INTRODUCTION TO
STATISTICAL METHOD

McGRAW-HILL SERIES IN PROBABILITY AND STATISTICS

David Blackwell and Herbert Solomon, *Consulting Editors*

INTRODUCTION TO STATISTICAL METHOD

Sylvain Ehrenfeld

Associate Professor of Industrial
and Management Engineering
School of Engineering and Applied Science
Columbia University

Sebastian B. Littauer

Professor of Industrial
and Management Engineering
Chairman of Department
School of Engineering and Applied Science
Columbia University

McGraw-Hill Book Company
New York   San Francisco   Toronto   London

INTRODUCTION TO STATISTICAL METHOD

Library of Congress Catalog Card Number 63-17595

19125

PREFACE

A knowledge of probability and statistical inference is becoming increasingly important to people in the fields of engineering, science, and industry. Many textbooks have been written which approach the subjects in various ways, some more rigorous and mathematical, some more pragmatic. What is unique about this book is that the two disciplines are presented from the viewpoint of their usefulness as tools to aid in the making of decisions while the treatment is on a level sufficiently rigorous to be of value to future mathematical statisticians.

The role that probability and statistics can play in the making of decisions is illustrated in the first chapter by showing how the techniques may be used to solve problems that occur in the work of engineers, scientists, and people in business and industry.

Chapters 2 to 5 provide a fundamental course in probability. They can be covered in one regular semester and are intended for second- or third-year students who have had a year of college mathematics. Each topic is introduced by an illustrative example, and other examples are given to clarify the principles that are established. When the book is used as a college text, the teacher can help greatly by developing the arguments presented, but it is sufficiently complete for home study and should be useful to nonstudents who are already engaged in professional practice. Exercises are included to give the reader a chance to test his achievement.

Chapters 7 to 10 provide a background in statistical inference. The material may be more than can be digested in one semester, but a balanced selection can readily be made. These chapters should provide the reader with an intuitively plausible foundation for experimental inference and also should serve as a sound basis for the advanced courses that will be taken by mathematical statisticians.

Chapter 6, which is on decision making, is designed to bridge the gap between probability and statistical inference. As far as the authors know, the material appearing here has not been presented from this perspective or emphasized elsewhere at the introductory level. It should be taken up at the point where it appears in the book, so that the reader, when studying the chapters on statistical inference, will already be aware of the requirements of decision making and the categories of inductive inference which it includes.

The closing chapter, Chap. 11, provides further insight into experimental inference by developing the concepts of statistical stability and the operation of statistical control. The chapter is short and presents only a few practical techniques, for it is intended primarily to show the relationship between statistical stability and valid statistical inference. Chapter 11, along with Chaps. 1 and 6, presents material in a way that is not found in other introductions to statistical methods; namely, these chapters attempt to unify the perspectives of probability and statistical inference and to show the essential role and valid basis of inductive inference.

When the book is used as a college text, the following selections of material are effective. For sophisticated students, the whole text can be studied in one year. For students who are not thoroughly grounded in symbolic manipulation, three terms may be required: in the first term, Chaps. 1 to 5; in the second, Chaps. 6, 7, and 8; and in the third, Chaps. 9, 10, and 11. On the other hand, a good one-year course can be given without Chaps. 8 and 9. While these chapters are very important, much work can be done in application with knowledge of the remaining chapters, and Chaps. 8 and 9 may be reserved for a later time. When only one semester is available for a course in probability, Chaps. 1 to 5 make a solid, self-contained unit.

The work on this book was begun while planning the probability and statistics program during the establishment of the department of industrial and management engineering at the Technion (Israel Institute of Technology). This project was supported by the ICA and was under a contract with New York University whose Professor Bernard Greidinger served as project director. One of the authors was attached to this project and had the opportunity to use early drafts of a number of chapters in his classes there; he received the full cooperation of his colleagues, as well as encouragement from the project director. The other author was then serving as vice president of the Technion and was encouraged by the president of the institution, General Yaacov Dori, to take substantial time from his administrative duties to prepare this text. On return to Columbia University, he was freed from some of his departmental duties by support from the Office of Ordnance Research (now called the Army Research Office). Both authors are most grateful for the cooperation, encouragement, and support they received.

We are grateful also to Professor Sidney Morgenbesser of the philosophy department of Columbia University for giving a critical reading of Chap. 6, although he must be completely exempted from responsibility for any inadequacies it may yet contain.

We are indebted to Sir Ronald A. Fisher, FRS, Cambridge, and to Dr. Frank Yates, FRS, Rothamsted; also to Oliver and Boyd Ltd., Edinburgh, for permission to reprint Table IV from their book "Statistical Tables for Biological, Agricultural, and Medical Research." We are also indebted to a number of other authors and publishers, as well as to journal editors, for use of tables and graphs. Specific acknowledgment is made in the text where this material appears.

The manuscript was guided through its various drafts with the devoted assistance of Mrs. Lucy Gottesman, Mrs. Marilyn Corne, and Mrs. Joyce Sofer at the Technion in Haifa; Mrs. Ruth Edelstein, Mrs. Suzanne Sen, and Mrs. Mary Beth Mahony of our department at Columbia; and Mrs. Myrtle Turner of New York City. Mrs. Edelstein was especially helpful in editing certain parts of the manuscript.

Sylvain Ehrenfeld
Sebastian B. Littauer

CONTENTS

1

VARIABILITY, EXPERIMENTAL INFERENCE, AND DECISION MAKING

In almost every aspect of our daily lives we are confronted with the necessity for making decisions resulting in action. Many of these decisions are made intuitively, but with the feeling that the action taken will yield a desired result. Were we to be asked on what we based the choice of our action, were we to try to explain how we arrived at our decision, were we confronted with the challenge as to how we knew that nature would act in a certain way, in short, were we to try to explain our mental processes, we should come up with a brief answer, namely, *it all results from experience*.

There is much truth in this statement, yet it requires considerable interpretation. What we mean in the first place is that, consciously or not, we observe our environment sometimes closely, although more often rather loosely. We have the feeling that we have learned from a set of previous observations of relatively similar situations that, in a situation of a given kind, a specified action usually results in a desired outcome. If we were to express ourselves in more sophisticated language, we might say that we have developed a method of inductive inference wherein, by unconsciously exercising some principles of probability in conjunction with statistical inferences following from observation, we can arrive at decisions which have a high chance of resulting in expected outcomes. Were we to characterize this activity in more fundamental terms, we might say that our task was that of giving meaning to experience. What we seek, then, are methods and techniques which will enable us so to approach a decision problem, that is to say, a problem of determining a course of action best suited to attaining certain ends, that we may be able systematically to take a sequence of specified steps in order to reach our goal. We want to do this with a strong conviction that our goal will be attained.

Consider some simple examples. Suppose we wish to cross a street where traffic is heavy.   How do we go about deciding where and when to cross?   In some cases the decision is made for us by law.   But where we are free to make the choice, we often do so at a corner.   We have sub-consciously calculated the risk of not reaching the other side of the street were we to cross at other places.   We rarely give serious thought as to just how we come to such a decision.   And it is a fact, evidenced by traffic accidents to pedestrians, that persons crossing streets at other than certain specified places do not always reach the other side on their own power.   If we think at all about where and when to cross a street, we do it on the basis of past observation.   We do not go into a formal study in order to make this decision.

Suppose we have another, closely related decision to make, namely, where to place a traffic light.   (The reader may take it for granted that traffic lights are placed only at street intersections, but he may be inter-ested to know that lights and pedestrian crossings at some distance from the intersections are in use.)   It is apparent to anyone that, in choosing between two intersections for the location of a traffic light allocated by the town budget, the density of traffic is one of the deciding factors. Without going into the problem any further, we may say that the deter-mination of traffic density is a problem of sufficient importance to require the use of a formal procedure.

It might prove interesting, and even amazing, to the reader to con-sider the many decisions he makes daily and to reflect on the observations involved and the techniques of inference used.

We are especially interested in problems arising in various engineering and industrial fields of operation.   It may serve us well to examine some practical problems characteristic of a broad range of problems which nat-urally lead to the use of statistical inference.

1.1   Example: variability in manufacturing process

In the field of steel fabrication it is common to have steel bars, rods, or rolled sheet, where the length of the individual piece is the important characteristic at the final stage of the operation.   A typical order might call for ten thousand 10-foot bars.   Let us suppose, for the present dis-cussion, that the manufacturer is naïve about the uniformity of the weights of the billets from which the bars are rolled.   He starts rolling the bars and makes only occasional spot inspections of the lengths of the bars.   When, however, he finds a bar of less than 9 feet and one of almost 12 feet in length, he begins to wonder what his lot of ten thousand will look like.   He is concerned because he is aware that the required lengths should not deviate so widely from the nominal length of 10 feet.   In fact, all such orders are given with definite specifications, and in this case, the specification was for 10-foot bars with a tolerance of ± 0.30 foot.   Obviously, if some of the bars deviate by more than a foot, there should be serious concern as to how many bars are within the tolerance limits. The manufacturer therefore decides to check thoroughly the first hundred bars. In Table 1.1 is given the 100 bar lengths in the order of their manufacture.

TABLE 1.1

Bar number	Bar length	Bar number	Bar length	Bar number	Bar length	Bar number	Bar length
1	10.23	26	10.15	51	10.45	76	9.53
2	10.03	27	9.22	52	10.59	77	10.36
3	10.74	28	10.69	53	9.25	78	10.10
4	10.51	29	10.97	54	9.65	79	10.97
5	10.70	30	10.99	55	10.69	80	9.63
6	10.07	31	9.85	56	9.74	81	10.79
7	8.94	32	10.09	57	9.47	82	10.54
8	9.82	33	10.39	58	9.76	83	10.22
9	9.76	34	10.10	59	10.38	84	9.77
10	9.72	35	9.87	60	10.11	85	10.48
11	11.23	36	10.65	61	9.74	86	10.06
12	9.73	37	9.40	62	10.00	87	9.68
13	9.67	38	9.52	63	9.92	88	10.37
14	10.64	39	10.60	64	9.19	89	9.89
15	10.02	40	10.21	65	10.19	90	9.23
16	9.84	41	10.12	66	10.30	91	10.76
17	9.90	42	10.01	67	10.38	92	9.87
18	10.35	43	9.57	68	9.93	93	9.79
19	11.76	44	9.75	69	9.83	94	10.43
20	10.16	45	10.21	70	10.38	95	9.87
21	9.97	46	9.52	71	10.44	96	10.18
22	10.27	47	10.26	72	10.48	97	9.65
23	10.46	48	10.97	73	10.53	98	9.78
24	10.28	49	9.86	74	9.74	99	9.77
25	11.47	50	9.98	75	10.09	100	10.06

Our concern arises from the fact that, while we want all bars to be precisely 10 feet long, we have found some which are much shorter and others which are much longer. We may ask ourselves whether this is a strange phenomenon. On reflection, however, we recall that upon duplicating the measurement of a rod diameter, the two results were not quite the same. When checking two "quarter pound" packages of butter, we find that there is a difference in their weights. In the chemistry laboratory duplicate weighings never came out quite the same. Let us look at these data again and single out one striking fact, namely, that bars which were supposed to be made in 10-foot lengths actually vary between 8.90

and 11.80 feet.   This is characteristic of results of all repetitive operations; if we attempt to make many repetitions of the same thing, the
resulting items will vary one from another.   In some cases the variation
will be great, and in other cases it will be small.   In some cases the variation will be symmetrical, while in other cases it will be skewed.   The
principal fact observed, however, in every case of repetitive operation is
the variability of the results.   This variability occurs not only when we
attempt to replicate the same thing by a mass operation but also when we
attempt repeated measurement of the same characteristic of one thing.

In our attempt to observe and interpret nature, to bring meaning
out of experience, we are challenged by the variability which pervades our
observations on essentially the same thing.   We have before us a practical problem of making decisions in connection with the manufacture of
10-foot bars.   We suspect that the variability in the lengths of the bars
already made is an inherent characteristic.   We suspect, further, that our
prime problem is to study the character of the variability of repetitive
operations in order to determine how important this is in the day-to-day
problem of satisfying human wants and needs.   With this aim in view,
we examine these data.

The techniques we use for the examination of the data depend to a
large extent on what we hope to accomplish.   In the foregoing discussion
it appears, on general scientific grounds, that in order to predict and to
make what we want, we must try to find out the nature of variability and
its effect on the thing we are trying to do.   Were we either customer or
manufacturer we might not be concerned with the scientific significance
of variability.   It is reasonable to expect, however, that many of us,
whatever our other interests may be, will be both affected by and concerned with the implications of variability and its cost.   Let us see,
then, what these effects and costs are in our present example.

First, let it be understood that bars whose lengths are between 9.70
and 10.30 feet can be used without question.   Initially, we shall suppose
that a bar whose length is less than 9.70 feet is scrapped and that a bar
with length greater than 10.30 feet is trimmed to a length of 10 feet.
This formulation actually occurs in practice.   The present approach will
be modified later on, in the sense that we shall consider the alternative
purpose for which the short bars might be used, as well as the cost of the
trimming operation.   The present formulation will be sufficient to illustrate the main point, namely, that variability can have significant
consequences.

In examining the data of 100 bar lengths we notice that any length
can be put into one of three groups, namely, within tolerance limits (that
is, 10 ± 0.30 feet), below 9.70 feet (short), or above 10.30 feet (long).
Scanning the 100 observations, we make the computations given in Table
1.2.   From the breakdown we see that 50 per cent of the bars are usable

without much ado; 34 per cent are usable after trimming; and finally, 16 per cent are not usable at all. We conclude that 84 per cent of the bars can be used (with suitable trimming of long bars) to satisfy the original order for bars whose lengths are within 10 ± 0.30 feet. Let us now consider how many feet of steel was used to obtain 84 out of 100 usable bars. The sum of the lengths of the 100 original bars equals 1,012 feet, and of this only 84 bars can be used. If there had been no variability, we should have used 1,000 feet (about the same number of feet) of steel, but 100 per cent of the bars would have been usable.

TABLE 1.2

Within tolerance limits	50%
Below 9.70 feet (short)	16%
Above 10.30 feet (long)	34%

The order was for 10,000 usable bars. Let us momentarily assume that the ratios indicated in Table 1.2 continue to be approximately 50, 16, and 34 per cent if more bars are rolled. This is a very crucial assumption and will be further discussed later in this chapter. If this is the case, in order to make 10,000 usable bars, we must roll approximately N bars, where N is obtained from $0.84 \times N = 10,000$. Therefore N equals 11,905. The total number of feet of steel needed to fulfill the required order is now computed to be

$$\frac{1,012}{84} \times 10,000 = 10.12N = 10.12 \times 11,905 = 120,479 \text{ feet}$$

The per cent loss in steel due to variability can now be computed by comparing 120,479 with the number of feet of steel needed when no variability is present. In the case of no variability, $10,000 \times 10$, or 100,000, feet of steel would be needed. Therefore

$$\text{Per cent loss} = \frac{120,479 - 100,000}{100,000} \times 100 \cong 20.5$$

This result means that, instead of using 100,000 feet of steel, one uses 120,479, that is, 20,479 feet extra! This result gives the per cent loss in steel for the following assumptions:

1. Setting is at 10 feet.
2. Tolerance limits are 10 ± 0.30 feet.
3. Steel bars whose lengths are below 9.70 feet and steel resulting from trimming long bars are altogether scrapped.
4. Percentage of short bars appearing among the 100 bars will remain approximately the same when more bars are made. This is called the *assumption of statistical stability*.

Before we discuss modification of this problem, let us consider assumption 1. It is clear that one effect of variability is that a setting of 10 feet will yield a certain number of short bars. It is reasonable, therefore, to consider settings other than 10 feet. An increase in setting would decrease the number of short bars, but would increase the amount of trimmed steel. Let us examine the effects of various settings. Instead of taking more measurements, let us assume that an increase in setting by amount t will increase all 100 bar lengths by the same amount t. In other words, we assume that the general character of the variability has

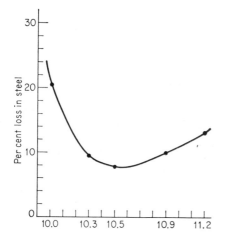

Figure 1.1   Per cent loss in steel vs. setting.

not changed with an increase in setting. The computations are straightforward and are exactly the same as those made previously. This procedure results in the curve shown in Fig. 1.1.

We see that the per cent loss is minimized at a setting of approximately 10.6 feet, with a percentage loss of about 8 per cent. At best, therefore, an order for ten thousand 10-foot bars will require approximately 108,000 feet of steel. Thus an explicit study of the variability in this case reduced the potential loss from 20 to 8 per cent.

Assumption 3 may be misleading in practical cases since bars outside the tolerance range can sometimes be used for other than the original purpose. In any case, bars whose lengths are outside the tolerance range cannot be used without some penalty of additional cost. In actual practice a short bar, one whose length is less than 9.70 feet, cannot be used for the purpose for which it was ordered. A variety of penalties can result from this. The largest penalty results if the bar cannot be used for an alternative purpose but must be sold as metal scrap. A lesser cost accrues when the bars can be used for some other purpose than originally intended. For example, the manufacturer may have customers who specify 9.75-foot bars and can therefore use some of the shorter bars. In this case the short bars may be sold for not much less than the original price. Additional costs may result from necessary storage and other handling charges. One need not go further into discussing the costs associated with short bars. Let us accept the fact that short bars entail a given penalty in money terms, which we shall denote by C_s. This is a simplification which, however, does not significantly affect the generality of the principle being studied. The cost penalty for long bars (longer than 10.30 feet) results from (1) the cost of the trimming operation, and (2) the loss in value of the trimmed steel. We shall denote the cost of trimming a steel bar by C_t. It will be assumed that the cost of scrap is proportional to the number of feet of scrap, namely, $C_p \times S$, where S is the number of feet of scrap steel and C_p is a proportionality factor. It is obvious that long bars need not be totally scrapped, since they can be used after trimming to fill the original order. The important point that concerns us here is the fact that the variability in the lengths of steel bars results in a financial penalty to the makers and users of these bars. And in the present case we have arrived at several types of costs, namely, C_s, C_t, and C_p, to which we can ascribe specific monetary values in particular instances. Given the actual sizes of a 100 or 1,000 or any other number of bars manufactured to the above specifications, we can calculate the cost or loss resulting from the fact of variability.

Suppose we knew that there were N_s short bars, N_l long bars, and S feet of scrap steel among the 100 bars considered previously. The total cost would then be given by

$$C = C_s N_s + C_t N_l + C_p S$$

where C is the monetary loss resulting from the undersize and oversize bars. In the data given, $N_s = 16$, $N_l = 34$, and $S = 23.40$ feet. The cost C would therefore be, in this case,

$$C = C_s(16) + C_t(34) + C_p(23.40)$$

In order to find N_s, N_p, and S for the 100 values given above, we must scan each number representing the lengths. Instead of just counting those numbers which are less than 9.70 and those which are larger than 10.30, let us determine the distribution of length for cell widths of 0.30 foot. For we are as much interested in how the values cluster about the specified nominal value of 10.00 feet as we are concerned with the extent of spread beyond the specified tolerances. Table 1.3 is a skeleton of a *tally* diagram.

In the first column, "cell interval," we put the various cell intervals (of length 0.30 foot), starting from about the lowest value of the 100 observations and continuing to approximately the largest value. In order to avoid overlapping of the cell intervals we exclude the right-hand side of the intervals. For example, the interval 8.50–8.80 includes all

lengths smaller than 8.80 and larger than or equal to 8.50.   The value
8.80 is therefore not in this interval.   Each of the 100 bar lengths falls
into one of the cell intervals.   We can count the number of lengths which
fall into the various intervals.   The results of the count are given in
column 3.   A simple way to obtain the count for the various intervals is
to look at each of the 100 bar lengths in order and to put a stroke next to
the cell interval for an observation which lies in that interval.   The result

TABLE 1.3

Cell number i	(1) Cell interval	(2) Tally	(3) Number N_i in cell i	(4) Cumulative number ΣN_j $(j \leqq i)$
1	8.50–8.80		0	0
2	8.80–9.10	/	1	1
3	9.10–9.40	////	4	5
4	9.40–9.70	⫽⫽ ⫽⫽ /	11	16
5	9.70–10.0	⫽⫽ ⫽⫽ ⫽⫽ ⫽⫽ ⫽⫽ /	26	42
6	10.0–10.3	⫽⫽ ⫽⫽ ⫽⫽ ⫽⫽ ////	24	66
7	10.3–10.6	⫽⫽ ⫽⫽ ⫽⫽ ///	18	84
8	10.6–10.9	⫽⫽ ////	9	93
9	10.9–11.2	////	4	97
10	11.2–11.5	//	2	99
11	11.5–11.8	/	1	100

of this procedure is indicated in column 2, labeled "tally."   Column 4
just gives the cumulative count.   For example, the number 42 in column
4, in the row corresponding to cell interval 9.70–10.0, indicates that 42
out of the 100 bar lengths have a length less than 10.0 feet.

From this tally diagram we can make a more formal picture, usually
called a frequency histogram.   When the frequencies, or counts, are
divided by the total number of observations (in this case 100), we obtain
a relative-frequency histogram, given in Fig. 1.2.

We are not merely interested in N_s, N_l, and S in these 100 bars; we
also are concerned with how many of them to expect among the next
1,000 or 10,000 or the like number of bars.   For this purpose we must
assume that the histogram of the next N bars will be essentially of the
same shape as the histogram in Fig. 1.2.   This means, for example, that
about the same fraction of the next N bars will be undersize as was found
to be so in the first 100 bars.   Since $N_s = 16$, we might expect the number
short for the next N bars to be $N \times {}^{16}\!/_{100}$.

We note that the ratio $N_s/100$ is the relevant quantity. In fact, we are interested in the relative frequency rather than the frequency itself. It is obvious that the cell heights for relative frequency are proportional to those for frequency. Hereafter, when considering the distribution of observed values resulting from a process, we shall utilize the histogram of relative frequencies.

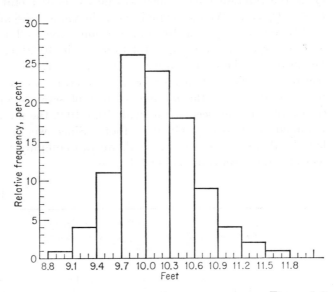

Figure 1.2

Now let us consider the actual cost of filling an order for 10,000 bars. Any cost, and for that matter any real quantity, can be determined only on the basis of certain specific assumptions. Let us examine our assumptions.

1. The process will yield a distribution of bar lengths in accordance with the histogram in Fig. 1.2.
2. The specifications are:
   a. The desired bar length is 10.00 feet.
   b. Bars will be acceptable if they are not shorter than 9.70 feet.
   c. Bars will be acceptable if they are not longer than 10.30 feet.
3. The cost per foot for producing a bar by this process is C_u.
4. The cost penalty for a short bar is C_s.
5. The cost penalty for the scrap of a long bar is $C_p S$.
6. The cost penalty of trimming is C_t.

In the first place, we note that a fraction f_s of bars produced will be short and unusable, so that we shall be obliged to produce more than

10,000 bars to fill our order.   It follows that

$$N(1 - f_s) = 10,000$$

and $N = 10,000/(1 - f_s)$, where N is the number of bars that we must produce.   Since $f_s = 0.16$, $N = 11,905$.   Furthermore, the loss due to short bars is C_sNf_s.   The loss due to trimming of long bars is NC_tf_l (f_l is the fraction long); the loss due to scrap metal from trimming is $C_pS = C_pNS'$.   We now explain how the values of S and S' are obtained.

In our example of 100 observations, five cell intervals contained lengths larger than the upper tolerance limit, 10.30 feet.   If a bar length lies in one of these five intervals, it must be trimmed.   The number of feet of steel trimmed varies with the interval.   For example, in the first interval, 10.3–10.6, the number of feet of scrap steel is approximately 0.45 foot.   In the second interval, 10.6–10.9, the number of feet of steel trimmed is approximately 0.75 foot.   Since we know how many bar lengths there are in each interval, we can compute the total number of feet of scrap steel from Table 1.4.

TABLE 1.4

Cell interval	Number of feet trimmed, l, per bar	Number of observations, N_l	$l(N_l)$
10.3–10.6	0.45	18	8.10
10.6–10.9	0.75	9	6.75
10.9–11.2	1.05	4	4.20
11.2–11.5	1.35	2	2.70
11.5–11.8	1.65	1	1.65
			23.40

The total number of feet of scrap steel (resulting from trimming) is therefore equal to 23.40 feet.   The value of S' is obtained from the relation $NS' = S$.   Thus S' is the average number of feet of scrap steel (trimmed) consumed in N bars.   The value of S' in this case is equal to 0.2340 foot.   The average number of feet of scrap in relation to long bars, however, is given by S divided by the number of long bars.   In this case, $23.40/34 = 0.9826$ foot.   In general, then, to compute S, we look at all intervals where long bars occur.   We compute how much steel must be trimmed if a bar length lies in that interval.   Suppose there are k such intervals, with trimmed scrap lengths $l_1, l_2, \ldots, l_k$.   Let the relative frequency of bar lengths in the k cell intervals be $f_1, f_2, \ldots, f_k$.   The values of S and S', respectively, are then computed from

$$S = l_1(Nf_1) + l_2(Nf_2) + \cdots + l_k(Nf_k) = NS'$$

The cost of steel for the usable bars is $NC_u(1 - f_s)10$, where C_u denotes the cost per foot for the manufacture of steel bars. Thus, adding the costs and losses, we have

$$C = NC_u(1 - f_s)10 + Nf_s(C_s) + Nf_l(C_l) + NC_p(S')$$
$$= N[10C_u(1 - f_s) + f_sC_s + f_lC_l + C_pS']$$

Therefore, for 10,000 bars,

$$C = \frac{10,000}{1 - f_s} [10C_u(1 - f_s) + C_sf_s + C_lf_l + C_p(S')]$$

If no variability were present, $f_s = f_l = S' = 0$ and the value of C would be C_0, given by $C_0 = 100,000C_u$. The per cent loss due to the fact of variability is

$$\frac{C - C_0}{C_0} \times 100 = \frac{1}{10(1 - f_s)}\left[\left(\frac{C_s}{C_u}\right)f_s + \left(\frac{C_l}{C_u}\right)f_l + \left(\frac{C_p}{C_u}\right)S'\right] \times 100 \quad (1.1.1)$$

Suppose, for the sake of illustration, that $C_p/C_u = 0.5$, $C_l/C_u = 0.2$, and $C_s/C_u = 1.5$. Then the per cent loss is (for setting of 10 feet)

$$\frac{1}{(10)(1 - 0.16)} [(1.5)(0.16) + (0.2)(0.34) + (0.5)(0.2340)](100) \cong 5$$

It is clear that this per cent loss is dependent on the values of the various costs.

It is natural to ask ourselves whether we can reduce such losses as result from variability of a manufacturing process. How many ways are open to us to reduce the loss penalties? We may consider at least the following approaches:

1. Reduce variability of process.
2. Widen specified tolerances.
3. Consider settings other than 10.00 feet.
4. Recondition or replace present machinery.

1.1.1 Reducing variability of process

Since the cost penalties resulted from the variability in length of the rolled bars, we might consider at first how this variability can be reduced. This is a practical engineering problem which long and hard experience has taught us to approach with care. In fact, in many cases variability can be reduced only by a substantial change in the process.

Under some circumstances, where we are able to determine causes of variability that can be eliminated, we may be able to reduce spread such as occurred in the rolled-bar lengths. At best, reducing the variability in the rolling process we are considering is a formidable task, requiring considerable engineering and statistical know-how. Since this is beyond our immediate aims, we shall not discuss this aspect further here. We shall return to it later when we are discussing statistical stability, in Chap. 11.

Suppose, however, that we could reduce the variability. Assume that we were able to obtain the histogram in Fig. 1.3 for another 100 rolled-bar lengths. Computation of the per cent loss in steel at a setting of 10 feet gives approximately 11 per cent. This is 8 per cent less than

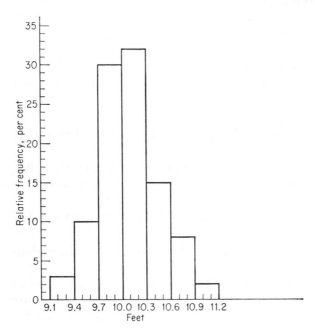

Figure 1.3

with the original variability. It is quite apparent that the per cent loss in steel decreases with decreased variability.

1.1.2 Wider specified tolerances

Tolerances are usually set to meet cost considerations and technical requirements for the use of manufactured articles. It often happens, however, that conscientious engineers specify narrower tolerances than are required. When both the purchaser and the manufacturer are confronted with a situation such as the one we are studying, they may with good reason question the practicality of the existing tolerances. For in their past experience they have often found it possible to make good use of out-of-tolerance parts. Suppose, then, that we could widen the specification to 10 ± 0.60 feet.

We readily find by a computation similar to that done for the original tolerances of ±0.30 foot that the per cent loss in steel at a setting of 10 feet is only 4.2 per cent.   It is clear that the setting of tolerance limits is an implicit recognition of the presence of variability.   Furthermore, the fact of variability often makes it worthwhile to give closer-than-usual scrutiny to the setting of tolerance limits.

1.1.3   Variation of bar-length setting

We assume now that we are not free to modify any of the engineering constraints, nor to replace machinery, nor to modify the process essentially.   Within the existing conditions we may, however, make any adjustments with respect to timing, tension on rolls, or settings (cutting position), and the like.   Such adjustments are expected in common practice and do not in essence change the process.   Let us consider the possibility of reducing losses resulting from out-of-tolerance parts by changing the cutter setting from 10 feet to some other value.

The effect of a change in setting has already been considered where only the amount of steel necessary for filling an order was of interest. The results for the per cent loss in steel as a function of the setting are given in Fig. 1.1.   Let us now consider the same question in relation to the various other costs.   The first question that arises is, shall we increase or decrease the setting?   Instead of exercising our intuition on a "best choice," let us explore the consequences of any change in setting, beginning with a large change, namely, an increase in setting of 0.30 foot.   We can examine what happens here by shifting the relative-frequency histogram 0.30 foot to the right.   (Recall that we assume no change in the distribution of lengths, so that the relative-frequency histogram remains unchanged.)   It becomes apparent that:

1. The number of short bars is materially decreased.
2. The number of parts needed to fill an order is decreased.
3. The number of long bars is increased.
4. The amount of trimming is increased.

What effect do these results of the increase in setting have on the loss penalties?

The answer to this question is obtained by computing the per cent loss for the various settings by means of Eq. (1.1.1).   The result of this computation is given in Fig. 1.4.   The best setting, in the sense that the loss is minimized, can readily be taken from the loss curves.   As could have been guessed, the best setting and loss curve depend on the values of the costs and penalties incurred for various contingencies such as short bars, trimming, and scrap steel.

1.1.4   Machinery reconditioning and replacement

It is common knowledge that variability of manufacturing processes can be reduced by replacing or reconditioning the machinery used.   This is, of course, common practice, but the decision to replace or recondition must be made on economic as well as technical grounds. We shall not go into the details here other than to make the observation that if the machinery in a process is not somewhere near the end of its life expectancy, replacement is not likely to be economically desirable unless some very

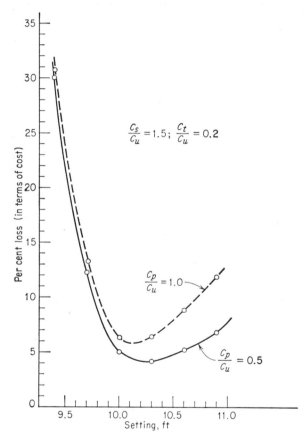

Figure 1.4 Per cent loss in cost vs. setting.

new features are incorporated in the new machine. There exist well-developed and rather effective techniques for determining the desirability of equipment replacement.

The decision to recondition machinery is of another nature. If the process has not been operating with satisfactory stability, then perhaps nonextensive changes will help bring about stable functioning and a reduction in variability. The decision to undertake such changes can be made with only a low risk of error by the use of statistical control methods. On the other hand, if the process has been working in a state of statistical stability for a reasonable length of time, and if during that time the variability has been too great, then, usually, extensive reconditioning will be necessary in order to reduce the variability. One must bear in mind, however, that even such extensive reconditioning may not reduce or even affect the variability. Certainly, a machine can be functioning at its lowest possible level of variability regardless of any modifications that may be made. Under such circumstances reduction in variability is impossible.

While both machinery replacement and its reconditioning are to be considered in order to reduce the variability of a process, one must be fully advised of the difficulty and complexity of the problem.

1.2 Experimental inference and cause systems

Is the Future as the Past? We return now to a question previously raised, namely, how can we be sure that the future will be as the past? A puzzling question implied in our first example is, if conditions were kept constant, why did the results vary? Even though we made an effort to keep conditions constant, there apparently were unnoticed changes going on. (We could, of course, have been more careful, but experience has shown that variations result even with the most extreme care.) It must also be remembered that increased care in keeping conditions "constant" may involve considerable expenditure of time, effort, and money. Is the extra cost warranted by possible reduction in variability?

Let us consider the above questions from a broader point of view. Presumably, each time that a steel bar was rolled, there was a *system of causes* operating. If we assume that a fixed set of causes leads to a definite result, we are led to conclude that the system of causes was varying. How can we study these changes in the system of causes? How extensive are these apparently minute changes?

It is very difficult at times to know what changes have occurred. There is, however, one thing that has changed, namely, time. Thus it seems natural to consider the results of an operating system of causes in time order. We do not imply that time produces change in an apparently constant system of causes, but we can at least identify the outcomes of the system of causes by the time of occurrence. We can, for example, represent length on a convenient vertical scale and time order of production on a horizontal scale. In doing so we can plot the various bar lengths in time order. This, however, might show nothing more than some ripples and an occasional high or low spot. A more sensitive method for detecting the degree to which the past and present may be relied upon as a guide to the future is studying the arithmetic averages of small samples. (The basis on which this method rests will be explained later, in Chap. 11.) The arithmetic average of a set of numbers, x_1,

$x_2, \ldots, x_n$, is defined as

$$\bar{x} = \frac{x_1 + x_2 + \cdots + x_n}{n}$$

It should be noted that $\bar{x}$ corresponds to the idea of the central value of a distribution. In our example of steel-bar length the arithmetic average of the numbers in Table 1.1 is 10.12 feet, which is close to the machine setting. Suppose we take the 100 observations from Table 1.1 and make of them 25 successive samples of 4 observations in a sample.

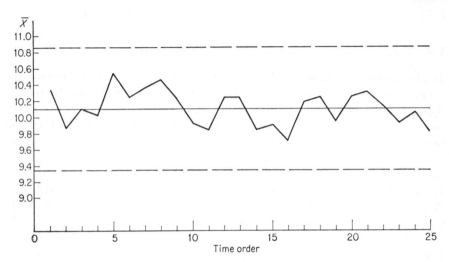

Figure 1.5

We then plot Fig. 1.5, which we proceed to explain. If all the 100 observations come from a homogeneous source, that is, if the bars are being rolled to an expected length of 10.00 feet under "constant" conditions, we may expect the following. There exists a source of bars whose arithmetic average is equal to (or very close to) the value obtained for the arithmetic average of the 100 bar lengths under consideration. The two dashed lines above and below the grand average span an interval within which most of the values of $\bar{x}$ should fall if the conditions under which these observations have been obtained have not basically changed. The setting of the dashed lines in this figure is partly based on the idea that, *if stability exists*, we expect a certain percentage of $\bar{x}$'s to fall outside the limits. This percentage can be computed by formal methods outlined in Chap. 11. It is usually set so small so that when an $\bar{x}$ falls outside these limits we have the choice of one of two alternatives: either a rare event has occurred or the assumption of stability is to be questioned. The basis for locating these dashed lines is also discussed in Chap. 11.

Hence, should we discover among these first 25 samples some $\bar{x}$'s above or below the dashed lines, we should suspect that conditions changed enough to warrant investigation.   We suspect that the "system of causes" affecting the variability of bar lengths is not a "constant system of chance causes."   The implication is that under such circumstances we are not confident about predicting an interval in which most future bar lengths may be expected to fall.   If, on the other hand, all the sample averages fall within the two "limit" lines, we may feel confident

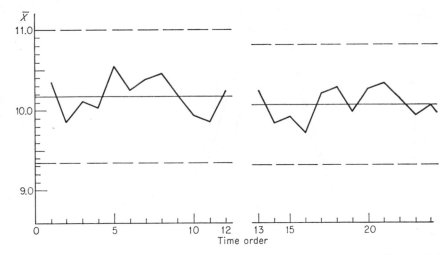

Figure 1.6

that the conditions under which the bar lengths have been determined are essentially constant.   If this is so, we may feel reasonably certain that future bar lengths will fall essentially within the same pattern as indicated in the histogram in Fig. 1.2.   Substantiating this statement requires a subtle argument, as well as assumptions other than those explicitly made.   A detailed discussion of this issue will be presented in Chap. 11.

Of course, we cannot maintain this confidence unless we continue to take periodic samples of four in time order and compare them with the limit lines in Fig. 1.5.   So long as such subsequent averages of samples of four fall within the limit lines so determined, we can maintain this confidence.   As soon as a sample average falls outside these limits, we must be prepared to doubt that the future will be as the past.   Let us compare the set of the first 12 groups with the following set of 13 groups of sample averages.   In Fig. 1.6 we have a graph similar to that of Fig. 1.5, split into two successive parts plotted side by side.   It is interesting to observe that the grand average of the first 12 samples is almost identical with that of the next 13 samples.   Furthermore, each of the 13 sample averages of the second set falls within the limit lines of the first set, and vice versa.   It is also interesting to note that the two histograms are very similar to one another and to the histogram for the 100 values (Fig. 1.7).

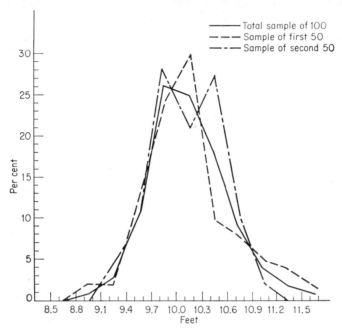

Figure 1.7

1.3   Example: variability in inventory

A class of problems where the fact of variability is an important aspect of the situation is found among inventory problems.   Some of these problems can be stated very simply, namely, how does one decide upon the amount of material to stock in preparation for an uncertain future? Both understocking and overstocking are undesirable.   For example, a warehouse buying perishables for the day will see them spoil if it buys too many and will lose potential customers if it buys too few.   In order to illustrate the significance of variability and to emphasize the need for a quantitative treatment of uncertainty, we consider a specific case.   A warehouse buys lots of a perishable food in the morning for $20 each and sells them during the day for $30.   Unsold lots at the end of the day are an outright loss.

If the same number of lots, say, five, are demanded by customers day after day, the warehouse owner would most certainly decide to order five lots each morning.   His daily profit in this case would be $50.   The experience of the warehouse owner, however, is that daily demand varies. At the beginning of the morning he is not certain how many lots will be demanded that day. Each morning he must decide how many lots to buy for that day. If he buys too many, he may be left with useless goods at the end of the day, and if he buys too few, he may lose potential sales. Since our warehouse owner is an observant and systematic sort of fellow he decides to keep a record of daily demand. He feels, and rightly so, that this record should be of help in his daily decision. His record for the distribution of daily demand during the first 100 days is shown in Table 1.5.

TABLE 1.5

Number demanded	0	1	2	3	4	5	6	7	8	9	10	11	12
Number of days		1	3	8	13	17	18	15	10	7	4	2	1	1

The average demand per day is

$$\bar{d} = \frac{(1)(3) + (2)(8) + \cdots + (10)(2) + (11)(1) + (12)(1)}{100} = 5.11$$

Thus $\bar{d}$ equals the total demand during the 100 days divided by 100. The above computation gives the values of $\bar{d}$ as approximately equal to 5.

Since $\bar{d}$ is equal approximately to 5, the warehouse owner decides to buy five lots each morning. On some days he will make money (varying amounts), while on other days he may lose money. He is confident, however, that five lots a day is a good decision. He feels that over a period of time his profits will average as high as can be expected. Let us see what effect variable demand has on daily profit. In order to make the computation, let us assume that the distribution in Table 1.5 will be approximately the same during the next 100 days. Again, we use the crucial assumption of stability that we have already discussed in the example in Sec. 1.1. If this assumption holds and our entrepreneur orders five lots daily, we can compute his total profit during these 100 days.

If only one lot is demanded on a day and he has ordered five, he has spent $100 and taken in only $30, a loss of $70. Let us compute the profit for days when 0, 1, 2, . . . , 12 lots are demanded. Since we know (by the assumption of stability) the frequency with which each number of lots is demanded, and since the warehouse owner each morning purchases five lots, we can compute his total profit during these 100 days as follows:

Total profit = $(1)(-\$100) + (3)(-\$70) + \cdots + (1)(50) = \$2{,}480$

This computation gives a total profit for the 100 days of $2,480. The average profit per day over this period is therefore $24.80. Note that the consequence of the fact of variability is an average loss of about $25 per day, or 50 per cent.

Should the warehouse owner purchase each morning the average expected demand per day? This may seem to be a reasonable, and even obvious, purchase procedure. In order to check whether this is the case, we perform a computation similar to the one we have just made for different order amounts. The results of this computation are given

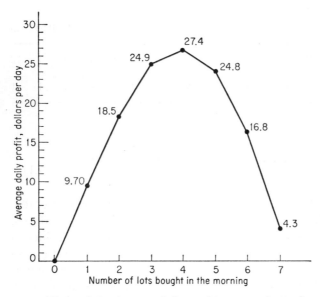

Figure 1.8   Average daily profit vs. morning order quantity.

in Fig. 1.8. This figure shows that the warehouse owner is better off if he buys four lots each morning instead of five. The average increase in daily profit is $2.60, a gain of approximately 10.5 per cent. We conclude that our reasonable or obvious rule of buying a number of lots equal to expected demand is not necessarily optimum. It is left to the reader to think of reasons for this. The point to be emphasized is that variability can have strange consequences.

The numerical quantities in this example were chosen for illustrative purposes, but the underlying principle and lesson to be learned from it reappear in more complex and important contexts. It is clear that those situations certainly warrant a closer look at uncertainty and its effects.

1.4   Example: variability in structural stress

Under certain conditions the central deflection D of a top-loaded column is given by

$$D = \frac{a}{1 - bP} \qquad (1.4.1)$$

where a, the initial eccentricity, and b are constants dependent on the length of the column and the material of which it is composed. P is the load applied. In this particular case, we are considering $a = 0.003$ and $b = 0.001$. Thus the deflection D is given by

$$D = \frac{0.003}{1 - (0.001)P} \qquad (1.4.2)$$

Furthermore, we suppose that it is undesirable for the value of D to be larger than 0.006 foot. From Eq. (1.4.2) we can compute that value of P, P_0 such that for all other values of P less than P_0, corresponding values of D are less than 0.006 foot. The value of P_0 so found is 500 psi. In order, however, to assure ourselves some margin of safety, we set $P_0 = 480$ psi.

Now we may ask whether we can assure ourselves that this condition will prevail in practice. Why do we ask this question? In actual practice we do not know with great accuracy the magnitude of load that the column is carrying. Even in laboratory experiments where we can "set" the load at a prescribed amount, we find on direct measurement that the true load differs from the load set by the laboratory machine. Hence, even in a laboratory experiment where repeated top loading of a column is performed at a "constant" setting, there will be in fact a distribution of load. It may turn out, of course, that the average of the true loads will be very close to the value of the load supposedly set by the machine.

Now consider a case of top loading of a column in practical use. For analytical purposes we may refer to one value at which the column is loaded. For a supposed loading of 480 psi we take actual measurements of the load from time to time until we have accumulated a few hundred observations of the magnitude of load at various times. The stipulated value is but the arithmetic average of a distribution of loads yielding the relative-frequency histogram in Fig. 1.9 (and the cumulative-frequency curve in Fig. 1.10). The source of concern is now apparent and should not be surprising when we consider real conditions. A column supporting a classroom floor may be full-loaded when 30 people are in the room or be minimum-loaded when the room is empty. We design in accordance with some practical condition, but we cannot economically keep pushing the expected load upward.   We must study what the effect of load variation is on D.

From the cumulative-frequency curve in Fig. 1.10 one finds $P \geq$ 480 psi for approximately 33 per cent of the observed loads; whence $D \geq 0.006$ for 33 per cent of the observed loads.   Let us give this condition a practical interpretation.   Suppose these observations had been made on an aluminum structural member of an aircraft wing.   Certain supports in wings are subject to loads under conditions the same as those

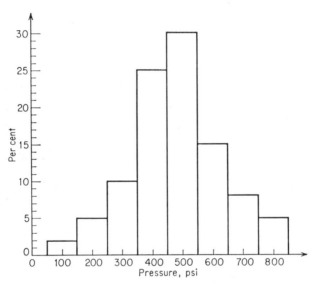

Figure 1.9

prevailing for top-loaded columns.   These loads vary considerably with the altitude of the plane, its air speed, and such sudden effects as are produced by sharp turns, steep climbs, high gusts, and the like.   Either under flight conditions or by means of simulation we can obtain samplings of the load distribution in time, which may be represented by the diagrams in Figs. 1.9 and 1.10.   On the other hand, the member under study is certainly subject to continuous loading, whereas our sampling is of only a finite number of instantaneous loads.   Let us assume that the relative frequency with which a given load appears in the histogram of Fig. 1.9 is equal to the percentage of the time in flight (under certain conditions) that the member considered is subject to the given load. Better still, consider the cumulative-frequency curve in Fig. 1.10: the member is subject to a load $P \geq 300$ psi 83 per cent of the time the aircraft is in flight under conditions like those tested.   It is subject to a load $P \geq 400$ psi 58 per cent of the time.   (One may, of course, use the cumulative-frequency curve for linear interpolation for loads other than those plotted.)

Returning to our question, is D ever greater than 0.006? From Fig. 1.10 we can find the frequency with which $P \geq 480$ psi; this is, in fact, 33 per cent. Hence, 33 per cent of the time during which the aircraft member is loaded as indicated in Fig. 1.10, $D \geq 0.006$. We may now ask ourselves, how can we prevent D from exceeding 0.006? But brief reflection is needed to modify the question: Is there an average

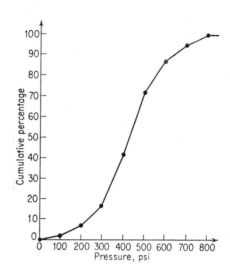

Figure 1.10

load, with the present load variability, for which $D \geq 0.006$ for less than a specified percentage of the time during which these load conditions apply? In order to answer this question bear in mind that we need not make further tests but need merely shift the frequency histogram of Fig. 1.9 left or right so as to apply to different average values of load. From each frequency histogram a cumulative-frequency curve for loss can be formed. And from each of these curves, by repeated solving of Eq. (1.4.2), one obtains a cumulative-frequency curve for D corresponding to a given mean value of P. Such a family of curves is given in Fig. 1.11.

At $D = 0.006$ foot, a vertical line intersecting each of the curves in Fig. 1.11 yields a set of percentages which are interpreted as follows: under the specified loading conditions, for an average load $\bar{P} = 580$ psi, $D \geq 0.006$ 60 per cent of the time. For even so low a mean load as $\bar{P} = 280$ psi, $D \geq 0.006$ 3 per cent of the time. Is D ever less than 0.006 all the time? This question does not have a practical answer. For any finite values of $\bar{P}$, even very small values, $D \geq 0.006$ *some* per cent of the time.

One may form another cumulative frequency from the family of curves in Fig. 1.11.   From the uppermost curve one obtains $D \geq 0.006$ foot 3 per cent of the time for $\bar{P} = 280$ psi; 13 per cent for $\bar{P} = 380$ psi; 33 per cent for $\bar{P} = 480$ psi; etc.   This is plotted in Fig. 1.12.   From this curve, for any value of $\bar{P}$, the ordinate gives the per cent of time that $D \geq 0.006$.   For example, when $\bar{P} \leq 430$ psi, $D \geq 0.006$ foot 20 per cent of the time.

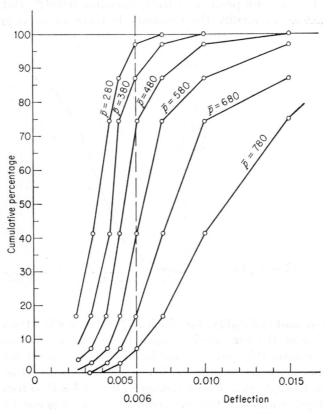

Figure 1.11

You may ask another question: Suppose we cannot tolerate $D \geq 0.006$ more than 1 per cent of the time; suppose further that under certain flying conditions we expect values of $\bar{P}$ to be as great as 320 psi; how shall we design the member under question?   There are at least two answers that may be considered.   One answer may be to design for a "stiffer" member such that for this member and $\bar{P} = 320$ psi, $D \geq 0.006$ less than 1 per cent of the time.   Another answer may be that both technical and economic requirements preclude the general changes which would be initiated by such a design change and that therefore the aircraft is not to be considered airworthy under the conditions referred to.

It must be borne in mind that the loads to which aircraft structural members are subject are not known with certainty. Nevertheless, modern statistical theory provides means whereby the risk of failure

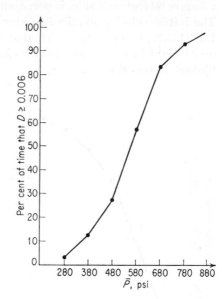

Figure 1.12   Percentage of the $D \geq 0.006$ versus $\bar{P}$.

of such structural supports can be reduced to a very low percentage which is practically acceptable.

1.5   Example: variability in ballistics

A problem frequently encountered today is that of determining the range of a projectile, in order to determine the relative frequency with which a given target can be hit.   The formulation given to this problem is similar to that of many engineering and industrial problems and is offered because of its simplicity.   Consider now a target whose center is situated at some distance R (called the range) from the gun.   Under certain conditions the following simple relation exists between initial projectile velocity v and the range R:

$$R = \frac{v^2}{g} \qquad (1.5.1)$$

(The assumption is made of zero air resistance and 45° gun elevation.) It appears quite simple to determine the projectile range when the initial velocity is known.   It should also be quite simple, therefore, with knowledge of the location of the target center, its shape, and size, to calculate the necessary initial velocity in order that any shot may hit the target center.   There is, however, one joker in this simple picture—the initial velocity cannot be held constant.   In order to study this we shall consider a specific case.

Suppose there is a target center 6,250 feet from a gun and the target, a square 60 feet on a side, is perpendicular to the plane of projectile flight. The initial velocity required to give the range 6,250 feet, obtained from Eq. (1.5.1), is 448.5 fps.   All that is required is to send the projectile on its flight in such a way that its initial velocity is 448.5 fps.   Here the "joker" enters the situation.

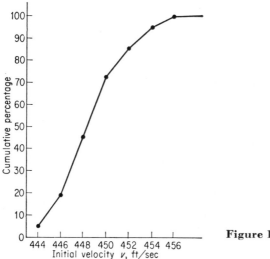

Figure 1.13

The initial velocity at which a projectile leaves the muzzle of a gun is influenced by many variables, among them weight of powder charge, temperature, humidity, and rifling of the muzzle.   It is not possible to hold all these variables constant.   At best, measurable variation in initial velocity results.   In order to cope with this effect we measure the variability of initial velocity under specified conditions and come up with the cumulative-frequency curve in Fig. 1.13, for $\bar{v} = 448.5$ fps.

It should be apparent that what we want to know is the variability in R due to the variability in v, for the values which R takes on determine the relative frequency of hits.   We obtain, then, a cumulative-frequency curve for R by the simple expedient of finding for the observed values of v in Fig. 1.13 the corresponding values of R.   For example, for $v = 446$ fps,

$$ R = \frac{(446)^2}{32.2} = 6,177.5 \text{ feet} $$

Since $v \leq 446$ fps 19 per cent of the time ($\bar{v} = 448.5$), it follows that $R \leq 6,177.5$ feet 19 per cent of the time.   By repetition of this computation, we obtain the cumulative curve for R, where $\bar{v} = 448.5$ fps.   This curve appears in Fig. 1.14.   We can now compute the percentage of hits when $\bar{v} = 448.5$ fps and when v has the variability given by its cumulative-frequency curve in Fig. 1.14.

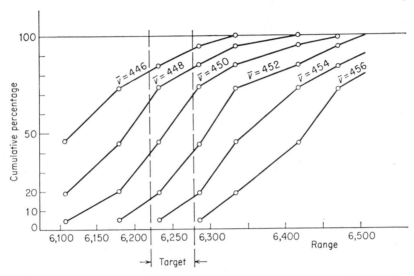

Figure 1.14

The target will be hit when R lies between 6,220 and 6,280 feet (6,250 $\pm$ 30 feet).   Now $R \leq 6,220$ feet 69 per cent of the time; $R \leq 6,280$ feet 85 per cent of the time.   Hence, when $\bar{v} = 448.5$ fps, the target will be hit 16 per cent of the time.   We may well wonder whether this low figure for hits is the best we can do.   We selected $\bar{v}$ to be 448.5 fps because it is the value obtained (approximately) from Eq. (1.5.1) when $R = 6,250$ feet.   We try a number of values for $\bar{v}$, each with the same variability that was observed for $\bar{v} = 448.5$ fps.   (Again this can be obtained by linear translation of the histogram for v so that the mean of v coincides with selected values.)   The cumulative curves are then computed by the procedure given in the example in Sec. 1.3.   Proceeding as above for each of the values of $\bar{v}$ in Fig. 1.14, we obtain the relative frequency of hits.   This is depicted in Fig. 1.15.   For $\bar{v} = 452$ feet we obtain 27 per cent as the relative frequency of hits.   Carrying this further, the greatest percentage of hits is 32 per cent, obtained for $\bar{v} = 450$ fps.   It is interesting to note that the mean velocity corresponding to the range of the target center, namely, $\bar{v} = 448.5$ fps, does not give the maximum percentage of hits.   In fact, the relative frequency of hits is doubled at the optimum mean initial velocity.

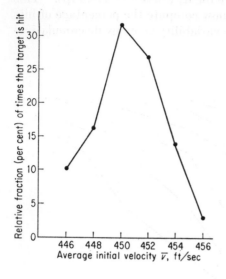

Figure 1.15   Per cent target hits vs. average initial velocity $\bar{v}$.

1.6 Example: variability in physical "constants"

Our conceptualization of the physical universe entails the notion of the existence of certain physical "constants."   For the present discussion, a physical constant is some entity possessing a numerical identification which is fixed under all circumstances in which it is used in determining other physical parameters.   The validity of this notion is not under consideration; it is accepted.   The velocity of light is one such constant; the charge on an electron is another.   A constant most commonly used is the earth's gravitational effect under specified conditions, usually denoted by g.   The notion of a "universal physical constant" would carry less conviction were it not possible to identify these quantities observationally.   This task has attracted the attention of distinguished scientists throughout history.   In some cases, as a result of the work of imaginative and brilliant experimenters, rather simple experiments, which can be performed by a student in the laboratory, have been devised to measure such constants.   We shall consider one of these experiments and its statistical implications.

Here we consider identifying numerically the gravitational constant g (supposedly) at sea level, latitude 40.0°N.   The experiment we use entails the free oscillation of a simple pendulum (Fig. 1.16).   We accept the assumptions that:

1. The pendulum consists of a point mass.

2. The pendulum is attached to a frictionless point of oscillation by a weightless string.

3. The only effect on the motion of the pendulum is that of gravity, as expressed by the "true" gravitational constant g (air resistance and the like are neglected).

Now the relationship among the variables involved is

$$T = 2\pi \sqrt{\frac{l}{g}} \tag{1.6.1}$$

where g is the gravitational constant to be estimated, l is the constant length of the pendulum, and T is the period of the free oscillation.   (θ is assumed "small.")

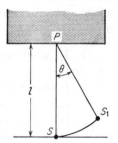

Figure 1.16

We can observe T directly, once we have established θ and l.   We emphasize again that we assume that both θ and l are known without error.   The formula used in relating g to the other variables is an approximation from an exact formulation in which θ is assumed to be small. Granting all these conditions, setting the pendulum on its course of free oscillation, we measure T as well as we can.   We make repeated observations on T since we are not inclined to rely on but one or two measurements of T.   We apparently are already aware of the presence of variability in even the best-planned and most accurately controlled experiment.   We now raise the question as to what effect this variability has on estimating g.

Suppose we have obtained the following N observations: T_1, T_2, . . . , T_N.   There seem to be at least two natural approaches to the estimation of g from the data.

1. Find the arithmetic average

$$\bar{T} = \frac{T_1 + T_2 + \cdots + T_N}{N}$$

and substitute $\bar{T}$ for T in Eq. (1.6.1) and solve for g, yielding g^*, where $g^* = 4\pi^2 l / \bar{T}^2$.

2. Determine $g_1, g_2, \ldots, g_N$ from Eq. (1.6.1), corresponding to the respective values of $T_1, T_2, \ldots, T_N$. Then obtain the arithmetic average

$$\bar{g} = \frac{g_1 + \cdots + g_N}{N}$$

It may not surprise the reader when he discovers that, in general,

$$g^* \neq \bar{g} \tag{1.6.2}$$

When this is the case, we want something more fundamental than the simplicity of an estimating procedure or its similarity to other accepted estimating procedures to serve as a criterion for choosing between the two methods of estimation.   We can readily see some issues arising which we might take into consideration in establishing a preferred estimating procedure:

1. In what way is one estimate more advantageous than another estimate?
2. Is one of these estimates more accurate than the other?
3. Is one of these estimates more precise than the other?
4. By what means can we discriminate between the relative accuracies and the relative precisions of different estimating procedures?
5. What set of criteria would you offer for preferring one procedure over another?

In raising this discussion we have not intended to answer these questions.   Our aim has been merely to illustrate the importance of developing systematic methods for handling the difficulties associated with estimating indirectly observed values under conditions of variability.   The subsequent developments in the text on probability and statistical inference will provide the necessary means for investigating such problems in a fruitful manner.

This chapter has been presented in order to introduce the reader by natural steps to the need for a systematic treatment of uncertainty.   We have tried to select problems which cover a varied range of engineering and industrial and scientific interest wherein the focus in the main has been on decision making under uncertainty.   All the problems have essential features in common and submit to common methods of treatment.   We have, however, used only the simplest conceptions and techniques for getting answers, and in some instances we merely emphasized the nature and importance of the problem.   We have avoided any attempt at rigor, and we have not introduced any formal concepts or definitions at this stage.   We have aimed primarily at stimulating the reader's interest in the principles and techniques that will be developed in the succeeding chapters.

In the development which follows, we shall return to a number of the problems which were examined here in a somewhat elementary fashion and treat them with more sophistication.   We have, however, tried explicitly to make the reader conscious of the following salient points.

Variability   There exists in most real situations the characteristic of variability.   Decisions that must be made on such a "simple" matter as a measurement of a physical dimension of a metal object is confounded by the variability encountered in repeated measurements.   Decision as to how to adjust a machine for rolling steel bars to a specified length is a complex problem because of the presence of variability in the results of a supposedly "constant" rolling process.   The principal factor to be dealt with in many important engineering, industrial, and scientific problems is the fact of variability.

Technical and Economic Consequences of Variability   Many technical decisions in the presence of variability (under uncertainty) are influenced by the cost consequences of variability, considered in the light of the purposes and aims of the technical operation in question.   It is to be expected, therefore, that accurate and effective decisions on engineering, industrial, and scientific problems require a close scrutiny of aims, purposes, and costs.   This, we hope, has been illustrated to some extent by the examples, especially where the occasional unexpected consequences of variability were at variance with "common intuition."   It even further emphasizes the need for a systematic quantitative treatment of uncertainty as exemplified in the concepts and techniques of probability, statistical inference, and statistical control.

Probability   The present treatment of the examples presented above has been, of necessity, empirical and arithmetical.   In consequence, the computations and manipulations were rather cumbersome and tedious. Distributions of observations were represented graphically or tabularly, but not formally.   Much simplification in the handling of these problems results from formal techniques.   These techniques constitute the field of probability and statistical inference.   We also indicated the inadequacy of some "simple" methods for the treatment of some problems.   In these problems it is essential that formal techniques be utilized.

Statistical Stability and Experimental Inference   A crucial assumption pervading the treatment of all the illustrative problems is that "the future is approximately as the immediate past."   In industrial and engineering practice this is often not the case.   In fact, a basic concern in these fields is how to attain that state of a situation in which one can be confident that the future imitates the past.   Such a situation is said to be in a *state of statistical stability.*   The validity of the application of probability and statistical inference is predicated upon the existence of a state of statistical stability. Attaining and maintaining statistical stability is a basic and profoundly important engineering and industrial task, essential in experimental inference and in accurate and effective decision making under uncertainty.

The actual practice of bringing about statistical stability and providing criteria for determining when this state does or does not exist is essentially based on the principles and techniques of statistical inference. We have the following interesting interplay of the concepts of statistical stability and statistical inference:

1. *Statistical stability* is essential for the validity of *statistical inference*.
2. *Statistical inference* is essential for establishing criteria for *statistical stability*.

These interesting relations, which together provide an essential part of experimental inference, will be developed in subsequent chapters.

The illustrative examples have been presented in order to emphasize the important roles of probability, statistical-inference, and statistical-stability concepts. Of necessity, however, some artifices have been used, which we hope have not vitiated the illustrative effectiveness of these problems. We hope, further, that the reader will now pursue the text with a genuine interest in the subject matter that is to be developed.

The foregoing exposition, together with these summarizing remarks, suggests the serious questions encountered in experimental inference and decision making. In particular, we have illustrated the difficulties which must be overcome in order to make effective decisions under uncertainty.

Exercises

1.1. Referring to the example in Sec. 1.1, find:

a. The best setting when $C_t/C_u = C_p/C_u = 0.5$ and $C_s/C_u = 0.4$.
b. The average number of feet of short bars when the setting is 10.0 feet.
c. The best setting and per cent loss in steel if the manufacturer wants to produce steel bars 30 feet long, with a tolerance ± 0.30 foot (assume that the character of variability is the same as in the text and that the criterion of optimum is the minimum per cent loss in steel).
d. Referring to (c) and assuming that a setting of 30 feet is used, the per cent long bars and the average number of feet of scrap steel for long bars.

1.2. Referring to the example in Sec. 1.3, find:

The curve of average daily profit vs. number of lots bought in the morning when unsold lots left at the end of day are not an outright loss but can be resold to the wholesaler for $10 per lot.

1.3. Referring to the example in Sec. 1.4, find:

a. $\bar{P}$, such that the per cent of loads $D \leq 0.007$ foot is about 85.

b. The histogram for D when $\bar{P}$ is 448 psi.

1.4. Referring to the example in Sec. 1.5, find:

a. Optimum $\bar{v}$ when the target center is at a range of 6,250 feet but is 100 feet square.

b. The frequency of target hits for this optimum $\bar{v}$.

c. The histogram for range R when $\bar{v}$ is 452 fps.

1.5. Two machines, A and B, each have 10,000 hours of life. Machine A costs $10,000, and machine B costs $15,000. Each machine produces parts which are sold at $1 apiece. The cost of production, disregarding the initial cost of the machine, is 50 cents per part. The machines do not produce parts at the same rate; moreover, the number of parts produced per hour varies. Fifty hours of observations yielded the following numbers of parts produced per hour:

Machine A

8	3	5	6	6	6	4	8	7	4
6	8	4	7	6	4	6	7	4	3
4	8	5	6	3	5	5	5	7	7
8	6	4	5	4	9	4	3	8	4
4	5	5	4	3	6	4	4	4	6

Machine B

7	7	8	8	5	5	7	9	7	4
4	5	7	7	7	8	7	6	8	8
10	7	8	7	3	9	7	10	8	8
4	7	3	7	7	7	7	8	7	8
8	7	6	3	7	7	8	8	7	8

a. Tabulate the cumulative frequency distributions for the above data.

b. Compute the mean profit per hour from machine A and from machine B, taking into account production costs.

c. An additional investment of $5,000 on machine B would reduce the production cost per part to 30 cents. Is this investment justifiable?

d. How many hours over the lifetimes of the machines does machine B work at a rate which is not less than that of machine A?

e. What other criteria for comparing the machines can you suggest?

1.6. A container is to be designed for a part. When part length is smaller than the container length, the gap is filled by felt pads 0.125 inch thick. Current experience with the production of containers and parts yields a distribution of their differences, E, given in the table below.   The cost of a felt pad is C_p.   The cost of an interference (part longer than container, that is, $E < 0$) is given by C_I.

Distribution of cell boundary, inches	Per cent
0.0355–0.0955	1
0.0955–0.1555	1
0.1555–0.2155	4
0.2155–0.2755	5
0.2755–0.3355	13
0.3355–0.3955	18
0.3955–0.4555	22
0.4555–0.5155	23
0.5155–0.5755	8
0.5755–0.6355	5

a. Find the arithmetic average of E (gap length).
b. Find the average number of felt pads used.
c. What cost do you expect for packing 1,000 containers when $C_p = 3$ cents? What assumptions are you making?
d. What would be the per cent interference if the average container length is reduced by 0.20 inch?   What cost (due to interference and felt pads) would be accrued in this case for the conditions in (c) (assume $C_I = 8$ cents)?
e. Plot per cent interference as a function of $\bar{r}$, where $\bar{r}$ is the average number of inches that the container length is reduced, assuming the above table.
f. Plot expected cost per container as a function of $\bar{r}$.
g. Find optimum $\bar{r}$.

2

SOME PRINCIPLES OF PROBABILITY

2.1 Experiments and their outcomes

We shall attempt to formalize our analysis of experiments. It may be well to ask ourselves, why formalize, and what constitutes formal analysis? But let us begin by asking why we perform an experiment. Why, for example, do we put a pendulum into free motion? We say we want to know the period of the pendulum. In fact, we risk little contradiction if we say that we usually take action in order to achieve specified objectives; we perform experiments in order to achieve specified objectives. The reader may ask how objectives are chosen, and we may rule this question out of bounds for the present discussion. The reader, however, may press for further enlightenment. We beg his indulgence and ask him to read on as we sketch some steps in the formal analysis of probabilities associated with experiments and let him judge the why and the value thereof.

For later discussion, we consider experiments E_1, E_2, . . . , E_9, briefly described as follows:

E_1 Tossing a coin once
E_2 Tossing a coin three times
E_3 Observing a piece of cloth one foot square coming from some process and sampled in a prescribed way
E_4 Calling Washington, D.C., on a Monday at 10 A.M. (no holiday)
E_5 Rolling steel bars (example in Sec. 1.1)
E_6 Observing deflection of a top-loaded column (example in Sec. 1.4)
E_7 Observing demand for lots on a particular day (example in Sec. 1.3)
E_8 Firing projectile on a target (example in Sec. 1.5)
E_9 Measuring period of a pendulum in a prescribed manner (example in Sec. 1.6)

Let us analyze experiment E_9. To begin with, we attempt an unambiguous specification of E_9—if possible, in somewhat colloquial terms—as follows.   Tie a string to a small lead sphere, and attach the other end of the string to a fixed point P so that $\overline{PS}$ measures 100 centimeters (Fig. 1.16).   Displace S to the right so that in the new position angle SPS_1 measures θ degrees, a "small" angle.   Release the sphere.   It descends freely and swings back and forth freely.   Let the pendulum make two "full" swings, and on its third full swing, note the chronometer readings when the pendulum passes the vertical position and again when it next passes the vertical from right to left.   The outcome is specified by the difference between these two chronometer readings.   (In Chap. 11 it will become apparent why we require two free swings before making the first measurement.)

This is a specification of E_9.   All conceivable outcomes of E_9 must be positive real numbers.   Call the first result t_1, the second t_2, etc., giving a set $\{t_i\}$.   What restrictions are there on $\{t_i\}$ (where we may assume for formal purposes that $i = 1, 2, \ldots, n \rightarrow \infty$)?   They are assuredly real numbers, and they are positive; they need not be integers; they are not restricted as to magnitude.   Hence the conceivable outcomes of E_9 can be said to be found among the positive real numbers.   To be sure, if the chronometer readings are limited to three significant figures to the right of the decimal point, and if the unit is in seconds, $\{t_i\}$ will be multiples of 0.001 second.   For example, the outcomes may be 0.000, 0.001, . . . , 0.015, . . . , 0.078, . . . , 0.099, 1.000, 1,001, . . . , 1.279, . . . , 11.300, . . . , etc., seconds.   We may say that "all conceivable outcomes of experiment E_9" are comprised of all positive numbers which, when multiplied by 1,000, yield integers.

Why, we may ask, were our outcomes limited to numbers with three places to the right of the decimal point?   This was so because in this experiment we could not distinguish, say, between 0.1011 and 0.1014 second on our chronometer.   Hence we were inclined to drop the fourth figure to the right of the decimal point.   Or again, we could not distinguish between 2.1735 and 2.1744.   Here we compromised by designating all numbers x such that $2.1735 \leq x \leq 2.1744$ as $x = 2.174$.

Suppose we could distinguish between 2.17388 and 2.17389, but not among numbers x such that $2.173885 \leq x \leq 2.173894$.   Then we should designate $x = 2.17389$.   We would express our measurement by numbers with five figures to the right of the decimal point, and our sample space would consist of all positive numbers with five figures to the right of the decimal point.   Another way of saying this is that all positive numbers which, when multiplied by 100,000, become integers are members of our sample space.

The foregoing is part of the formal analysis of concepts of experiments and their outcomes, as well as their representation by numbers.   Such an analysis may help us predict the outcomes of future repetitions of experiments.   Let us perform E_1, the coin-tossing experiment, as follows. Place a United States penny on the thumb, and rest the index finger against the thumb with light pressure.   Raise the thumb upward with a snap motion, displacing the penny upward in rotary motion.   Let the penny fall freely on a fixed flat surface, and when it comes to rest read the visible face of the penny.   The result will be designated as either H (head) or T (tail).   The conceivable outcomes are just H and T, which constitute the sample space of E_1.   (No, we do not conceive of the penny as either remaining aloft or resting on its circumferential edge.)   This is a discrete sample space; it is not comprised of numbers.   It is advisable to think of outcomes of experiments as not necessarily representable by numbers, but merely as definite, identifiable "situations."   In the case of E_9, the outcomes were given as time magnitudes, to each of which there corresponded uniquely a positive real number which corresponded, also uniquely, to a point of the real half line $[0, \infty]$. E_1 yields a discrete sample space not necessarily associated with real numbers.

Consider next the sample space of E_2.   Quite intuitively, we can list the conceivable outcomes:

$$
\begin{array}{ll}
HHH & THH \\
HHT & THT \\
HTH & TTH \\
HTT & TTT
\end{array}
$$

We have exhausted all outcomes; there are but eight of them, each distinct from the other.   This is again a discrete sample space, apparently nonnumerical, or at least not necessarily so.   We shall develop this example further in the next chapter.

Let us recapitulate.   We have specified an experiment in words in such a way that others can carry out essentially the same steps in performing the experiment.   Furthermore, having specified the experiment, we believe that we can repeat it in essentially the same way.   We have included observation of the outcome in the specification of some experiments and have called attention to each distinct conceivable outcome. For E_9 there are conceivably an infinite number of outcomes, whereas for E_1 and E_2 there are a finite number of possible outcomes.   We have indicated that an outcome may be representable in a variety of forms, the essence of an outcome being its identifiability and its uniqueness. For E_1 one possible outcome is H.   We can think of and focus attention on H in response to whatever question is put to us about E_1.   The totality of outcomes of E_1 $\{H,T\}$ can be represented in several ways.

The outcomes of E_9 are represented by numbers; these numbers can be associated with points on a line.   Note that, usually, we can associate an outcome of an experiment, however it is observed, with a point. These points can, in general, be associated with a space with whose geometric and metric properties we are familiar.   We have referred to the totality of outcomes for a given experiment as a sample space.   An individual outcome is called a sample point (although outcome is certainly a satisfactory name when referring to sample space).   The concepts of experiment, outcome, sample space, and sample point are instruments in the formal analysis of probability which help us anticipate the consequences of certain well-defined activities (experiments).   The formal analysis helps us anticipate results in a reproducible manner.   It helps us predict the results of experiment so that we can initiate action which yields desired objectives.

We have now essentially defined experiment and outcome, key concepts, and one other concept, namely, observation.   Recall that in the specifications of experiments we sometimes referred to the act of observation.   Furthermore, there are experiments which consist primarily of observation.   For example, we may be interested in determining the "required" number of turnstiles at the entrance to a subway.   As a first step one may want to know the number of people passing through the turnstiles.   This requires an act of observation: count the number of people who enter the subway portal during a specified number of minutes on a specified day at a specified time.   Such an act of observation may be called an experiment.   Observation is not limited to the counting of people or objects; observation can be considerably involved. In E_6 the observation is not performed without skill, and the observation is the essence of the experiment, although not the "all" of the experiment. Bear in mind that as we have used the term experiment, manipulation of the variables need not necessarily be required; observation can constitute experiment.

2.2   Sample space

We have referred to the results of experiments as outcomes.   We have considered some specific experiments and their outcomes.   For purposes of consistency and clarity, we shall designate each possible outcome of an experiment as a *sample point*.   The totality of all possible outcomes of an experiment is called the sample space of the experiment.

Definition: sample space   The totality of possible sample points resulting from an experiment is designated as the sample space of the experiment.

It is apparent from the examples considered that some sample spaces are finite while others can be considered to be infinite.   In particular, the sample space of E_2 definitely consists of eight sample points, and is called a finite sample space.   On the other hand, sample spaces can be infinite, at least conceptually.   We specified experiment E_9 with a least count of 0.0001 second.   If we consider the elapsed time for one full swing of the pendulum to be bounded, there are only a finite number of possible sample points. Instead of specifying an upper bound, it may be more convenient to consider the elapsed time unbounded. In this case the sample space consists of an infinite number of sample points.

These sample points are isolated one from another by at least the magnitude of the least count. Now suppose that we let the least count in E_9 become smaller. It is convenient here, and in many other experiments, to conceptualize the sample space as consisting of a continuum of sample points. Such sample spaces are referred to as *continuous sample spaces*.

2.2.1 Events

In most cases we are interested in particular combinations of the sample points. A few examples will illustrate this notion.

Example 2.1 Conceptually, the sample points corresponding to E_5 (rolling steel bars to a specified length) are nonnegative and can be conveniently thought of as positive real numbers. The sample space S then consists of all points on the positive real axis,[1]

$$S = \{x: \quad x > 0\}$$

Some sets of interest are:

1. Steel bars of length 10 ± 0.30 feet, that is, bars within tolerance limits. The corresponding set is

$$S = \{x: \quad 9.70 \leq x \leq 10.30\}$$

2. Bar lengths greater than 10.30 feet, that is, bars that are too long and must be trimmed. The corresponding set is

$$S = \{x: \quad x > 10.30\}$$

Example 2.2 E_2 was the experiment of tossing a coin three times. For convenience we can describe the sample space corresponding to E_2 as a set composed of triplets such as (H,H,T) which denotes the outcome: head on first two tosses and tail on the last toss. The sample space consists of eight triplets, namely:

s_1:	(H,H,H)	s_5:	(T,H,H)
s_2:	(H,H,T)	s_6:	(T,H,T)
s_3:	(H,T,H)	s_7:	(T,T,H)
s_4:	(H,T,T)	s_8:	(T,T,T)

---

[1] $S = \{x: x > 0\}$ reads: the set of all values of x for which $x > 0$. This notation is used further in denoting point sets, as well as $S = \{x|x > 0\}$.

Some sets of interest are:

1. Heads on the first toss. The subset of the sample space corresponding to this specification is composed of the sample points s_1, s_2, s_3, and s_4.

2. At least one tail. The corresponding subset is composed of s_2, s_3, s_4, s_5, s_6, s_7, and s_8.

In each of the examples given above, subsets of the sample space were selected for special consideration. Sample points which fall into a selected set are said to correspond to a specified event. For example, results of experiment E_5 that consist of bars of length 10 ± 0.30 feet constitute the *event*, bars within tolerances. Again, in E_2 the specification heads on the first toss is an event and corresponds to a subset of the sample space. We now have the following definition.

Definition: event   An event of an experiment E is defined as a collection (set) of sample points of the sample space, S of E. An event is thus a subset of the set S and is well defined, if and only if the description of the event enables us to classify unambiguously each and every sample point as either belonging or not belonging to the event.

The notion of event is singled out for consideration and formal definition because our main interest, in a formal study of experiments and their outcomes, is, clearly, to make predictions about the occurrence of events of special interest.

2.2.2 Compound events

In Example 2.1 we expressed interest in the events, bars within tolerance and bars too long. We might also have referred to bars which are too short. We are, however, also interested in the class of usable bars, which comprises not only those within tolerance, but also the long bars which can be trimmed to usable size. In order to facilitate computations of probabilities and costs involved in the rolling of steel bars we shall specify the events involved in formal terms:

Event A (bars within tolerances): $A = \{x: \ 9.70 \leq x \leq 10.30\}$
Event B (bars too long): $B = \{x: \ x > 10.30\}$
Event C (short bars): $C = \{x: \ 0 \leq x < 9.70\}$
Event D (usable bars): $D = \{x: \ x \geq 9.70\}$

Every sample point of the sample space S in this experiment falls into one of the sets A, B, or C. This is equivalent to saying that one of the events A, B, or C must occur.

This decomposition could have been made in another way. Obviously, the "sum" of sets C and D also exhausts the sample space S, for a bar is either too short or usable. Let us note here that a sample space can be decomposed in more than one way. It is also evident that some events are decomposable in terms of others. In particular, the set D is the "sum" of sets A and B; usable bars consists of within-tolerance bars and long bars.

We shall formalize some useful notions of events and sets, beginning with definitions.

Definition: complement event An event, in the sample space S, consisting of all points not contained in event A, will be called the complement of A and will be denoted by $\bar{A}$; that is, to each event A, there corresponds another event $\bar{A}$, defined by the condition "A does not occur." Simple geometric representation is given in Fig. 2.1.

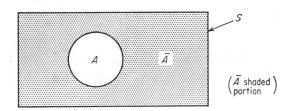

Figure 2.1 Complement.

Definition: union (logical sum) The union of two sets A and B is defined as a set C such that

$$C = A + B = \{x: \quad x \in A \quad or \quad x \in B\}$$

where $x \in A$ means "x belongs to the set A."

The verbal description corresponding to the union of two events is "either or." Thus, "either A or B" occurs is seen to include all the sample points of the set $A + B$. In the previous example of the steel

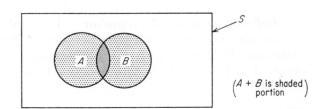

Figure 2.2 Union.

bars the union of the sets A and B was equal to the set D. It is clear that for any sample space and any event A,

$$S = A + \bar{A}$$

Definition: intersection   The intersection of two events A and B is defined as

$$C = A \cdot B = \{x:\ x \in A \qquad and \qquad x \in B\}$$

Note that the set C contains all those points which are *both* in A and in B.

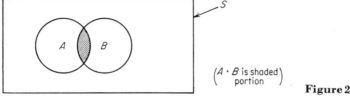

$\begin{pmatrix} A \cdot B \text{ is shaded} \\ \text{portion} \end{pmatrix}$

Figure 2.3   Intersection.

Definition: inclusion   The event B is said to include the event A if $x \in A$ implies that $x \in B$.   This relationship is formally denoted by

$$A \subset B$$

The occurrence of the event A logically implies the occurrence of event B. In the example of the steel bars an occurrence within tolerance certainly implies usability.

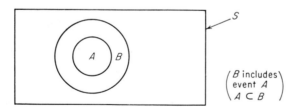

$\begin{pmatrix} B \text{ includes} \\ \text{event } A \\ A \subset B \end{pmatrix}$

Figure 2.4   Inclusion.

Definition: mutual exclusion   The events A and B are said to be mutually exclusive if they do not contain any points in common. More formally, if $C = A \cdot B = \phi$ (where ϕ denotes the empty set), then events A and B are said to be mutually exclusive.

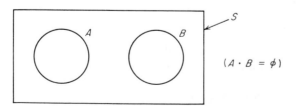

$(A \cdot B = \phi)$

Figure 2.5   Mutual exclusion.

Example 2.3   To illustrate these definitions, we refer back to Example 2.2.   Denote the event heads on the first toss by A, the event at least one tail by B, and the event two tails by C.   It follows, then, that:

1. $A + B$ consists of the whole sample space: $A + B = S$.
2. $A \cdot B$ consists of the points s_2, s_3, and s_4.
3. $C \subset B$.
4. $\bar{A}$ consists of the points s_5, s_6, s_7, and s_8.
5. B consists of the points s_2, s_3, s_4, s_5, s_6, s_7, and s_8.
6. C consists of the points s_4, s_6, and s_7.
7. $B \cdot \bar{C}$ consists of the points s_2, s_3, s_5, and s_8.

A brief résumé in both verbal and symbolic form of relations among events (sets) follows.

Verbal description	Set notation
The event A has not occurred	$\bar{A}$
Either the event A or B has occurred	$A + B$
Simultaneously the events A and B have occurred	$A \cdot B$
The event A but not B has occurred	$A \cdot \bar{B}$
The occurrence of A implies the occurrence of B	$A \subset B$
The events A and B cannot occur simultaneously	$A \cdot B = \phi$

The outcomes of experiments can now be looked upon as sample points.   Events are sets of sample points.   It has been shown that some events, called compound events, are combinations of other events.   A central problem in the analysis of experiments is to reduce compound events that are of interest to combinations of events whose probabilities are more readily accessible.

2.3   Measure of probability

In the previous sections we have developed some definitions in order to simplify the notions of events.   An important and ever-present feature of the examples discussed is the assumption of stability.   In the example of rolling steel bars it is necessary to assume that the initial sample yielded relative frequencies of short, long, and satisfactory steel bars which would, in some sense, persist if more bars were rolled.   It is clear that such an assumption is necessary to make meaningful statements concerning the bar-length setting for the rolling process which would minimize costs for rolling 10,000 bars.

Consider an event A and let $N_k(A)$ denote the number of times event A has occurred when an experiment is repeated k times.   As an example, consider the event where the steel-bar length lies within tolerance (that is, 10 ± 0.30 feet). It is clear that $N_k(A)$ will vary with increasing k. Under certain circumstances, there is reason to believe that, even though $N_k(A)$ fluctuates with k, the fraction $N_k(A)/k$ will, for large k, remain "stable." The stable value which $N_k(A)/k$ approaches is associated with the idea of the probability of A. Thus we write

$$\frac{N_k(A)}{k} \approx P(A)$$

This is understood to mean that, for k "large," the value of $N_k(A)/k$ stabilizes to some value $P(A)$.

Formally, the notion of probability measure can be given by the following definition.

Definition: probability of event A With a given experiment, we assume the existence of a function P, which assigns a number $P(A)$ to each event A in the sample space S. The number is called the *probability* of event A. Some properties of this function are:

1. $P(S) = 1$.
2. $P(A) \geq 0$.
3. If $A \cdot B = \phi$, then $P(A + B) = P(A) + P(B)$.

The calculus of probabilities can be developed from properties 1, 2, and 3 considered as axioms.[1] Properties 1 to 3 are natural ones if we keep in mind the interpretation of probabilities in terms of relative frequencies. These relations should be verified by the reader. The usefulness of probabilities in describing reality depends on particular circumstances. Let it suffice at this point to say that its value has been shown in a wide variety of circumstances.

It should be emphasized that $P(A)$ refers to both event A and the experiment under consideration. For example, when one discusses the probability of functioning of a component (that is, its reliability) one is talking about the component *plus* its reaction to the environmental conditions implied in the specification of the experiment. When one discusses probabilities, it is essential to keep in mind the experiment under consideration.

The assumption of stability is the connection between our *formal* notion of probability and the *empirical* evidence of regularities in the behavior of certain events in sequences of repeated experiments. Such correspondence between relative frequencies and assigned probabilities is well known to exist in most gambling games. Statistical regularities have also been found to exist in phenomena of interest to engineers, scientists, businessmen, government officials, and, in general, all

---

[1] To assure the existence of P, satisfying 1 to 3, we must, for complicated sample spaces, restrict the class of events to those called measurable.

decision makers. It is clear that statistical regularity is vital to successful decision making in the face of uncertainty.

2.3.1   Example of calculating probabilities of events

Consider again the example in Sec. 1.1. Assume that the process of rolling steel bars to a 10-foot length is stable. Let the relative frequency of occurrence of 100 bars as tabulated in Table 1.3 be representative of future occurrences. Define events A_1, A_2, . . . , A_{11} as the occurrence of bars whose lengths fall, respectively, into cell numbers 1 to 11. The assignment of probabilities can be quite arbitrary so long as the resulting 11 numbers satisfy the properties set down in our definition.

Nevertheless, the relationship among the actual occurrences of bars of different lengths and good empirical sense leads us to make the following probability assignment: to each event A_i assign probability equal to the cell frequency divided by the total number of occurrences. This yields Table 2.1.

TABLE 2.1

Event	Probability $P(A_i) = p_i$
A_1	0.00
A_2	0.01
A_3	0.04
A_4	0.11
A_5	0.26
A_6	0.24
A_7	0.18
A_8	0.09
A_9	0.04
A_{10}	0.02
A_{11}	0.01

The lower tolerance is 9.70 feet; the upper tolerance is 10.30 feet. Thus the event short bars (event C in Sec. 2.2.2) consists of the logical sum of events A_1, A_2, A_3, and A_4. Hence, since the events A_1, . . . , A_4 are mutually exclusive,

$$P(C) = P(A_1) + P(A_2) + P(A_3) + P(A_4)$$
$$= 0.00 + 0.01 + 0.04 + 0.11 = 0.16$$

Similarly, the number of usable bars is the event which is the complement of event C. Thus the probability of obtaining usable bars is $1 - P(C) = 0.84$. The probabilities of other compound events can be obtained in a similar manner.

In Sec. 2.6 we elaborate on the rules for combining probabilities of events and develop, somewhat rigorously, some of the essential elements of a probability calculus.

For purposes of illustration, before leaving this section, we return to our coin-tossing example.

2.3.2 Example of events in coin tossing

Consider the experiment of tossing a coin three times. The sample space consists of eight members. Let us suppose that all the outcomes $s_1, s_2, \ldots, s_8$ are equally likely; that is, in terms of the relative-frequency interpretation of probability, the relative frequency $N_k(s_j)/k$ approaches $\frac{1}{8}$. In order to find the probabilities associated with various events, we use property 3 (on page 44). For example, the probability that at least one tail occurs is calculated from $P(B) = p(s_2) + p(s_3) + \cdots + p(s_8) = \frac{7}{8}$. For any finite discrete sample space with sample points $x_1, x_2, \ldots, x_N$, we can completely specify the probability function P if we are given $p_1, p_2, \ldots, p_N$ such that

$$0 \leq p_j \leq 1 \qquad j = 1, \ldots, N$$

and

$$p_1 + p_2 + \cdots + p_N = 1$$

The value of p_j is, of course, meant to be the probability that outcome x_j occurs.

2.4 Conditional probability

2.4.1 Illustrative example

We have so far introduced the notion of probability and indicated its relationship with the frequency of events occurring in repeated trials. In order to clarify these concepts further, we consider the following exercise in sampling.

A box contains 10 items, of which 3 are defective.
A sample of 2 is drawn from the box in the following way: first one is drawn; then a second is drawn *without replacing* the first.

We have spelled out this method of sampling to distinguish it from sampling with replacement; namely, the second drawing occurs only after the first item drawn has been replaced. We shall show later that the sample spaces and the probability of various events depend upon the kind of sampling procedure that is used. Let us consider the case of sampling without replacement and find the probability that both items drawn are defective.

The sample space in this experiment consists of all possible pairs of items drawn from 10 items which could result from the sampling procedure. Let us label the 10 items $I_1, I_2, \ldots, I_{10}$. For convenience, we suppose the three defective items to be I_1, I_2, I_3. The sample space is composed of 90 possible outcomes, of the form (I_i, I_j) with $i \neq j$ and $(i = 1, \ldots, 10; j = 1, \ldots, 10)$. Let the event A_1 be the event with I_i defective (that is, $i = 1$, 2, 3) and A_2 the event with I_j defective (that is, $j = 1$, 2, 3). The event A, which is *both* I_i and I_j defective, is the intersection of sets A_1 and A_2 (that is, $A = A_1 \cdot A_2$).

The probability we are seeking, then, is $P(A) = P(A_1 \cdot A_2)$. To find $P(A)$ we must know the probabilities of the basic outcomes in the sample space. The value of $P(A)$ is then the sum of all the probabilities associated with outcomes in the set A. For example, if we assume that all 90 points are equiprobable (that is, the probability assigned each of the 90 possible outcomes is $\frac{1}{90}$), we find that $P(A)$ is $N/90$, where N equals the number of outcomes in the set A. In many problems such a procedure is cumbersome. In general, it is desirable to decompose $P(A_1 \cdot A_2)$ into probabilities involving only events A_1 and A_2 separately. In order to study the possibility of this, we resort to the frequency interpretation of probability. It is emphasized that the frequencies we consider do not *define* the probabilities in question, but merely provide the motivation for the definition.

2.4.2   Probabilities of "conditional" events

For any event, let $N_k(A)$ denote the number of occurrences of event A in a series of k trials of the experiment under consideration. In a previous section we found that $N_k(A)/k$ fluctuated, and that for k "large" it seemed to "stabilize," under certain conditions, to a definite number. This number was identified with probability $P(A)$. For k "large" we want the probability assignment on the sample space to be such that $N_k(A)/k$ is "close" to $P(A)$. Thus we write

$$P(A_1 \cdot A_2) \approx \frac{N_k(A_1 \cdot A_2)}{k} \qquad (2.4.1)$$

We multiply numerator and denominator of the right-hand side of Eq. (2.4.1) by $N_k(A_1)$ and obtain

$$P(A_1 \cdot A_2) \approx \frac{N_k(A_1 \cdot A_2)}{N_k(A_1)} \frac{N_k(A_1)}{k} \qquad N_k(A_1) > 0 \qquad (2.4.2)$$

The term $N_k(A_1)/k$ is recognized as the relative frequency of occurrence of event A_1 and is identified as approximately equal to $P(A_1)$. The term $N_k(A_1 \cdot A_2)/N_k(A_1)$ requires further interpretation. Suppose that in the series of k trials we considered only those occurrences where A_1 *has* occurred. The relative frequency of occurrence of A_2 under the condition that A_1 *has* occurred is then $N_k(A_1 \cdot A_2)/N_k(A_1)$. If we assume that the relative frequency of A_2, under the condition that A_1 has occurred (a conditional events), is "stable," we are motivated to define a conditional probability $P(A_2 \mid A_1)$, where $P(A_2 \mid A_1)$ is for "large" k close to $N_k(A_1 \cdot A_2)/N_k(A_1)$.   Thus we write

$$P(A_2 \mid A_1) \approx \frac{N_k(A_1 \cdot A_2)}{N_k(A_1)}$$

From Eq. (2.4.2) we therefore expect that $P(A_2 \mid A_1)$ will be so interpreted as to be close to $P(A_1 \cdot A_2)/P(A_1)$.

   Definition: conditional probability   The conditional probability of event A_2 on the condition that A_1 has occurred is

$$P(A_2 \mid A_1) = \frac{P(A_1 \cdot A_2)}{P(A_1)} \qquad P(A_1) > 0 \qquad (2.4.3)$$

When $P(A_1) = 0$, $P(A_2 \mid A_1)$ is undefined.

   From this definition we obtain the form of the *multiplication rule*

$$P(A_1 \cdot A_2) = P(A_1)P(A_2 \mid A_1) = P(A_2)P(A_1 \mid A_2) \qquad (2.4.4)$$

We have decomposed $P(A_1 \cdot A_2)$ into a probability of event A_1 and a probability of event A_2 under the condition that A_1 *has* occurred.   The expression in Eq. (2.4.3) could also have been approached by writing

$$P(A_2 \mid A_1) \approx \frac{N_k(A_1 \cdot A_2)/k}{N_k(A_1)/k} \approx \frac{P(A_1 \cdot A_2)}{P(A_1)} \qquad (2.4.5)$$

The concept of conditional probability and the multiplication rule are often of value since $P(A_1 \cdot A_2)$ may be difficult to compute from the original probability assignments on the sample space, while $P(A_1)$ and $P(A_2 \mid A_1)$ may be much simpler to find.

   We now use the multiplication rule to find the probability of drawing at random[1] in two trials (without replacement) two defective items from a box containing 10 items of which 3 are defective.   In this case, we easily find that $P(A_1) = \frac{3}{10}$.   The value of $P(A_2 \mid A_1)$ is obtained by considering the fact that, if the first item drawn is defective (A_1 has occurred), the number of items remaining in the box is 9, of which 2 are defective.   Thus $P(A_2 \mid A_1) = \frac{2}{9}$.   The multiplication rule then gives

$$P(A) = P(A_1 \cdot A_2) = \frac{3}{10} \cdot \frac{2}{9} = \frac{1}{15}$$

(The reader may check this result by referring back to the original sample space.)

   Let us consider the previous situation, with the difference that the sampling is to be performed with replacement.   In this instance $P(A_1)$ is

---

[1] Random sampling is a process of selection of elements from a population so that the outcomes are equiprobable.   In practice, it is often difficult to show that a selection process is random.

still equal to $\frac{3}{10}$ but $P(A_2 \mid A_1)$ is also equal to $\frac{3}{10}$. This is so, for when the first item drawn is replaced, there still remain 3 defectives among the items when the second random drawing takes place. Thus

$$P(A_1 \cdot A_2) = \frac{3}{10} \cdot \frac{3}{10} = \frac{9}{100}$$

It is clear that the knowledge that A_1 has occurred does not affect the probability of A_2 occurring [that is, $P(A_2 \mid A_1) = P(A_2)$].

We have, therefore,

Sampling with replacement: $P(A) = \frac{9}{100} = 0.090$

Sampling without replacement: $P(A) = \frac{1}{15} = 0.067$

2.5   Independence

2.5.1   Independent events

Referring to the previous example, we note that the probability of the event two defectives in two trials is dependent upon whether the selection in the second trial is independent or not of the selection in the first trial. For in order to have two defectives in two trials, the first item drawn must be a defective. The probability of drawing a defective on the second trial depends on whether or not the first item is replaced.

If the first item is replaced, the probability of a defective on the second trial is the same as the probability of drawing a defective on the first trial. Otherwise the probabilities change on successive trials. The multiplication rule

$$P(A_1 \cdot A_2) = P(A_1)P(A_2 \mid A_1)$$

then yields different results, depending upon whether or not $P(A_2 \mid A_1)$ depends on A_1. If $P(A_2 \mid A_1)$ does not depend on A_1, we have

$$P(A_2 \mid A_1) = P(A_2)$$

as in our example. It follows, then, that

$$P(A_1 \cdot A_2) = P(A_1)P(A_2 \mid A_1) = P(A_1)P(A_2)$$

when the $P(A_2 \mid A_1)$ is independent of the occurrence or nonoccurrence of A_1. In this case, the events A_1 and A_2 are said to be independent.

Definition: independence of two events   Two events A and B are said to be *independent* when

$$P(A \mid B) = P(A)$$

or when
$$P(A \cdot B) = P(A)P(B)$$

These two conditions are equivalent one to the other. This is evident from the multiplication rule. The advantage of the independence of two events A and B lies in the simplification of the multiplication rule.

This is all the more evident when we consider the probability of k simultaneous events A_1, A_2, . . . , A_k.

The multiplication rule becomes

$$P(A_1 \cdot A_2 \cdot \cdots \cdot A_k) = P(A_1)P(A_2) \cdots P(A_k)$$

for k independent events.   In fact, we may define k events as independent when this multiplication rule holds.   For nonindependent events defined as other than independent events, the multiplication rule can be quite involved.

2.5.2   Independent experiments

Discussion of independent events would have little merit were there not empirical meaning attached to the notion of independent experiments. These concepts can be fruitfully extended to experiments.   Suppose we have k experiments, E_1, E_2, . . . , E_k.   Another experiment, E, is defined as the joint experiment of performing E_1, E_2, . . . , E_k.   For example, Let E_j ($j = 1$, . . . , k) be the toss of a coin.   The sample space corresponding to E_1 consists of two outcomes, namely, H (heads) and T (tails). Let E_2 be another toss of a coin and let E_3, . . . , E_k be defined similarly. The combined experiment $E = (E_1, E_2, . . . , E_k)$ is the tossing of a coin k times.   The outcomes of E are k-tuples of the form $(X_1, X_2, . . . , X_k)$, where X's can be either H or T.   One possible outcome is $(H, H, T, H,$ . . . $,H)$.   Let A_1, A_2, . . . , A_k be k events (sets of the sample space of E), where A_j specifies an event relating only to E_j (i.e., the occurrence of the event A_j depends only on the outcomes of E_j).   The experiments E_1, E_2, . . . , E_k are said to be *independent* when

$$P(A_1 \cdot A_2 \cdot \cdots \cdot A_k) = P(A_1)P(A_2) \cdots P(A_k) \qquad (2.5.1)$$

for all A_1, A_2, . . . , A_k of the type specified above.

Thus the model for two independent tosses of a coin is that for which $P(H, T)$ is given by the product $P(H) \cdot P(T)$, with (H, T) denoting the event heads on the first toss and tails on the second.   To put it another way, two experiments E_1 and E_2 are independent when the probability of an event A_2 resulting from E_2 does not depend on what happens as a result of experiment E_1; that is,

Prob (event resulting from E_2 | event resulting from E_1)

$$= \text{Prob (event resulting from } E_2)$$

In the example of tossing two coins,

Prob (H in second toss | T in first toss) = Prob (H in second toss)

The definition used here for independence of k events is usually called *k-wise* independence.   The concept of *mutual* independence makes the additional requirement that the events also be 2, 3, . . . , $(k - 1)$-

wise independent. For k experiments, however, the two types of independence are equivalent.

The question of deciding when, in fact, a series of experiments conforms to the model of independence may sometimes be a very difficult statistical problem in itself. The independence of experiments $E_1, \ldots,$ E_k allows us to find probabilities in the sample space of E by referring to the simpler experiments $E_1, E_2, \ldots, E_k$. The fact that this reduction occurs when there is independence is the reason this concept has such a central place in probability theory and statistical inference. The model of independence, just described, has been fruitfully applied in a variety of circumstances.

The next example will clearly demonstrate how the assumption of independence can simplify the calculation of probabilities of complex events from simpler ones.

2.5.3 Example of independent events

Two machines, A and B, consist of N_A and N_B components, respectively. The operation of A and B does not, however, depend in the same way on the successful functioning of their components. For the operation of A all N_A components must function successfully. For B, it is sufficient that at least one of the N_B components functions successfully. Let r_A and r_B be the reliabilities of the components of A and B, respectively; that is, the reliabilities of all A components are equal and denoted by r_A and the reliabilities of all B components are also equal and denoted by r_B. Reliability of A is measured by the probability of successful functioning of A at any time during a specified time interval. If all components are assumed to act independently, what are the reliabilities R_A and R_B of machines A and B? (Examples of such a system might be circuits with all switches in series, A; or all in parallel, B.) To answer this question, we consider machines A and B in turn.

For the operation of A all components must function. The reliability R_A is therefore

$$R_A = \text{Prob (all } N_A \text{ components function)}$$

Let $A_1, \ldots, A_{N_A}$ denote the events of the set of experiments, each of which consists of the operation of the respective components of A, namely, $1, 2, \ldots, N_A$. Then $R_A = \text{Prob} (A_1 \cdot A_2 \cdot \cdots \cdot A_{N_A})$. Since we have assumed the independence of each component, we obtain

$$R_A = r_A \cdot r_A \cdot \cdots \cdot r_A = (r_A)^{N_A}$$

Thus R_A decreases with increasing N_A. For machine B we have $R_B = \text{Prob (at least one component functions)}$. To calculate R_B we note that the probability F_B of machine B failing is given by $F_B = 1 - R_B$. Thus we have $R_B = 1 - \text{Prob (all } N_B \text{ components fail)}$.

Since the failure of machine B implies the failure of all N_B components, it is clear, the probability of failure of any component being $1 - r_B$, that the probability of all N_B components failing simultaneously is

$$F_B = (1 - r_B)^{N_B}$$

Thus $$R_B = 1 - F_B = 1 - (1 - r_B)^{N_B}$$

The value of R_B increases with increasing N_B.

Suppose that $r_A = 0.75$, $N_A = 2$, and $r_B = 0.2$. How large must N_B be so that $R_B > R_A$? From the previous equations we obtain

$$R_A = (0.75)^2 = 0.5625$$

and $$R_B = 1 - (1 - 0.2)^{N_B} = 1 - (0.8)^{N_B}$$

On solving the equation $0.5625 = 1 - (0.8)^{N_B}$, we obtain the value of N_B such that $R_B > R_A$. Rather than try to solve a transcendental equation, we may calculate R_B for successive values of N_B, obtaining the following result:

N_B	R_B
1	0.2000
2	0.3600
3	0.4880
4	0.5904

Therefore, when the number of components N_B of machine B is 4 or greater, the reliability of machine B is greater than that of machine A.

2.6 Combination of probabilities

In this section we present certain rules of combination which will simplify the computation of probabilities. The aim here, as previously, is to express the probabilities of certain events in terms of the probabilities of other events. The development of this section is formal in the sense that we assume as given the sample space with certain prescribed probabilities associated with the outcomes. The immediate relevance of this model to actual outcomes of experiments is not under consideration at present; the usefulness of the rules will be readily established.

2.6.1 Addition rule

If a set A in the sample space S is decomposed into k disjoint sets A_1, A_2, . . . , A_k, then

$$P(A) = P(A_1) + P(A_2) + \cdots + P(A_k) \tag{2.6.1}$$

As a special case we have

$$S = A + \bar{A}$$

Therefore
$$1 = P(S) = P(A) + P(\bar{A})$$

and
$$P(A) = 1 - P(\bar{A})$$

We have used this result in Sec. 2.5.3, where event A denoted successful functioning and $\bar{A}$ unsuccessful functioning. In that case, $R_B = 1 - F_B$.

An interesting example of this rule is found by considering various decompositions of the sample space S into two disjoint sets. A possible decomposition is the following. Consider any two sets A and B in S. Form sets C and D, where $C = A + B$ and $D = \bar{A} \cdot \bar{B}$. The reader may readily verify the fact that sets C and D are complementary to each other. Therefore

$$S = C + D = (A + B) + \bar{A} \cdot \bar{B}$$

Using the addition rule for probabilities, we obtain

$$P(S) = 1 = P(A + B) + P(\bar{A} \cdot \bar{B})$$

from which it follows that

$$P(A + B) = 1 - P(\bar{A} \cdot \bar{B})$$

2.6.2 Multiplication rule

In developing the concept of conditional probability we have stated the following relationship:

$$P(A \cdot B) = P(A)P(B \mid A) = P(B)P(A \mid B)$$

for any two sets A and B. This is but a rule of combination, obtaining the probability of the simultaneous occurrence of A and B in terms of the probabilities of A and B. Note, however, that one must first obtain either the conditional probability of B given A or the conditional probability of A given B. Again, in the case of the independence of A and B, we have the simplified rule

$$P(A \cdot B) = P(A)P(B)$$

The multiplication rule is especially useful in the case of independent events.

The multiplication rule for k sets A_1, A_2, . . . , A_k is

$$P(A_1 \cdot A_2 \cdot \cdot \cdot \cdot \cdot A_k)$$
$$= P(A_1)P(A_2 \mid A_1)P(A_3 \mid A_1 \cdot A_2) \cdot \cdot \cdot P(A_k \mid A_1 \cdot \cdot \cdot A_{k-1})$$

where $P(A_j \mid A_1 \cdot A_2 \cdot \cdot \cdot \cdot \cdot A_{j-1})$ denotes the conditional probability of A_j under the condition that event $A_1 \cdot A_2 \cdot \cdot \cdot \cdot \cdot A_{j-1}$ has occurred. For independence we have

$$P(A_1 \cdot A_2 \cdot \cdot \cdot \cdot \cdot A_k) = P(A_1)P(A_2) \cdot \cdot \cdot P(A_k)$$

2.6.3   Decomposition rule

Often the computation of the probability of an event B can be simplified by considering the event B in conjunction with other events.   Suppose, then, in the sample space S we have an event B and also k disjoint events $A_1, A_2, \ldots, A_k$ which completely exhaust S.   That is to say,

$$S = A_1 + A_2 + \cdot \cdot \cdot + A_k$$

We shall proceed now by means of the addition and multiplication rules to find an expression for $P(B)$ in terms of $P(A_j)$ $(j = 1, \ldots, k)$ and $P(B \mid A_j)$ $(j = 1, \ldots, k)$.   The manipulation follows.

Any event B can be expressed as $B \cdot S$, yielding

$$B = B \cdot S = B \cdot (A_1 + \cdot \cdot \cdot + A_k) = B \cdot A_1 + B \cdot A_2 + \cdot \cdot \cdot + B \cdot A_k$$

Since the A's are disjoint, it follows that $B \cdot A_1, B \cdot A_2, \ldots, B \cdot A_k$ are also disjoint.   The probability of B can then be expressed, in consequence of the addition rule, as

$$P(B) = P(B \cdot A_1) + P(B \cdot A_2) + \cdot \cdot \cdot + P(B \cdot A_k)$$

Applying the multiplication rule to each term, we obtain

$$P(B \cdot A_j) = P(A_j)P(B \mid A_j) \qquad j = 1, \ldots, k$$

Hence
$$P(B) = \sum_{j=1}^{k} P(B \mid A_j)P(A_j)$$

Since, in practice, it is often much simpler to obtain the $P(A_j)$ and $P(B \mid A_j)$ than it is to compute $P(B)$ directly from the probability assignments on the sample space, this decomposition rule can be very useful. We shall illustrate its value with a number of examples.   These examples are chosen so as to parallel real situations, but have been much simplified in their computational aspects.

Example 2.4   Experience with the daily production of a machine gives the following probabilities for the number of items produced:

Number produced	1	2	3
Probability	0.10	0.30	0.60

Furthermore, the probability of defective items being produced is equal to 0.03.   Defectives are assumed to occur independently.   What is the probability of no defectives during a day's production?

Let A_1, A_2, A_3 be, respectively, the events 1, 2, and 3 items produced during a day. The probability of event B, no defective items produced in a single day, is given by

$$P(B) = P(A_1)P(B \mid A_1) + P(A_2)P(B \mid A_2) + P(A_3)P(B \mid A_3)$$

$P(A_1)$, $P(A_2)$, and $P(A_3)$ are assigned as in the table above. The conditional probabilities are readily found by considering the probability of the occurrence of defectives on condition, respectively, that one, two, or three items are produced in a single day. The probability of no defectives on a given day if only one item is produced on that day is 1 minus the probability of a defective. The remaining conditional probabilities are similarly obtained. The results are

$$P(B \mid A_1) = 1 - 0.03 = 0.97$$
$$P(B \mid A_2) = (1 - 0.03)(1 - 0.03) = (0.97)^2$$
$$P(B \mid A_3) = (1 - 0.03)^3 = (0.97)^3$$

Substituting these values, we obtain

$$P(B) = (0.10)(0.97) + (0.30)(0.97)^2 + (0.60)(0.97)^3 = 0.93$$

Example 2.5   There are two machines, A and B, with the following distribution for the number of parts produced per hour on each:

	Distribution, number produced per hour									
	1	2	3	4	5	6	7	8	9	10
Machine A	0.02	0.05	0.10	0.25	0.23	0.11	0.09	0.09	0.05	0.01
Machine B	0.03	0.07	0.10	0.10	0.40	0.10	0.10	0.07	0.02	0.01

Machines A and B are assumed to act independently of one another. What is the probability that A produces more them B? What is the probability that A and B produce the same number of parts? Let N_A and N_B be the number of parts produced, respectively, by machines A and B. Then

$$\text{Prob } (N_A > N_B) = \sum_{j=1}^{10} P(N_A > N_B \mid N_B = j)P(N_B = j)$$

The probabilities $P(N_B = j)$ are given in the table above. The conditional probabilities, Prob $(N_A > N_B \mid N_B = j)$, are precisely equal to Prob $(N_A > j)$ and can be obtained by summing up the appropriate probabilities for machine A. For example,

Prob $(N_A > 10) = 0$
  Prob $(N_A > 9) = $ Prob $(N_A = 10) = 0.01$
  Prob $(N_A > 8) = $ Prob $(N_A = 9) + $ Prob $(N_A = 10)$
$$= 0.05 + 0.01 = 0.06$$

In general,

$$\text{Prob } (N_A > j) = \sum_{u=j+1}^{10} \text{Prob } (N_A = u)$$

Thus

$$\text{Prob } (N_A > N_B) = (0.01)(0.02) + (0.06)(0.07) + \cdots$$
$$+ (0.98)(0.03) = 0.4189$$

We now compute the probability that $N_A = N_B$.

$$\text{Prob } (N_A = N_B) = \sum_{j=1}^{10} \text{Prob } (N_A = N_B \mid N_B = j) \text{ Prob } (N_B = j)$$
$$= \sum_{j=1}^{10} \text{Prob } (N_A = j) P(N_B = j) = (0.02)(0.03)$$
$$+ (0.05)(0.07) + \cdots + (0.01)(0.01) = 0.1585$$

Example 2.6 A machine has a distribution of lifetimes as given below. Furthermore, there are two types of failures, I and II. The probability of the failure type depends on the lifetimes as indicated below.

Month	1	2	3	4	5	6	7	8	9	10
Probability of life	0.40	0.30	0.10	0.06	0.05	0.03	0.03	0.01	0.01	0.01
Probability of failure I	0.01	0.02	0.03	0.08	0.10	0.20	0.26	0.30	0.30	0.40
Probability of failure II	0.99	0.98	0.97	0.92	0.90	0.80	0.74	0.70	0.70	0.60

What is the probability of failure I?
Let m be the number of months of life; then

$$\text{Prob } (\text{failure I}) = \sum_{j=1}^{10} \text{Prob } (\text{failure I} \mid m = j) \text{ Prob } (m = j)$$
$$= (0.01)(0.40) + (0.02)(0.30) + \cdots + (0.40)(0.01) = 0.0466$$

2.7   Combinatorial formulas

In order to facilitate the computations of probabilities we need some combinatorial relations.   The formulas to be developed will be especially helpful in computing probabilities for events resulting from experiments with equiprobable outcomes.   Suppose there are N possible outcomes, of which n imply the occurrence of an event A; then the probability of event A is given by the fraction n/N.   Finding n frequently involves tedious counting.   The combinatorial formulas often provide a convenient and compact way of finding n.   To obtain the desired results it is useful to prove some combinatorial rules.

2.7.1   Multiplication—rule 1

If one operation can be done in u different ways and if, after it is done in any of these ways, a second operation can be done in any one of v ways, then the two things can be done in the stated order in $u \cdot v$ ways.

PROOF.   For each way of doing the first operation, there are v ways of doing the two operations in the stated order.   Hence, since there are u ways of doing the first operation, there are $u \cdot v$ ways of doing the two operations in the stated order.

It becomes clear that this basic rule also holds when more than two operations are involved.   In general, if the jth operation ($j = 1, \ldots, k$) can be done in u_j ways, then the k operations can be done in the stated order in $u_1 \cdot u_2 \cdot u_3 \cdots u_k$ ways.

Example 2.7   A system has 20 switches.   A switch is either open or closed.   The state of the system is described by indicating for each switch whether it is open or closed.   How many states of the system are there?

Any switch can be in either one of two positions.   Since there are 20 switches, rule 1 states that the number of states of the system is given by $2 \cdot 2 \cdot 2 \cdots 2 = 2^{20}$.

Example 2.8   A factory has available eight punch presses of four different tonnage capacities, T_1, T_2, T_3, and T_4, such that $T_1 < T_2 < T_3 < T_4$.   For any item requiring the punching operation, only a punch press with a specified minimum tonnage capacity can be used.   We list the number of presses which have given tonnage capacities:

Tonnage capacity	T_1	T_2	T_3	T_4
Number of presses	2	1	3	2

An order is received to punch six different items, a, b, c, d, e, and f, whose minimum tonnage-capacity requirements are:

Item	Tonnage capacity, minimum requirement
a	T_2
b	T_2
c	T_2
d	T_3
e	T_3
f	T_1

In how many different ways can the items be assigned to presses so that no punch press is working on more than one item?

The answer can be obtained by applying rule 1 and considering how many ways each item can be assigned.   Starting with the items needing the highest minimum tonnage, we find that item d can be scheduled on any of five presses.   Item e can be scheduled, after d has been assigned, on any one of the remaining four presses consistent with its requirements. Continuing in this way we find:

Item	Number of assignments
d	5
e	4
a	4
b	3
c	2
f	3

The application of rule 1 then gives the number of possible technologically feasible assignments as equal to the product $5 \cdot 4 \cdot 4 \cdot 3 \cdot 2 \cdot 3 = 1,440$.

2.7.2   Permutations—rule 2

Consider a set of n different things arranged in a set of numbered places.   Let r of the n objects be chosen and arranged in the first r places. Any such arrangement is called a permutation.

Any permutation of r out of n things results from two acts.   The first is the act of selecting the r things; the second act arranges them in a particular order.   The possible permutations of two letters from among a, b, and c are ab, ba, bc, cb, ca, ac.   The first act selected three pairs of letters; the second act put them in their possible orders, yielding $3 \times 2 = 6$ different permutations of two letters selected from among three. Another way of referring to this is the number of permutations of three items taken two at a time denoted by $_3P_2$.   The number of permutations of all three letters can be readily determined and is found to be six. The general rule for the number of permutations $_nP_r$ of n things taken r at a time is

$$_nP_r = n(n-1)(n-2) \cdots (n-r+1) = \frac{n!}{(n-r)!}$$

called the permutation rule.

PROOF. In any permutation we can fill the first place by any of n things; the second place by any of the $(n-1)$ things remaining after the first place is filled; the third place by any of the $(n-2)$ things remaining; finally, the rth place by any of the $[n-(r-1)]$ things remaining after the $(r-1)$st place is filled. Hence, according to rule 1, all r places in a permutation of the n things, taken r at a time, can be filled in $n(n-1)(n-2) \cdots (n-r+1)$ different ways.

As a special case $(r=n)$ we obtain the result that the number of permutations of n different things, taken n at a time, $_nP_n$, is $n!$.

Example 2.9 The manufacture of a sheet-steel item requires the following operations: (a) shearing, (b) blanking, (c) punching holes (piercing), (d) degreasing, (e) trimming, (f) painting, and (g) drying.

The order of some of these operations can be interchanged, but others cannot. Operation a must be first, and b must be second. The operations d, f, and g must be in the stated order, without any intervening operations, but could possibly come after trimming (e) or piercing (c). As well, e and c can be in any order. How many sequences of operations are technically feasible?

Since operations a and b must come first and second for technical reasons, they can be omitted from consideration at the moment. Furthermore, since operations d, f, and g must be in the stated order, they can be considered as one group, which we shall label G. Thus there remain three operations [i.e., trimming (e), piercing (c), and G], which we are free to put into any order. The number of different sequences possible is the number of different permutations of three things taken three at a time, $_3P_3 = 6$. The different orders are:

a	b	e	c	d	f	g
a	b	e	d	f	g	c
a	b	c	e	d	f	g
a	b	c	d	f	g	e
a	b	d	f	g	e	c
a	b	d	f	g	c	e

2.7.3 Combinations—rule 3

In the previous section we were concerned not only with the r items which were chosen from n, but also with the possible ways in which the r chosen items were ordered. In some cases, however, we are interested only in the objects selected when r objects are chosen from among n objects without regard to their order. Such an unordered selection is called a *combination*. The total number $_nC_r$, of possible combinations of selections of r items from among n objects, is given by the following combination rule:

$$_nC_r = \frac{_nP_r}{r!} = \frac{n!}{r!(n-r)!} = \binom{n}{r}$$

PROOF. With each combination, containing r things, we can form $r!$ permutations of the things taken r at a time. Hence, since there are $_nC_r$ different combinations, there are $(_nC_r)(r!)$ different permutations. That is, $_nP_r = (_nC_r)(r!)$, or $_nC_r = {_nP_r}/r!$.

Since $_nP_r = n(n-1) \cdots (n-r+1)$, we have

$$\frac{_nP_r}{r!} = \frac{n(n-1) \cdots (n-r+1)}{r!}$$

$$= \frac{n(n-1) \cdots (n-r+1)(n-r)!}{(n-r)!r!} = \frac{n!}{r!(n-r)!}$$

Example 2.10 A telephone exchange contains 10 lines. A line can be busy or available for calls. It is assumed for the present illustration that the lines act independently. Furthermore, let the probability of a particular line being busy be 0.80 during the morning period. What is the probability of there being at least three free lines at any given time during the morning period?

Let n denote the number of available lines, and $p(k)$ the probability that n equals k. Thus the probability we are seeking is

$$\text{Prob } (n \geq 3) = p(3) + p(4) + \cdots + p(10)$$

Since
$$p(0) + p(1) + p(2) + \cdots + p(10) = 1$$

we obtain
$$\text{Prob } (n \geq 3) = 1 - p(0) - p(1) - p(2)$$

Although one can readily find the value of $p(1)$ and $p(2)$, it is useful for future purposes to find a general expression for $p(k)$. The probability that any set of k lines will be free while the other $10 - k$ lines are busy is given (because of the independence assumption) by the product

$$\underset{(k \text{ times})}{(0.20)(0.20) \cdots (0.20)} \times \underset{(10 - k \text{ times})}{(0.80)(0.80) \cdots (0.80)} = (0.20)^k(0.80)^{10-k}$$

We are not, however, interested in any particular k lines, but in all combinations of lines where k are available and $10 - k$ are busy. Since the probability is the same for each set, we must multiply the product by the number of such combinations. Rule 3 provides the answer to the number of combinations of 10 lines taken k at a time as equal to $_{10}C_k$.

Hence

$$p(k) = {}_{10}C_k(0.20)^k(0.80)^{10-k} = \frac{10!}{k!(10-k)!}(0.20)^k(0.80)^{10-k}$$

and

$$p(0) = \frac{10!}{0!10!}(0.20)^0(0.80)^{10} = 1(0.80)^{10} = 0.10737$$

$$p(1) = \frac{10!}{1!9!}(0.20)^1(0.80)^9 = 10(0.20)^1(0.80)^9 = 0.26844$$

$$p(2) = \frac{10!}{2!8!}(0.20)^2(0.80)^8 = 45(0.20)^2(0.80)^8 = 0.30199$$

Therefore

Prob $(n \geq 3) = 1 - (0.10737) - (0.26844) - (0.30199) = 0.3222$

This example has yielded an illustration of the *binomial distribution,* which is further described below.

Let us consider N independent trials of an experiment E. Suppose that the probability of an event A occurring as the result of a given trial is p. It follows that the probability that A does not occur is $1 - p$. We are interested in the probability $p(k)$ that the event A will occur k times in N repeated trials. (For purposes of probability calculations, independent trials of an experiment E can be considered as equivalent to independent experiments.) Because of the independence of the repeated trials, we have

$$p(k) = \frac{N!}{k!(N-k)!}p^k(1-p)^{N-k}$$

This equation plays a fundamental role in probability theory and its applications. We shall return to the binomial distribution with more detailed discussion and applications in subsequent chapters.

2.8 Random variable

In much experimental activity it may not be practically feasible to identify each outcome, although it may be readily possible to determine whether or not an outcome belongs to a certain set of the sample space. In general, therefore, we decompose the sample space into disjoint sets, each of which can represent an event of interest. Furthermore, we are usually interested in associating each of these events with a numerical value. We illustrate with the following example.

Example 2.11 The experiment consists of observing the number of boys and the number of girls in a family of a community. For the purpose of this example we shall not specify how the families are selected so long as the selection is not influenced by the number or sex of the children in the family. Suppose now that we let B denote boy and G

denote girl.   The possible outcomes are: none, B, G, BB, BG, GG, BBB, BBG, BGG, GGG, etc., enumerated as below with respect to events, number of boys, number of girls, and number of children.

Possible outcomes	Numerical value attached to outcome		
	X, no. of boys	Y, no. of girls	Z, no. of children
None	0	0	0
B	1	0	1
G	0	1	1
BB	2	0	2
BG	1	1	2
GG	0	2	2
BBB	3	0	3
BBG	2	1	3
BGG	1	2	3
GGG	0	3	3
$BBBB$	4	0	4
. . .	. . .	. . .	. . .

It is apparent that specifying all possible outcomes is a tedious job. On the other hand, in a particular case we may be interested only in the number of children in a family. Z gives this quantity.   We may also be interested in the number of boys and also the number of girls in the family.   These values are represented by X and Y, respectively.   There are, of course, other numerical associations with the outcomes which can be of interest.   As a matter of fact, we may not be interested in the number of boys or girls in a family, but rather in the yearly outlay for children's clothing.   It might be next to impossible to get accurate figures about the actual outlay for children's clothing.   On the other hand, we may get information on the cost of children's clothing, as well as some estimate as to the required number of items used per year.   Then, from the following formula,

$$W = aX + bY$$

where a is the yearly outlay per boy and b is the yearly outlay per girl, we obtain a numerical value for the yearly family outlay for children's clothes.

Example 2.12   Now let us refer back to the example in Sec. 1.3, in which we considered the activity of a warehouse.   Our experiment consisted of observing the daily demand D of a perishable item.   The sales of this item yield a daily profit P, dependent, of course, on the fixed morning purchase quantity Q. With a purchase cost of \$20 and a selling price of \$30, the profit is

$$P = \begin{cases} 30D - 20Q & \text{if } D \leq Q \\ 10Q & \text{if } D > Q \end{cases}$$

Our interest is in P, although the outcomes of our experiment are represented by D. P is a function defined on the sample space of the experiment. The function P as well as the function W is defined on the sample spaces of the respective experiments described. These functions, which focus interest on special aspects of the sample space, are called *random variables*. Formally, we have the following definition.

Definition: random variable A numerically defined function on a sample space is called a *random variable*.

We shall illustrate with a case taken from engineering practice.

Example 2.13 In Chap. 1 we studied the problem of filling the gap E between container and part being packed. The gap was filled by felt pads 0.125 inch thick. The sample space consisted of the container's length L_2 and part length L_1. Several random variables are of interest here (see Exercise 1.6):

Gap length (E):

$$E = L_2 - L_1$$

Number (approximate) of felt pads needed to fill gap, X:

$$X \cong \begin{cases} \dfrac{E}{0.125} & \text{if } E > 0 \\ 0 & \text{if } E \leq 0 \end{cases}$$

Total cost due to felt pads and interference, Y:

$$Y \cong \begin{cases} C_p X & \text{if } E \geq 0 \\ C_I & \text{when } E < 0 \end{cases}$$

where C_p is the cost of a felt pad and C_I is the cost of an interference $(E < 0)$.

It should be pointed out that, whereas the outcomes of the experiment dealt with lengths, we are primarily interested in the cost consequence of these lengths. It is not practical to set up the experiment in such terms as to observe cost directly, yet the important random variable is the cost resulting from the outcomes of the process (experiment).

Most of us have some intuitive notions about chance occurrences. Our experience has required us to make predictions in terms of probabilities. Yet, unless these notions are not only consistently used but also represented in formal terms, we lack any measure of confidence in the predictions. Furthermore, examination of the formal representation of fundamental probability concepts highlights and focuses attention upon the underlying assumptions which are often unconsciously made. Thus, by attempting to formalize these fundamental probability notions, one is forced to examine underlying presuppositions and their consequences. We have explicitly put our assumptions in formal terms in order to avoid any hidden contradictions and circularities. We are then provided with simple numerical means for obtaining desired practical predictions from experimental inquiry.

We have referred to any activity of probabilistic interest in terms of "experiment and its outcomes." To avoid ambiguity and to provide explicit means for calculation, we have formalized the outcomes of experiments with elementary notions of set theory, using the concepts *sample point, event,* and *sample space.* In particular, the formalization enables us to establish useful and convenient relations between frequency of occurrence of events and measures of probability. In this connection the concept of *random variable* is introduced, which provides the basis for unambiguous discussion of distribution functions presented in the next chapter.

Finally, on the basis of this conceptualization of probability, we demonstrated various rules of the probability calculus in simple and unambiguous fashion. These rules enable us to perform probability computations routinely without recurrent recourse to fundamental analysis of the sample space involved. The basis is thus set for introducing distribution theory and the subsequent treatment of decision problems.

We may not close this chapter without acknowledging that other interpretations of probability than the one presented here are currently accepted. In practice, however, essentially the same probability calculus is employed in spite of the differences among fundamental concepts as well as among various interpretations of the results of the probability calculus.

EXERCISES

2-1. A bag contains 25 items, of which 5 are defective. A random sample of two are drawn (without replacement). What is the probability:

 a. Of both being good?
 b. Of both being bad?
 c. Of at least one being good?
 d. Of (*a*), (*b*), and (*c*) if sampling is with replacement?

2-2. In the assembling of a machine three different parts are used, originating from three independent processes. Let the probability that parts are defective be p_1, p_2, and p_3. What is the probability, in (*a*) to (*c*), that:

 a. All parts are satisfactory?
 b. No parts are satisfactory?
 c. At least two parts are satisfactory?

d. What are the answers to (*a*) to (*c*) if part 3 is not independent of part 2 but is independent of part 1? Let the probability that part 3 is defective when part 2 is be p_3' and the probability that part 3 is defective when 2 is not be p_3''.

2-3. A girls' club lists the following vital statistics of its membership:

Color of hair	Color of eyes	
	Blue	Brown
Blonde	15	8
Brunette	9	12
Red	1	0

a. If you arrange a blind date with one of the club members, what is your chance of meeting:

  i. A blonde?
  ii. A blue-eyed blonde?
  iii. Either a blonde or a redhead?
  iv. Either a brunette or a brown-eyed girl?

b. It is raining when you meet the girl. Her hair is completely covered. However, her sparkling blue eyes bid you welcome. What is the probability that she is blonde?

c. A boys' club invites the girls' club to send ten of its members to a party. What is the probability of at least two brunettes among the ten?

d. Are the two events being a redhead and having blue eyes independent? Why?

2.4. In a group of 15 people, a person tells a rumor to a second person, who in turn repeats it to a third person, etc. At each step the recipient of the rumor is chosen at random from the remaining 14 people. Find the probability, in (*a*) and (*b*), that the rumor will be told two times without:

a. Returning to the originator.

b. Being repeated to any one person.

c. What is the answer to (*a*) and (*b*) if the rumor is told three times?

d. What are the answers to (*a*) and (*b*) when the rumor is told twice but two people are chosen at random from the other 14 at each stage?

2.5. Referring to Sec. 2.5.3 of the text, find R_B when the operation of machine B depends on the successful functioning of at least three of the N_B components. How large must N_B be in this case? (Use r_A, N_A, and r_B as given in the text.)

2.6. Suppose a lot contains N items, D of which are defective. A random sample of n items is inspected. If the sample contains no defectives, then the lot is accepted; if one or more defectives are found, the lot is rejected. Find an expression for the probability that the lot will be accepted.

2.7. A bag contains N similar chips, each with a number on it. The numbers are $1, 2, \ldots, N$. Thus, to each chip there is a corresponding unique integer. A sample of n chips is chosen at random. Let M be the maximum number found on the chips in the sample.

a. What values can M take on?

b. What is the probability that $M \leq k$ for $k = 2, 3, 4$, when $N = 10$ and $n = 3$?

 c. What is the probability that $M = 4$ for M and n as in (*b*)?

 d. What is the answer to (*b*) when chips are sampled with replacement?

2.8. Experience with the daily production of a machine gives the following probabilities for producing numbers of parts per day:

Number of parts per day	1	2	3	4	5	6	7	8	9	10
Probability	0.10	0.10	0.30	0.25	0.10	0.05	0.05	0.03	0.01	0.01

Furthermore, the probability of a defective part being produced is equal to 0.03.

 a. What is the probability of producing at least two parts per day?

 b. Find the probability of having no more than three defectives per day.

 c. If frequency interpretation of probability is reasonable, how many defectives can be expected in a month (30 days)?

2.9. The probability of having various numbers of children in a family is assumed to be given by:

Number of children	0	1	2	3
Probability	0.20	0.50	0.25	0.05

Furthermore, assume a 50–50 chance that a child born will be a boy or a girl.

 a. Describe the sample space.

 b. What is the probability that a family has at least two children?

 c. If it is known that a family has one boy, what is the probability that there are two children in a family?

 d. Find the probability that the family has one boy.

 e. Let the random variable X denote the number of boys in a family. Find $P(X = 0)$, $P(X = 1)$, $P(X = 2)$, and $P(X = 3)$.

 f. What is the probability that a family has more boys than girls?

2.10. A fair coin is tossed three times independently. The first two tosses resulted in heads. What is the probability that the third toss will result in heads?

2.11. There are two machines, A and B, with the following distribution for the number of parts produced per hour (assume that machines A and B act independently).

	1	2	3	4	5	6	7	8	9	10
A	0.02	0.05	0.10	0.25	0.23	0.11	0.09	0.09	0.05	0.01
B	0.03	0.07	0.10	0.10	0.40	0.10	0.10	0.07	0.02	0.01

 a. Describe the sample space.

Find the probability, in (*b*) to (*g*),

 b. Of A producing at least 4 parts per hour.

 c. Of B producing no more than 2 parts per hour.

d. Of *A* producing less than 2 and *B* more than 8 per hour.
e. Of *B* producing more than *A*.
f. Of *A* producing at least 50 per cent more than *B*.
g. Of *A* producing more than *B* when it is known that *B* produced 2.
h. Which machine do you prefer (in terms of productivity)? Explain.

2.12. A part has a distribution of lifetimes as given. Furthermore, there are two types of failures, I and II. The probability of the failure type depends on the lifetime as indicated.

	Month									
	1	2	3	4	5	6	7	8	9	10
Probability of life	0.40	0.30	0.10	0.06	0.05	0.03	0.03	0.01	0.01	0.01
Probability of I	0.01	0.02	0.03	0.08	0.10	0.20	0.26	0.30	0.30	0.40
Probability of II	0.99	0.98	0.97	0.92	0.90	0.80	0.74	0.70	0.70	0.60

Find the probability:

a. That the part lives at least 2 months.
b. That the part lives 6 months when it known to have lived 3 months already.
c. Of failure type II.

A failure of type I has occurred:

d. Find the probability of the part's having lived 6 months.
e. Find the probability of the part's having lived no more than 2 months.

Suppose a machine has three parts, with life characteristics as given before. Furthermore, the machine fails if (1) at least two parts die of failure type II or (2) at least one part dies of failure type I. Find the probability:

f. Of failure (1) in 2 months.
g. Of failure (2) in 3 months.
h. Of failure [either (1) or (2)] in 2 months.
i. Of surviving at least 5 months.

2.13. A group of bombers is sent to a destination. The probability that a bomber will reach the destination is $\frac{1}{2}$, regardless of the size of the group.

a. If three bombers are sent, what is the probability of at least one getting through?
b. How many bombers should be sent, so that the chance of at least one getting through is at least 90 per cent?

Each bomber carries two bombs. The probability of a hit, when a bomb is dropped, is $\frac{2}{3}$.

c. How many bombers should be sent, so that the probability of at least one target hit may be at least 90 per cent?

2.14. A fair die is tossed twice. Find the probability that the second result will be:

a. Greater than the first result.
b. Equal to the first result.
c. Smaller than the first result.

2.15. Letters in the Morse alphabet are formed by a succession of dashes and dots with repetitions permitted. How many letters is it possible to form with three symbols or less?

2.16. A train arrives at a station every hour on the hour. A passenger arrives at the station at random. What is the probability that he will have to wait less than 15 minutes for a train?

2.17. A point is chosen at random on a line segment, dividing it into two parts. What is the probability that the ratio of the lengths of the parts (either combination) is less than $\frac{1}{3}$?

2.18. What is the minimum number of independent tosses of a fair coin necessary so that the probability of at least one head is more than 90 per cent?

2.19. A fair coin is tossed repeatedly.

a. What is the probability that the first head occurs after three tosses?
b. Find the probability that the third head occurs at the tenth toss.

2.20. The probability of one accident occurring in a small time interval of length Δt is $\lambda(\Delta t)$. Assume that accidents occur independently in nonoverlapping time intervals. Also, neglect the possibility of more than one accident occurring in a time interval.

a. What is probability of three accidents in a time interval of length T?
b. What is probability of no accidents in length of time T?
c. What happens in (a) and (b) when $\Delta t \rightarrow 0$?

2.21. Suppose the outcome of an experiment is described in terms of a random variable X which can take on two possible values, 1 and 2, with equal probability. The experiment is repeated independently n times, and the arithmetic average $\bar{X}$ of X, for the n results, is calculated.

a. What values can $\bar{X}$ take on?
b. What is the probability that $\bar{X}$ will take on these values when $n = 2, 3,$ and 4? What interesting observation can you make?

2.22. A certain manufactured item consists of three critical components. An item will be classified as defective if *any* of the three components is defective. Suppose $\frac{1}{10}$, $\frac{1}{5}$, and $\frac{1}{3}$ are the respective probabilities that the first, second, and third components will be defective and that components can be considered to operate independently. If five items are produced, what is the probability that at least three of the items will be not be defective?

2.23. A system is composed of two components A and B in series; that is, the system functions only if both A and B operate. Each component is made up of a number of subcomponents in parallel; that is, the component functions if any one of its subcomponents operate. Assume that the operations of all subcomponents are independent. Suppose there are N_A and N_B subcomponents in A and B, respectively, and that p_A and p_B denote the probability of functioning of a subcomponent of A and B, respectively. Let P_S be the probability that the system functions.

a. Find an expression for P_S in terms of p_A, p_B, N_A, and N_B.

b. Let $p_A = 0.4$ and $p_B = 0.2$.   Find values of N_A and N_B which will maximize P_S subject to the restriction that $N_A + N_B \leq 5$.

2.24. Suppose there are N distinct elements a_1, a_2, . . . , a_N. Let $a_i > a_j$ denote the precedence relationship that a_i precedes a_j in a permutation of the N elements.

a. How many permutations of a_1, a_2, . . . , a_N are there?

b. How many permutations of a_1, a_2, . . . , a_N satisfy the restriction $a_1 > a_2$?

c. Find the number of permutations with restrictions $a_1 > a_2$ and $a_4 > a_1$.

d. Find the number of permutations with restriction $a_1 > a_2$, $a_4 > a_1$, and $a_4 > a_2$.

2.25. Using the axioms for probability in Sec. 2.3, show that

a. $P(\phi) = 0$

b. $P(A) \leq 1$

c. $P(A + B) = P(A) + P(B) - P(A \cdot B)$

2.26. If A, B, and C are three subsets of the sample space S, show that

a. $A \cdot (B + C) = A \cdot B + A \cdot C$

b. $A + B$ is the complement of $\bar{A} \cdot \bar{B}$

2.27.   Describe the sample space in Example 2.4.

2.28. Let A_1, A_2, . . . , A_k be k mutually exclusive sets such that $A_1 + A_2 + \cdots + A_k = S$.   If B is any set, prove *Bayes' rule*, which states that for any i,

$$P(A_i \mid B) = \frac{P(B \mid A_i)P(A_i)}{\displaystyle\sum_{j=1}^{k} P(B \mid A_j) P(A_j)}$$

2.29. Show that if two events A and B are independent, then A and the complement of B, $\bar{B}$ are independent.

2.30. A set has N distinct elements.   How many subsets are there?   HINT: See Example 2.7.

3

DISTRIBUTION FUNCTIONS

3.1 Univariate distribution functions

3.1.1 Cumulative distribution functions

In experiment E_2 (Example 2.2) of tossing a coin three times, we are not interested in all the conceivable outcomes. Usually, we are interested in events such as those relating to the number of heads, the number of tails, and the like. We have, of course, the eight outcomes $s_1, s_2, \ldots, s_8$, to which we have made the probability assignment such that all outcomes are equiprobable. Specifically, this means $P(s_i) = \frac{1}{8}$ $(i = 1, \ldots, 8)$. It is apparent that we can refer to the number of heads as a random variable since it is a function on the original sample space. Let us consider various possible random variables such as:

$$X: \quad \text{the number of heads}$$
$$Y: \quad \text{the number of tails}$$
$$Z: \quad \text{the difference between } X \text{ and } Y \ (X - Y)$$

But before analyzing these random variables, consider another interpretation of Z.

Two persons whom we shall call Peter and Paul match pennies. If a head occurs, Peter pays Paul $1. On the other hand, if a tail occurs, Paul pays Peter $1. The random variable Z is, in fact, the amount Paul has at the end of three tosses. Another random variable, W, can be obtained by considering at each stage who is leading. The random variable W is the number of trials at which Paul leads Peter.

The values taken on by the random variables X, Y, Z, and W are given in Table 3.1.

It would seem quite natural for Paul to ask how frequently Z was positive. Or he might be interested in the frequency with which he would always be ahead. Let us compute the probability that Z is positive. This is obtained directly by counting the number of s's which yield Z's that are greater than zero. These are s_1, s_2, s_3, and s_5. Thus

$$P(Z > 0) = p(s_1) + p(s_2) + p(s_3) + p(s_5) = \tfrac{1}{2}$$

TABLE 3.1

Elements of sample space	Random variable			
	X	Y	Z	W
$s_1 = (H,H,H)$	3	0	3	3
$s_2 = (H,H,T)$	2	1	1	3
$s_3 = (H,T,H)$	2	1	1	2
$s_4 = (H,T,T)$	1	2	-1	1
$s_5 = (T,H,H)$	2	1	1	1
$s_6 = (T,H,T)$	1	2	-1	0
$s_7 = (T,T,H)$	1	2	-1	0
$s_8 = (T,T,T)$	0	3	-3	0

We might ask what, in general, is the probability that Z is less than or equal to any real number. For example, it is quite obvious that

$$P(Z \leq -3.01) = 0$$
$$P(Z \leq -3.00) = \tfrac{1}{8}$$
$$P(Z \leq -2.00) = \tfrac{1}{8}$$
$$P(Z \leq -1.00) = \tfrac{1}{2}$$
$$P(Z \leq 0) = \tfrac{1}{2}$$
$$P(Z \leq 1) = \tfrac{7}{8}$$
$$P(Z \leq 2) = \tfrac{7}{8}$$
$$P(Z \leq 3) = 1$$

Note that the $P(Z \leq a)$, where a is any real number, is a nondecreasing real function of a.

These steps can be repeated for X, Y, and W, yielding analogous results. As a matter of fact, the foregoing procedure can be used with any random variable. Such functions are called cumulative distribution functions.

Definition: cumulative distribution function (*CDF*) The *cumulative distribution function* (*CDF*) of a random variable X, defined on a sample space S with probability measure P, is given by

$$F(t) = \text{Prob}\ [X(s) \leq t] \equiv P[X(s) \leq t]$$
$$\equiv \text{probability of occurrence of a set of}$$
$$\text{outcomes in } S \text{ such that the numerical}$$
$$\text{value } X(s) \text{ associated with outcomes in}$$
$$\text{that set is not greater than } t \qquad (3.1.1)$$

In order to indicate the dependence of the CDF on the random variable, we shall sometimes write $F_X(t)$ instead of $F(t)$ to avoid possible confusion. It will be shown that the probabilities of many complicated events describable in terms of X can be computed from the function $F_X(t)$.

Returning to our example, we can now specify the cumulative distribution functions F_X, F_Y, F_Z, and F_W of X, Y, Z, and W, respectively. The graph of F_Z is given in Fig. 3.1.

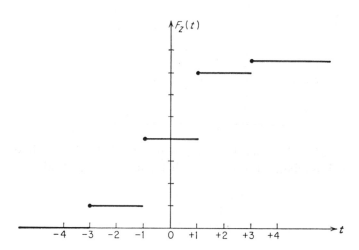

Figure 3.1 *CDF* of *Z*.

Example 3.1 Let us reconsider the example in Sec. 1.3. Suppose that the random variables of interest are the daily demand D and the daily profit P. It is clear that the values of P depend on both the outcomes D and on the morning purchasing quantity Q. In order to derive the CDF of P we first consider the CDF of D. In this case the values which D takes on are identical with the values of the sample points in the sample space itself. Bear in mind, however, that D is also a random variable.

The CDF of D is symbolically represented as

$$F_D(t) = \text{Prob } (D \le t)$$

In order to compute $F_D(t)$ we assume that the record of demand for the first hundred days, as given in Table 1.5, truly reflects the frequencies which would occur if more days were observed. Again, the assumption of stability is seen to be vital for the useful application of our formalism.

We obtain the *CDF* as follows:

t	Prob $(D \leq t)$	t	Prob $(D \leq t)$
0	0.01	7	0.85
1	0.04	8	0.92
2	0.12	9	0.96
3	0.25	10	0.98
4	0.42	11	0.99
5	0.60	12	1.00
6	0.75		

This is plotted in Fig. 3.2.

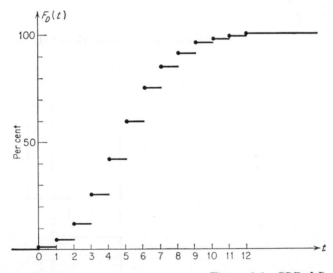

Figure 3.2   *CDF* of *D*.

We now consider the *CDF* of the daily profit *P*. To indicate the dependence of *P* and its *CDF* on *Q* we write the *CDF* as

$$F_P(t \mid Q) = \text{Prob } (P \leq t \mid Q)$$

Once the value of *Q* is chosen, the *CDF* of *P* is determined. On the other hand, for different choices of *Q*, different *CDF*s result. Such a constant as *Q* is an example of what is called a *parameter* of the *CDF*. In order to compute $F_P(t \mid Q)$, we first plot *P* as a function of *D* (Fig. 3.3) and a particular value of *Q*. *P* is given by

$$P = \begin{cases} 30D - 20Q & \text{if } D \leq Q \\ 10Q & \text{if } D > Q \end{cases}$$

Thus, for any value, say, t_0, $F_p(t_0)$ can be obtained by considering the fact that the values of D for which $P \leq t_0$ are given by the set of D's such that

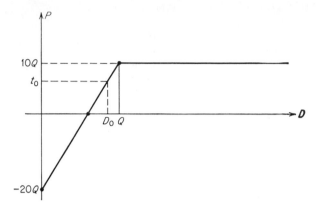

Figure 3.3 P as a function of D.

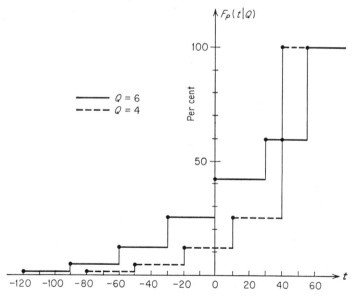

Figure 3.4   *CDF*s of P for $Q = 4$ and $Q = 6$.

$D \leq D_0$.   Thus

$$F_P(t_0 \mid Q) = \text{Prob } (P \leq t_0) = \text{Prob } (D \leq D_0) = F_D(D_0)$$

$F_D(D_0)$ can be computed for any t_0.   The dependence of the *CDF* on the parameter Q follows from the fact that D_0 depends on both t_0 and Q. The *CDF*s of P for $Q = 4$ and 6, respectively, are given in Fig. 3.4.

Properties of the CDF

1. $F_X(t)$ is nondecreasing
2. $F_X(-\infty) = 0$
3. $F_X(+\infty) = 1$

These three properties follow, obviously, from the definitions of probability and of the cumulative distribution function.

4. $$\text{Prob } (a < X \leq b) = F_X(b) - F_X(a) \qquad (3.1.2)$$

This result can be derived by considering the following events:

$$A_1: \quad \{s: \quad a < X(s) \leq b\}$$
$$A_2: \quad \{s: \quad X(s) \leq a\}$$
$$A_3: \quad \{s: \quad X(s) \leq b\}$$

It is clear that

$$A_3 = A_2 + A_1 \qquad \text{and} \qquad A_1 \cdot A_2 = \phi$$

Thus $$P(A_3) = P(A_2) + P(A_1)$$
and $$F_X(b) = F_X(a) + \text{Prob } (a < X \leq b)$$

which gives the desired result.

As a special case, when $b = \infty$, we have the *TDF* (*tail distribution function*):

5. Prob $(X > t) = 1 - F_X(t)$

3.1.2 Probability distribution functions

In the very nature of experiments and their outcomes it is difficult to arrive at other than discrete sample spaces. The examples presented so far have been chosen for simplicity to develop the notion of the *CDF* of a random variable. Let it be emphasized that these examples have dealt only with discrete sample spaces. A little reflection will show that most measurement results in discrete quantities. Any resort to a continuous scale of measurement requires an approximation to, or an idealization of, the concrete process involved in experimentation and measurement. In general, as in our examples, for all cases of discrete sample spaces we can represent the *CDF* as follows:

$$F_X(t) = \Sigma p(s) \qquad (3.1.3)$$

where the summation is over all s such that $X(s) \leq t$.

This form often does not provide the most convenient and compact way to make probability computations. It may be quite difficult to specify the various sets of s to which a specific value of $X(s)$ corresponds, yet one can readily attach a probability to the values of X for which $X(s) \leq t$. We may look upon an experiment E and its corresponding sample space S as transformed by the random variable X into a new experiment E_X and its associated sample space S_X. Note that the new experiment may be conceived as consisting of the old experiment E together with the observation $X(s)$.

If S has a finite number of sample points, then $X(s)$ can take on only a finite set of values.   (The converse, however, is not necessarily true.)

Let us consider a general discrete random variable $X(s)$.   Suppose the values which X can take on to be $\ldots, x_{-N}, \ldots, x_{-1}, x_0, x_1, \ldots, x_N, \ldots$, where N can be an arbitrarily large integer.   Let us assume that we can take the set of values, $\ldots, x_{-N}, \ldots, x_{-1}, x_0, x_1, \ldots, x_N, \ldots$, as being in ascending order.

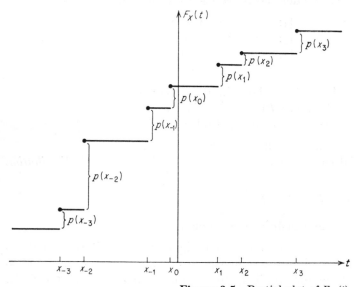

Figure 3.5   Partial plot of $F_X(t)$.

Let us try to rewrite the general CDF of a random variable X by first collecting all the points s in S such that $X(s) = x_i$.   To this set of elements there corresponds a probability denoted by $p(x_i)$ which can be written as

$$p(x_i) = \Sigma p(s) \qquad (3.1.4)$$

where the summation is over all s such that $X(s) = x_i$.

Now consider some t lying in the interval $x_r \leq t < x_{r+1}$.   It is clear that the probability that $X \leq t$ can be obtained summing $p(x_i)$ over all i from $-\infty$ to r.   This can be represented by a double sum as follows:

$$F_X(t) = \text{Prob } [X(s) \leq t] = \sum_{i=-\infty}^{r} \Sigma p(s)$$

over all s such that $X(s) = x_i$, which equals

$$\sum_{i=-\infty}^{r} p(x_i) \qquad \text{where } x_r \leq t < x_{r+1} \qquad (3.1.5)$$

We can specify $p(x_i)$ unambiguously by the definition of a probability function.

Definition: probability function (*PF*)   The function $p(x)$ as specified in Eq. (3.1.4) is called the *probability function* (*PF*) of the discrete random variable X.   It is clear that

$$p(x_i) \geq 0 \qquad \text{for all } i$$

$$\sum_{i=-\infty}^{\infty} p(x_i) = 1$$

The *CDF* of X can be plotted as in Fig. 3.5.   Bear in mind that the probability function, as just defined, is restricted to random variables which

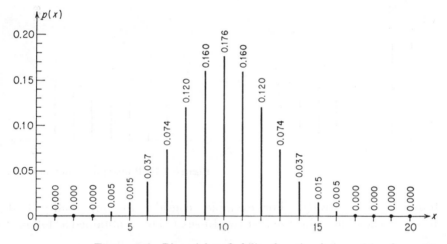

Figure 3.6   Binomial probability function for $p = \frac{1}{2}$ and $n = 20$.

take on a denumerable set of values.   Such random variables we have called *discrete*.

Example 3.2   Consider the experiment of tossing a penny coin 20 successive times.   Observe whether a head or a tail occurs after each toss.   The outcomes consist of sequences of heads (H) and tails (T). Let us assume that all 2^{20} outcomes are equiprobable.   The random variable X, to be considered, is the number of heads.   The probability function of X can be obtained from the binomial distribution.   The *PF* of X is

$$p(x) = {}_{20}C_x(\tfrac{1}{2})^x(\tfrac{1}{2})^{2-x} = \frac{{}_{20}C_x}{2^{20}}$$

The graph of $p(x)$ is given in Fig. 3.6.

Another random variable of interest is W, the number of times Paul leads Peter during the play of this game.   The *PF* of W is given in Fig. 3.7.   Unlike X, the probability distribution of W is higher at the ends than at the middle.   The value $W = 10$ is the least likely.   The intuitive interpretation is that, if Paul is leading at any stage, Peter must get a long winning streak in order to pull ahead; the influence of the few initial

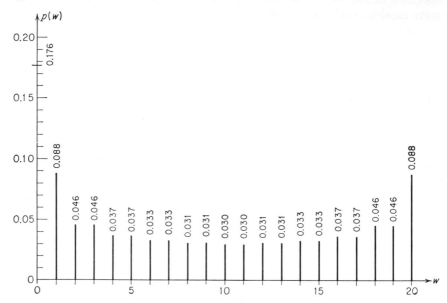

Figure 3.7   Probability function of W.

tosses is quite strong.   For example, consider the probability that $W = 20$ when Paul wins the first two tosses.   This is obtained as follows:

$$\text{Prob } (W_{20} = 20 \mid W_2 = 2) = \frac{P(W_{20} = 20 \quad \text{and} \quad W_2 = 2)}{P(W_2 = 2)}$$

where W_N denotes the random variable W for N coin tosses.   Since $W_{20} = 20$ implies $W_2 = 2$, we obtain

$$P(W_{20} = 20 \text{ and } W_2 = 2) = P(W_{20} = 20)$$

Thus

$$P(W_{20} = 20 \mid W_2 = 2) = \frac{P(W_{20} = 20)}{P(W_2 = 2)} = \frac{0.088}{0.250} = 0.352$$

In other words, if Paul wins the first two tosses, the chances that he will be ahead for the whole 20 tosses is 35.2 per cent.   This may at first seem to be rather high.

3.1.3   Probability density function (*PDF*)

We have so far restricted ourselves intentionally to discrete random variables.   The advantage of this is that we may be intuitively convincing and mathematically precise in making probability assignments and deriving cumulative distribution functions. It is furthermore true that most real experiments, as we have already noted, lead to discrete sets of measurements. Nevertheless, we do aim in most of scientific inquiry to refine the accuracy of our measurements to the point where it seems fruitful to represent these outcomes and their associated random variables on a continuous scale. This is commonly done in the physical sciences, where mass density, density of electrical charge, pressure on a surface, and other physical quantities are treated as continuous variables. This has been common practice and has been fruitful for centuries, in spite of the fact that all measurements are limited by a finite lower bound of least count. Similarly, in treating random variables and their CDFs in a general manner, it will turn out to be useful to approximate many CDFs by continuous functions. This procedure is especially valuable for random variables which can assume a great many values that are closely spaced, as, for example, measurements of length taken to the nearest 0.0001 inch.

To develop this idea, let us consider automatically filling 5-pound bags of sugar where the least count is 0.01 pound. Suppose we weigh a sample of 1,500 filled bags to an accuracy of 0.01 pound. We shall set up the histogram and probability function for these values taken to represent a random variable of the outcomes of the experiment. In Table 3.2 we have the distribution of the values of this random variable X equals the outcomes. (In keeping with our requirement of stability, we shall assume that these 1,500 outcomes are "representative" of the long-run outcome of the process.) A histogram of $p(x)$ is given in Fig. 3.8. The CDF is

$$F_X(t) = \text{Prob } (X \leq t) = \sum_{x_i \leq t} p(x_i)$$

This computation yields the graph illustrated in Fig. 3.9.

TABLE 3.2

x	Number of occurrences	$p(x) = $ number/1,500
5.05	5	0.003
5.04	30	0.020
5.03	40	0.027
5.02	200	0.133
5.01	300	0.200
5.00	425	0.284
4.99	320	0.213
4.98	150	0.100
4.97	15	0.010
4.96	10	0.007
4.95	5	0.003

Note, in Fig. 3.8, that the longest spike represents 425 actual weighings at 5.00 pounds. Suppose we were able to make these measurements to the nearest 0.001. In deriving Fig. 3.8, we should have ten times as many spikes to plot. Furthermore, the greatest number of weighings at any one particular value, such as 4.978 pounds, would be approximately one-tenth as great as the number of weighings at the nearest 0.01 value,

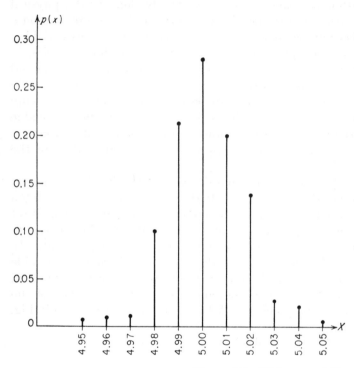

Figure 3.8 Histogram of X.

namely, 4.98 pounds. In fact, looking again at the value 5.00, we might get something like 40 weighings at 5.001. The *CDF* now has 110 jumps, each of which we expect to be approximately one-tenth the magnitude of those in Fig. 3.9. There are ten times as many steps; the jumps between successive steps are approximately one-tenth as great as those in Fig. 3.9. Of greatest importance is the fact that

$$F_X(t) = 0 \qquad \text{for } t \leq 4.944$$
$$F_X(4.949) = 0.0017$$
$$F_X(5.000) = 0.491$$
$$F_X(5.050) = 0.998$$

and
$$F_X(t) = 1.00 \qquad \text{for } t > 5.054$$

This function is nonnegative, nondecreasing, zero at $-\infty$, 1.0 at $+\infty$, and is a CDF. Comparing this with the original CDF in which measurements were made no closer than 0.01 pound, we find the difference in values of $F(t)$ to be small for common values of t.

We ask the reader now to indulge his imagination. Imagine that one can make these measurements of the weights of "5-pound" bags of sugar to 0.0001 pound. There would now be 1,100 possible outcomes, and the random variable could have 1,100 possible values between 4.9445 and 5.0544. Obviously, successive values which the random variable

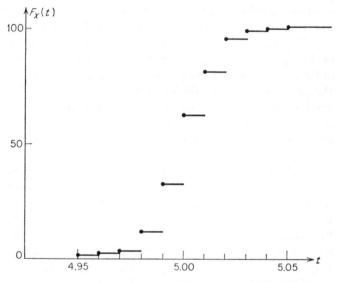

Figure 3.9 CDF of X, $F_X(t)$.

can take on differ by as little as 0.0001 inch. Furthermore, the CDF in this instance will not differ appreciably from the CDF previously discussed. It is a very cumbersome procedure to perform probability calculations for random variables, taking on so many closely spaced yet discrete values. In doing this, we are obliged to tally some thousands of numbers. Suppose we approximate the last CDF by a continuous differentiable (except for a finite number of points) $F^*(t)$, such that

$$F^*(t) \text{ is nondecreasing}$$
$$F^*(-\infty) = 0$$
$$F^*(+\infty) = 1$$

Suppose, further, that the approximating $F^*(t)$ is made equal to the limit of the successive discrete CDFs. Each of the respective discrete CDFs is explicitly defined. This can be done for a very wide range of random variables that are encountered in engineering and business experience. Let us suppose, further, that we can perform the usual analytical operations for this approximating CDF.

Consider now the probability function resulting from going through steps analogous to those used in the procedure for obtaining an approximating CDF, $F_X(t)$. For example, the spike of the probability function at $t = t_i$ is equal to the difference between the corresponding values of the CDF at t_{i+1} and t_i. Bear in mind that the spikes equal the probability that the random variable will take on the values at which the spikes are plotted. Furthermore, this is the measure of the probability that the random variable will take on any value halfway between the predecessor and the successor of the value at which the spike was plotted.

The probability function in Fig. 3.8 refers to occurrences in intervals of 0.01 pound. From the next stage of measurement we obtained probabilities for occurrences falling in intervals of 0.001 pound. Note that the ratio of the probabilities at the spikes divided by the magnitude of the interval between successive points remains substantially constant in the successive probability functions. Again, we can approximate this by a continuous function in such a way that at the spikes the value of the approximating function times the magnitude of the interval of least count is approximately equal to the probability represented at the spike.

Let us present the preceding argument more formally. Let $p(x_i \mid \Delta)$ denote the probability at the spike value x_i when measurement s can be made to a least count Δ. We have assumed, and indicated it to be "reasonable," that $p(x_i \mid \Delta)/\Delta$ (Δ small) can be usefully approximated by a constant depending on x_i, which we shall designate by $f(x_i)$. Thus we may represent $p(x_i \mid \Delta)$ approximately by $f(x_i)\Delta$.

We can approximate the CDF of X as follows:

$$F_X(t) = \text{Prob } (X \le t) = \sum_{x_i \le t} p(x_i \mid \Delta) \sim \sum_{x_i \le t} f(x_i)\Delta$$

Observe that the last summation is of the form of a finite sum approximating a definite integral of $f(x)$ with respect to x. We may then assert the following relations:

$$F_X(t) \sim \sum_{x_i \le t} f(x_i)\Delta \sim \int_{-\infty}^{t} f(x)\ dx$$

We can, however, select the approximating function $F_X^*(t)$ in such a way that

$$F_X^*(t) = \int_{-\infty}^{t} f(x)\ dx \qquad \text{where } \frac{dF_X^*(t)}{dt} = f(t)$$

(This discussion is necessarily nonrigorous; the mathematical details required for rigor are beyond the scope or interest of this text.)

The new function $f(x)$ is called the probability density function (PDF) and is formally defined as follows.

Definition: probability density function (PDF)   A function $f(x)$ is said to be a *probability density function* (PDF) if

$$f(x) \geq 0$$
$$\int_{-\infty}^{+\infty} f(x) \, dx = 1$$

The present argument was developed to make plausible the practical use of continuous random variables and their associated CDFs and PDFs, where the original sample space was necessarily discrete.   Once one has obtained practical representations of random variables and their associated CDFs and PDFs resulting from certain experiments, one can use continuous distribution functions to perform probability calculations in connection with idealized experiments.   To be sure, in the subsequent applications of such idealization, comparison with actual experiments must justify the use of continuous distributions.

We have stressed the PDF in particular because of its intimate relation to the CDF and because of its convenience in representing numerous experimental situations.

Example 3.3   One frequently encounters such operational problems as determining the number of toll gates required at highway entrances, the number of turnstiles at a subway entrance, the number of servers at a cafeteria, the number of telephone lines to service an urban area.   A common feature of these problems is that in each there is a timewise variable demand for service which can be economically satisfied by a specific number of servers.   In the case of highway entrances where toll must be paid, it is well known that the number of cars arriving in a given time interval cannot be predicted exactly; the time elapsed between successive arrivals, called the *interarrival time,* cannot be predicted exactly.   Nevertheless, extensive studies have been made of interarrival times of cars at toll gates, and the following characteristics seem to apply to most highway toll-gate systems:

1. The arrival times are part of a stable process during specified time intervals at specified times of the day and year.   For example, at the New Jersey approach to the George Washington Bridge between 2 and 3 P.M. on Tuesdays, Wednesdays, and Thursdays during the first three weeks of May, the distribution of interarrival time is stable.   There are but two qualifications, namely, that there be no special public occasion or exceptional change in weather.

2. The interarrival times cannot be predicted individually.   Naturally, one of the important variables influencing the extent of need for the toll gates is the interarrival time.   It is further apparent that the

interarrival time is a random variable whose distribution is essential to "quantitative" solution of the toll-gate problem.

For our present purposes, we shall investigate the *CDF* and the *PDF* of the random variable X denoting the interarrival time. Under many circumstances it appears that the time of arrival of a car at the toll gate is not influenced by the time of arrival of the preceding car. More formally, this observation can be expressed as follows:

$$\text{Prob } (X > t + s \mid X > t) = \text{Prob } (X > s)$$

Starting with this as given and the rules of combination for probabilities, we shall derive the *CDF* of the random variable X. Let

$$A_1 \text{ be the set } (X > t)$$
$$A_2 \text{ be the set } (X > t + s)$$

It follows that $A_1 \cdot A_2 = A_2$ since the relation $X > t + s$ implies $X > t$. Therefore

$$P(A_2 \mid A_1) = \frac{P(A_1 \cdot A_2)}{P(A_1)} = \frac{P(A_2)}{P(A_1)}$$

By our initial assumption,

$$P(X > t + s \mid X > t) = P(A_2 \mid A_1) = P(X > s)$$

whence
$$\frac{P(X > t + s)}{P(X > t)} = P(X > s)$$

This relation is more conveniently expressed in terms of the tail distribution function (*TDF*), here denoted by $G_X(t)$. We obtain, then,

$$\frac{G_X(t + s)}{G_X(t)} = G_X(s) \qquad \text{and} \qquad G_X(t + s) = G_X(t)G_X(s)$$

This relationship determines $G_X(t)$. We must still show whether $G_X(t)$ is unique, and we must derive its form. It can be shown by mathematical argument (beyond the scope of this text, however) that the only continuous, monotonic, nonincreasing, and nonvanishing solution of the above functional equation is

$$G_X(t) = e^{-\theta t} \qquad \text{where } \theta \geq 0$$

Therefore the *CDF* of X is

$$F_X(t) = 1 - e^{-\theta t}$$

and the *PDF* is obtained as

$$f_X(t) = \left[\frac{dF_X(u)}{du} \right]_{u=t} = \theta e^{-\theta t}$$

In this case, θ is a parameter of the distribution.   The above is called the *exponential distribution*.

3.2   Discrete bivariate distribution function

3.2.1   Joint probability function

In many industrial processes an end product is the result of the joint effect of more than one random variable.   These random variables may be defined on the same sample space or on different sample spaces.   A very common experience is that of mating a thread screw with a nut, or packing an item for snug fit into a container.   In both cases (and there are an endless number of others), the inner dimension resulting from one process must match the outer dimension of another process.   Exercise 1.6 offers an excellent case in point.

Recall that we are placing a large fragile item into a container so that it will fit without shifting back and forth during handling.   The item is essentially cylindrical in shape and can be made to fit along its cylindrical surface without difficulty.   There is, however, variation in both the length of the item L_1 and the length of the container L_2.   As described in Exercise 1.6, there are several random variables of interest, in particular, $E = L_2 - L_1$.   There are a number of events of special interest, for example, that of the container length being greater than or equal to the part length, $E \geq 0$.

Let us consider a sample space of pairs of values of L_2 and L_1.   This consists of sets of points in the first quadrant of the plane, with axes l_1 and l_2.   The event $E \geq 0$ consists of all those points on or above the line $l_2 = l_1$.   The probability assignment on space (l_1, l_2) is given by the function $p(l_1, l_2)$.   The probability of the event $E \geq 0$ is

$$P(E \geq 0) = \sum_{l_2 \geq l_1} p(l_1, l_2) \tag{3.2.1}$$

The function $p(l_1, l_2)$ is called the joint probability function of the random variables L_1 and L_2.

Definition: joint probability of two discrete random variables X and Y   The joint probability function of two discrete random variables X and Y which jointly take on the pairs of values (x_i, y_j) $(i, j = -\infty, \ldots, -1, 0, 1, \ldots, +\infty)$ is denoted by $p(x_i, y_j)$, where $p(x_i, y_j) = $ Prob $(X = x_i$ and $Y = y_j)$.

Some properties which $p(x_i, y_j)$ must satisfy are:

1. $p(x_i, y_j) \geq 0$
2. $\sum_i \sum_j p(x_i, y_j) = 1$

Properties 1 and 2 are essential counterparts of the basic properties required of single random variables: property 1 asserts the nonnegativeness of probability; property 2 asserts the fact that the total probability over the sample space is unity.

Example 3.4 Let us reconsider Exercise 1.6 with the following probability assignments, which are derived from an industrial problem. From Table 3.3 on the joint probability distribution, we can determine

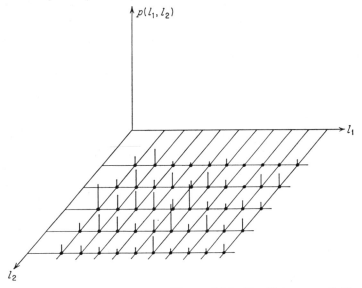

Figure 3.10   Bar histogram $p(l_1, l_2)$.

the probabilities of various events. (Table 3.3 is represented in Fig. 3.10.) We refer to the gap length E as a random variable of special interest, and, in particular, we shall find the probability that $E \geq 0$ using Eq. (3.2.1). We simply refer to Table 3.3 and select those cells for which $l_2 \geq l_1$ and add the numbers in these cells. We can do this more systematically by rewriting Eq. (3.2.1) as follows:

$$P(E \geq 0) = \sum_{l_2 \geq l_1} p(l_1, l_2) = \sum_{l_2 = 5.00}^{5.16} \sum_{l_1 = 4.76}^{l_1 = l_2} p(l_1, l_2) \qquad (3.2.2)$$

Another event of interest is $E < 0$, namely, the occurrence of an interference between the part and the enclosure of the container. The expression for finding the probability of this event is

$$P(E < 0) = \sum_{l_2 < l_1} p(l_1, l_2) = p(5.04, 5.00) + p(5.08, 5.00)$$
$$+ p(5.12, 5.00) + p(5.08, 5.04) + p(5.12, 5.04) + p(5.12, 5.08)$$
$$= 0.005 + 0.005 + 0.005 + 0.010 + 0.015 + 0.010 = 0.050$$

Since $P(E \geq 0) = 1 - P(E < 0)$, we can obtain $P(E \geq 0)$ without resorting directly to Table 3.3.

TABLE 3.3
Probability Assignments in Packing Problem

l_2 \ l_1	4.76	4.80	4.84	4.88	4.92	4.96	5.00	5.04	5.08	5.12
5.00	0.000	0.080	0.005	0.000	0.000	0.000	0.000	0.005	0.005	0.005
5.04	0.030	0.000	0.035	0.100	0.000	0.080	0.020	0.060	0.010	0.015
5.08	0.015	0.020	0.010	0.050	0.200	0.020	0.080	0.020	0.025	0.010
5.12	0.035	0.000	0.040	0.000	0.000	0.000	0.000	0.005	0.000	0.000
5.16	0.010	0.000	0.010	0.000	0.000	0.000	0.000	0.000	0.000	0.000

We may wish further to compute the probabilities of other aspects of the random variable E. In the present example the distribution of the values of E directly affects the cost of the packing operation. In this case, then, we need the *PF* of E in a form which lends itself to systematic computation. We want to know, for example, the probability that one filler will be needed to give a snug fit. A single filler is required when $E = 0.12, 0.16, 0.20$. The filler used in this case is a felt pad 0.125 inch thick. The pad can be compressed up to 0.01 inch if necessary. Hence the probability of one filler is

$$P(E = 0.12) + P(E = 0.16) + P(E = 0.20)$$

The *PF* of E is

$$p(x) = \text{Prob}\ (E = x) = \text{Prob}\ (L_2 - L_1 = x) = \sum_{l_2} p(l_2 - x, l_2)$$

Bear in mind that this summation takes place only over points $(l_2 - x, l_2)$ belonging to the sample space. In a particular instance, when $x = 0.12$, the points in question are $(4.88,5.00)$, $(4.92,5.04)$, $(4.96,5.08)$, $(5.00,5.12)$, and $(5.04,5.16)$. The points lie on the diagonal beginning with the fourth cell of the first row, descending to the right. The *PF* for the other values of x are similarly obtained by summing along the appropriate diagonals. The numerical value of the probability of requiring one felt pad is therefore

$$\text{Prob (one felt pad)} = p(0.12) + p(0.16) + p(0.20)$$
$$= 0.02 + 0.305 + 0.165 = 0.490$$

In general, probabilities $E = x$ are found by diagonal summation over probability assignment of points on the sample space. More generally, finding the probabilities of events in a bivariate sample space requires summing the joint probability function systematically over selected sets of points.

Example 3.5   In Example 2.11 we consider the number of boys and girls in a community.   On the sample space the univariate random variables X (number of boys in a family) and Y (number of girls in a family) were defined.   The bivariate random variable (X,Y) can be represented on a two-dimensional plane by means of the integral points of the first quadrant.   The probability assignment on the basic sample space will lead to a joint probability function defined for those integral points (the sample points).   More formally, we have a function

$$p(i,j) = \text{Prob } (X = i \text{ and } Y = j)$$

For the number of children in a family, the random variable $Z = X + Y$ can be studied directly from the joint PF $p(i,j)$.   The PF of Z is

$$P(z) = \text{Prob } (Z = z) = \sum_{i+j=z} p(i,j) = \sum_{i=0}^{z} p(i, z - i)$$

Bear in mind that in this summation z is a fixed number.   Furthermore, if $z = 5$, we must sum the joint PF over all these points for which $i + j = 5$. These points lie on a diagonal.   In fact, the probability that Z equals any z constitutes a summation of the joint PF over a diagonal in the sample space.   The sum of random variables and their distribution functions play a central role in statistical theory.

3.2.2   Joint cumulative distribution function

Often, in cases such as the packaging of a fragile cylindrical part, the process for making the part is well controlled at the lower specification but varies considerably at the upper specification.   This happens because the lower specification is critical with respect to technical performance of the part whereas the production manager is not perturbed about interference in packaging.   His effectiveness is judged more immediately and directly by sampling on his finished product rather than on how economically it can be packed.   The container manufacturer, on the other hand, is anxious to avoid interference and so allows his containers to trail off somewhat on the longer side.   The manager of the plant manufacturing and packing the part is concerned with the overall economy of the plant operation.   Hence, while he is quite satisfied with the control of the part's lower specification, he is particularly interested in the joint variation of the part length and the container length.   While he is not able to exercise direct influence on the container manufacturer, he does have the power of persuasion, provided he is supported by data on the distribution of the part and container lengths.   When containers seem to be too long and must be filled with felt pads at excessive cost, he may argue that the distribution of his part lengths is narrow and that his lower specification is quite satisfactory.   Of the data appearing in Table

3.3, the basis for the part manufacturer's approval of the containers serves to induce the container manufacturer to work toward the high side. Hence this situation results in a diverse tendency between part and container lengths, which must be overcome by an influence which considers the joint distribution of these quantities. The important event in this connection is, therefore, the probability that $L_1 \leq t_1$ and $L_2 \leq t_2$, where t_1 and t_2 are appropriately selected. This probability is the cumulative probability distribution of the joint random variable (L_1, L_2). This joint CDF can be found from the joint PF $p(l_1, l_2)$ as follows:

$$F_{L_1, L_2}(t_1, t_2) = \text{Prob } (L_1 \leq t_1 \text{ and } L_2 \leq t_2)$$
$$= \sum_{l_2 \leq t_2} \sum_{l_1 \leq t_1} p(l_1, l_2) \tag{3.2.3}$$

Definition: joint CDF of two discrete random variables X and Y The joint CDF of X and Y is

$$F_{X,Y}(t_1, t_2) = \text{Prob } (X \leq t_1 \text{ and } Y \leq t_2) = \sum_{y_i \leq t_2} \sum_{x_i \leq t_1} p(x_i, y_j)$$

Some properties of the joint CDF of two discrete random variables X and Y are:

1. $F_{X,Y}(-\infty, y_j) = 0$ for all y_j
   $F_{X,Y}(x_i, -\infty) = 0$ for all x_i
2. $F_{X,Y}(+\infty, +\infty) = 1$
3. $F_{X,Y}(t_1, t_2) \leq F_{X,Y}(t'_1, t_2)$ when $t_1 \leq t'_1$
   $F_{X,Y}(t_1, t_2) \leq F_{X,Y}(t_1, t'_2)$ when $t_2 \leq t'_2$

Properties 1 and 2 are analogous to those of CDFs of univariate random variables; property 3 is a generalization of the monotonicity property of univariate CDFs.

Returning to the plant manager's concern with the distribution of L_1 and L_2, we find that he intuitively suggested trying to cut the part length at 5.00 feet in order to avoid interference and simultaneously to cut the container length at 5.08 feet in order to minimize felt-pad costs. He is interested in knowing the probability that $L_1 \leq 5.00$ and $L_2 \leq 5.08$. This is given by

$$F_{L_1, L_2}(5.00, 5.08) = \sum_{l_2 \leq 5.08} \sum_{l_1 \leq 5.00} p(l_1, l_2) = 0.745 \tag{3.2.4}$$

It is apparent that the manager's attempt to diagnose the potential economy of the processes under consideration is not adequate. This is a decision problem involving the joint probability distribution, the joint CDFs, and the distribution of E, wherein a cost function involving one or more of these distributions, the loss from interference and from felt pads, is to be minimized. Part of this problem was dealt with in Exercise 1.6.

3.2.3 Marginal probability function

In Example 3.4 we discussed the joint PDF of the random variables L_1 and L_2. The probability assignments are given in Table 3.3. From these assignments we were able to compute the probability of various events specified by relationships between L_1 and L_2. Results of the study of E lead us to consider changing the average gap length. It seems natural, therefore, since E is dependent on L_1 and L_2, to consider the variations of L_1 and L_2 separately. Our table, however, presents the probability of L_1 for different values of L_2 and vice versa. Under the present conditions, fitting a part to a container has entailed some selection in order to reduce the cost of packing with felt pads. On the other hand, the plant manager believes it would be less expensive if the packing were unselected, provided the gap between part and container were narrower than at present but not so narrow as to lead to undue interference.

Toward this end we look at the distributions of L_1 and L_2. Selecting the smallest value of L_2, namely, 5.00, let us compute the probability of interference $(E < 0)$. We are, in fact, seeking in more formal terms

$$\text{Prob } (E < 0 \mid L_2 = 5.00)$$

which is equal to

$$\frac{\text{Prob } (E < 0 \text{ and } L_2 = 5.00)}{\text{Prob } (L_2 = 5.00)}$$

This is readily computed from Table 3.3 by looking at the first column. The numerator is

$$
\begin{aligned}
\text{Prob } (E < 0 \text{ and } L_2 &= 5.00) \\
&= p(5.04,5.00) + p(5.08,5.00) + p(5.12,5.00) \\
&= 0.005 + 0.005 + 0.005 \\
&= 0.015
\end{aligned}
$$

The denominator is obtained by adding all the joint probabilities in the column for which $L_2 = 5.00$; that is,

$$\text{Prob } (L_2 = 5.00) = \sum_{l_1 = 4.76}^{5.12} p(l_1, 5.00) = 0.10$$

Analysis of the problem indicates that one should look for the probability that L_2 equals other values than 5.00, since interference can take place at those values as well. We are generally interested, therefore, in

$$p_{L_2}(l_2) = \text{Prob } (L_2 = l_2) = \sum_{l_1} p(l_1, l_2)$$

We note that $p_{L_2}(5.00) = 0.10$; $p_{L_2}(5.04) = 0.35$; $p_{L_2}(5.08) = 0.45$; $p_{L_2}(5.12) = 0.08$; and $p_{L_2}(5.16) = 0.02$. This is a univariate probability function, called the *marginal probability function* of L_2.

Since we know that L_1 can take on values larger than 5.00, there is some chance of interference when the container of that size is selected. This is also true for $L_2 = 5.04$ and $L_2 = 5.08$. Hence, one immediate suggestion is to raise the minimum value of the container lengths in order to reduce interference. On the other hand, the possible economy from reduced interference may be negated by the increase in the number of felt pads required. For the moment we shall not pursue the calculation of the optimum size of containers but define the marginal probability function which has given evidence of its importance.

Definition: marginal probability functions for the discrete bivariate random variable (X,Y) The marginal probability functions for (X,Y) are defined as

$$p_X(x_i) = \sum_{y_j} p(x_i, y_j) \qquad \text{for all } x_i$$

$$p_Y(y_j) = \sum_{x_i} p(x_i, y_j) \qquad \text{for all } y_j$$

where (x_i, y_j) are the values taken on by the bivariate random variable (X,Y) with joint probability function $p(x_i, y_j)$. Note that marginal probability functions obey the properties of univariate probability functions.

Of course, in deciding on what action to take to reduce losses due to interference, we must also keep the cost of felt pads as low as possible. We must therefore consider the probability function of L_1 as well as L_2. The problem of minimizing losses in our packing problem requires use of the joint probability function of the two random variables (L_1, L_2) and also particular knowledge of their marginal distributions.

3.2.4   Conditional probability function

It may be well, in connection with the study of interference $(E < 0)$, to emphasize the variation of E with L_2. Setting down the formal relations will put into perspective the importance not only of the marginal probabilities, but also of the conditional probabilities. We have, again,

$$\text{Prob } (E < 0 \mid L_2 = l_2) = \frac{\text{Prob } (E < 0 \text{ and } L_2 = l_2)}{\text{Prob } (L_2 = l_2)} = \sum_{l_1 > l_2} p(l_1 \mid l_2)$$

where

$$p(l_1 \mid l_2) = p(L_1 = l_1 \mid L_2 = l_2) = \frac{p(l_1, l_2)}{\text{Prob } (L_2 = l_2)} = \frac{p(l_1, l_2)}{p_{L_2}(l_2)}$$

Note that probabilities connected with interference can be computed from $p(l_1 \mid l_2)$, called the *conditional probability function* of L_1 given L_2, the individual terms of which are conditional probabilities. In some cases, computation of desired probabilities is performed more simply by means of conditional probabilities than by recourse to the original probability assignments; this is shown for the univariate case in the discussion of conditional probabilities in Chap. 2. Furthermore, the dependence of the variation of either of the random variables in terms of the other is brought into focus by the conditional probabilities.

Definition: conditional probability functions for discrete bivariate random variables (X,Y) The conditional probability functions $p(x \mid y)$ of X with respect to Y and $p(y \mid x)$ of Y with respect to X are

$$p(x_i \mid y_j) = \frac{p(x_i,y_j)}{p_Y(y_j)} \qquad \text{for all } x_i,\ y_j \text{ and } p_Y(y_j) > 0$$

$$p(y_j \mid x_i) = \frac{p(x_i,y_j)}{p_X(x_i)} \qquad \text{for all } x_i,\ y_j \text{ and } p_X(x_i) > 0$$

Note that, for a given y_j, the function $p(x_i \mid y_j)$ satisfies the requirements for a univariate probability function.

3.3   Generalization to many dimensions

There is no limit on the number of random variables which might come under joint consideration. In practice, it is not uncommon to consider jointly three or more random variables. In the theoretical consideration of N-fold repetitions of experiment, inferences can be made more tractable by considering the repetitions as an N-fold compound experiment. Simply, the tossing of a coin 50 times can be thought of as the compound experiment of tossing 50 coins. Similarly, the analysis of five supposedly identical specimens of a chemical compound for the percentage content of a given element can be treated as yielding outcomes $(X_1,X_2, \ . \ . \ . \ ,X_5)$, where X_i is the per cent content of the ith analysis. The quintuple $(X_1,X_2, \ . \ . \ . \ ,X_5)$ is here considered as a sample point in a five-dimensional sample space. Random variables on such many-dimensional sample spaces are studied with multidimensional distribution functions. The forms of these multivariate distribution functions are quite analogous to those of the bivariate case. (The term multivariate does, of course, include the bivariate case. It is convenient, however, to use the **term** bivariate when dealing in two dimensions.)

Consider, then, a k-dimensional discrete sample space and the corresponding k-dimensional random variable $(X^{(1)},X^{(2)}, \ . \ . \ . \ ,X^{(k)})$ whose sample points s are representable by k-tuples of the form $s = (x^{(1)},x^{(2)}, \ . \ . \ . \ ,x^{(k)})$. Specific points are designated as

$$(x_{i_1}{}^{(1)},x_{i_2}{}^{(2)}, \ . \ . \ . \ ,y_{i_k}{}^{(k)})$$

where the $i_1, i_2, \ldots, i_k$ each take on the values $-\infty, \ldots, -1, 0,$ $+1, \ldots, +\infty$.

We have here an analogy between the univariate, bivariate, and multivariate cases. The univariate and bivariate cases are special cases of the k-variate case, for $k = 1$ and 2, respectively. Geometrically, each sample point s corresponds to a point in the k-dimensional space. For example, in three dimensions ($k = 3$), each particular point can be represented by a 3-tuple $(x_{i_1}^{(1)}, x_{i_2}^{(2)}, x_{i_3}^{(3)})$ as shown in Fig. 3.11. The forms of

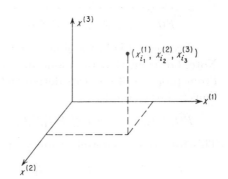

Figure 3.11

the multivariate marginal and conditional probability functions, as well as the *CDF* for the multivariate case, are given below.

3.3.1 Multivariate probability function $p(x^{(1)}, \ldots, x^{(k)})$

$$p(s) = p(x^{(1)}, \ldots, x^{(k)})$$
$$= \text{Prob} \ (X^{(1)} = x^{(1)} \text{ and } X^{(2)} = x^{(2)} \cdots \text{ and } X^{(k)} = x^{(k)})$$

This function obeys the following properties (nonnegativeness, unit sum):

1. $p(x_{i_1}^{(1)}, \ldots, x_{i_k}^{(k)}) \geq 0$ for all $i_1, i_2, \ldots, i_k$
2. $\sum_{i_1} \sum_{i_2} \cdots \sum_{i_k} p(x_{i_1}^{(1)}, x_{i_2}^{(2)}, \ldots, x_{i_k}^{(k)}) = 1$

3.3.2 Multivariate cumulative distribution function $F(t_1, \ldots, t_2)$

This function is denoted by

$$F(t_1, t_2, \ldots, t_k) = \text{Prob} \ (X^{(1)} \leq t_1, X^{(2)} \leq t_2, \ldots, X^{(k)} \leq t_k)$$
$$= \sum_{x^{(1)} \leq t_1} \sum_{X^{(2)} \leq t_1} \cdots \sum_{x^{(k)} \leq t_k} p(x^{(1)}, \ldots, x^{(k)})$$

The properties of the univariate and bivariate cases are but special properties of the general case.   These properties are:

1. $F(-\infty,t_2, \ldots ,t_k) = 0$ for all values of $t_2, \ldots , t_k$
   $F(t_1,-\infty,t_3, \ldots ,t_k) = 0$ for all values of $t_1, t_3, \ldots , t_k$
   . . . .
   $F(t_1,t_2, \ldots ,t_{k-1},-\infty) = 0$ for all values of $t_1, t_2, \ldots , t_{k-1}$
2. $F(+\infty,+\infty, \ldots ,+\infty) = 1$
3. $F(t_1,t_2, \ldots ,t_k) \leq F(t'_1,t_2, \ldots ,t_k)$ when $t_1 \leq t'_1$
   $F(t_1,t_2, \ldots ,t_k) \leq F(t_1,t'_2,t_3, \ldots ,t_k)$ when $t_2 \leq t'_2$
   . . . .
   $F(t_1, \ldots ,t_{k-1},t_k) \leq F(t_1, \ldots ,t_{k-1},t'_k)$ when $t_k \leq t'_k$

Property 3 is but a generalization of the monotonicity requirement. Note, however, that the monotonicity holds separately for each variable. From property 3 one can derive the monotonicity for various combinations.   For example,

$$F(t_1,t_2,t_3, \ldots ,t_k) \leq F(t'_1,t'_2,t_3, \ldots ,t_k) \qquad \text{when } t_1 \leq t'_1, \ t_2 \leq t'_2$$

This follows immediately from property 3:

$$F(t_1,t_2,t_3, \ldots ,t_k) \leq F(t'_1,t_2,t_3, \ldots ,t_k) \leq F(t'_1,t'_2,t_3, \ldots ,t_k)$$

3.4   Continuous multivariate distribution functions

In the univariate case the probability function for a discrete random variable was generalized to establish a probability density function by increasing indefinitely the number of sample points.   While no detailed or complete argument was developed, a sufficient indication of the procedure was presented to lend conviction to the usefulness of the result. The multivariate probability density function can also be established by a generalization of the univariate procedure.   We shall give a heuristic argument for the bivariate case and state the result for the general case.

Consider the graphical representation of a bivariate probability function of a discrete random variable (X,Y).   Suppose that measurements are given in each variable to a least count of one unit.   The lengths of the spikes at the integral points of the sample space add up to unity.   Suppose now that the outcomes of the experiment can be measured to a least count of 0.1 unit in each variable.   We get (approximately) 100 times as many sample points.   At each of these we can represent the probability of occurrence by a spike.   In order to estimate the magnitude of these spikes, consider the point (3,2) of the original sample, now denoted as (3.0,2.0) in the new sample space.   Suppose $p(3,2) = 0.22$.   Then consider all new sample points (x,y) such that $2.5 \leq x \leq 3.4$ and $1.5 \leq y \leq 2.4$, of which there are 100.   The sum of these spikes is 0.22, and each of them is approximately 0.0022; that is, $p(x,y)$ in the chosen rectangle is approximately 0.01 of that of $p(3,2)$.

Assume now that the least count is successively reduced and the number of sample points proportionately increased. The sample points tend to fill the (x,y) plane. The spike lengths, however, decrease to 0, although their sum remains 1. Thus the spike lengths have lost their usefulness for making probability calculations, and we must restore the meaningfulness of the relative frequency of occurrence of the bivariate outcome (X,Y).

Consider now, for the original sample space, the ratio of the spike length to the area of the square of which it is the center. As the least count decreases, this ratio remains approximately constant. At whatever state in the reduction of the least count one considers the set of sample points, these ratios remain approximately constant through the successive stages in the reduction of the least count. We express this more formally as $p(x,y \mid \Delta,\Delta)/\Delta^2$, Δ small, which can be practically approximated by a constant [depending on (x,y)]. We shall designate this constant by $f(x,y)$. Now we can assert that

$$p(x,y \mid \Delta,\Delta) \approx f(x,y)(\Delta^2) \tag{3.4.1}$$

By a similar argument the same result can be obtained for different least counts, Δx and Δy, provided that Δx, Δy both are "small," and Eq. (3.4.1) becomes

$$p(x,y \mid \Delta x, \Delta y) \approx f(x,y)\, \Delta x\, \Delta y \qquad \Delta x,\, \Delta y \text{ small} \tag{3.4.2}$$

In accordance with the general definition of a function it should be noted that since $f(x,y)$ is defined at every point of the plane, it is a function of (x,y), where $-\infty \le x \le +\infty$ and $-\infty \le y \le +\infty$.

Definition: bivariate probability density function   A function $f(x,y)$ is said to be a *bivariate probability density function* if

$$f(x,y) \ge 0$$
$$\int_{-\infty}^{+\infty} \int_{-\infty}^{+\infty} f(x,y)\, dx\, dy = 1$$

The *CDF* for continuous bivariate random variables can be obtained quite directly from the discrete bivariate *CDF* and the continuous bivariate *PDF*. Starting with

$$F_{X,Y}(t_1,t_2) = \text{Prob }(X \le t_1,\, Y \le t_2) = \sum_{x_i \le t_1} \sum_{y_j \le t_2} p(x_i,y_j \mid \Delta x,\, \Delta y)$$
$$\approx \sum_{x_i \le t_1} \sum_{y_1 \le t_2} f(x_i,y_j)(\Delta x\, \Delta y)$$

Observe that the last summation is of the form of a finite sum approximating a definite integral of $f(x,y)$. This may be expressed by the following approximate relations:

$$F_{X,Y}(t_1,t_2) \approx \sum_{x_i \le t_1} \sum_{y_j \le t_2} f(x_i,y_j)\, (\Delta x)\, (\Delta y) \approx \int_{-\infty}^{t_1} \int_{-\infty}^{t_2} f(x,y)\, dx\, dy$$

Therefore the continuous approximation to the discrete bivariate CDF, $F_{X,Y}(t_1,t_2)$, is chosen so that

$$F_{X,Y}(t_1,t_2) \approx \int_{-\infty}^{t_1} \int_{-\infty}^{t_2} f(x,y) \, dx \, dy = F_{X,Y}^*(t_1,t_2)$$

Utilizing the "continuous" approximation to the discrete bivariate CDF allows us to make probability calculations by integration of the continuous bivariate PDF. The following relation holds between continuous CDF and PDF:

$$\left(\frac{\partial^2 F_{X,Y}^*(t_1,t_2)}{\partial t_1 \partial t_2} \right)_{t_1=x, t_2=y} = f(x,y)$$

Analogous to the univariate case, the continuous bivariate CDF and PDF are related to each other as integral and derivative, respectively.

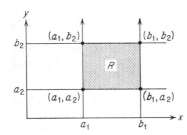

Figure 3.12

We can make use of both the continuous PDF and CDF to make probability calculations of events, in particular, when the event is represented by a rectangle R in the plane as in Fig. 3.12. The computation is made as follows:

$$\begin{aligned} \text{Prob}\,((x,y) \text{ in } R) &= \text{Prob}\,(a_1 \leq X \leq b_1;\, a_2 \leq Y \leq b_2) \\ &\approx \int_{a_1}^{b_1} \int_{a_2}^{b_2} f(x,y) \, dx \, dy \\ &= F_{X,Y}^*(b_1,b_2) - F_{X,Y}^*(a_1,b_2) - F_{X,Y}^*(b_1,a_2) + F_{X,Y}^*(a_1,a_2) \end{aligned}$$

The relation is approximate when discrete probability assignments on the plane are given. Obviously, the closeness of the approximation depends on the size of the least count and the "smoothness" of the probability assignments.

We shall often study real situations in terms of continuous random variables where probability density functions replace probability functions in idealized experiments. The usefulness of this idealization depends upon the closeness with which real situations are described thereby. Practical examples will be developed in subsequent chapters.

Now we shall give the form of the continuous marginal and conditional probability density functions.

Bivariate Marginal Probability Density Function $f_X(x)$, $f_Y(y)$

$$f_X(x) = \int_{-\infty}^{+\infty} f(x,y)\, dy \qquad \text{and} \qquad f_Y(y) = \int_{-\infty}^{+\infty} f(x,y)\, dx$$

These are univariate probability functions and therefore can be used to compute probabilities on X or Y individually. For example,

$$\text{Prob } (a \le X \le b) = \int_a^b \int_{-\infty}^{+\infty} f(x,y)\, dy\, dx = \int_a^b f_X(x)\, dx$$

Conditional Probability Density Functions of X **Given** Y **and** Y **Given** X; $f(x \mid y)$, $f(y \mid x)$

$$f(x \mid y) = \frac{f(x,y)}{f_Y(y)} \qquad f_Y(y) > 0$$

$$f(y \mid x) = \frac{f(x,y)}{f_X(x)} \qquad f_X(x) > 0$$

For a given value of y, $f(x \mid y)$ is a univariate PDF, and similarly, for a given value of x, $f(y \mid x)$ is a univariate PDF. Again, these functions can be used to make probability calculations. For example,

$$\text{Prob } (a \le X \le b \mid y) = \int_a^b f(x \mid y)\, dx$$

The notion can be generalized to many dimensions directly. (Practice is offered in the exercises.)

3.5   Independence

Recall the packing problem where, among other events of interest, we were concerned with $L_1 \le t_1$ and $L_2 \le t_2$. The probability of this inequality can be calculated from the bivariate CDF of L_1 and L_2. The form of the computation is as follows:

$$F_{L_1,L_2}(t_1,t_2) = \text{Prob } (L_1 \le t_1 \text{ and } L_2 \le t_2) = \sum_{l_1 \le t_1} \sum_{l_2 \le t_2} p(l_1,l_2) \qquad (3.5.1)$$

For this computation it is necessary to resort to the probability-assignment table (Table 3.3) and pick out the required terms for summing. In the present case, even though there are but 5 levels for L_1 and 10 levels for L_2, there are in all 50 terms which can contribute to the CDF. For the bivariate case, the number of terms in the probability-assignment table increases as the product of the number of levels of observation of each random variable. Loosely stated, we can say that as the number of levels of each individual random variable is doubled, the number of bivariate probability assignments is quadrupled; for the trivariate case, the number of probability assignments increases eightfold, and so on.

Hence the computation of multivariate CDFs, as well as other computations on higher sample spaces, can be extremely cumbersome. It seems to be worthwhile to seek a means for generating all the probability assignments from the marginals. In certain cases this will contain the essence of all the probability assignments. To see how this can come about, let us examine further the bivariate probability assignments.

We have

$$p(l_1,l_2) = \text{Prob } (L_1 = l_1 \text{ and } L_2 = l_2)$$
$$= \text{Prob } (L_1 = l_1 \mid L_2 = l_2) \text{ Prob } (L_2 = l_2)$$
$$= p(l_1 \mid l_2) \cdot P_{L_2}(l_2)$$

The probability assignments can be expressed as a product of a marginal and a conditional probability. The conditional-probability term contains the dependence of L_1 on L_2. Suppose, however, that the events $L_1 = l_1$ and $L_2 = l_2$ were independent events for all l_1 and l_2. Then

$$p(l_1 \mid l_2) = \text{Prob } (L_1 = l_1 \mid L_2 = l_2)$$
$$= \text{Prob } (L_1 = l_1)$$
$$= p_{L_1}(l_1) \text{ and } p(l_1,l_2) = p_{L_1}(l_1) \cdot p_{L_2}(l_2) \qquad (3.5.2)$$

This is precisely the form we desire since it can yield the 50 terms of the probability assignment from knowledge of only the 15 marginal terms. Generally, for m terms of the marginal of X and n terms of the marginal of Y, the mn probability assignments are determined by taking the appropriate products. This result can be expressed more formally.

Definition: independence of two discrete random variables X, Y Two discrete random variables X and Y are said to be *independent* when the events $X = x$ and $Y = y$ are independent for all (x,y).

This is merely an extension of the notion of independence already discussed in connection with experiments and events. The reader can readily show that this definition is equivalent to the condition expressed in Eq. (3.5.2). It will become increasingly apparent that much of probability calculation becomes tractable and that much of probability analysis becomes formally elegant under the condition of independence.

Making use of the independence concept, we reformulate Eq. (3.5.1).

$$F_{L_1,L_2}(t_1,t_2) = \sum_{l_1 \leq t_1} \sum_{l_2 \leq t_2} p(l_1,l_2)$$
$$= \sum_{l_1 \leq t_1} \sum_{l_2 \leq t_2} p_{L_1}(l_1) p_{L_2}(l_2)$$
$$= \left[\sum_{l_1 \leq t_1} p_{L_1}(l_1) \right] \left[\sum_{l_2 \leq t_2} p_{L_2}(l_2) \right] = F_{L_1}(t_1) F_{L_2}(t_2) \qquad (3.5.3)$$

Here again, the product rule holds and serves to simplify computation.

Before illustrating the notion of independence, we shall state it for both the k-variate discrete and continuous random variables.

Definition: independence of k discrete random variables X_1, X_2, . . . , X_k The k discrete random variables X_1, X_2, . . . , X_k are said to be *independent* when the events $X_1 = x_1$, $X_2 = x_2$, . . . , $X_k = x_k$ are independent for all $(x_1, x_2, \ldots , x_k)$. This is equivalent to

$$p(x_1, x_2, \ldots , x_k) = p_{X_1}(x_1) p_{X_2}(x_2), \ldots , p_{X_k}(x_k)$$

Definition: independence of k continuous random variables X_1, X_2, . . . , X_k The k continuous random variables X_1, X_2, . . . , X_k are said to be *independent* when $f(x_1, x_2, \ldots , x_k) = f_{X_1}(x_1) f_{X_2}(x_2), \ldots ,$ $f_{X_k}(x_k)$. Independence in the k-variate case, as in the bivariate case, is also equivalent to the product rule for the CDFs.

Example 3.6 Suppose that the manufacture of a complete assembly requires k operations in sequence:

$$\text{Raw material} \to X_1 \to X_2 \to \cdots \to X_k \to \text{final product}$$

Let X_i be the random variable denoting the possible number of times operation i can be performed per day. Let Z be the number of items produced per day. The random variable Z is related to $X_1, \ldots , X_k$ as follows: $Z = \min (X_1, X_2, \ldots , X_k)$. That is, Z is the minimum value of $X_1, \ldots , X_k$.

If $X_1, \ldots , X_k$ has CDFs $F_{X_1}(t)$, $F_{X_2}(t)$, . . . , $F_{X_k}(t)$ and if they are independently distributed, then the CDF of Z can be obtained as follows.

First note that $Z > t$ only if all $X_i > t$. Since the TDF is

$$P(X_i > t) = 1 - F_{X_i}(t)$$

we obtain

$$P(Z > t) = [1 - F_{X_1}(t)][1 - F_{X_2}(t)] \cdots [1 - F_{X_k}(t)]$$

Thus

$$F_Z(t) = 1 - P(Z > t) = 1 - [1 - F_{X_1}(t)][1 - F_{X_2}(t)] \cdots [1 - F_{X_k}(t)]$$

Consider the special cases where $k = 2, 3$ and $F_{X_1}(t) = F_{X_2}(t) = F_{X_3}(t)$. Let the random variables take on the following values:

$x =$

	0	5	10	15	20	25	30
Prob $(X = x)$	0.00	0.05	0.10	0.35	0.25	0.15	0.10
$F_X(t)$	0.00	0.05	0.15	0.50	0.75	0.90	1.00
$F_Z(t)$ $(k = 2)$	0.00	0.10	0.28	0.75	0.94	0.99	1.00
$F_Z(t)$ $(k = 3)$	0.00	0.14	0.38	0.875	0.985	1.00	1.00

In Fig. 3.13 are given the *TDF*s for $k = 1, 2,$ and 3.

This quite simplified example is patterned after situations which arise commonly in manufacturing practice. It is evident that were the rates of production not independent, estimate of the probability of producing more than certain quantities of final assemblies would be quite a cumbersome task.

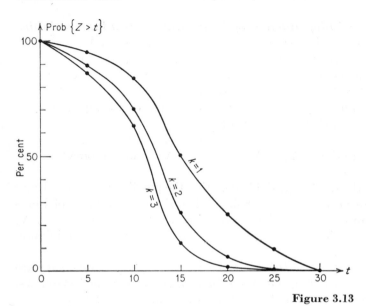

Figure 3.13

We shall illustrate the significance of independence further by application of the concept to the packing problem. In Eq. (3.2.4) we computed the probability that $L_1 \leq 5.00$ and $L_2 \leq 5.08$ by means of the *CDF* $F_{L_1, L_2}(5.00, 5.08)$. This involved adding 21 terms of Table 3.3, yielding

$$F_{L_1, L_2}(5.00, 5.08) = 0.745$$

Similarly, one can compute $F_{L_1, L_2}(4.92, 5.04) = 0.250$. By the product rule for independent random variables, however,

$$F_{L_1, L_2}(4.92, 5.04) = F_{L_1}(4.92) \cdot F_{L_2}(5.04)$$
$$= (0.64)(0.45) = 0.288$$

Interestingly enough, the two results differ by an amount greater than that which can be attributed to computational error. The random variables part length and container length are not independent of one another; the product rule does not apply. It does not necessarily follow that nonindependence is undesirable. The question of whether or not to achieve independence of the random variables is part of a broader decision problem involving specifications for these variables, among other considerations, in order to minimize the cost of packing this part. The important implication of the present problem is that independence is not to be taken for granted. *Independence is not an abstract notion. It is inherent in the circumstances of experiment.* The basic and fundamental element of independence is the independence of experiments.

EXERCISES

3.1. A fair coin is tossed independently n times, and the average number $\bar{X}$ of heads noted.

    a. Find the probability function of $\bar{X}$ when $n = 1, 2, 3$, and 4.
    b. Find the *CDF* of $\bar{X}$ when $n = 1, 2, 3$, and 4.
    c. Find the probability function of the number of tosses until the first head appears.
    d. The first toss resulted in heads. Find the probability that after five tosses the accumulated number of tails is greater than the accumulated number of heads.

3.2. Let the time to failure of an item be described in terms of a random variable L with probability function $p(l)$.

l, days	1	2	3	4	5	6	7	8	9	10
$p(l)$	0.10	0.15	0.20	0.15	0.12	0.10	0.08	0.05	0.03	0.02

    a. Plot the *CDF* of L.
    b. Find the probability that $L = 5$ conditional on $L \geq 2$.
    c. Find the probability that $L > 5$ conditional on $L \geq 2$.

Two items have independent lifetimes L_1 and L_2, each with the probability function $p(l)$.

    d. Describe the joint probability function of L_1 and L_2.
    e. Find the probability function of $L_1 + L_2$.
    f. Find the probability function of min (L_1, L_2).
    g. N items have independent lifetimes $L_1, L_2, \ldots, L_N$, each with the probability function $p(l)$. Find a way of computing the *CDF* of min $(L_1, L_2, \ldots, L_N)$, the time until the first failure.

3.3. The time to failure of a machine is described by a random variable L, with probability function $p(l)$, as in Exercise 3.2. If the machine fails, it is repaired at a cost c_1. After repair we assume the machine starts a new lifetime as new. To reduce costs the possibility of maintenance is being considered. Thus every m days after starting a new lifetime, the machine is given maintenance at a cost c_2 (c_2 usually is less than c_1). We assume that after maintenance the machine is as new. A cycle for the machine is defined to be the length of time either until after a repair for a failure or after maintenance (when a new lifetime begins).

  a. Find the probability function of cycle length for $m = 2$, 3, and 8.
  b. Find the probability that the cycle ends with failure (failure before maintenance) for $m = 2$, 3, and 8.
  c. Using the frequency interpretation of probability, estimate how many days pass until the end of the Nth cycle when N is large, for $m = 2$, 3, and 8.
  d. What long-run cost do you expect for N cycles, for $m = 2$, 3, and 8, and $c_1 = 10$ and $c_2 = 5$?
  e. What long-run cost *per day* do you expect for $m = 2$, 3, and 8 and $c_1 = 10$ and $c_2 = 5$?
  f. Which of $m = 2$, 3, and 8 is best for $c_1 = 10$ and $c_2 = 5$?
  g. What is the answer to (f) when $c_1 = 20$ and $c_2 = 10$?
  h. What is the answer to (f) when $c_1 = 10$ and $c_2 = 2$?

3.4. X_1, X_2, and X_3 are independent random variables, identically distributed, each with probabilities of assuming the values $+1$ and -1 equal to $\frac{1}{2}$. Further define the random variables U and V as follows:

$$U = X_1 + X_2$$
$$V = X_1 + X_3$$

  a. Give the joint distribution of U and V.
  b. Are U and V statistically independent? Demonstrate your answer.

3.5. A fair coin is tossed repeatedly and independently.

  a. Find the expression for the probability that after trial $2k$ the number of heads equals the number of tails.
  b. It is known that the first two tosses resulted in heads. Find the probability of an equal number of heads and tails at the end of toss $2k$.
  c. Compare answers for (a) and (b) for $k = 3$ and 4.
  d. What is the probability of an equal number of heads and tails for the first time at the end of the sixth toss?

3.6. A machine has three critical components. The times to failure of the three components are independently and identically distributed random variables, with CDF equal to $F(t)$.

  a. In order for the machine to function, all three components must function. What is the CDF of the time to failure of the machine?
  b. In order for the machine to function, at least one of the components must function. What is the CDF of the time to failure of the machine?
  c. If the CDF of component failure time is $F(t) = 1 - e^{-\theta t}$ (exponential with parameter θ), what are answers to (a) and (b)? Comment on the result.

3.7. A retailer stocks a product which deteriorates rapidly on the shelf. The product costs the retailer $2; he prices it at $5 on the day it is stocked but reduces the price to $1 on the following day. Product which has not been sold by the end of the second day is scrapped at a total loss. The retailer estimates from experience the probability distributions given for the demand for fresh product and demand for day-old product. Further, he has reason to believe that fresh- and day-old-product demand are independent. How many units should he stock?

Fresh product		Day-old product	
Demand	Probability	Demand	Probability
0	0.00	0	0.10
1	0.30	1	0.20
2	0.40	2	0.30
3	0.30	3	0.30
4	0.00	4	0.10

3.8. A molecule in a gas has a velocity V which is a random variable with probability density $f(v)$, where

$$f(v) = ave^{-v^2} \qquad v \geq 0$$

a. Find a so that $f(v)$ is a probability density function.

b. The kinetic energy E of the particle is given by the relationship $E = mV^2/2$. Find the CDF and PDF of E.

3.9. A piece of equipment has two major components, A and B, connected in series. Furthermore, component B has two subcomponents in parallel and A has only one subcomponent. The lifetime of the subcomponent in A is described by a random variable L_1, with CDF $F_A(t)$. The lifetimes of the two subcomponents of B are L_2 and L_3 with CDF $F_B(t)$. All three components are assumed to act independently. Thus the machine functions only if both A and B are operating. B functions if either one of its subcomponents work, and A functions if its subcomponent operates. Let L denote the lifetime of the machine. Find the CDF of L.

3.10. The life of a part of a machine is described by a random variable L, with the exponential PDF ae^{-at} $(t \geq 0)$. A spare part is available.

a. Find the CDF of the part.

b. What is the joint distribution function of the part and spare if they are independent?

c. Find the PDF of the combined life of the part in the machine and the spare.

3.11. Suppose the length of a telephone call to have the exponential PDF $\frac{1}{2}e^{-t/2}$ (t in minutes).

a. What is the probability that a call will last more than 3 minutes? Between 3 and 3.5 minutes?

b. An operator is timing a call. It started 2 minutes ago. Find the probability that it ends within a minute.

3.12. Let X and Y be two random variables with joint probability density function (PDF) given by $f(x,y)$, where

$$f(x,y) = e^{-(x+y)} \qquad x \geq 0, y \geq 0$$

Let $U = X - Y$ and $V = X + Y$.

a. Find the CDF of U and V.

b. Find the PDF of U and V.

c. Are X and Y independent?

d. Find the joint PDF of U and V.

e. Are U and V independent?

3.13. A motor-car trip is made from location A to location B, which takes T hours. Suppose a continuous record of the speedometer reading $S(t)$ is given as a function of time t, where $0 \leq t \leq T$. Describe and explain how you would find the distance covered from A to B using $S(t)$.

3.14. A PDF sometimes used to describe income distribution is given by Pareto's distribution

$$f(x) = \begin{cases} \left(\dfrac{r}{A}\right)\left(\dfrac{A}{x}\right)^{r+1} & x \geq A \\ 0 & x < A \end{cases}$$

where $r > 0$. Find the CDF corresponding to this PDF.

3.15. Let X have a uniform distribution in the interval $-1 \leq x \leq +1$. Find the PDF:

a. Of X^3.
b. Of $|X|$.
c. Of $\cos \pi X$.

4

PROPERTIES OF DISTRIBUTIONS

It is common in scientific work to attempt the description of important aspects of complicated phenomena by relatively few numbers. Similarly, it will be useful to focus on certain features of probability distributions by describing them by a limited set of quantities. The distribution function of a random variable does, of course, contain all the needed information for the purposes of probability calculations. Nevertheless, the solution of many problems requires knowledge of only particular aspects of the relevant distributions. In this chapter we shall describe certain features of distributions by a few numbers and analyze the properties of random variables in terms of these numbers.

4.1 Percentiles

In Example 3.1 we discussed the CDFs of the random variables, daily demand D, and daily profit. We might ask for the probability that Q_0, a particular value of the ordering quantity Q, is sufficient to meet the daily demand. The answer is obtained from the CDF of D as follows:

Prob (Q_0 units are sufficient to meet daily demand)
$$= \text{Prob } (D \leq Q_0) = F_D(Q_0) \quad (4.1.1)$$

For example

Prob (7 units are sufficient to meet daily demand)
$$= F_D(7) = 0.85 \quad (4.1.2)$$

For each value of Q, then, we can compute $F_D(Q)$, which relates the above probability to the order quantity Q. It is natural, now, to ask the reverse question, namely, what Q will meet daily demand with a probability of at least P? This type of question can be answered by looking at the inverse function.

Thus the order quantity sufficient to meet demand with probability at least 0.60 (60 per cent) is 5; for 0.92 (92 per cent) it is 8. We can plot these probabilities against Q.   This curve can be obtained from $F_D(t)$ and is plotted in Fig. 4.1.

The values of Q corresponding to the P's are called P *percentiles*. For each P the corresponding Q is denoted by Q_P, in order to denote this dependence.   Thus the 60 percentile of D is 5, the 92 percentile is 8.

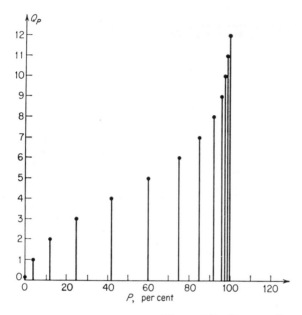

Figure 4.1 P versus Q_P.

In short, the P percentile of D, Q_P, is obtained as a solution of the equation

$$F_D(Q_P) = P \tag{4.1.3}$$

Since this distribution is discrete and Q_P can take on only the values $0, 1, 2, \ldots , 12$, there are only 13 percentiles corresponding to the solution of the above equation.   For continuous distributions, however, there may be an infinite number of percentiles.

Definition: P percentile of a random variable X Given a random variable X and its *CDF* $F_X(t)$, the P percentile x_P is the smallest solution of the equation

$$F_X(x_P) = P \tag{4.1.4}$$

where $0 \leq P \leq 1$ (or expressed in per cent between 0 and 100).

In other words, the probability that the random variable X is less than or equal to x_P is P.   In the discrete case, suppose X takes on the values $\cdots x_{-1}, x_0, x_1 \cdots x_i \cdots$; then x_P can take on only these values.   The percentiles are obtained from the equation

$$\text{Prob } (X \le x_s) = \sum_{i=-\infty}^{s} p(x_i) \tag{4.1.5}$$

Thus x_s is the percentile corresponding to Prob $(X \le x_s)$.   It should be clear that the P percentiles of a random variable yield its CDF.

An important task in many situations is to find the CDF of a function of a random variable: in other words, given the CDF $F_X(t)$ of the random variable X, to find the CDF $F_W(t)$ of the random variable $W(X)$, some function of X.

This problem occurs particularly in situations involving profit, cost, loss, and the like, all of which are random variables.   For instance, in Example 3.1, the profit is a function of the random variable D, as plotted in Fig. 3.3.   In the steel-bar problem (the example of Sec. 1.1) the cost is a function of the random variable bar length.   Another example is in the packing problem (Exercise 1.6), where cost is a function of gap length E.   The percentiles, as will be shown, provide a natural method for handling the above problem, when $W(X)$ is a monotone (nondecreasing or nonincreasing) function.   The result is summed up in the following theorem.

***Theorem* 4.1**   If $W_1(X)$ is a nondecreasing function and $W_2(X)$ is a nonincreasing function of X, then the P percentiles of W_1 and W_2, W_{1P} and W_{2P}, are

$$W_{1P} = W_1(x_P)$$
$$W_{2P} = W_2(x_{1-P})$$

where x_P and x_{1-P} are the P and $1 - P$ percentiles of X, respectively.

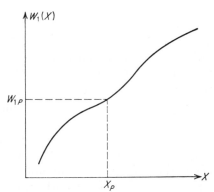

Figure 4.2 $W_1(x)$ versus X.

We indicate the method of proof for W_1 in the case of a continuous random variable.   The value of x_P is obtained from $F_X(x_P) = P$.   Referring to the graph of W_1 versus X in Fig. 4.2, one recognizes that

$$F_{W_1}(W_{1P}) = \text{Prob } (W_1 \le W_{1P}) = \text{Prob } (X \le x_P) = P \tag{4.1.6}$$

for the set $W_1(x) \leq W_{1P}$ is equivalent to the set of x's where $x \leq x_P$. Note that W_1 is a random variable while W_{1P} is a constant. The proof for W_2 is similar.

From the P percentiles of W_1 and W_2 one can readily obtain the CDFs of W_1 and W_2. In fact, we have used the above technique numerically, in several previous examples, namely:

1. Distribution of central deflection D as function of pressure (psi) P (the example of Sec. 1.4), where $D = 0.003/(1 - 0.001P)$.

2. Distribution of range R as a function of initial velocity v from the nondecreasing functional relationship (the example of Sec. 1.5), where $R = v^2/g$.

3. The daily profit P as a function of daily demand D as shown in Fig. 3.3.

4.2 Measures of central tendency

4.2.1 Mode, median, and mean

It is natural, in many problems, to be concerned with the central tendency of distributions. This concern is implicit in the use of such concepts as most probable, average, and long-run effects of the repeated use of a policy. In fact, we shall show that the notions of "average" and "long run" are closely connected. There are various measures of central tendency, each of which have their use in particular contexts. While all these measures have some notion of a typical or representative state in common, they are different in other important respects. For example, when we speak of an average mileage on a trip, we imply that this number is typical. If a car is going at an average speed of 40 mph, then, even though it is varying in speed, we may compute the total number of miles traversed in h hours by the product of the average speed 40 and h, the number of elapsed hours of travel. In all likelihood, if we were traveling on a highway where the speed limit was 40 mph, we should be traveling most of the time at somewhat above 40 mph or somewhat below that speed. In fact, one's speed, as a random variable, would very likely be based on an almost symmetrical distribution about an arithmetic mean value of 40. We should not necessarily be traveling much of the time at "exactly" 40 mph. Yet it makes sense to say that 40 was our typical speed, a value which was the *central tendency* about which our speeds fluctuated. The sense in which average is here used, especially since speed is represented as a continuous random variable, is quite different from the sense in which we say "the number of children in an average family is 3." The usual sense of the latter statement is that, in the community studied, more families have 3 children than any other number.   Another sense is that the arithmetic mean is 2.6 or 3.2 (or the like) and that the nearest integer to the arithmetic mean is 3.   The interpretation of average in other (or another) of these senses depends on the use to which the notion of average is to be put.

We want to note that the arithmetic mean may not be at all typical. Again referring to average speed, in a trip of 200 miles, one may travel most of the way on a divided four-lane highway, yet pass through a few cities.   On the highway one may travel well over 40 mph all the time, and through the city, well under 25 mph, "averaging" 40 mph.   This arithmetic mean is useful, but it is not always typical, that is, not modal. It is not the most frequent speed nor the central tendency about which the speeds varied.   The reason is that this distribution of speeds is bimodal.   There is more than one central tendency or typical speed. We must take this circumstance into account when interpreting the term average, or the more uniquely defined term arithmetic mean.

Again referring to the "average" family, we may say there is one boy in the average family.   By this we usually mean that there are more families with one boy than with none or with more than one.   Or we may mean that the arithmetic mean is, say, 0.9 boys per family or 1.3 boys per family.   For some uses "one boy" is the more significant interpretation, whereas, if one were planning a gymnasium or summer-camp facilities, the arithmetic mean may be the needed number—the meaningful "average."

There is still another meaningful interpretation of central tendency, namely, that of the median.   The median value of a random variable is its fiftieth percentile.   It is as likely that the random variable is above the median as below it.   In a specific sense the median is a central value. Yet in many circumstances the median is not actually realized; in particular, this can occur for a discrete random variable.

Other interpretations of average value or central tendency are in use, and in some cases these other interpretations are most appropriate.   Here we shall, however, limit our consideration to the *arithmetic mean*, the *median*, and the *mode*.   In the scope of our interest, the arithmetic mean is the most useful and most used of the specifications of central tendency. We shall precisely define each of these concepts, giving principal attention to the arithmetic mean.   We begin with the mode.

Definition: mode of random variable X A *mode* of random variable X is a most probable value that X assumes.   For a continuous random variable a mode is a maximum of the *PDF*.   It is clear that a mode is not necessarily unique.

Definition: median of a random variable X The *median* of a random variable X is the 50 percentile of X.   In the continuous case the median always exists, whereas in the discrete case, not all percentiles need exist.

Before defining the notion of mean value, let us consider again Example 3.1. There the outcome of the experiment was the daily demand D. For each outcome there is associated a certain profit P, dependent on the ordering quantity Q; that is, the values P takes on depend on Q. How do we assess whether a certain value of Q is "good" or not? How do we compare different policies of ordering various quantities Q?

Let us follow up, then, the consequences of choosing a particular Q. Suppose that N days have passed. Let N_0, N_1, N_2, . . . , N_{12} be the frequency of occurrence of demand of 0, 1, 2, . . . , 12 items, respectively, where

$$N_0 + \cdots + N_{12} = N \qquad (4.2.1)$$

In each day there is associated a value of P. Let the corresponding profits for the 13 types of demand days be P_0, P_1, P_2, . . . , P_{12}. Therefore, on N_i days there was a profit P_i, where $i = 0, 1, \ldots, 12$. The total profit TP for these N days is

$$TP = P_0N_0 + P_1N_1 + \cdots + P_{12}N_{12} = \sum_{i=0}^{i=12} P_iN_i \qquad (4.2.2)$$

The total profit *per* day is TP/N, which is

$$\frac{TP}{N} = P_0\left(\frac{N_0}{N}\right) + P_1\left(\frac{N_1}{N}\right) + \cdots + P_{12}\left(\frac{N_{12}}{N}\right) \qquad (4.2.3)$$

From the assumption of stability and the frequency interpretation of probability, we have

$$\frac{N_i}{N} \approx \text{Prob}\,(D = i) = p_i \qquad i = 0, 1, \ldots, 12 \qquad (4.2.4)$$

Thus $$\frac{TP}{N} \approx P_0p_0 + P_1p_1 + \cdots + P_{12}p_{12} \qquad (4.2.5)$$

The quantity on the right of Eq. (4.2.5) is called the expected value of the random variable P, denoted by $E(P)$, or sometimes the mean value of P. It is clear, then, that there is an intimate connection between the "long-run" value and the expected value. This connection is clarified in the theorem called the *law of large numbers*, which corresponds to the so-called "law of averages," demonstrated in a later section. A natural means for comparing different Q's is thus provided by $E(P)$. The expected value of P, $E(P)$, depends on Q since P_0, . . . , P_{12} depend on Q by virtue of the relation

$$P_i = \begin{cases} 30i - 20Q & i \leq Q \\ 10Q & i > Q \end{cases} \qquad (4.2.6)$$

More generally, let a policy or an experiment lead to outcomes s_1, . . . , s_k with probabilities p_1, p_2, . . . , p_k. Suppose, further, that with each outcome s_j is associated an evaluation $c_j = C(s_j)$. A natural evaluation of the policy is the expected cost $E(C)$, where

$$E(C) = c_1 p_1 + c_2 p_2 + \cdots + c_k p_k \qquad (4.2.7)$$

For the value $E(C)$ is, in fact, the cost per day we can "expect" in the long run. For many trials of the experiment (or repeated carrying out of a policy) N, say, we can "expect" approximately a cost of $NE(C)$. Intuitively we select cost per day as an effective quantity by means of which to evaluate a policy whose individual daily outcomes are evaluated in terms of cost. Such evaluation is often made in terms of utility (and sometimes as value). We shall discuss the notion of utility in Chap. 6.

In the example just cited and, in fact, in all the examples discussed in this work, the *arithmetic mean* plays a significant role. It represents to us the single number which significantly characterizes a random variable over its range of occurrence. Our search into the behavior of the random variable is centered in the arithmetic mean. We are all quite familiar with the arithmetic mean as defined for a specific set of observed values. For a random variable, even when defined on a discrete sample space, this definition, in order to avoid being cumbersome, must be generalized in terms such as given in Eq. (4.2.7). We shall refer to the arithmetic mean as the expected value and define it here for discrete sample spaces. Later we shall generalize this to continuous sample spaces.

Definition: expected value of a random variable X, $E(X)$, ***defined on a discrete sample space*** S The *expected value* of the random variable X, $E(X)$, is defined by

$$E(X) = \sum_{s \text{ in } S} X(s) p(s)$$

Example 4.1   Let us compute the expected value of the number of heads X in the experiment of tossing three coins. The sample space consists of eight points $s_1, s_2, \ldots, s_8$, each with probability assignment $\frac{1}{8}$. Thus $E(X)$ is given by (see Table 3.1)

$$E(X) = (3)p(s_1) + (2)p(s_2) + \cdots + (0)p(s_8) = 1.5 \qquad (4.2.8)$$

Note that the summation had as many terms as there are sample points in the sample space. If the number of sample points is large, this may be a difficult task to carry out. In Example 3.2 we consider the experiment of tossing a coin 20 times. In this case there are 2^{20} sample points. To find the expected number of heads, we must, for each sample point, multiply the number of heads by 2^{-20} and sum over all 2^{20} points. It is clear that simplified procedures would be helpful. We may reconsider the above problem by thinking of a new experiment where the 20 coins are tossed and the number of heads observed. The number of sample points is then reduced to 21, consisting of 0, 1, 2, $\ldots$, 20 heads. The probability for each of these points is, of course, given by the probability function $p_X(x)$ of the random variable X. And this we know to be the binomial distribution function $B(x,\frac{1}{2},20) = \dfrac{20!}{x!(20-x)!}\,(\frac{1}{2})^{20}$. We can compute $E(X)$ now as follows:

$$E(X) = (0)p_X(0) + (1)p_X(1) + \cdots + (20)p_X(20) = 10 \quad (4.2.9)$$

That the result for $E(X)$ is the same for both conceptions of the experiment (tossing 1 coin 20 times or tossing 20 coins and counting heads) and their corresponding sample spaces is apparent from

$$E(X) = \sum_s X(s)p(s) = \sum\sum X(s)p(s) \quad (4.2.10)$$

over x and all s such that $X(s) = x$, which equals

$$\sum_x x \sum_{X(s)=x} p(s) = \sum_x x p_X(x)$$

Similarly, one can obtain the expected value $E[G(X)]$ of any function $G(X)$ of X without having to find the probability function of $G(X)$. If we think of the sample space as having outcome values of X, then the previous argument yields the result

$$E[G(X)] = \sum_x G(x)p_X(x)$$

Example 4.2 Referring to Example 2.10 let us compute the expected number $E(n)$ of available telephone lines at any given time during the morning period. From the definition we have

$$E(n) = \sum_k k \,\text{Prob}\,(n = k) = \sum_k k p(k)$$

The function $p(k)$ is given by

$$p(k) = \frac{10!}{k!(10-k)!}\,(0.20)^k(0.80)^{10-k} \quad (4.2.11)$$

Therefore

$$E(n) = \sum_{k=0}^{10} \frac{k\,10!}{k!(10-k)!}\,(0.20)^k(0.80)^{10-k}$$

$$= (10)(0.20) \sum_{k=1}^{10} \frac{9!}{(k-1)!(10-k)!}\,(0.20)^{k-1}(0.80)^{10-k} \quad (4.2.12)$$

If we let $m = k - 1$, we have

$$E(n) = (10)(0.20) \sum_{m=0}^{9} \frac{9!}{m!(9-m)!}\,(0.20)^m(0.80)^{9-m}$$

$$= (10)(0.20) = 2 \quad (4.2.13)$$

The summation above is equal to 1 because it is the sum of probabilities of 0, 1, . . . , 9 lines being available for the case when there are 9 lines, which is given by the expansion of the binomial $(0.2 + 0.8)^9 = 1$.

Example 4.3 An important task in the transmission of messages by telegraph is the design of a suitable code. One relevant consideration

TABLE 4.1
Morse-code Letter Frequency

Letter	Code	Time	Probability
A	· —	5/24	0.0821
B	— · · ·	9/24	0.0137
C	— · — ·	11/24	0.0300
D	— · ·	7/24	0.0456
E	·	1/24	0.1368
F	· · — ·	9/24	0.0143
G	— — ·	9/24	0.0143
H	· · · ·	7/24	0.0613
I	· ·	3/24	0.0717
J	· — — —	13/24	0.0005
K	— · —	9/24	0.0039
L	· — · ·	9/24	0.0378
M	— —	7/24	0.0274
N	— ·	5/24	0.0769
O	— — —	11/24	0.0852
P	· — — ·	11/24	0.0228
Q	— — · —	13/24	0.0004
R	· — ·	7/24	0.0704
S	· · ·	5/24	0.0677
T	—	3/24	0.0938
U	· · —	7/24	0.0143
V	· · · —	9/24	0.0104
W	· — —	9/24	0.0078
X	— · · —	11/24	0.0026
Y	— · — —	13/24	0.0078
Z	— — · ·	11/24	0.0003

in the efficiency of codes is the duration in transmitting messages. In effect, then, we must study the transmission time for the various letters when using a particular code. It is well known that the letters of the alphabet do not occur equally frequently. Furthermore, a code is, of course, intended for use over long periods. Thus, in the efficiency of a code, we must consider the time of transmission for the letters as well as the frequency of the letters. We have, here, a situation where the "long run" is the relevant criterion for the comparison of different codes. We shall compute the expected time for transmitting a letter for the Morse code. Each letter is composed of dots (·), dashes (–), and spaces between dots and dashes. The transmission times for dot and dash are approximately $\frac{1}{24}$ and $\frac{3}{24}$ second, respectively. The time taken up by space is $\frac{1}{24}$ second. Thus, for each letter, we can compute the length of time for transmission. For example, the code for the letter D is (– · ·) and the time for transmission is $\frac{7}{24}$ second. In Table 4.1 is given the code for each letter, the time of transmission, and the probability of occurrence.

The expected transmission time per letter denoted by E is

$$E = (\tfrac{5}{24})(0.0821) + (\tfrac{9}{24})(0.0137) + \cdots + (\tfrac{11}{24})(0.0003) = 0.2440$$

Thus, on the average, with the Morse code it takes about $\frac{1}{4}$ second to transmit a letter. It is possible to construct codes which have a smaller value of E than the Morse code. However, the value of E is not the only relevant factor in the efficiency of codes. Among other considerations is that of errors in transmission. These questions have, of late, received much attention.

4.2.2   Expected value and its properties

In this section we demonstrate some properties which simplify the computation of expected values for many cases. In particular, we find the expected values of linear combinations and products of random variables. The merits of these results are shown in the examples to follow.

Theorem 4.2   If $a_1, \ldots, a_N$ are N arbitrary constants and $X_1, X_2, \ldots, X_N$ constitute an arbitrary set of N random variables, then

$$E(a_1X_1 + a_2X_2 + \cdots + a_NX_N) = a_1E(X_1) + a_2E(X_2) \\ + \cdots + a_NE(X_N) \quad (4.2.14)$$

PROOF

$$E(a_1X_1 + a_2X_2 + \cdots + a_NX_N)$$
$$= \sum_s [a_1X_1(s) + a_2X_2(s) + \cdots + a_NX_N(s)]p(s)$$
$$= a_1 \sum_s X_1(s)p(s) + \cdots + a_N \sum_s X_N(s)p(s)$$
$$= a_1E(X_1) + a_2E(X_2) + \cdots + a_NE(X_N)$$

Example 4.4   We refer to Example 4.2. We demonstrate a simple method for computing $E(n)$ by the use of Theorem 4.2. Let $X_1, X_2, \ldots, X_{10}$ be the following random variables:

$$X_i = \begin{cases} 1 & \text{if } i\text{th line is free} \\ 0 & \text{otherwise} \end{cases} \qquad (4.2.15)$$

Thus
$$\text{Prob } (X_i = 1) = 0.20$$
$$\text{Prob } (X_i = 0) = 0.80$$

Furthermore, the number of free lines n is given by $n = X_1 + X_2 + \cdots + X_{10}$. From Theorem 4.2 we have, therefore, $E(n) = E(X_1) + E(X_2) + \cdots + E(X_{10})$. Now

$$E(X_i) = (1) \text{ Prob } (X_i = 1) + (0) \text{ Prob } (X_i = 0) = \text{Prob } (X_i = 1)$$
$$= 0.20$$

Thus $E(n) = (10)(0.20) = 2$.

The foregoing type of argument can be easily generalized to any series of binomial experiments. Suppose, for example, that we specify

$$p = \text{Prob (success in a trial)}$$

Then
$$E \text{ (number of successes in } N \text{ trials)} = Np$$

We often require the expected value of a product of random variables. There is a rule for the expectation of the product of independent random variables which corresponds to the product rule for probabilities of independent events. We show these in the following theorem.

***Theorem* 4.3** If two random variables X and Y are independent, then

$$E(XY) = E(X)E(Y)$$

In order to demonstrate this result, let the joint probability function of X and Y be $p(x,y)$. Then

$$E(XY) = \sum_x \sum_y xy\,p(x,y)$$

When X and Y are independent we have

$$p(x,y) = p_X(x)p_Y(y)$$

Thus

$$E(XY) = \sum_x \sum_y xy\,p_X(x)p_Y(y) = \sum_x x\,p_X(x) \sum_y y\,p_Y(y) = E(X)E(Y)$$

Example 4.5 In the example of Sec. 2.5.3, we saw that the functioning of a system comprised of components may depend on the components in various ways. We shall describe three different types of situations. Throughout we shall assume that the components function independently. Consider these examples:

1. There are k components, and the system functions only when *all* its components function.   Let

$$X_i = \begin{cases} 1 & \text{if } i\text{th component functions} \\ 0 & \text{otherwise} \end{cases}$$

Thus $E(X_i) = \text{Prob } (i\text{th component functions}) = R_i$

where R_i is called the reliability of the ith component.   Consider

$$Z = X_1 X_2 \cdot \cdot \cdot X_k$$

Then Z is 1 or 0, according to whether the whole system functions or not. Thus

$$R = \text{Prob } (Z = 1) = E(Z) = E(X_1)E(X_2) \cdot \cdot \cdot E(X_k)$$
$$= R_1 R_2 \cdot \cdot \cdot R_k$$

2. The system functions if *any* of the components function.   Let

$$Z' = 1 - (1 - X_1)(1 - X_2) \cdot \cdot \cdot (1 - X_k)$$

We see that $Z' = 1$ if *any* of the X's is equal to 1.   Thus

$$R' = \text{Prob } (Z' = 1) = 1 - E(1 - X_1)E(1 - X_2) \cdot \cdot \cdot E(1 - X_k)$$
$$= 1 - (1 - R_1) \cdot \cdot \cdot (1 - R_k)$$

The results for R and R' are, of course, the same as in the example of Sec. 2.5.3.   To demonstrate further the convenience of using the above type of representation, we find the reliabilities of combinations of the systems in 1 and 2.

3. There are k primary components.   Each primary component is made up of N subcomponents.   The system functions only if *all* primary components function.   Each primary component functions if *any* of the subcomponents function.   Let

$$X_{ji} = \begin{cases} 1 & \text{if } i\text{th subcomponent of } j\text{th primary component functions} \\ 0 & \text{otherwise} \end{cases}$$

Furthermore, let

$$Z'' = [1 - (1 - X_{11}) \cdot \cdot \cdot (1 - X_{1N})]$$
$$[1 - (1 - X_{21})(1 - X_{22}) \cdot \cdot \cdot (1 - X_{2N})] \cdot \cdot \cdot$$
$$[1 - (1 - X_{k1}) \cdot \cdot \cdot (1 - X_{kN})]$$

Since the reliability of the system R'' is given by

$$R'' = \text{Prob } (Z'' = 1) = E(Z'')$$

we have

$$R'' = [1 - (1 - R_{11}) \cdot \cdot \cdot (1 - R_{1N})]$$
$$\cdot \cdot \cdot [1 - (1 - R_{k1}) \cdot \cdot \cdot (1 - R_{kN})]$$

If $R_{ji} = R$, then

$$R'' = [1 - (1 - R)^N]^k$$

4.2.3 Conditional expectation

In the steel-bar problem (the example of Sec. 1.1) we sought the average amount of steel trimmed from *the long bars*. We shall now do this problem in accordance with principles stated in Chaps. 2 and 3 and express the result in terms of conditional expectation. For simplicity, let us assume that the random variable bar length L can take on only 11 values, whereas S respresents the scale of measurement of the bars:

S	s_1	s_2	s_3	s_4	s_5	s_6	s_7	s_8	s_9	s_{10}	s_{11}
L	8.65	8.95	9.25	9.55	9.85	10.15	10.45	10.75	11.05	11.35	11.60

The sample space has 11 sample points. The event long bar corresponds to the set A of sample points s_7, s_8, s_9, s_{10}, and s_{11}. We assume that the probabilities on the sample space are given by $p_1, p_2, \ldots, p_{11}$. Let us suppose that N bars are rolled and that the frequencies of the various lengths are $N_1, N_2, \ldots, N_{11}$. The number of long bars N_L is given by $N_L = N_7 + N_8 + N_9 + N_{10} + N_{11}$. For each long bar there is a certain corresponding length of trimmed steel given by:

Length of long bar	s_7	s_8	s_9	s_{10}	s_{11}
Amount of trimmed steel, ft	0.45	0.75	1.05	1.35	1.65

The total amount of steel trimmed from long bars, T_L, is given by

$$T_L = (0.45)N_7 + (0.75)N_8 + \cdots + (1.65)N_{11}$$

The average length of trimmed steel *per long bar* is given by

$$\frac{T_L}{N_L} = (0.45)\left(\frac{N_7}{N_L}\right) + \cdots + (1.65)\left(\frac{N_{11}}{N_L}\right)$$

where, from the frequency interpretation,

$$N_L \approx N(p_7 + p_8 + p_9 + p_{10} + p_{11}) = NP(A)$$

and $N_i \approx Np_i$ $(i = 7, \ldots, 11)$. Thus

$$\frac{T_L}{N_L} \approx (0.45)\left[\frac{p_7}{P(A)}\right] + \cdots + (1.65)\left[\frac{p_{11}}{P(A)}\right]$$

$$= \frac{1}{P(A)}[(0.45)p_7 + (0.75)p_9 + \cdots + (1.65)p_{11}]$$

The quantity on the right is called the conditional expectation of the random variable trimmed length t, under the restriction given by the event A. It is denoted by $E(t \mid A)$. The result sought is given by

$$\frac{T_L}{N_L} \approx E(t \mid A)$$

We now have the following definition.

Definition: conditional expectation   The *conditional expectation* of a random variable X subject to a restriction given by the event A of the sample space is defined as follows:

$$E(X \mid A) = \frac{1}{p(A)} \sum_{s \text{ in } A} X(s)p(s) \tag{4.2.16}$$

Although the application of this definition may be cumbersome, one can simplify the computation in many cases in terms of the conditional probability function.   Suppose that the event A is given in terms of a random variable Y as follows: $A = [s: \ Y(s) = y]$
Then we have

$$
\begin{aligned}
E(X \mid A) &= \frac{1}{p_Y(y)} \sum_{x} \sum_{X(s)=x} x p_{X,Y}(x,y) \\
&= \sum_{x} x \left[\frac{1}{p_Y(y)} \sum_{x} p_{X,Y}(x,y) \right] \\
&= \sum_{x} x p(x \mid y) = E(X \mid y)
\end{aligned}
$$

Thus we have expressed $E(X \mid y)$ as an expected value of a conditional distribution.

We now demonstrate a basic result about the relationship between the conditional and unconditional expectation.   The result below, stated as Theorem 4.4, will enable us to simplify many computations of expected values.

Theorem 4.4   If X and Y are two random variables, then

$$E(X) = E_Y[E_X(X \mid Y)] \tag{4.2.17}$$

where the subscripts denote the fact that the inner expectation is taken over the x's and the outer over the y's.

PROOF

$$
\begin{aligned}
E_Y[E_X(X \mid Y)] &= E_Y \left[\sum_{x} x p(x \mid y) \right] = \sum_{y} \left[\sum_{x} x p(x \mid y) \right] p(y) \\
&= \sum_{y} \sum_{x} x p(x \mid y) p(y) = \sum_{y} \sum_{x} x p(x,y) \\
&= \sum_{x} x \left[\sum_{y} p(x,y) \right] = \sum_{x} x p(x)
\end{aligned}
$$

Also, it is easily shown that, in general, if the sample space is divided up into the event A and its complement $\bar{A}$, then

$$E(X) = p(A)E(X \mid A) + p(\bar{A})E(X \mid \bar{A}) \qquad (4.2.18)$$

These results are useful since $E(X \mid A)$, $E(X \mid \bar{A})$, or $E(X \mid y)$ may be simpler to compute than the desired $E(X)$. This corresponds to the decomposition rule for probabilities. We shall now give a number of examples illustrating the foregoing principles.

Example 4.6 Suppose that customers coming into a store have a distribution of demand given by the probability function $p_D(d)$. Furthermore, suppose that the number of customers per day, N, has a probability (of occurrence) function $p_N(n)$. The expected demand per day can be obtained by applying Theorem 4.4 to the random variables N and D by breaking up the computation into stages. We first note that on days when there are n customers (that is, $N = n$), the demand is $D_1 + D_2 + \cdots + D_n$; whence the expected daily demand, when $N = n$, is given by (assuming D and N are independent)

$$E(\text{demand} \mid N = n) = E(D_1 + D_2 + \cdots + D_n) = nE(D)$$

Then we average these results according to the likelihood of obtaining days with various values of N. Thus

$$\begin{aligned}
E(\text{demand}) &= \sum_n E(\text{demand} \mid N = n)p_N(n) \\
&= \sum_n nE(D)p_N(n) \\
&= E(D) \sum_n np_N(n) = E(D)E(N)
\end{aligned}$$

Example 4.7 A common sampling-inspection procedure, used in industry to help assure a desired quality level of a product, is given by the numbers n and c. The sampling plan, denoted by $S(n,c)$, is carried out as follows:

1. Inspect sample of n pieces drawn at random from a lot of N pieces.
2. If the number of defectives $X \leq c$, accept the lot; otherwise inspect the remainder of the uninspected pieces in the lot.
3. Replace all defective pieces by nondefective pieces.

We are usually interested in the expected fraction defective resulting from application of this plan. In order to compute this value, called the AOQ, let Y be the number of defective items left after sample inspection when the sampling plan $S(n,c)$ is used. We have, then, applying Eq. (4.2.18),

$$E(Y) = P(X \leq c)E(Y \mid X \leq c) + P(X > c)E(Y \mid X > c)$$

We further note that all defective items in the sample are replaced and that, since the proportion of defectives is p, we have an expected value of defectives of $(N - n)p$ in the uninspected remainder. Therefore the whole lot is, after inspection,

$$E(Y \mid X \leq c) = (N - n)p \qquad \text{and} \qquad E(Y \mid X > c) = 0$$

Also, when N is large and the probability of a defective is p,

$$P(X \leq c) \cong \sum_{x=0}^{c} \frac{n!}{x!(n - x)!} \, p^x(1 - p)^{n-x}$$

is a close approximation. Thus the outgoing proportion of defectives AOQ may be given by

$$AOQ = E\left(\frac{Y}{N}\right) = \left(1 - \frac{n}{N}\right) p \cdot P(X \leq c)$$

For N large we obtain

$$AOQ \approx P(X \leq c)p = p \sum_{x \leq c} \frac{n!}{x!(n - x)!} \, p^x(1 - p)^{n-x}$$

The value of AOQ depends on p, n, and c. It can be shown that AOQ as a function of p (for n and c fixed) has a maximum. Let

$$AOQL = \max_{0 \leq p \leq 1} AOQ$$

where $AOQL$ denotes the average outgoing quality limit. We are assured, therefore, that the average outgoing quality AOQ is no worse (greater) than $AOQL$. There are tables giving $AOQL$ as a function of n and c. For example, for $N = 1,500$, $c = 2$, $n = 65$, the $AOQ \leq AOQL = 2$ per cent.

Example 4.8 In various areas of engineering and science, such as industrial engineering, chemistry, and ecology, one is interested in the cumulative change of a system varying with time. Some examples are diminishing of stock as a function of time, variation of position of a molecule with time, and the wandering of an animal species. In these and many other cases, certain magnitude changes occur in the system at various times. The times of occurrence as well as the magnitudes of the changes may be chance phenomena.

In this example we consider a simple case (developments in later chapters will provide for treatment of more complicated and realistic models). Nevertheless, even this simple example exhibits features which appear in more sophisticated models. Suppose that a particle moves according to the following scheme. During each second it moves one unit either forward or backward; each move is made with equal probability. We suppose, further, that the decision made before each step as to which direction to take is independent of what has occurred in the previous steps. What is the expected distance of this wandering particle from the origin after N steps?

Let X_1, X_2, . . . , X_n be a series of independent random variables such that

$$\text{Prob } (X_i = +1) = \text{Prob } (X_i = -1) = \tfrac{1}{2}$$

The position of the particle, after N steps D_N, is given by $D_N = X_1 + X_2 + \cdots + X_N$. The quantity we seek is $E|D_N|$, where $|D_N|$ denotes the absolute value of D_N. We take advantage of the decomposition rule for probabilities at each stage, and at the Nth stage decomposition is made in terms of the $(N-1)$st stage. If $p_N(i)$ denotes the probability that the particle after N steps is at position i, then $p_N(i) = \text{Prob } (D_N = i)$.

By what sequence of steps could the particle have gotten to i? If the particle is at i at the Nth step, it was either at $i-1$ or at $i+1$ at the $(N-1)$st step. By the decomposition rule we have

$$p_N(i) = \tfrac{1}{2}p_{N-1}(i-1) + \tfrac{1}{2}p_{N-1}(i+1) \tag{4.2.19}$$

Equation (4.2.19) allows us to compute $p_N(i)$ recursively. We shall see, however, that we need not find all the values of $p_N(i)$ in order to compute $E|D_N|$. First express D_N in terms of p_N:

$$E|D_N| = \sum_{s=-\infty}^{+\infty} |s|p_N(s) = 2 \sum_{s=1}^{\infty} s p_N(s)$$

Then multiply both sides of Eq. (4.2.19) by i and sum, obtaining

$$E|D_N| = 2 \sum_{i=1}^{\infty} i p_N(i) = \tfrac{1}{2} \times 2 \sum_{i=1}^{\infty} i p_{N-1}(i-1)$$

$$+ \tfrac{1}{2} \times 2 \sum_{i=1}^{\infty} i p_{N-1}(i+1)$$

$$= \sum_{t=0}^{\infty} (t+1)p_{N-1}(t) + \sum_{t=2}^{\infty} (t-1)p_{N-1}(t)$$

$$= 2 \sum_{t=1}^{\infty} t p_{N-1}(t) + \sum_{t=0}^{\infty} p_{N-1}(t) - \sum_{t=1}^{\infty} p_{N-1}(t)$$

which reduces to

$$E|D_N| = E|D_{N-1}| + p_{N-1}(0)$$

Note that $E|D_{N-1}| = E|D_{N-2}| + p_{N-2}(0)$; whence by iteration one obtains

$$E|D_N| = E|D_1| + p_1(0) + p_2(0) + \cdots + p_{N-1}(0)$$

Furthermore, $E|D_1| = 1$ and $p_s(0) = 0$ when s is odd, since it is impossible for the particle to return to 0 in an odd number of steps. Again, since

$$p_{2r}(0) = \frac{(2r)!}{(r!)^2} 2^{-2r}$$

$$E|D_N| = 1 + \sum_{r=1}^{s} \frac{(2r)!}{(r!)^2} 2^{-2r}$$

where $s = (N-1)/2$ for N odd, and $(N-2)/2$ for N even. For example, after three steps,

$$E|D_3| = 1 + \frac{2!}{(1!)^2} \times 2^{-2} = 1 + \frac{2}{4} = 1.5$$

Had we computed this value the "long way," we should have been obliged to enumerate the eight possible paths that the particle could take, as shown in Table 4.2, in order to be able to compute $E|D_3|$.

TABLE 4.2

Step 1	Step 2	Step 3	D_3
r	r	r	3
r	r	l	1
r	l	r	1
r	l	l	1
l	r	r	1
l	r	l	1
l	l	r	1
l	l	l	3

NOTE: r denotes right, l denotes left.

Since all the paths have probability $\frac{1}{8}$, we have

$$E|D_3| = (3 + 1 + \cdots + 1 + 3)/8 = \frac{12}{8} = 1.5$$

It is obvious that such direct computation becomes tedious even for moderate values of N. For large N it can be shown that

$$E|D_N| \sim 0.79788 \sqrt{N}$$

For $N = 3$ this approximation gives 1.38. The reader may well check this formula for several large values of N to be convinced of its accuracy.

That $E|D_N|$ increases proportionately with the square root of N will be demonstrated in a later chapter. It is interesting to note the expected change of position *per step*, namely,

$$E \frac{|D_N|}{N} \sim \frac{0.79788}{\sqrt{N}}$$

This quantity varies inversely as the square root of the number of steps N, whereas the cumulative change of position, the displacement after N steps, varies directly as the square root of the number of steps.   This type of change of position, illustrated in a rather simple example, is somewhat typical of important and more complicated behavior of "systems."

4.3   Measures of variation

It is clear from the numerous examples discussed previously, particularly in Chap. 1, that variability presents a central difficulty in the formulation of effective decision policies.   Thus it is evident that it is worthwhile establishing suitable measures of variability in terms of which the effects of variability on the consequences of decisions can be appraised.

Let us consider the example of Sec. 1.1, where our concern with variation arose from the fact that bar lengths did not remain within tolerances. One suitable measure of variation in this case might be the probability that bar lengths are within tolerance.   Another measure, related to the above, is expressed in terms of intervals containing various proportions of the population.   For instance, $X_{0.95} - X_{0.05}$ contains 90 per cent, $X_{0.75} - X_{0.25}$ contains 50 per cent, of the population.   Such measures are useful in various contexts, as in a study of income distribution.

Various other measures are available.   One such is the *expected deviation*, which is defined as $E|X - m|$, where m is the mean value of the random variable X.   This quantity measures the amount of concentration around m.   A measure related to the above, but in more popular use, is the *variance*, which is defined below.   This measure is convenient since it is quite tractable for computational and analytical purposes. This will become clearer with later developments.

4.3.1   Variance, standard deviation, and their properties

Definition: variance   The variance $V(X)$ of a random variable X, with mean m, is given by

$$V(X) = E[(X - m)^2]$$

The variance is a measure of the concentration of a distribution around the mean.   A value of zero for the variance indicates that all the probability is concentrated at one point, the mean.   Since $V(X)$ is of the order of X^2, the dimensionality of V is that of X^2.   The square root of V, the *standard deviation*, is introduced as a measure of variability of the same dimensionality as that of X.

Definition: standard deviation   The *standard deviation* $\sigma(X)$ of a random variable X is given by

$$\sigma(X) = \sqrt{V(X)}$$

We now demonstrate some properties of $V(X)$ and $\sigma(X)$.

1. If X is a random variable with mean m, then $V(X) = E(X^2) - m^2$.
This result is obtained directly by expanding the expression defining $V(X)$.

2. If a is any constant, then $V(aX) = a^2V(X)$.
This can be verified directly from the definition

$$V(aX) = E[(aX - am)^2] = E[a^2(X - m)^2] = a^2V(X)$$

3. If X and Y are independent random variables, then $V(X + Y) = V(X) + V(Y)$.

This is verified again directly from the definition

$$\begin{aligned} V(X + Y) &= E\{[X + Y - E(X) - E(Y)]^2\} \\ &= E\{[X - E(X)]^2\} + E\{[Y - E(Y)]^2\} \\ &\quad + 2E\{[X - E(X)][Y - E(Y)]\} \end{aligned}$$

where the last term vanishes because of the independence of X and Y.

From the above results it follows, for instance, that if $a_1, \ldots, a_N$ are any constants and $X_1, \ldots, X_N$ are independent random variables, then

$$\begin{aligned} V(a_1X_1 + a_2X_2 + \cdots &+ a_NX_N) \\ &= a_1^2V(X_1) + a_2^2V(X_2) + \cdots + a_N^2V(X_N) \end{aligned}$$

Consider some special, but important, examples of the above relations. If $X_1, X_2, \ldots, X_n$ are N independent random variables with the same variance V, then

$$V(X_1 + X_2 + \cdots + X_N) = NV$$

and
$$\sigma(X_1 + X_2 + \cdots + X_N) = \sigma\sqrt{N}$$

Note the square-root characteristic. Furthermore,

$$V(\bar{X}) = V\left(\frac{X_1 + X_2 + \ldots + X_N}{N}\right) = \frac{V}{N}$$

and
$$\sigma(\bar{X}) = \sigma\left(\frac{X_1 + X_2 + \ldots + X_N}{N}\right) = \frac{\sigma}{\sqrt{N}}$$

It is to be noted that for a common mean m and large N the distribution of the random variable $\bar{X}$ clusters more and more closely around m.

Example 4.9 Referring to Example 4.2, let us find the variance $V(n)$ of the available telephone lines at any given time during the morning.

$$V(n) = \sum_{k=0}^{10} k^2 p(k) - E^2(n)$$

$$= \sum_{k=0}^{10} k^2 p(k) - 4$$

$$= \sum_{k=0}^{10} \frac{k^2 10!}{k!(10-k)!} (0.20)^k (0.80)^{10-k} - 4$$

Instead of making this direct computation, we shall utilize result 3 above. Let X_i be a random variable such that

$$X_i = \begin{cases} 1 & \text{if } i\text{th telephone is available} \\ 0 & \text{otherwise} \end{cases}$$

Thus $n = X_1 + X_2 + \cdots + X_{10}$ and $E(X_i) = \text{Prob } (i\text{th telephone available}) = 0.20$. Thus $E(n) = 10E(X) = 10(0.20) = 2$. The variance of any X_i is obtained directly as follows:

$$V(X_i) = E(X_i^2) - (0.20)^2 = (0.20) - (0.20)^2 = (0.20)(0.80) = 0.16$$

Thus

$$V(n) = 10(0.16) = 1.6 \qquad \text{and} \qquad \sigma(n) = \sqrt{1.6}$$

In general, for any series of N independent binomial trials with probability of success equal to p, we have

$$E(\text{number of successes}) = Np$$
$$V(\text{number of successes}) = Np(1 - p)$$

The word "success" is a generic term indicating the occurrence of an event we designate as a success. Thus the occurrence of a defective in a production process, the appearance of a 6 on the toss of a die, or the occurrence of rainfall on a particular day might be such events.

Example 4.10 In a series of independent binomial trials, each with probability of success equal to p, it is interesting to find the number of trials W following a success and up to and including the next success. Since W is a random variable, we also want $E(W)$ and $V(W)$. The probability function of W, that is, the probability that we have to wait w trials for a success, denoted by

$$p(w) = \text{Prob } (W = w)$$

is clearly $(1 - p)^{w-1} p$ $(w = 1, 2, \ldots, \infty)$, since $W = w$ if, and only if, there are $w - 1$ failures and then 1 success. But we must first show that

$p(w)$ is a probability function; that is, $p(w)$ summed from 1 to ∞ equals 1. This follows readily:

$$\sum_{w=1}^{\infty} p(w) = p \sum_{w=1}^{\infty} (1-p)^{w-1} = p \sum_{s=0}^{\infty} (1-p)^s = p\left(\frac{1}{p}\right) = 1$$

The above is called the *geometric distribution*.

To find $E(W)$, we compute

$$E(W) = \sum_{w=1}^{\infty} wp(w) = \sum_{w=1}^{\infty} wp(1-p)^{w-1}$$

$$= p \sum_{w=1}^{\infty} w(1-p)^{w-1} = -p\frac{d}{dp}\left[\sum_{w=1}^{\infty}(1-p)^w\right]$$

$$= -p\frac{d}{dp}\,1-p = \frac{1}{p}$$

Thus, if the probability of an event is 0.5, on the average, there are two trials between successive occurrences of the event.

The variance $V(W)$ is computed as follows:

$$V(W) = \sum_{w=1}^{\infty} w^2 p(w) - \frac{1}{p^2} = \sum_{w=1}^{\infty} w^2 p(1-p)^{w-1} - \frac{1}{p^2}$$

However,

$$p\sum_{w=1}^{\infty} w^2(1-p)^{w-1} = -p\sum_{w=1}^{\infty} w\frac{d}{dp}[(1-p)^w] = -p\frac{d}{dp}\left[\sum_{w=1}^{\infty} w(1-p)^w\right]$$

$$= -p\frac{d}{dp}\left[(1-p)\sum_{w=1}^{\infty} w(1-p)^{w-1}\right]$$

$$= -p\frac{d}{dp}\left(\frac{1-p}{p^2}\right) = \frac{2-p}{p^2}$$

Thus $$V(W) = \frac{2-p}{p^2} - \frac{1}{p^2} = \frac{1-p}{p^2}$$

Going one step further, we may ask for the expected value and variance of the number S_N of trials up to and including the Nth success. Let $W_1, W_2, \ldots, W_N$ denote the number of trials up to the first success, between the first and second success, etc. Then $W_1, W_2, \ldots, W_N$ are independent, and all have the geometric distribution. Furthermore, it is clear that $S_N = W_1 + W_2 + \cdots + W_N$. Thus

$$E(S_N) = NE(W) = \frac{N}{p} \quad \text{and} \quad V(S_N) = NV(W) = \frac{N(1-p)}{p^2}$$

4.3.2 Conditional variance

Conditional probabilities were introduced because they arise naturally in many situations. The notion of conditional variance, which is indicated when a random variable is defined conditionally upon a given set in the sample space, is useful in simplifying many probability calculations.

Definition: conditional variance For a random variable X conditional upon the set A in the sample space S, the variance is referred to as a *conditional variance*. Analogous to the ordinary variance, it is obtained from the following relation:

$$V(X \mid A) = E(X^2 \mid A) - E^2(X \mid A)$$

Suppose that we consider set A specifically as consisting of those elements s of the sample space S for which $Y(s) = y$. For random variables X and Y it follows from the definition that

$$V(X \mid A) = V(X \mid Y) = E(X^2 \mid Y) - E^2(X \mid Y)$$

We can now connect the conditional and unconditional expectation and variance in a way which provides for "stagewise" computation of the variance of a random variable, which is, however, specified conditionally. We shall establish this result formally as a theorem and then apply it to Example 4.6, where the simplification obtained is readily evident.

Theorem 4.5 For any two random variables X and Y, the variance $V(X)$ is given by

$$V(X) = E[V(X \mid Y)] + V[E(X \mid Y)] \qquad (4.3.1)$$

We shall give the formal argument which serves generally as a useful technique. Expand each term on the right of Eq. (4.3.1), applying the definition of conditional variance as needed:

$$E[V(X \mid Y)] = E[E(X^2 \mid Y) - E^2(X \mid Y)] = E(X^2) - E[E^2(X \mid Y)]$$
$$V[E(X \mid Y)] = E[E^2(X \mid Y)] - E^2[E(X \mid Y)] = E[E^2(X \mid Y)] - E^2(X)$$

Addition of the two equations yields

$$E[V(X \mid Y)] + V[E(X \mid Y)] = E(X^2) - E^2(X) = V(X)$$

Example 4.11 In Example 4.6 we required the variance V of the daily demand D. The daily demand is determined in part by the number of customers n on a given day and by the specific demand of each customer. Hence, on any day, n is but one value of the random variable N, and on each day for a given number of customers n, there are n identical random variables $D_1, D_2, \ldots, D_n$, where on that day $N = n$. It becomes simpler to consider $N = n$ constant, first, and then to let N behave as a random variable. Thus we may say that

$$V(D_1 + D_2 + \cdots + D_N) = E[V(D_1 + D_2 + \cdots + D_N \mid N = n)]$$
$$+ V[E(D_1 + D_2 + \cdots + D_N \mid N = n)]$$

for a given value n taken on by N, the random variable which represents the number of customers per day.

Proceeding in accordance with known relations, we have

$$E(D_1 + D_2 + \cdots + D_N \mid N = n) = nE(D)$$

and $V(D_1 + D_2 + \cdots + D_N \mid N = N) = nV(D)$. Hence

$$V(D_1 + D_2 + \cdots + D_N) = E[NV(D)] + V[NE(D)]$$
$$= E(N)V(D) + V(N)E^2(D)$$

Example 4.12 Instances where Theorem 4.5 is very useful are those involved with *mixing*. These problems are frequent in engineering and science. Some examples are those in industrial engineering where final product is a mixture originating from various sources, in chemistry where a vessel contains a mixture of several products, etc. In all these cases the final product is a mixture, in certain proportions, of several sources. Given the characteristic of the sources and the proportions of the final mixture due to each of these sources, what are the characteristics of the final product?

Suppose there are k sources with k means m_1, m_2, . . . , m_k and k variances V_1, V_2, . . . , V_k. Let the final product be a mixture of these sources in proportions p_1, p_2, . . . , p_k. What is the mean $E(X)$ and variance $V(X)$ of the mixed population? From Theorems 4.4 and 4.5 we have

$$E(X) = E[E(X \mid i)] = \sum_{i=1}^{k} p_i m_i = m$$

and

$$V(X) = E[V(X \mid i)] + V[E(X \mid i)]$$

But

$$E[V(X \mid i)] = E(V_i) = \sum_{i=1}^{k} p_i V_i$$

and

$$V[E(X \mid i)] = V(m_i) = \sum_i p_i(m_i - m)^2$$

Thus

$$V(X) = \sum_i p_i V_i + \sum_i p_i(m_i - m)^2$$

It is clear that the variation of a final product is very much affected by variation among the means of the sources. This indicates the possible hazard in mixing sources whose means differ considerably.

4.4 Approximations to mean and variance of functions of random variables

In many problems it is important to compute the expected value and variance of a function $G(X)$ of a random of variable X. One direct approach is to find the probability function of $G(X)$ and to apply the appropriate definitions. Thus if $G(X)$ takes on the values $g_1, g_2, \ldots, g_k$ with probability $p_1, p_2, \ldots, p_k$, then

$$E[G(X)] = \sum_i g_i p_i \quad \text{and} \quad V[G(X)] = \sum_i g_i^2 p_i - E^2[G(X)]$$

Somewhat more simply, without finding the probability function of $G(X)$, one can apply the definitions of mean and variance directly, obtaining for discrete random variables

$$E[G(X)] = \sum_x G(x)p(x)$$

and
$$V[G(X)] = \sum_x G^2(x)p(x) - E^2[G(X)]$$

Nevertheless, for many functions $G(X)$, the above procedure may still be too unwieldy for computational purposes. An approximation to the mean of $G(X)$ which is more tractable is given in the following theorem, whose plausibility we show, but which we do not prove.

Theorem 4.6 Let a random variable X have mean m and variance $V(X)$. Then the expected value of $G(X)$ is given, approximately, by

$$E[G(X)] \simeq G(m) + \frac{G''(m)}{2} V(X)$$

where $G''(m)$ denotes the second-order derivative of G evaluated at m. [$G(X)$ must be assumed to possess a second-order derivative at $X = m$.] The following argument essentially substantiates the theorem if $G(X)$ can be expressed by a Taylor-series expansion,

$$G(X) \simeq G(m) + G'(m)(X - m) + \frac{G''(m)}{2}(X - m)^2$$

From the expectation of both sides and the fact that $E(X - m) = 0$ and $E[(X - m)^2] = V(X)$, it follows by direct substitution that

$$E[G(X)] \simeq G(m) + \frac{G''(m)}{2} V(X)$$

as we hoped to show.

Theorem 4.7 The variance $V[G(X)]$ is given approximately by

$$V[G(X)] \simeq [G'(m)]^2 V(X)$$

Expanding again to one term and a remainder, we obtain

$$G(X) \simeq G(m) + G'(m)(X - m)$$

Taking expected values directly, we obtain

$$E[G(X)] \simeq G(m)$$

Again from the variance of both sides of the expansion we find

$$V[G(X)] \simeq E[G(X) - G(m)^2] \simeq [G'(m)]^2 V(X)$$

The closeness of approximation in particular cases depends, of course, on the nature of the function $G(X)$ and can often be investigated by closer scrutiny of the error term in the Taylor-series expansion. In most cases, however, this result is found sufficiently accurate for practical purposes. (See also Exercise 2.9.)

Example 4.13 Let us return to the example of Sec. 1.6, where we consider two methods of estimating the gravitational constant g by means of N independent observations of the period of a pendulum in free oscillation. The notion of a series of N independent observations of a random variable is here meant to correspond to a series of independent experiments, each one of which consists of observing an oscillation of the pendulum. Recall that the two methods of estimating g consisted of the following. Observe $T_1, T_2, \ldots, T_N$.

Method 1

$$\bar{g} = \frac{g_1 + g_2 + \cdots + g_N}{N}$$

where

$$g_i = \frac{4\pi^2 l}{T_i^2} \qquad i = 1, 2, \ldots, N$$

Method 2

$$g^* = \frac{4\pi^2 l}{\bar{T}^2}$$

where

$$\bar{T} = \frac{T_1 + T_2 + \cdots + T_N}{N}$$

Let us compute the approximate means and variances of $\bar{g}$ and g^*, respectively. For the mean

$$E(\bar{g}) = E(g_i) = E\left(\frac{4\pi^2 l}{T_i^2}\right) = 4\pi^2 l E\left(\frac{1}{T_i^2}\right)$$

$$E(g^*) = 4\pi^2 l E\left(\frac{1}{\bar{T}^2}\right)$$

Applying Theorem 4.6 and denoting $E(T_i)$ by m and $V(T_i)$ by σ^2, we find

$$E(\bar{g}) \simeq 4\pi^2 l \left(\frac{1}{m^2} + \frac{3}{m^4} \sigma^2 \right)$$

We now must use the appropriate value of $E(T_i) = m$ in the equation for $E(\bar{g})$. Suppose that the ith measurement of T yields

$$T_i = 2\pi \sqrt{\frac{l}{g}} + \epsilon_i$$

where T_i is composed of a so-called "true" value, g stands for the "true" g, and ϵ_i is an error term which incorporates the error of measurement. The "true" part of $2\pi \sqrt{l/g}$ is not a random variable; whence the error portion ϵ_i is a random variable. Hence in

$$E(T_i) = 2\pi \sqrt{\frac{l}{g}} + E(\epsilon_i)$$

we assume now that $E(\epsilon_i) = 0$ and that the variance of ϵ_i is $V(T_i)$.

We then obtain, by substitution, $2\pi \sqrt{l/g}$ for m.

$$E(\bar{g}) \simeq g + \frac{3g^2 \sigma^2}{4\pi^2 l}$$

Analogously, we find

$$E(g^*) \simeq g + \frac{3g^2 \sigma^2}{4\pi^2 l N}$$

Application of Theorem 4.7 yields

$$V(\bar{g}) \cong \frac{g^3 \sigma^2}{\pi^2 l N} \cong V(g^*)$$

These results indicate that g^* clusters more closely around "g" as $N \to \infty$, whereas $\bar{g}$ clusters around "g" + "a finite quantity" independent of N. Yet both the variances approach zero.

The results of the previous theorems can be extended to the case of a function of several variables. If $X_1, X_2, \ldots, X_k$ are k independent random variables with means $m_1, m_2, \ldots, m_k$ and variances $\sigma_1^2, \sigma_2^2, \ldots, \sigma_k^2$, respectively, then for a wide class of functions $F(X_1, X_2, \ldots, X_k)$,

$$E[F(X_1, X_2, \ldots, X_k)] \cong F(m_1, m_2, \ldots, m_k) + \sum_{i=1}^{k} \left(\frac{\partial^2 F}{\partial X_i^2} \right) \sigma_i^2$$

and

$$V[F(X_1, X_2, \ldots, X_k)] \cong \sum_{i=1}^{k} \left(\frac{\partial F}{\partial X_i} \right)^2 \sigma_i^2$$

where all the derivatives are evaluated at $m_1, m_2, \ldots, m_k$.

Example 4.14   In a variety of problems, the ratio of two quantities is of primary interest.   It is typical in some of these cases, however, that the two quantities in question are not known exactly, but must be estimated by repeated experiment, where the experiment is conventionally called measurement.   Suppose, then, that we have two series of independent measurements $X_{11}, X_{12}, \ldots, X_{1N_1}$ and $X_{21}, X_{22}, \ldots, X_{2N_2}$ such that

$$E(X_{1i}) = m_1 \qquad i = 1, \ldots, N_1$$
and
$$E(X_{2j}) = m_2 \qquad j = 1, \ldots, N_2$$

Furthermore, denote $V(X_{1i})$ by σ_1^2 and $V(X_{2j})$ by σ_2^2.

The quantity of interest is then m_1/m_2.   One approach is to estimate m_1/m_2 in terms of the respective arithmetic means.

$$\bar{X}_1 = \frac{1}{N_1} \sum_{i=1}^{N_1} X_{1i} \qquad \bar{X}_2 = \frac{1}{N_2} \sum_{j=1}^{N_2} X_{2j}$$

An estimate of m_1/m_2 frequently used is $\bar{X}_1/\bar{X}_2$.   In order to decide if this estimate is "adequate," we shall compute the approximate mean and variance of $\bar{X}_1/\bar{X}_2$.   As a by-product, we may gain insight into how large N_1 and N_2 should be.   Direct application of the generalizations of Theorems 4.6 and 4.7 yields

$$E \left(\frac{\bar{X}_1}{\bar{X}_2} \right) \cong \frac{m_1}{m_2} \left[1 + \frac{2}{N_2} \left(\frac{\sigma_2}{m_2} \right)^2 \right]$$
and
$$V \left(\frac{\bar{X}_1}{\bar{X}_2} \right) \cong \left(\frac{m_1}{m_2} \right)^2 \left[\frac{1}{N_1} \left(\frac{\sigma_1}{m_1} \right)^2 + \frac{1}{N_2} \left(\frac{\sigma_2}{m_2} \right)^2 \right]$$

Thus it is clear that $\bar{X}_1/\bar{X}_2$ is, in general, not an unbiased estimate of m_1/m_2 and that the extent of bias depends mostly on the variation of the denominator.

4.5   Bounds of Variation

4.5.1   Tchebycheff's inequality

In the previous sections we have attempted to characterize distributions with regard to their location and variation without specifying the distribution in detail. The mean and variance describe basic aspects of a distribution. We can reasonably expect the mean and variance to impose restrictions on any distribution function, and of course this is indeed the case. For this reason the mean and variance are in widespread use in characterizing distribution functions. Given the mean and variance, what, then, can be said about the probability distribution, *without further specification of the distribution?* One major result in this direction is Tchebycheff's inequality, which gives bounds on the probability of deviations from the mean in terms of the variance. The following theorem expresses this famous inequality.

Theorem 4.8   If the random variable X has mean m and variance $V(X)$, then, for any $c > 0$,

$$\text{Prob } (|X - m| \geq c) \leq \frac{V(X)}{c^2}$$

PROOF. Let us divide the sample space into the set A and its complement set $\bar{A}$ as follows:

$$A = (|X - m| \geq c) \quad \text{and} \quad \bar{A} = (|X - m| < c)$$

Then, by the decomposition rule for expectations, we have

$$\begin{aligned}
V(X) &= E[(X - m)^2] \\
&= E[(X - m)^2 \mid A]p(A) + E[(X - m)^2 \mid \bar{A}]p(\bar{A}) \\
&\geq E[(X - m)^2 \mid A]p(A)
\end{aligned}$$

Furthermore, for sample points in the set A, $(X - m)^2 \geq c^2$. Thus

$$E[(X - m)^2 \mid A] \geq c^2$$

Combining these results we obtain

$$V(X) \geq E[(X - m)^2 \mid A]p(A) \geq c^2 p(A)$$

whence $\qquad p(A) = \text{Prob } (|X - m| \geq c) \leq \dfrac{V(X)}{c^2}$

A useful special case of this result is obtained by choosing $c = k\sigma$, which yields

$$\text{Prob } (|X - m| \geq k\sigma) \leq \frac{1}{k^2}$$

The upper bound $1/k^2$ is usually much larger than the true probability. Nevertheless, in some problems this bound is quite useful.

4.5.2   The law of large numbers

We have seen that the arithmetic average tends to cluster closer and closer around the mean as the sample size is increased. We can expect this to happen when we look at the generation of the expected value. Suppose, for example, that a random variable can take on values x_1, x_2, . . . , x_k with probabilities p_1, p_2, . . . , p_k. The mean value is then given by

$$m = x_1 p_1 + x_2 p_2 + \cdot \cdot \cdot + x_k p_k$$

Suppose now that we take N independent observations on the sample space $(x_1, x_2, \ldots, x_k)$. If N_1, N_2, . . . , N_k is the number of times x_1, x_2, . . . , x_k occurs, the arithmetic average $\bar{X}_N$ is

$$\bar{X}_N = \frac{N_1 x_1 + N_2 x_2 + \cdot \cdot \cdot + N_k x_k}{N} \qquad N = N_1 + N_2 + \cdot \cdot \cdot N_k$$

Recall that the meaning of "a random variable takes on the value x with probability p_i" is that

$$\frac{N_i}{N} \cong p_i$$

as $N \to \infty$. This may also be denoted by $N_i/N \cong p_i$ for large N. Hence

$$\bar{X}_N = x_1 \left(\frac{N_1}{N} \right) + x_2 \left(\frac{N_2}{N} \right) + \cdot \cdot \cdot \left(\frac{N_k}{N} \right)$$
$$\cong x_1 p_1 + x_2 p_2 + \cdot \cdot \cdot x_k p_k = m$$

As $N \to \infty$, $\bar{X}_N \to m$. This is not a proof—it is a suggestion of possible proof.

We wish further to estimate how rapidly $\bar{X}_N$ approaches m and how probable are certain deviations of $\bar{X}_N$ from m. To make an "exact" computation requires further knowledge of p_1, p_2, . . . , p_k Tchebycheff's inequality allows us, however, to obtain an upper bound. In Chap. 5, when we discuss the central limit theorem, we shall see how one can get even better approximations for large N. For the present, for any $c > 0$, we have

$$P_N = \text{Prob} \left(|\bar{X}_N - m| \geq c \right) \leq \frac{\sigma^2}{c^2 N}$$

where $\sigma^2 = V(X)$; whence, as $N \to \infty$, $\sigma^2 > 0$, $P_N \to 0$. This relationship is known as the *law of large numbers*. More generally, we have the following theorem.

Theorem 4.9 Let X_1, X_2, . . . , X_N be a series of independent random variables with means m_1, m_2, . . . , m_N and variances σ_1^2,

$\sigma_2^2, \ldots, \sigma_N^2$. Furthermore, let

$$\bar{X}_N = \frac{X_1 + X_2 + \cdots + X_N}{N}$$
$$V_N = \sigma_1^2 + \sigma_2^2 + \cdots + \sigma_N^2$$
$$M_N = \frac{m_1 + m_2 + \cdots + m_N}{N}$$

Then, for any $c > 0$,

$$\text{Prob } (|\bar{X}_N - M_N| \geq c) \to \infty \; 0 \text{ as } N \to \infty \qquad \text{when } V_N/N^2 \to 0.$$

The proof rests on the fact that

$$V(\bar{X}_N) = \frac{1}{N^2} (\sigma_1^2 + \sigma_2^2 + \cdots + \sigma_N^2) = \frac{V_N}{N^2}$$

and $$\text{Prob } (|\bar{X}_N - M_N| \geq c) \leq \frac{V(\bar{X}_N)}{c^2} = \frac{V_N}{c^2 N^2}$$

4.6 Continuous random variables

In this chapter we have restricted ourselves, until now, to discrete distributions. As we have observed in Chap. 3, however, continuous distributions can play an important role conceptually as well as in simplifying computations, particularly in problems with random variables taking on many closely spaced values. Similarly, it is advantageous to consider continuous distributions in connection with expected values and other parameters. All the quantities studied so far have their counterpart for continuous distributions. To illustrate and motivate subsequent ideas, we discuss a continuous analogue to the geometric distribution discussed in Example 4.10.

Example 4.15 We shall consider a particular mode of time-order occurrence of events. Suppose that a specific event is uniquely defined and that we observe the time of each occurrence of this event. Examples of the types of events being considered are the time a customer arrives at a store, the time at which an auto passes a specific position on the road, the time of occurrence of an accident in a factory, and the time of failure of a given piece of equipment. For a given event, denote the times of occurrence in nondecreasing order as follows: $t_1 \leq t_2 \leq t_3 \leq \cdots$. A particular random variable of interest is T, the time interval between the successive occurrences of the event. We assume that the system is in a state of statistical stability. The time intervals between events are t_1, $t_2 - t_1$, $t_3 - t_2$, $t_4 - t_3$, $\ldots$. Stability in this case implies that the random variables $(t_i - t_{i-1})$, representing these time intervals, all have the same distribution. Physically, this implies that if the system were observed for a long time and if a histogram of the observations $(t_i - t_{i-1})$ $(i = 2, 3, \ldots)$ were made, the histogram would approach a limiting form with increasing time. Still another way to view this is that the frequency of any event relating to the successive time intervals approaches a definite value as $t \to \infty$. We shall now propose conditions for a particular system of this type.

To begin with, we assume:

1. Occurrences in nonoverlapping time intervals are independent. This also implies that the successive time intervals are independent. This assumption, in spite of being very restrictive, has been found to fit many operating systems quite adequately.

2. If $p(\Delta)$ denotes the probability of one occurrence in the time interval Δ, then for Δ "small," we have $p(\Delta) \cong \theta\Delta$. We assume that events occur discretely, namely, that for Δ small enough, the probability of two occurrences in the interval Δ is so small that it can be ignored.

Now consider the time axis to be divided into segments of length Δ. Then we can associate with each segment a binomial experiment whose probability of success is denoted by $p(\Delta)$. Moreover, according to assumption 1, these experiments are independent. As we stated above, a random variable of this system which is of genuine interest is the time interval between successive occurrences of the primary event. In our atomized linear time manifold this is equivalent to the counting of the number of segments between two successive segments in which the event occurred. Let us denote this random variable by T; whence, if we designate the number of segments which correspond to a particular value t of T by n, $n\Delta = t$ $(n = 0, 1, 2, \ldots)$ represents the various values which the random variable T can take on. A simple verbal description of random variable T is the time interval during which the primary event does not occur. In order to avoid ambiguity we shall modify the description of T slightly. To each Δ segment in which the primary event has occurred, attach the preceding sequence of segments in which there is no occurrence of the event. Again designate this number of segments (trials) by n so that the values which T takes on are designated again by $t = n\Delta$, $n \geq 1$. Then we may express the probability that a success —"the event"—will occur on the nth Δ segment after the preceding success, or what is the same probability, namely, the probability of time interval t between successive "successes" as follows:

$$\text{Prob } (T = t = n\Delta) \equiv P(t) = [1 - p(\Delta)]^{n-1}p(\Delta)$$

If we wish to calculate these probabilities, we must reduce the preceding expression to one which is analytically tractable—and meaningful for T, a continuous random variable. The values t which T can take on must therefore cover a continuous domain, perhaps $(0, \infty)$, and Δ must be able to shrink to zero. We can do this by utilizing the assumptions that $t = n\Delta$ and $p(\Delta) \cong \theta\Delta$; whence

$$[1 - p(\Delta)]^{n-1}p(\Delta) \cong \frac{(1 - \theta\Delta)^{t/\Delta}}{1 - \theta\Delta}\, \theta\Delta$$

For a given pair (θ, t) as $\Delta \to 0$,

$$(1 - \theta\Delta)^{t/\Delta} \to e^{-\theta t}$$

Hence we can evaluate $P(t)/\Delta$ for Δ vanishing:

$$\lim_{\Delta \to 0} P(t)/\Delta = \lim_{\Delta \to 0} \left[\frac{(1 - \theta\Delta)^{t/\Delta}}{1 - \theta\Delta} \right] \frac{\theta\Delta}{\Delta}$$
$$= \theta e^{-\theta t} \qquad t \geq 0$$

(The juggling with limits is entirely justifiable in rather simple terms.) According to our definitions, $P(t)$ is the probability distribution or probability function of random variable T, and therefore $\theta e^{-\theta t}$ is the *PDF* of T; whence

$$P(t) \cong \theta e^{-\theta t}\Delta \equiv f(t)\Delta$$

We are interested in $f(t)$, the *PDF* of T, which was introduced in Chap. 3 under other considerations; it is called the exponential. Note that assumption 1 above is equivalent to the assumption of the independence of interarrival times between successive cars made in Chap. 3. Note also that the attachment of the last segment to the interval between successes made for analytical simplicity and formal equivalence to interarrival times.

We are usually interested in the mean value of T, which can be attained from the facts at hand by standard techniques. According to definition,

$$E(T) = \sum t_i P(t_i) \cong \sum t_i \theta e^{-\theta t_i}\Delta$$
$$\cong \int_0^\infty t\theta e^{-\theta t}\, dt = \frac{1}{\theta}$$

(Note that by definition $t_i = i\Delta$.)

The variance of T can also be obtained directly as follows:

$$V(T) = \sum_{i=1}^{i=\infty} t_i^2 P(t_i) - \frac{1}{\theta^2} \cong \int_0^\infty t^2 \theta e^{-\theta t}\, dt - \frac{1}{\theta^2} = \frac{1}{\theta^2}$$

In general, as we have observed in Chap. 3, a random variable taking on many closely spaced values can sometimes be approximated by a probability density function $f(x)$, where $f(x) \cong P(x \mid \Delta)/\Delta$, with Δ the interval of least count.

Furthermore, the expected value of a function $G(x)$ of the random variable X can be approximated in terms of $f(x)$ as follows:

$$E[G(X)] = \sum_x G(x)P(x) = \sum_x G(x)f(x)\Delta \cong \int_{-\infty}^{\infty} G(x)f(x)\, dx$$

Thus the mean and variance can be approximated by an integration process which may sometimes be more convenient than summation. This discussion leads to a definition of expectation for continuous random variables.

Definition: expected value   Let the random variable X have a probability density function $f(x)$. Then the *expected value* of $G(X)$ is defined by

$$E[G(X)] = \int_{-\infty}^{\infty} G(x)f(x)\, dx$$

In a similar manner conditional means and variances can be defined in terms of the conditional *PDF*s. The properties of the parameters relating to discrete random variables discussed in previous sections carry over directly for continuous random variables if the above definitions are utilized.

Example 4.16   We refer back to Example 4.8. It will be shown in Chap. 5 that the distribution function of D_N for N "large" can be approximated by a continuous probability density function $\phi(x;m,\sigma^2)$, called the *normal distribution*, with parameters m and σ^2, which is defined as follows:

$$\phi(x;m,\sigma^2) = \frac{1}{\sigma\sqrt{2\pi}} \exp\left[-\frac{1}{2}\left(\frac{x-m}{\sigma}\right)^2 \right] \qquad -\infty \leq x \leq \infty$$

where m and σ^2 are parameters which can be verified by integration to be equal to the mean and variance, respectively. Furthermore, it can be checked that this is a *PDF* by integrating over the range of definition to obtain 1. The *PDF* $\phi(x;m,\sigma^2)$ is a symmetrical bell-shaped curve clustered around m whose spread depends on σ^2. This distribution plays a central role in probability theory. A graphical representation of $\phi(x;0,\sigma^2)$ for $\sigma^2 = 1$ and 4 is given in Fig. 4.3.

The distribution function of D_N (N large) can be approximated by $\phi(x;m,\sigma^2)$ by choosing m and σ^2 equal to the mean and variance of D_N. Thus $m = E(D_N) = 0$ and

$$\sigma^2 = V(D_N) = V(X_1 + X_2 + \cdots + X_N) = NV(X) = N$$

Then

$$E|D_N| \cong \int_{-\infty}^{+\infty} \frac{|x|}{\sqrt{2\pi N}} \exp\left(-\frac{x^2}{2N}\right) dx = 2 \int_{0}^{\infty} \frac{x}{\sqrt{2\pi N}} \exp\left(-\frac{x^2}{2N}\right) dx$$

$$= \sqrt{\frac{2}{\pi}} \sqrt{N} = 0.79788 \sqrt{N}$$

It will be shown in Chap. 5 that the distribution of a sum of N independent random variables can be approximated for large N under very good conditions by $\phi(x;m,\sigma^2)$. This important result is called the *central limit theorem*.

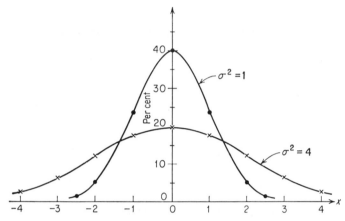

Figure 4.3 $\phi(x;0,\sigma^2)$ for $\sigma^2 = 1$ and $\sigma^2 = 4$.

4.7 Moments and moment-generating function

4.7.1 Moments

In the previous section we discussed parameters describing the *location* and *variation* of distribution functions. The mean and variance, while very helpful for describing and studying distribution functions, do not give the whole picture. Some other features of a distribution function of interest are *skewness* and flatness or peakedness, called *kurtosis*.

The mean of a random variable X is defined as the expected value of X, given CDF $F(x)$. The variance of X is defined as the expected value of $(X - m)^2$. Some other measures descriptive of the distribution of X can be obtained from the expected values of other suitably chosen functions of X. We shall give some formal definitions.

Definition: central moments The kth *central moment* μ'_k of a random variable X is defined as

$$\mu'_k = E(X^k)$$

Definition: moments around the mean The kth *moment around the mean* μ_k of a random variable X is given by

$$\mu_k = E[(X - m)^k]$$

Thus we see that the mean is μ_1' and the variance is μ_2. The third moment around the mean, μ_3, is generally used as a measure of asymmetry of skewness. For a symmetrical distribution, $\mu_3 = 0$. However, a value of $\mu_3 = 0$ does *not* imply symmetry. A distribution f_1 with $\mu_3 > 0$ is said to be skewed to the right, while an f_2 with $\mu_3 < 0$ is said to be skewed to the left (Fig. 4.4).

The fourth moment about the mean, μ_4, is a measure of peakedness since it gives relatively large weight to values far away from the mean.

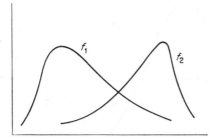

Figure 4.4

Generally, the mean and variance are very useful, while the higher moments are, in practice, of marginal usefulness. The importance of the moments, as we shall see, is that the whole sequence, μ_k or μ_k', usually is unique to a particular distribution, so that to each sequence μ_k there is a corresponding unique distribution, under most circumstances. Before exploring this further we wish to point out that it is mostly a matter of convenience whether we deal with central moments μ_k' or with moments around the mean μ_k, since they are related to each other. This can be observed from the fact that $(X - m)^k$ can be expressed in terms of powers of X, using the binomial theorem. Thus

$$(X - m)^k = \sum_{s=0}^{k} (-1)^s \frac{k!}{s!(k-s)!} \, m^s X^{k-s}$$

Therefore

$$\mu_k = E[(X - m)^k] = \sum_{s=0}^{k} (-1)^s \frac{k!}{s!(k-s)!} \, m^s \mu_{k-s}'$$

For example,

$$V(X) = \mu_2 = \mu_2' - 2m^2 + m^2 = E(X^2) - m^2$$

An important classical problem in probability is the question of finding conditions when a sequence of numbers represents the moments of a distribution function uniquely. It is quite a difficult problem and beyond the scope of this text. As we have remarked previously, however, the moments, apart from being descriptive, have their importance because of uniqueness. This is summed up in the following result: *Under quite general conditions the moments μ_k' ($k = 1, 2, \ldots$) determine a unique distribution function.*

Furthermore, an important related result is the following. Let Z_N ($N = 1, 2, \ldots$) be a sequence of random variables with CDF F_N; let u_{kN}' be the kth central moment of Z_N; let F be a CDF with central moments μ_k'. Then, *under quite general conditions, $F_N \to F$ as $N \to \infty$ when $\mu_{kN}' \to \mu_k'$ for $N \to \infty$ and $k = 1, 2, \ldots$.* This result is of great importance in obtaining approximations to distribution functions.

More exact statements of these results and the conditions under which they hold will not be developed here.

Example 4.17 We have previously remarked that the distribution function of the arithmetic average $\bar{X}_N$ of a series of independent random variables often approaches that of the normal distribution when N is large. One way this can be demonstrated is by showing that the central moments of $\bar{X}_N$ approach those of the normal for increasing N. This can, in fact, be demonstrated, but is very laborious. To indicate the method, we show that the first four central moments approach those of the normal in the special case of identically distributed random variables, all with finite moments. We suppose, for convenience, that X's all have zero mean.

From the definition of the normal distribution $\phi(x;0,\sigma^2)$ (Example 4.16), it directly follows that

$$\mu_{2k+1}' = 0 \qquad k = 0, 1, 2, \ldots$$
and
$$\mu_{2k}' = (1)(3)(5) \cdots (2k-1)\sigma^{2k} \qquad (4.7.1)$$

These equations give all the moments (about the mean) of the normal distribution. We leave the demonstration of the above to the reader as an exercise in integration. Now let

$$Z_N = \frac{X_1 + X_2 + \cdots + X_N}{\sqrt{N}} = \sqrt{N}\,\bar{X}_N$$

where $X_1, X_2, \ldots$ are independently and identically distributed random variables, each with mean zero and variance σ^2. The central moments μ_{kN}' of Z_N are given by

$$\mu_{kN}' = E[(\sqrt{N}\,\bar{X}_N)^k] = N^{-k/2}E(X_1 + X_2 + \cdots X_N)^k$$

For $k = 1$, we have

$$\mu'_{1N} = N^{-\frac{1}{2}}E(X_1 + X_2 + \cdots + X_N) = 0$$

For $k = 2$, we have

$$\mu'_{2N} = \frac{1}{N} E(X_1 + \cdots + X_N)^2 = \frac{1}{N} (\sigma^2 + \cdots + \sigma^2) = \sigma^2$$

We study $\sqrt{N}\, \bar{X}_N$ instead of $\bar{X}_N$ for the purpose of normalizing the result so that $\mu'_{2N} = \sigma^2$, which agrees with the result in Eq. (4.7.1) for $k = 1$.

The higher moments are obtained by using the multinomial theorem (expansion) as follows:

$$(X_1 + X_2 + \cdots X_N)^k = \sum \frac{k!}{s_1! s_2! \cdots s_N!} X_1^{s_1} X_2^{s_2} \cdots X_N^{s_N}$$

where summation is over all $s_1, s_2, \ldots, s_N$, with $s_1 + \cdots + s_N = k$. Thus, because of the independence,

$$E(X_1 + \cdots + X_N)^k = \sum \frac{k!}{s_1! s_2! \cdots s_N!} E(X_1^{s_1}) E(X_2^{s_2}) \cdots E(X_N^{s_N})$$

where summation is over $s_1 + s_2 + \cdots + s_N = k$.

For $k = 3$,

$$\mu'_{3N} = N^{-\frac{3}{2}}E \left(\sum_i X_i^3 + 3 \sum_{i \neq j} X_i^2 X_j + 6 \sum_{i \neq j \neq r} X_i X_j X_r \right)$$

$$= \frac{N\mu'_3}{N^{\frac{3}{2}}} = N^{-\frac{1}{2}}\mu'_3 \to 0 \quad \text{as } N \to \infty$$

$$\mu'_{4N} = N^{-2}E \left(\sum_i X_i^4 + 4 \sum_{i \neq j} X_i^3 X_j + 12 \sum_{i \neq j \neq r} X_i^2 X_j X_r \right.$$

$$\left. + 6 \sum_{i \neq j} X_i^2 X_j^2 + 24 \sum_{i \neq j \neq r \neq l} X_i X_j X_r X_l \right)$$

$$= N^{-2} \left[N\mu'_4 + \frac{6\sigma^4 N(N-1)}{2} \right] = \frac{\mu'_4}{N} + 3\sigma^4 - \frac{3\sigma^4}{N} \to 3\sigma^4$$

The first four moments of the random variable $\sqrt{N}\, \bar{X}_N$ approach those of the normal distribution as $N \to \infty$. Iteration of the present technique will yield the same result for all higher moments. These results were obtained under certain restrictions which can be removed. In Chap. 5 these restrictions will be relaxed and more general results, expressed in the form of the central limit theorem, will be discussed.

4.7.2   Moment generating function

The moments of a distribution are important, as we have seen, since they can in many cases characterize a distribution uniquely. However, the moments are often difficult to compute and not very convenient to work with. We therefore introduce the moment-generating function which "contains" all the moments of a distribution and is usually more tractable to mathematical manipulation than are the individual moments themselves.

Definition: moment-generating function   The *moment generating function* $M_X(t)$ of a random variable X is given as a function of a variable t as follows:

$$M_X(t) = E(e^{tX})$$

The term moment-generating function arises from the fact that $M_X(t)$ does "generate" all the moments. Furthermore, under most conditions, there is a unique correspondence between the central moments $\mu'_k (k = 1, 2, \ldots)$ and $M_X(t)$.

To demonstrate these aspects we expand e^{tX} into a power series:

$$e^{tX} = 1 + tX + \frac{1}{2} t^2 X^2 + \frac{1}{3!} t^3 X^3 + \cdots$$

Thus

$$M_X(t) = E(e^{tX}) = 1 + t\mu'_1 + \frac{1}{2} t^2 \mu'_2 + \frac{1}{3!} t^3 \mu'_3 + \cdots$$

This is a power series in t whose coefficients are related, systematically, to the central moments. Also, by differentiating $M_X(t)$ and evaluating the results at $t = 0$, we can express the moments in terms of the derivatives of M. Thus

$$M_X^{(1)}(t) = \mu'_1 + \frac{2}{2} t\mu'_2 + \frac{3}{3!} t^2 \mu'_3 + \cdots + \frac{k}{k!} t^{k-1} \mu'_k + \cdots$$

evaluated at $t = 0$ is

$$M_X^{(1)}(0) = \mu'_1$$

From the second derivative we obtain

$$M_X^{(2)}(t) = \mu'_2 + t\mu'_3 + \frac{1}{2!} t^2 \mu'_4 + \cdots$$

which yields $M_X^{(2)}(0) = \mu'_2$ upon setting $t = 0$.

In a similar manner we obtain

$$\mu'_k = M_X^{(k)}(0) = \left(\frac{d^k M_X(t)}{dt^k} \right)_{t=0} \qquad k = 1, 2, \ldots$$

We can indicate some uses for $M_X(t)$. Suppose that we have two random variables X and Y whose moment-generating functions $M_X(t)$

and $M_Y(t)$ are identical for t in an interval containing $t = 0$. We shall show then that *all* the moments of X and Y are equal.

$$U(t) = M_X(t) - M_Y(t) = (\mu'_{1X} - \mu'_{1Y})t + (\mu'_{2X} - \mu'_{2Y})\frac{t^2}{2} + \cdots$$

which equals zero in the interval containing $t = 0$. Hence the derivatives of $U(t)$ exist at $t = 0$ and equal zero there. Therefore

$$U^{(k)}(0) = \mu'_{kX} - \mu'_{kY} = 0 \qquad k = 1, 2, \ldots$$

In this and subsequent results we merely wish to indicate the approach without going into existence, convergence, and other mathematical questions. We now quote an important result, similar to one stated previously, for moments. Let Z_N be a series of random variables with CDF F_N and moment-generating functions $M_{Z_N}(t)$. Let F be a CDF with moment-generating function $M(t)$. Then, *under quite general conditions, if $M_{Z_N}(t) \to M(t)$ for an interval of values of t including $t = 0$, $F_N \to F$.*

The moment-generating function often serves as a convenient device for establishing many important statistical relations. Before giving an example of this we need some simple properties of $M_X(t)$. Some of these are:

1. For any constant C we have

$$M_{CX}(t) = E(e^{CtX}) = M_X(Ct)$$
$$M_{X+C}(t) = E[e^{t(X+C)}] = e^{Ct}M_X(t)$$

2. If X and Y are independent random variables, then

$$M_{X+Y}(t) = E[e^{t(X+Y)}] = E(e^{tX})E(e^{tY}) = M_X(t)M_Y(t)$$

Thus, for $X_1, X_2, \ldots, X_N$ independent and $C_1, C_2, \ldots, C_N$ any constants, we have

$$M_{C_1X_1+\cdots+C_NX_N}(t) = M_{X_1}(C_1t)M_{X_2}(C_2t) \cdots M_{X_N}(C_Nt) \qquad (4.7.2)$$

This result is very useful in studying sums of independent random variables, as we shall show in the next example.

Example 4.18   We often need the distribution of the sum of two independent normal random variables. This can be done quite simply with the aid of the moment-generating function. First, let us find the moment-generating function of the normal distribution with mean m and variance σ^2 by straightforward integration.

$$M_X(t) \qquad \text{for} \qquad f(x) = \frac{1}{\sqrt{2\pi}\,\sigma} e^{-\frac{1}{2}\left(\frac{x-m}{\sigma}\right)^2}$$

is found to be

$$M(t) = e^{tm + \frac{1}{2}t^2\sigma^2} \tag{4.7.3}$$

Suppose now that X and Y are two independent normal random variables with respective means m_1 and m_2 and respective variances σ_1^2 and σ_2^2. Direct substitution of Eq. (4.7.3) in (4.7.2) yields

$$M_{X+Y}(t) = M_X(t)M_Y(t) = (e^{tm_1 + \frac{1}{2}t^2\sigma_1^2})(e^{tm_2 + \frac{1}{2}t^2\sigma_2^2})$$
$$= e^{t(m_1 + m_2) + \frac{1}{2}t^2(\sigma_1^2 + \sigma_2^2)}$$

a form which is that of the moment-generating function of the normal distribution with mean $m_1 + m_2$ and variance $\sigma_1^2 + \sigma_2^2$, since the moment-generating function is unique. It follows that the *PDF* of the random variable $X + Y = Z$ is

$$f(z) = \frac{1}{\sqrt{2\pi}\sqrt{\sigma_1^2 + \sigma_2^2}} \exp\left\{-\frac{[z - (m_1 + m_2)]^2}{2(\sigma_1^2 + \sigma_2^2)}\right\}$$

We can say this in other words: if random variables X and Y are as given above, then the distribution of $X + Y$ is normal with mean $m_1 + m_2$ and variance $\sigma_1^2 + \sigma_2^2$.

4.8 Statistical simulation

The study of phenomena, in many branches of science, engineering, and industry, is often complicated by uncertainties in measurement as well as by high variability in the basic variables of the system. Consequently, effective decision making with regard to such systems depends on assessing the effects of these variations. Some simple examples of the ramifications of variability were described in Chap. 1. In subsequent chapters we develop some principles of probability in order to enable us to answer questions arising in situations of variability and uncertainty with some measure of confidence. It is somewhat disillusioning, however, to discover that questions which arise when problems are realistically formulated are too often rather difficult to answer, if not altogether unanswerable analytically. In order to meet this all-too-frequent contingency, methods have been devised which pretend to replicate the "real" situation and, by computations or by simulated action, yield empirical answers.

Suppose, for example, we wish to study possible changes affecting traffic behavior at a busy intersection. An action, among others, which may come under consideration is varying the timing of the signal lights at intersections. One can do this actually at the scene of many intersections—an excellent operational experiment—with, however, questionable results. In the first place, one may disrupt traffic, and in the second place one may never include the range of optimal timing even with a thousand variations.   And of course such an experiment would be inordinately expensive and require an inordinately long time.   This dilemma is common in operations and operational problems.   And as a matter of fact, one of the characteristics of the new popular field of operations research is that, in order to make an "optimal" choice of policy among possible alternatives for action on an operations situation, one must give some play to the interaction between experiment, observer, and the situation under study.   This kind of inquiry, which calls upon the whole instrumentality of probability and statistical inference, is in strong contrast to so-called basic and *pure* scientific inquiry in which the interaction under investigation can be isolated in a laboratory environment, if not realistically symbolized in conceptual formalism.   We are led, then, to consider representations of complex operations situations which permit the observer to "play" with the situation without disturbing it or paying an "inordinate price" for the privilege.

It might be well to recall a number of situations—usually called engineering problems—in which the dilemma discussed above occurs. Harbors have a way of silting so that channels become impassable: how can we study harbor silting?   A target-seeking missile system is designed: how shall one evaluate the effectiveness of such a system?   It is obvious that practical experimentation is quite restricted.   A complex servo-control system is designed to steer a ship: how shall the effectiveness of such a system be tested?   An inventory policy is dependent upon an empirically determined demand forecast which does not lend itself readily to analytical form.   At best the demand is expressible graphically.   The choice of an "optimal" inventory policy (material-purchase or work-scheduling plan) requires minimizing the expected value of a complicated cost function entailing the graphical demand.   How shall this minimization be accomplished?

In the situations introduced above, it is necessary (1) to represent the behavior of a complicated operation under controlled variation of the input variables, while the whole system may be further subjected to certain random variations, and (2) to obtain, under these circumstances, the values of particular output variables over a wide range, either continuous or discrete, of values of the input variables.   We shall give a simple example of a situation in which some of the basic data can only be introduced in either tabular form or graphically.   In treating this problem, the behavior of an input is expressible only in terms of some past history—observations which are approximated over the possible range of occurrence graphically.   These inputs may occur "at random," meaning that any particular value of an input variable is not predictable but occurs as though chosen by random selection from a group of numbers which possess the same probability distribution (PF or CDF) as does the input variable considered.   We therefore must provide a method for successive selection of values of the given input variable so that the total set of values used in obtaining the set of output values has the distribution given by the graphical representation.   Explanation can best be made in a specific simple example.

Example 4.19   A common problem in industrial production concerns the maintenance of machines in working order, and a perplexing aspect is holding down the cost.   Look at the life history of a machine: It is put to work at time t_0, and at time t_1 it becomes inoperative (breaks down).   The machine is repaired—restored to working order.   Let us assume that the repaired machine is as good as new and that, when the machine breaks down again, the elapsed working time from first restoration to the second breakdown is describable in the same terms as was

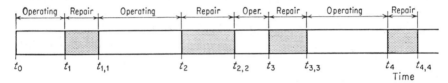

Figure 4.5

the first working period.   Again, following the second breakdown, there is a second restoration, and the same sequel.   We represent this in the time scale of Fig. 4.5.

The successive elapsed times to breakdowns, $t_1 - t_0 \equiv X_1, t_2 - t_{1,1} \equiv X_2, \ldots, t_n - t_{n-1,n-1} \equiv X_n$, may be considered to be selected randomly from some universe of values belonging to the random variable X.   We repeat: X is a random variable whose specific values are $X_1, X_2, \ldots, X_n, \ldots$.   These values constitute a distribution.   In the present problem we cannot express this distribution by a mathematical expression, but we have a long past history on our machine from which we can establish a graphical representation of $F(t)$, the *CDF* of random variable X. A particular value X_i of X is the uninterrupted working time of our machine during the ith period. X_i is independent of all the preceding $i - 1$ values of X which occurred.   We make another assumption about our machine: its future is statistically the same as its past.   By this we mean that the observed lengths of uninterrupted working periods in the future are expected to have the same *CDF* as do those of the past, and both periods are in statistical control with the same parameters.

Why all this discussion?   We have a problem, and we want to learn what to do about it.   We have been servicing our machine each time it breaks down, and we note that the average length of repair time is quite long.   We have determined the cost of repair service during the past quarter (3 months) and have found it to be too high.   We wonder whether we can cut this cost.   The values we pursue here are simple;

in this particular case there is one value, low repair cost. Such technical knowledge as we can muster indicates that our repair service is excellent and as economical as can be hoped for. But on occasion some of the repairmen have given machines what is euphemistically called maintenance service. So-called maintenance consists of adjusting some fittings, replacing some smaller parts (and refurbishing the removed parts if salvageable), additional oiling and greasing, realigning, and the like. Such service was done while the machine appeared to be in good operating condition, and the maintenance service time was roughly estimated to be less than one-third that of "usual" repair service time. (This experimental maintenance has been done only when the machine was temporarily idle and a repairman was free.) It seems intuitively likely—at least worthy of the thought—that a scheduled regular maintenance service might, in actual fact, cost less "on the average" than does breakdown repair service. How shall we find out?

An obvious answer is not often tenable: conduct regular maintenance service for some weeks or months and compare costs. One such test run, with a scheduled repair interval of, say, 10 days, takes 3 months, or some 63 working days. But "10 days maintenance" may not yield least cost; we try another test for another 3 months; and so on. If we could simulate the different situations on paper and determine the minimum-cost maintenance interval, we should save considerable expense and reduce the likelihood of erroneous decision. How do we proceed?

We get the data that we need, namely, a sequence of "lifetimes" (lengths of uninterrupted operating intervals), a sequence of repair times, and a sequence of maintenance times. We get these data by simulating the operating-process characteristics, with random selection of numbers from universes of random numbers which possess the same CDFs of the respective process characteristics. In Fig. 4.6, two CDFs, $z = F(x)$ ($0 \leq z \leq 1$), of operating times are graphically represented. These curves have the form that we may encounter in practice. We shall obtain from curve I a sequence of values of X, $x_1, x_2, \ldots, x_n$ such that, if they were reconstituted into a cumulative frequency diagram, the diagram would "look like" curve I in Fig. 4.6. In fact, the diagram would approach $F(x)$ as $n \to \infty$. Any point (x,z) of $z = F(x)$ is interpreted to mean Prob $(X \leq x) \equiv F(x) = z$. Furthermore, Prob $(a \leq X \leq b) = F(b) - F(a)$. We want a random sequence of values of X. We could do this by taking 50, 100, or 1,000 (etc.) equally spaced numbers between 0 and 50, where 50 represents the practical maximum of X. Suppose we mark off points 0.5, 1.5, 2.5, $\ldots$, and 49.5 on the X axis and project vertical lines to curve $F(x)$. At the intersections we project horizontally upon the Z axis, getting points $z_1, z_2, \ldots, z_{50}$. These points have this meaning: Prob $(17.5 < X \leq 18.5) = F(18.5) - F(17.5)$. Another approximate interpretation is: if X takes on integral values 1,

2, . . . , 50, Prob $(X = 18) = F(18.5) - F(17.5) \equiv p_{18}$. That is to say, to each value x_i $(i = 1, 2, \ . \ . \ . , 50)$, there corresponds a probability of occurrence p_i. We could then mark identical circular thin disks with these integers, each integer x_i occurring with relative frequency p_i and actual frequency Np_i, where N is a large integer, so that all Np_i are approximately integers. Thus each value x_i appears Np_i times, and as is obvious, $\sum\limits_{i=1}^{50} Np_i = N$. (This process requires some necessary adjustment, and in particular when Np_i lies midway between two integers. We can leave these adjustments to the ingenuity of the reader.)

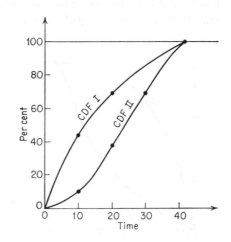

Figure 4.6

Now we get down to business. We place all N disks into a "mixing barrel" or cage (bingo!) and make random independent withdrawals, one disk at a time, noting its number. The outcome is a random sequence of x_i numbers [equivalent to the operating times of one machine if we used $F(t)$] which simulates how these numbers would occur in practice for a random variable with $CDF = F(x)$. This is, however, a very tedious job, which we can avoid by taking advantage of existing sets of random numbers drawn from the uniform distribution. Such sets of random independent selections from a uniform distribution of the unit integers 0, 1, . . . , 9 have been made, studied, and tested, so that now one need merely refer to such tables, select a digit from the table, by chance, and apply any rule consistently for getting as long a random sequence as one wishes. In order to get a random sequence of numbers between 0 and 99, one need merely find a starting pair of digits and follow with consecutive pairs.

We can make use of this method by recognizing that we can consider $Z \equiv F(X)$ to be uniformly distributed between 0 and 1. Assume 100 equal percentiles between 0.00 and 1.00. To each $Z_i \equiv F(X_i)$ there is a corresponding $X_i = x_i$ on the abscissa such that Prob $(X \leq x_i) = Z_i$. Consider $Z_b = 0.50$ and $Z_a = 0.40$; Prob $(x_a < X \leq x_b) = Z_b - Z_a = 0.10$. Hence numbers between x_a and x_b will occur 10 per cent of the time. Again, let $Z_d = 0.90$ and $Z_c = 0.80$; whence numbers between Z_d and Z_c also occur 10 per cent of the time. But note the difference between the spread of $x_d - x_c$ and $x_b - x_a$. Thus the numbers on the x scale will occur, independent of their time order of selection, with the same relative frequency that yields the original CDF, Prob $(X \leq x) = F(x)$. We have demonstrated this procedure in an empirical manner for an $F(x)$ represented graphically. In other words, if random variable X has CDF $F(x)$, then the random variable $Z = F(X)$ has the uniform distribution in interval $[0,1]$. That is, Prob $(Z \leq z) = z$ $(0 \leq z \leq 1)$.

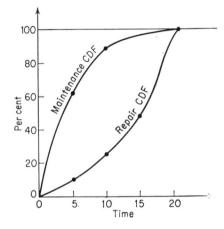

Figure 4.7

Thus a series of observations on X; x, x_2, . . . , x_n can be obtained from a series of observations on Z; z_1, z_2, . . . , z_n by solving for x_i, from $z_i = F(x_i)$. (See Exercise 4.11.)

We shall now use this technique for answering the questions on preventive maintenance which were raised on introducing this example. Consider the CDFs in Fig. 4.6, which represent (as labeled) two different (possible) lifetimes of a given machine. In Fig. 4.7 we have the CDFs of the maintenance times and repair times, respectively. We have chosen these distributions so as to illustrate a definite point and have therefore exaggerated the length of maintenance—the method of analysis is valid, independent of the specific form of the CDFs. We are looking for histories of breakdowns (in accordance with given lifetime distributions), a history of maintenance times, and a history of repair times. We need a table of random numbers from which we make random independent selections of sequences of two digit numbers, to which correspond lifetimes, maintenance times, and repair times, respectively. Assuming that we have a table of random numbers available, we have obtained three random sequences RNL, RNM, and RNR of numbers (Table 4.3). Each of these sequences is a sample of a possible sequence of occurrences with the given respective distributions.   Following the technique illustrated above, we obtain the respective lifetimes, repair time, and maintenance time.

We are now able to construct a history of the machine's behavior for a lifetime distribution and for a given maintenance interval of T days,

TABLE 4.3

RNL	Lifetime I	Lifetime II	RNM	Maintenance time	RNR	Repair time
41	9	21	54	4	14	7
48	11	22	83	9	96	20
39	9	20	30	2	28	11
73	21	29	07	1	95	19
49	11	22	69	6	85	18
37	9	20	62	5	02	1
87	23	34	71	6	41	14
94	35	37	64	5	74	18
12	4	11	99	3	45	15
14	4	12	37	11	71	17
74	21	29	90	9	69	17
31	7	18	85	5	04	2
11	4	10	61	1	46	15
08	3	9	08	2	67	17
61	14	1	27	7	73	18
70	19	28	77	2	70	17
02	1	1	23	1	90	19
25	6	16	17	3	57	16
90	32	36	37	3	19	8
65	16	27	40	3	70	17

given the repair-time and maintenance-time histories in Table 4.3.   To illustrate, suppose that $T = 10$ days.   The machine begins normal operation and continues for 9 days before breaking down.   The length of repair is then 7 days, the first number in the repair-time sequence.   Again the machine starts a new, normal operation which could continue for 11 days.   Our maintenance schedule, however, requires that after 10 days the machine be given a maintenance overhaul.   The first number in the maintenance-time history is 4 days, after which the machine goes back into normal operation for a third hitch.   This endures 9 days, and then a 20-day repair.   One 180-day history is illustrated in Fig. 4.8, for $T = 10$,

25, and ∞ days, respectively. The machine-utilization percentage is readily calculated. The results are tabulated in Table 4.4 and graphed in Fig. 4.9. The effects of the difference in distribution of lifetime are quite apparent. Under lifetime I preventive maintenance affords no

TABLE 4.4

T	% utilization with CDF I	% utilization with CDF II
5	36	48
10	55	61
15	55	75
20	55	82
25	55	65
∞	55	60

economy, since for no finite T is the per cent utilization greater than for $T = \infty$, no preventive maintenance. On the other hand, for distribution II, $T = 20$ days offers the greatest machine utilization, 82 per cent, whereas with no preventive maintenance, the utilization is only 60 per cent.

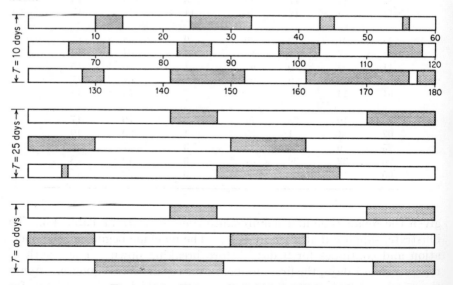

Figure 4.8   History of machine for lifetime II ($T = 10, 25, \infty$).

A more comprehensive treatment would have to include other costs such as those for maintenance and repair.

The foregoing results derive from a history of only 180 days. What the results would be like for indefinitely long histories will be considered in a later chapter on confidence intervals. Given certain assumptions, statistical estimates can be made for the length of a machine history necessary for estimating machine-utilization percentage within a specified degree of accuracy. This discussion has been merely illustrative of problems involved and of the nature of possible results.

Example 4.20 We further illustrate the simulation technique, with a discussion of some aspects relating to storage problems. Storage

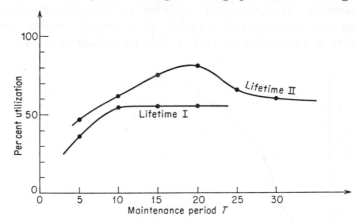

Figure 4.9   Per cent utilization versus T.

space is often a necessary element in a system involving the flow of material. For example, in manufacturing storage space is often needed between stages of the production process, especially when there are uncertainties and lags between the stages. Warehousing capacity is also a necessity for most finished products which must be distributed in accordance with demand. A similar situation occurs in a store which orders and receives goods periodically. Dams represent another class of essential storage facility wherein input and output are in magnitudes

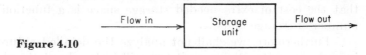

Figure 4.10

which vary continuously. The dam serves to provide storage and control of outflow under conditions of uncertainty of inflow.

The structure of these and many other problems can be visualized as in Fig. 4.10.

Both the flows in and out may have probabilistic elements in them. An important factor relating to these problems is the capacity of the storage unit. We have remarked that the function of storage is accommodation at various stages in the flow of material. How much is this accommodation worth? The answer, of course, depends on the possible consequences for goods not accommodated, as well as the cost of maintaining the storage unit.

If the storage capacity is made small, there will be frequent demand for storage which cannot be met. This involves undesirable consequences in terms of possible dislocations or costs because the goods were stored elsewhere at greater expense. On the other hand, a large-capacity storage area may be unused much of the time, and thus wasteful. The optimum storage capacity depends on *balancing* the costs due to not having storage space available when needed (during periods of peak activity) as against the cost of building and maintaining the storage area.

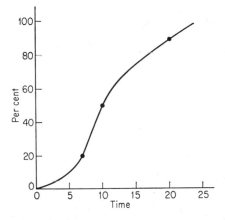

Figure 4.11 *CDF* of *I*.

We shall not delve into the various economic questions involved. For the purposes of illustration, we focus on only one relevant aspect, namely, the amount of storage capacity which is needed but cannot be accommodated. This quantity will be measured in terms of storage units, where a storage unit means storage of one item for 1 day. Thus two items, each needing 3 days of storage, have the same number of storage units (i.e., six) as one item needing 6 days of storage. In a sense, we assume that the cost of extra needed storage space is a function only of the number of storage units.

Furthermore, we shall not analyze the detailed nature of the flow in and out of the storage unit but will look only at the changes in the required storage space. Thus, from time to time, there is a change in needed storage space. The change is positive if material flows in and negative when some flows out. We assume that the successive intervals between changes are random variables independently and identically distributed. Also, the intervals and the changes are assumed to be independent. The evolution of the process can be described as follows. After interval I_1, there is a change D_1; after a further interval I_2, a change D_2; etc. We assume that the I's are independent, with CDF as given in Fig. 4.11. The D's are also independent, with CDF as shown in

Fig. 4.12. In order to simulate the process, we use a table of random numbers in conjunction with graphs of the *CDF*s.

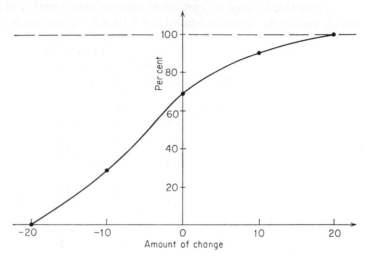

Figure 4.12 *CDF* of *D*.

In Table 4.5 we have two columns of random numbers labeled *RN*. Adjacent to each such column are the computed observations. With these values we simulate the process. Let us start with 10 items in the

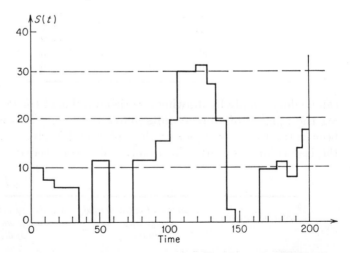

Figure 4.13 *S(t)* versus *t*.

store. From the table we observe 8 days until a change occurs. The amount of change is a removal of two items from the store, leaving 8 until the next change occurs after another 8 days. This process is continued to any desired length.   Figure 4.13 gives the amount of needed storage $S(t)$ as a function of time for 200 days.

From this history we can easily compute the number of storage units which cannot be accommodated for various storage capacities S.   This

TABLE 4.5

RN	Internal I	RN	Change D
38	8	64	− 2
37	8	68	− 1
97	21	41	− 8
21	6	93	+11
73	14	07	−15
07	3	31	−10
60	11	94	+11
83	16	77	+ 3
10	4	83	+ 5
39	8	94	+11
59	11	72	+ 1
38	8	65	− 2
30	7	31	−10
65	12	08	−15
27	7	43	− 7
91	18	93	+10
68	13	71	+ 1
48	9	62	− 2
06	3	81	+ 5
10	4	85	+ 6

can be done simply by drawing a horizontal line at the value S and counting the number of storage units above the line.   This computation has been carried out for various values of S and is given in Table 4.6.   In the last column we give the number of extra needed storage space per

TABLE 4.6

Storage capacity S	Number of extra needed storage units in 200 days	Number of extra needed storage units per 30 days
10	1,221	183.15
15	500	75.00
20	261	39.15
25	131	19.65
30	8	1.20

month (30 days). This is simply obtained by multiplying the total for 200 days by $\frac{3}{20}$. The result is plotted in Fig. 4.14.

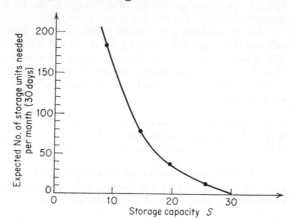

Figure 4.14 Required monthly storage units vs. storage capacity.

In order to find the optimum value of S we need to consider the various economic aspects of the problem, coupled with the results as given in Fig. 4.14.

EXERCISES

4.1. Suppose the lifetime of an item X has the exponential density function

$$f(x) = \begin{cases} \theta e^{-\theta x} & \text{if } x \geq 0 \\ 0 & \text{otherwise} \end{cases}$$

A profit Z of an item depends on its lifetime as follows:

$$Z = \begin{cases} -2 & 0 \leq x \leq 1 \\ 1 & 1 < x \leq 2 \\ 3 & 2 < x \leq 3 \\ 5 & x > 3 \end{cases}$$

a. Find expected profit $E(Z)$ and variance $V(Z)$ when $\theta = 2$.
b. Suppose θ can be set at θ for a cost $C(\theta) = 2/\theta^2$. What is best θ?

4.2. A density function $f(x)$ of a random variable X is as follows:

$$f(x) = \begin{cases} 0 & x < 0 \\ cx & 0 \leq x \leq 6 \\ 0 & x > 6 \end{cases}$$

a. What must c be?
b. What is $E(X)$ and $V(X)$?
c. Find Prob. $(1 \leq X \leq 5)$.

4.3. A manufacturer and buyer have the following deal. The buyer inspects 10 items selected at random, with each item replaced after inspection, from a certain lot. If he finds two or less defectives, he pays $1,000 for the lot. If he finds eight or more defectives, he pays $200 for the lot. Otherwise, he pays $500 for the lot. Suppose the actual proportion of defectives in the lot is 0.20. What is the expected amount of money that the buyer will pay?

4.4. A machine is to be set to dimension a part. Specifications for the part calls for the dimension (denoted by X) to fall within the interval (10,11). Assume X is a continuous random variable having a uniform distribution over the interval $(d - 4, d + 4)$. Suppose that the machine is such that the value of d can be adjusted by the setting. What should d be to minimize the expected cost if the relevant costs are as follows:

If $X < 10$, the part is scrapped at cost S.
If $X > 11$, the part can be reworked at cost R.
If the part meets specification, the cost is zero

4.5. The frequencies at which certain plants suffered from three principal diseases were registered over a long period. Experiments were conducted for various numbers of treatments, and the results are given:

Disease	Damage per plant	Relative frequency of disease after receiving:				
		No treatment	1 treatment	2 treatments	3 treatments	4 treatments
1	3.5	0.42	0.15	0.12	0.10	0.09
2	4.0	0.355	0.12	0.08	0.06	0.05
3	6.0	0.21	0.09	0.04	0.03	0.02

Let the cost of treatment per plant be $0.50.

a. Assuming that the three diseases occur independently, how much damage will you expect for a plantation containing 10,000 plants after receiving no treatment? Two treatments?
b. What is the gain of the fourth treatment over the third?
c. Is it worth giving four treatments as compared with three treatments?
d. What is the probability of a plant with no treatments suffering all three diseases? Only from the first?

4.6. A random variable X can take on only nonnegative values ($X \geq 0$). If the *CDF* of X is $F(t)$ and the expected value of X is denoted by $E(X)$, prove

$$E(X) = \int_0^\infty [1 - F(t)] \, dt$$

4.7. Let X and Y be independent random variables with geometric probability functions having parameters p_1 and p_2, respectively.

a. Find *PF* of $Z = \min (X,Y)$.
b. Find $E(Z)$.
c. Find Prob. $(X > Y)$.

4.8. Two processes, A and B, are available for synthesizing penicillin. Let the random variable Y denote the yield of this drug. With process A the density function of Y is given by

$$f(x) = \begin{cases} \frac{1}{5} & 10 \le x \le 15 \\ 0 & \text{otherwise} \end{cases}$$

With process B, the density function of Y is given by

$$f(x) = \begin{cases} \dfrac{x - 10}{18} & 10 \le x \le 16 \\ 0 & \text{otherwise} \end{cases}$$

a. Which process provides the greater mean yield?
b. Which process provides the greater probability that $Y > 11$?
c. What are the variances of Y for process A and B?

4.9. Suppose X and Y are two random variables with the following joint probability function:

X	Y	Probability
1	1	$\frac{1}{3}$
1	2	$\frac{1}{4}$
1	3	$\frac{1}{12}$
2	1	$\frac{1}{6}$
2	2	$\frac{1}{12}$
2	3	$\frac{1}{12}$

a. Find the probability function of Y, given $X = 1$.
b. Find the probability function of Y, given $X = 2$.
c. Evaluate $E(Y \mid X = 1)$.
d. Evaluate $E(Y \mid X = 2)$.
e. Find the probability function of $X + Y$ and $X - Y$.

4.10. X_1 and X_2 are random variables with $E(X_1) = 3$, $V(X_1) = 2$, $E(X_2) = 5$, and $V(X_2) = 1\frac{2}{3}$.

a. Find $E(X_1 - X_2)$.
b. Find $V(X_1 - X_2)$. Assume independence.
c. Give an upper bound, using Tchebycheff's inequality, of

$$\text{Prob} \left[|3(X_1 + X_2) - E(3(X_1 + X_2))| > 10 \right]$$

4.11. Suppose that X is a random variable with CDF equal to $F(t)$. Show that the random variable $Z = F(X)$ has a uniform distribution over the interval $[0,1]$.

4.12. Suppose Y has a uniform distribution over the interval $[0,1]$. Find a function $G(Y)$ of Y such that $G(Y)$ has the exponential distribution function with mean m.

4.13. Prove relation 4.7.3.

4.14. Plot percentiles of random variables given in Exercises 3.2 and 2.7.

4.15. For the random variable L in Exercise 3.2:

a. Find the percentiles of L^2 and plot. Use the result to find the CDF of L^2.
b. Find the percentiles and CDF of $1/L$.

4.16. Let $X_1, X_2, \ldots, X_N$ be N independent random variables with a uniform distribution in the interval [0,1].

a. Find the moment-generating function $M_{X_1}(t)$ for X_1.
b. Find the moment-generating function $M_{S_N}(t)$ of $S_N = X_1 + X_2 + \cdots + X_N$.
c. Find the moment-generating function $M_{\bar{X}}(t)$ of

$$\bar{X} = \frac{X_1 + X_2 + \cdots + X_N}{N}$$

4.17. Refer to Exercise 3.9. If L_1 has an exponential distribution with mean M_A and L_2 and L_3 an exponential distribution with mean M_B:

a. Find the *CDF* of L.
b. Find the *PDF* of L.
c. Find $E(L)$.

4.18. Ten machines are in operation. Every once in a while a breakdown occurs. A repairman, if he is available, repairs it. The machine is then assumed to be as new and starts operation again. Assume that the time until breakdown of any machine is described by a random variable I. Furthermore, suppose that the repair time for any broken-down machine is described by a random variable S. We assume that

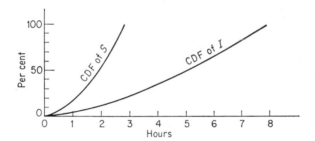

there is a pool of r repairmen available. If a machine breaks down and all r repairmen are busy fixing other machines, it must wait until a repairman is free to start repairing the machine. We shall assume a first-come, first-served rule. Let the *CDF* of I and S be as given in the accompanying figure. Assume that successive values of I and S are independent.

Use the Monte Carlo technique to estimate the following:

a. Per cent idle time of machines for $r = 1, 2, 3, \ldots, 10$.
b. Per cent idle time of repairmen for $r = 1, 2, \ldots, 10$.
c. The expected number of breakdowns per 30-day period.
d. Let C_R denote the daily cost of having a repairman and C_M the daily cost of an idle machine. Describe how you would find the optimum value of r.
e. If $C_R = \$20$ and $C_M = \$50$, what is the best value of r?

4.19. A storage depot has a supply of 50 of a critical item needed for field usage. The field needs one item on hand at all times. The field life of an item is exponentially distributed with a mean m, which depends on the length of time t (in weeks) it has been in storage. Suppose that this relationship is given by $m = 20/t$. The stockpile in the depot has been in storage for varying lengths of time as follows:

Length in storage, weeks	1	2	3	4	5	6	7	8	9	10
Number		3	7	10	15	5	3	2	3	1	1

When an item fails in the field it is immediately replaced by an item from the storage depot. Two policies for issuing items are under consideration. One policy is FIFO (first in first out); that is, the oldest item on hand is issued. The other policy is LIFO (last in first out). The newest one is issued with the LIFO policy. Use the Monte Carlo method to find the following:

    a. The expected time until the 50 items are used up for FIFO policy.
    b. Same as (*a*) for LIFO policy.
    c. How do the results in (*a*) and (*b*) change if the field requires 5 items at all times?
    d. List some factors relevant to the choice between LIFO and FIFO.

4.20. Suppose a process can be in one of two states, A or B. Furthermore, after each unit of time the state may change. Let p ($p \neq 0$ or 1) equal the probability of changing state. Assume that the decision at each stage is independent of those at other stages. Assume that the process starts in state A. Let P_N denote the probability that at the end of the Nth stage the process is in state A

    a. Find the expression for P_N. (HINT: Let $X_j = +1$ or -1 according to whether a change of state occurs on the jth trial. Then consider product $X_1 X_2 \cdots X_N$.)
    b. What happens to the value of P_N when N goes to infinity?
    c. What is result of (*a*) and (*b*) if the starting state is B?

4.21. Let X be a random variable which can take on the positive-integer values 1, 2, 3, . . . , with probabilities P_1, P_2, P_3, ... Let $T_n = \text{Prob } (X \geq n) = P_n + P_{n+1} + P_{n+2} + \cdots$.

    a. Show that $E(X) = T_1 + T_2 + T_3 + \cdots$.
    b. Use result of (*a*) to obtain the following lower bound on $E(X) : E(X) \geq 2 - P_1$.
    c. Use result of (*a*) to obtain lower bound: $E(X) \geq 3 - 2P_1 - P_2$.

4.22. Referring to Example 4.8, find $E|D_4|$ and $E|D_5|$ from the formula, and directly compare with the approximation $E|D_N| \simeq 0.79788 \sqrt{N}$.

4.23. Refer to Sec. 1.4, where the formula $D = a/(1 - bP)$ is presented. Suppose that a and b are estimated from data giving estimates $\hat{a}$ and $\hat{b}$ where $E(\hat{a}) = a$, $E(\hat{b}) = b$, $V(\hat{a}) = \sigma_a{}^2$, and $V(\hat{b}) = \sigma_b{}^2$. Let the random variable $\hat{D} = \hat{a}/(1 + \hat{b}P)$.

Find $E(\hat{D})$ and $V(\hat{D})$ approximately in terms of the previous quantities, $E(P)$ and $V(P)$. Assume $\hat{a}$ and $\hat{b}$ independent.

4.24. Referring to Exercise 3.14, find the mean and variance of Pareto's distribution.

4.25. Consider the following acceptance sampling plan specified by the numbers (s,n), where $n \leq 2s$. Accept the batch as soon as, and only when, a successive s nondefectives are observed before n items are tested. For a device which can operate more than once, accept when a run of s successful operations is observed in n or fewer operations. Assume that the performances for successive trials are independent.

Let the probability of failure equal p.

a. Find the probability of accepting at the rth trial.
b. Show that the probability of acceptance is given by
$$(1 - p)^s[(n - s)p + 1].$$

4.26. It takes 0.5 minute to walk from the third floor to the first floor of a building; the same trip takes 0.1 minute by elevator. The waiting time L for an elevator to arrive has the following probability density function:

$$f_L(t) = \begin{cases} \frac{1}{3} & 0 \le t \le 3 \\ 0 & \text{otherwise} \end{cases}$$

Suppose an individual uses the following action rule; if the elevator does not arrive within x minutes, he then walks. Let T denote the time it takes to get from the third to the first floor using the above rule.

a. Compute $E(T)$ as a function of x.
b. Which x minimizes $E(T)$?
c. Which x maximizes $E(T)$?
d. Interpret (*a*), (*b*), and (*c*).

4.27. X is said to have a uniform distribution if it has the *PDF* $f_X(x) = 1$ for $0 \le x \le 1$ and zero otherwise.

a. Find the *CDF* of X.
b. Find $E(X)$ and $V(X)$.

4.28. Let X and Y be two random variables. The *covariance* is defined by cov $(X,Y) = E\{[X - E(X)][Y - E(Y)]\}$. Demonstrate:

a. cov $(X,Y) = E(XY) - E(X)E(Y)$.
b. cov $(aX + b, cY + d) = ac$ cov (X,Y).
c. $V(X + Y) = V(X) + V(Y) + 2$ cov (X,Y).
d. If X and Y are independent, then cov $(X,Y) = 0$.
e. If $X_1, X_2, \ldots, X_N$ are independent random variables with common σ^2 and $U = \Sigma c_i X_i$ and $W = \Sigma d_i X_i$, then cov $(U,W) = \sigma^2 \Sigma c_i d_i$.

4.29. Obtain a better approximation to $V[G(X)]$ (than that given in Theorem 4.7) by using $E[G(X)]$ as given in Theorem 4.6 and a Taylor series expansion to a second-order term.

5

SOME USEFUL DISTRIBUTIONS

Practical problem solving entails a variety of aspects of decision making involving random variables.   In engineering, science, and industry certain distributions of the random variables of interest have been found to be very useful in practice.   Some of these distributions have been referred to in examples in the earlier chapters.   Now we shall endeavor to give some empirical background leading to use of these distributions.

5.1   Distributions related to series of independent binomial experiments

Perhaps the simplest example of a sequence of experiments is that of independent binomial experiments as introduced in earlier chapters.   We recall that in this conceptualization we focus attention on an experiment E and its associated sample space S.   We consider independent repetitions of E.   Furthermore, for each repetition, we observe whether an event which we designated as a "success" does or does not occur. Another way to view this is to consider the series in terms of independent random variables X_1, X_2, X_3, . . . , where X_i is equal to 1 or 0, with probabilities p and $1 - p$, respectively, according to whether the event occurs or not on the ith repetition of experiment E.   In this section we are concerned with various distributions which arise in connection with this basic representation.   Various distributions result in answer to certain questions we can ask concerning the series of independent experiments.   Some of these questions are as follows:

1. How many times does a success occur in N repetitions?   The answer is obviously expressible as the sum $Z_N = X_1 + X_2 + \cdots + X_N$. Hence Z_N itself is a random variable.   We are interested in the distribution associated with Z_N.

2. How many trials are required in order to achieve the first success? (Let us include the trial at which the success occurs.)   The relevant random variable may be designated by W.   After the so-called "first

163

success," one may repeat the experiment again and count the number of trials following the last success and up to and including the next success.

3. How many trials are required up to and including the kth success? The random variable in this case is $S_k = W_1 + W_2 + \cdots + W_k$. Note that S_k is a natural generalization of $W = S_1$.

We have seen (Example 4.15) that the above representation can also be used in connection with certain types of time-ordered events. As indicated in Example 4.15, it leads to continuous distributions. We shall show, however, that there are continuous analogues of the distributions arising in questions 1, 2, and 3 above. We shall now describe and summarize the properties of distributions, which will help answer the questions we have raised.

5.1.1   Binomial distribution

This basic distribution has already been introduced in connection with various examples. The random variable Z_N can take on values j from 0 to N. The distribution has parameters p and N and is given by

$$\text{Prob}\,(Z_N = j) = \binom{N}{j} p^j (1 - p)^{N-j} = \binom{N}{j} p^j q^{N-j} \qquad j = 0, 1, \ldots, N$$

The mean and variance can, of course, be calculated directly from the expression of Z_N as the sum of X's. Thus, since

$$E(X_i) = p \qquad \text{and} \qquad V(X_i) = p(1 - p) = pq$$
$$\text{we have} \qquad E(Z_N) = Np \qquad \text{and} \qquad V(Z_N) = Npq.$$

The moment-generating function can be obtained as follows:

$$M_{Z_N}(t) = M_{X_1}(t) M_{X_2}(t) \cdots M_{X_N}(t)$$

Now
$$M_{X_i}(t) = E(e^{tX_i}) = pe^t + q \tag{5.1.1}$$

Thus
$$M_{Z_N}(t) = (pe^t + q)^N \tag{5.1.2}$$

The moments of Z_N can be obtained directly by differentiation of $M_{Z_N}(t)$.

5.1.2   Geometric distribution

In order to find the distribution of W we note that the event $W = j$ can occur if, and only if, $X_1 = X_2 = \cdots = X_{j-1} = 0$ and $X_j = 1$. Thus

$$\text{Prob}\,(W = j) = q^{j-1}p \qquad j = 1, 2, \ldots$$

We note that W is, strictly speaking, defined on the infinite sample space specified by the possible sequences $(X_1, X_2, \ldots)$.

The mean and variance have already been derived in Example 4.10 and found to be

$$E(W) = \frac{1}{p} \quad \text{and} \quad V(W) = \frac{1-p}{p^2} = \frac{q}{p^2}$$

The moment-generating function can be found directly from the definition as follows:

$$M_W(t) = \sum_{j=1}^{\infty} e^{tj} q^{j-1} p = \frac{p}{q} \sum_{j=1}^{\infty} (e^t q)^j = \frac{pe^t}{1 - qe^t} \qquad (5.1.3)$$

The last sum is obtained by noting that it is a geometric series, where t is taken small enough so that $e^t q < 1$.

5.1.3 Pascal distribution

A natural generalization of W, as we have seen, is S_k. The mean and variance, derived in Example 4.10, are

$$E(S_k) = E(W_1 + \cdots + W_k) = \frac{k}{p} \quad \text{and}$$

$$V(S_k) = V(W_1 + \cdots + W_k) = \frac{kq}{p^2}$$

Note that the mean and variance were derived without explicitly finding the distribution function of S_k.

In order to find the distribution of S_k, consider how S_k can equal j. First, $S_k = j$ implies success on the jth trial. Furthermore, $S_k = j$ implies that the first $j - 1$ trials resulted in $k - 1$ successes. The above events, which we denote by A_1 and A_2, are independent, and their joint occurrence is equivalent to the event $S_k = j$. Thus

$$\text{Prob } (S_k = j) = \text{Prob } (A_1) \text{ Prob } (A_2)$$

We have

$$\text{Prob } (A_1) = p \quad \text{and} \quad \text{Prob } (A_2) = \binom{j-1}{k-1} p^{k-1} q^{j-k}$$

Therefore

$$\text{Prob } (S_k = j) = \binom{j-1}{k-1} p^k q^{j-k} \qquad j = k, k+1, \ldots$$

The moment-generating function of S_k is

$$M_{S_k}(t) = M_{W_1}(t) M_{W_2}(t) \cdots M_{W_k}(t) = \left(\frac{pe^t}{1 - qe^t} \right)^k$$

5.1.4 Poisson distribution

We now reconsider a particular representation of time-ordered events. This model forms the continuous analogue to the discrete series of independent binomial trials, when N is large and p is small. In fact, we can think of the series of events as being obtained by repetitions of the experiment, say, every Δ seconds. Furthermore, we assume the probability of success during interval Δ, $p(\Delta)$ to be $\theta\Delta$, proportional to Δ (Example 4.15). We now ask for the number of times the event occurs in a specified time interval. If the time interval is $(0, T)$ and the time axis divided into lengths Δ, we have $N = T/\Delta$ repetitions of the basic experiment. From the binomial distribution the probability that the number of successes $Y = j$, for subdivision of duration Δ, is

$$\text{Prob}\,(Y = j \mid \Delta) = \binom{N}{j} p^j(\Delta)[1 - p(\Delta)]^{N-j}$$

Since $N = T/\Delta$ and $p(\Delta) \cong \theta\Delta$, it follows that

$$\text{Prob}\,(Y = j \mid \Delta) \cong \frac{N(N-1)\cdots(N-j+1)}{(1-\theta\Delta)^j j!}\theta^j\Delta^j(1-\theta\Delta)^N$$

$$= \frac{[N\Delta][N\Delta - \Delta]\cdots[N\Delta - (j-1)\Delta]}{(1-\theta\Delta)^j j!}\theta^j(1-\theta\Delta)^N$$

$$= \frac{(1-\theta\Delta)^{T/\Delta}\theta^j}{j!}\left(\frac{T}{1-\theta\Delta}\right)\left(\frac{T-\Delta}{1-\theta\Delta}\right)$$

$$\cdots\left[\frac{T-(j-1)\Delta}{1-\theta\Delta}\right]$$

Thus, as $\Delta \to 0$, we have

$$\text{Prob}\,(Y = j \mid \Delta) \to \frac{(\theta T)^j}{j!}e^{-\theta T}$$

This is called the *Poisson distribution*, which gives the probability that $Y = j$ in the interval $[0, T]$.

It is clear that the above distribution can also be used as an approximation to the binomial when p is small and N large but Np a moderate value θT. This can be seen directly from the above development by letting $\Delta = T/N$ and $p = \theta\Delta$ and thus $Np = \theta T$. If p is small and N large, this is equivalent to Δ small; hence the approximation. The Poisson can be used not only for events in time, but also for events in space, such as faults in a piece of fabric, the empirical basis being that the area (or volume) can be divided into many small parts where the probability of a fault occurring in each part is small and where the occurrence or nonoccurrence of a fault, in any part, is independent of occurrences in other parts. The interpretation of T, in such cases, can be area or volume or the like.

The mean and variance can be computed directly from the distribution or from the binomial and going to the limit. Thus

$$E(Y) = Np \cong \frac{T}{\Delta} \theta\Delta = \theta T$$

$$V(Y) = Np(1 - p) \cong \frac{T}{\Delta} \theta\Delta(1 - \theta\Delta) \cong \theta T$$

A direct computation from the Poisson gives the same result, namely, that the mean and variance are both equal to θT.

The moment-generating function can be obtained directly or from the binomial and going to the limit. Thus

$$M_Y(t) \cong [p(\Delta)e^t + 1 - p(\Delta)]^N \cong (\theta\Delta e^t + 1 - \theta\Delta)^{T/\Delta}$$
$$= [1 - \theta\Delta(1 - e^t)]^{T/\Delta} \cong e^{-\theta T(1-e^t)}$$

An important property of the Poisson distribution is *additivity*. Suppose that $Y(T)$ denotes the Poisson random variable with respect to the interval of length T. Furthermore, let the interval T be divided into two parts of length T_1 and T_2. From the physical interpretation it is obvious that $Y(T_1 + T_2)$ has the same distribution as $Y(T_1) + Y(T_2)$. This is so, since the number of successes in T is the sum of those of T_1 and T_2. This can also be verified from the moment-generating function

$$M_{Y(T_1)+Y(T_2)}(t) = e^{-\theta T_1(1-e^t)}e^{-\theta T_2(1-e^t)} = e^{-\theta(T_1+T_2)(1-e^t)} = M_{Y(T_1+T_2)}(t)$$

In general, we have the result that if Y_j $(j = 1, 2, \ldots, N)$ have independent Poisson distributions with means m_j, then $Y_1 + Y_2 + \cdots + Y_N$ has a Poisson distribution with mean $m_1 + m_2 + \cdots + m_N$.

5.1.5 Exponential distribution

We have discussed the exponential distribution in some of the previous examples. In one case, Example 3.3, we derived the distribution from the property that

$$\text{Prob } (X > t + s \mid X > t) = \text{Prob } (X > s)$$

where X is the time between events. The above emphasizes the basic independence characteristic of this model.

Another derivation, as given in Example 4.15, involved the empirical basis of the distribution and showed how it is a continuous analogue of the geometric distribution. In fact, the exponential distribution is an approximation to the geometric distribution when N is large and p is small.

We can also derive the exponential distribution directly from the Poisson distribution. In order to do this, let us find the CDF of X by considering the event $X > t$ for any specified t. The event $X > t$ implies that the event has not occurred in the time interval $[0,t]$. The probability of this event is found from the Poisson to be

$$\text{Prob } (X > t) = \text{Prob (no event in } [0,t]) = \frac{(\theta t)^0}{0!} e^{-\theta t} = e^{-\theta t}$$

Therefore the CDF of X is

$$F_X(t) = 1 - \text{Prob } (X > t) = 1 - e^{-\theta t}$$

The PDF of X, $f_X(t)$, is found by differentiating $F_X(t)$, yielding

$$f_X(t) = \theta e^{-\theta t} \qquad t \geq 0$$

The mean and variance of X have already been found in Example 4.15 and are $E(X) = 1/\theta$ and $V(X) = 1/\theta^2$. Thus, while in the Poisson the mean and variance are equal, in the exponential the mean and standard deviation are equal.

The moment-generating function can be found by integration:

$$M_X(t) = E(e^{tX}) = \theta \int_0^\infty e^{tx} e^{-\theta x} \, dx = \frac{\theta}{\theta - t} \int_0^\infty (\theta - t) e^{-x(\theta - t)} \, dx = \frac{\theta}{\theta - t}$$

The higher moments of X can be computed directly from $M_X(t)$.

Example 5.1   Component parts of industrial equipment are often characterized by the fact that their lifetimes, the lengths of time during which the components operate effectively, are represented by random variables with exponential distributions. Some complex equipment is so constituted that the failure of any component means the failure of the equipment. It is interesting to know the distribution of the lifetime for the complex equipment under these circumstances, where apparently the lifetime desired is a random variable which is the minimum of a set of random variables.

Let $X_1, X_2, \ldots, X_N$ be N random variables, each having an exponential distribution with parameters $\theta_1, \theta_2, \ldots, \theta_N$, respectively. Given, then, that the CDF of X_i $(i = 1, 2, \ldots, N)$ is

$$F_{X_i}(t) = \text{Prob } (X_i \leq t) = 1 - e^{-\theta_i t}$$

we seek the CDF of $Z_N = \min (X_1, X_2, \ldots, X_N)$. It turns out to be rather simple to find the CDF of Z_N if we assume that the X_i are independent random variables. For if we routinely formulate

$$F_{Z_N}(t) = \text{Prob } (Z_N \leq t) = 1 - \text{Prob } (Z_N > t)$$

we need merely express the last term so that Z_N is the minimum of $\{X_i\}$. Obviously, for independent X_i,

$$\text{Prob }(Z_N > t) = \text{Prob }(X_1 > t)\, \text{Prob }(X_2 > t) \cdots \text{Prob }(X_N > t)$$

It follows directly that

$$\begin{aligned} F_{Z_N}(t) &= 1 - e^{-\theta_1 t} e^{-\theta_2 t} \cdots e^{-\theta_N t} \\ &= 1 - e^{-(\theta_1 + \theta_2 + \cdots + \theta_N)t} \end{aligned}$$

This is, of course, an exponential distribution. It turns out, then, that the exponential distribution has the interesting property that *the minimum of a set of independent random variables possessing exponential CDFs with parameters θ_1, θ_2, . . . , θ_N is a random variable itself with exponential distribution and parameter $\theta_1 + \theta_2 + \cdots + \theta_N$.* A useful corollary, which seems intuitively obvious, is that, for N "identical" components, the parameter is $N\theta$.

This property of the exponential distribution, in particular for N identical independent random variables, helps materially in the experimental estimation of component life. For suppose that the lifetime X of a part is assumed to be exponentially distributed, with mean life $1/\theta$, which we wish to estimate experimentally. The usual procedure is to put N of these (identical) components into operation under "identical" independent conditions. The estimate of $1/\theta$ is then,

$$\bar{X} = \frac{(X_1 + X_2 + \cdots + X_N)}{N}$$

the average of the lifetimes observed. It may be that the greatest of the values $\{X_i\}$ is many times greater than the least, so that the test may last for an interminably long time. We do know, however, that the mean value of a random variable which has an exponential distribution with parameter θ is $E(X) = 1/\theta$. Therefore the mean value of $Z_N = \min(X_1, X_2, \ldots, X_N)$ for N "identical" components is 1 divided by the parameter, which describes the exponential distribution belonging to Z_N. This parameter we have just shown to be $N\theta$; whence

$$E(Z_N) = \frac{1}{N\theta}$$

In order to estimate the mean life $1/\theta$, we may therefore measure the time to the first failure and multiply by N. Thus our estimate is NZ_N.

One may ask about the properties of the estimator $\bar{X}$ and NZ_N. First, it is obvious that both estimators $\bar{X}$ and NZ_N are unbiased. The variances

$$V(\bar{X}) = \frac{1}{N\theta^2}$$

$$V(NZ_N) = N^2V(Z_N) = \frac{N^2}{N^2\theta^2} = \frac{1}{\theta^2}$$

show that $\bar{X}$ is a more precise estimate than NZ_N. On the other hand, the estimator $\bar{X}$ requires waiting until all N items fail, whereas the estimator NZ_N requires waiting for only the first failure. The durations of each procedure are max $(X_1, X_2, \ldots, X_N)$ and Z_N, respectively. The expected duration, using estimate NZ_N, is

$$E\,(Z_N) = \frac{1}{N\theta}$$

The expected duration, using estimator $\bar{X}$, can be shown to be

$$E[\max\,(X_1, X_2, \ldots, X_N)] = \frac{1}{\theta}\left(\frac{1}{N} + \frac{1}{N-1} + \frac{1}{N-2} + \cdots \right.$$
$$\left. + \frac{1}{2} + 1\right)$$

which is clearly much larger than $1/N\theta$. For example, if $N = 3$, then the expected duration, using NZ_N, is $1/3\theta$, while for $\bar{X}$ it is $(1 + \frac{1}{2} + \frac{1}{3})(1/\theta) = 11/6\theta$. In choosing between the two methods, one must weigh the loss in precision against the gain in time. Other alternative procedures are available, as for example estimating $1/\theta$ from the time to failure of the first k out of N components under test.

5.1.6   Erlang distribution

Suppose we ask for the interval of time U_k, during which there are k occurrences of success. This random variable's distribution is a natural generalization of the exponential which is the special case for $k = 1$. Moreover, it is the continuous analogue of the Pascal distribution. As a matter of fact, U_k is the sum of k independent exponential random variables, $X_1, X_2, \ldots, X_k$, since X_1 is the time interval to the first success, X_2 the time interval from the first to and including the second success, etc. The mean and variance of U_k are directly derived as follows:

$$E(U_k) = E(X_1 + X_2 + \cdots + X_k) = \frac{k}{\theta}$$

$$V(U_k) = V(X_1 + X_2 + \cdots + X_k) = \frac{k}{\theta^2}$$

The PDF of U_k can be derived in several ways. First, from the empirical picture, as described in Example 4.15, we can obtain the distribution of U_k as a limit of the Pascal distribution. A more direct approach, however, is to consider the event $t \leq U_k \leq t + \Delta$. This event is equivalent to the joint occurrence of the two events

$$A_1: \quad k - 1 \text{ occurrences in } [0,t]$$
$$A_2: \quad 1 \text{ occurrence in } [t, t + \Delta]$$

whence it follows that

$$\text{Prob } (t \leq U_k \leq t + \Delta) = P(A_1)P(A_2)$$

Again, from the assumptions in Sec. 5.1.4, $P(A_2) \cong \theta\Delta$, and from the Poisson distribution,

$$P(A_1) = \frac{e^{-\theta t}(\theta t)^{k-1}}{(k - 1)!}$$

Thus we have

$$\text{Prob } (t \leq U_k \leq t + \Delta) \cong \frac{\theta e^{-\theta t}(\theta t)^{k-1}}{(k - 1)!} \Delta$$

But the last expression is equivalent to the probability of the occurrence of the random variable U_k in an interval of "small" length Δ, which is equivalent to the product of the PDF of U_k by Δ. Thus the PDF of U_k is

$$f_{U_k}(t) = \frac{\theta e^{-\theta t}(\theta t)^{k-1}}{(k - 1)!}$$

We can obtain the moment-generating function readily by noting that U_k is the sum of k independent exponential random variables whose MGF is $\theta/(\theta - t)$; whence

$$M_{U_k}(t) = \left(\frac{\theta}{\theta - t}\right)^k$$

In situations where a machine has a vital part without which it cannot function, some $k - 1$ spares are usually provided in order to ensure continued operation. Suppose that it is possible to make instantaneous replacements and that each of these k parts has a lifetime distributed exponentially with parameter θ. The combined life may then be represented by the random variable $X_1 + X_2 + \cdots + X_k$, where all the X_i are identically and independently distributed. The combined life then has the Erlang distribution with parameters θ and k. If, on the other hand, we have the requirement that all k parts must function, the machine life is then given by $Z_k = \min (X_1, X_2, \ldots, X_k)$, which has the exponential distribution with parameter $k\theta$.

The six distributions which have been presented are interrelated as indicated in Fig. 5.1, and their definitions and certain properties are summarized in Table 5.1.

The Poisson process, which we have discussed above, has wide application in engineering, industry, and the sciences. Because this process entails discrete occurrences which are independent—that is, the proba-

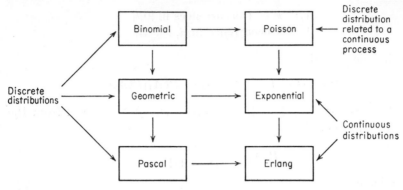

Figure 5.1

bility of the occurrence of the given event in any time interval is independent of the number of previous occurrences—it does not apply to many situations where its simplicity is desired. This model implies a "memoryless" process, such as failure of material randomly without deterioration. Nevertheless, there are many complex non-Poisson proc-

TABLE 5.1

Distribution	Probability function, or PDF	Range of random variable and of parameter	Mean	Variance	Moment-generating function
Binomial	$\binom{N}{j} p^{i} q^{N-i}$	$j = 0, 1, \ldots, N$ $0 \leq p \leq 1$	Np	Npq	$(pe^{t} + q)^{N}$
Geometric	$q^{j-1}p$	$0 \leq p \leq 1$ $j = 1, 2, \ldots$	$\dfrac{1}{p}$	$\dfrac{q}{p^{2}}$	$\dfrac{pe^{t}}{1 - qe^{t}}$
Pascal	$\binom{j-1}{k-1} p^{k} q^{i-k}$	$j = k, k+1, \ldots$	$\dfrac{k}{p}$	$\dfrac{kq}{p^{2}}$	$\left(\dfrac{pe^{t}}{1 - qe^{t}}\right)^{k}$
Poisson	$\dfrac{(\theta T)^{i}}{j!} e^{-\theta T}$	$j = 0, 1, \ldots$ $m = \theta T \geq 0$	$m = \theta T$	m	$e^{-m(1-e^{t})}$
Exponential	$\theta e^{-\theta t}$	$t \geq 0$ $\theta \geq 0$	$\dfrac{1}{\theta}$	$\dfrac{1}{\theta^{2}}$	$\dfrac{\theta}{\theta - t}$
Erlang	$\dfrac{\theta(\theta t)^{k-1} e^{-\theta t}}{(k-1)!}$	$\theta \geq 0$ $t \geq 0$	$\dfrac{k}{\theta}$	$\dfrac{k}{\theta^{2}}$	$\left(\dfrac{\theta}{\theta - t}\right)^{k}$

esses which can be effectively studied by means of this model, and we shall consider an example.

Example 5.2 Suppose we have a machine whose functioning depends on some delicate mechanism which needs very careful adjustments. From time to time the mechanism fails and an adjustment is made. If the adjustment has been properly made, the interval until the next breakdown X_2 is exponential with parameter θ_2. If the adjustment has not been properly carried out, the lifetime X_1 is exponential with parameter θ_1 (where $1/\theta_1$ is usually much smaller than $1/\theta_2$). Consider

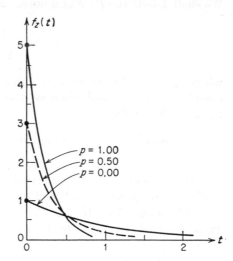

Figure 5.2 $f_Z(t)$ versus t.

the case where the probability of a proper adjustment is p. What is the lifetime Z of the machine? This random variable is given by

$$Z = \begin{cases} X_1 & \text{when adjustment is proper (probability } p) \\ X_2 & \text{otherwise (probability } q) \end{cases}$$

where X_1 and X_2 are random variables.

The PDF $f_Z(t)$ can be obtained by using the decomposition rule for probabilities as follows:

$$f_Z(t) = pf_{X_1}(t) + qf_{X_2}(t) = p\theta_1 e^{-\theta_1 t} + q\theta_2 e^{-\theta_2 t}$$

A graph of this PDF for $\theta_1 = 5$ and $\theta_2 = 1$ and for several values of p is given in Fig. 5.2.

The mean and variance can be obtained directly from $f_Z(t)$ or in terms of the conditional means and variances. This type of mixture of exponential distributions, called the hyperexponential distribution, has been found to represent many situations satisfactorily.

5.2   Normal and related distributions

In previous sections we have indicated that the sum of independent random variables can approximate a random variable with a normal distribution.   The normal distribution has, therefore, a very wide range of application and has been extensively studied.   Its properties will be given in some detail.

5.2.1   Normal distribution

We shall denote the *PDF* of a normally distributed random variable X by

$$\phi(x;m,\sigma^2) = \frac{1}{\sigma\sqrt{2\pi}}\, e^{-\frac{1}{2}\left(\frac{x-m}{\sigma}\right)^2}$$

where X can take on all real values: $-\infty \le x \le +\infty$.   The *PDF* is completely determined when m, the $E(X)$, and σ^2, the $E(X - m)^2$, are known.   The *CDF* is

$$\text{Prob } (X \le x) \equiv \Phi(x;m,\sigma^2) = \frac{1}{\sigma\sqrt{\pi}} \int_{-\infty}^{x} e^{-\frac{1}{2}\left(\frac{u-m}{\sigma}\right)^2} du$$

In Example 4.18, the normal distribution was shown to enjoy the additivity properties which will now be formally proved.

   Theorem **5.1**   If X_1, X_2, . . . , X_N are independent random variables, each having *CDF* $\Phi(x;m_i,\sigma_i{}^2)$, $i = 1, 2, \ldots , N$, then

$$Z = a_0 + a_1 X_1 + a_2 X_2 + \cdots + a_N X_N$$

has *CDF*

$$\Phi\left(x; a_0 + \sum_{i=1}^{N} a_i m_i, \sum_{i=1}^{N} a_i{}^2 \sigma_i{}^2\right)$$

where $a_0, a_1, a_2, \ldots , a_N$ are arbitrary constants and

$$E(Z) = a_0 + \Sigma a_i m_i$$
$$V(Z) = \Sigma a_i{}^2 \sigma_i{}^2$$

   This result can be obtained quite directly from the properties of the moment-generating function.   For

$$M_X(t) = E(e^{tX}) = \frac{1}{\sigma\sqrt{2\pi}} \int_{-\infty}^{\infty} e^{xt}\, e^{-\frac{1}{2}\left(\frac{x-m}{\sigma}\right)^2} dx$$

and on letting $(x - m)/\sigma = v$ transforms into

$$M_X(t) = \frac{e^{mt} e^{\sigma^2 t^2/2}}{\sqrt{2\pi}} \int_{-\infty}^{+\infty} e^{-\frac{1}{2}(v-\sigma t)^2} dv = e^{mt+\sigma^2 t^2/2}$$

This general result can be applied to

$$M_Z(t) = E(e^{Zt}) = E(e^{a_0 t + a_1 X_1 t + \cdots + a_N X_N t})$$

When $E(e^{Zt})$ is written out as an integral it is an N-dimensional integral, where, however, the statistical independence of the X_i implies the independence of the x_i with respect to integration. It follows then that

$$
\begin{aligned}
E(e^{Zt}) &= E(e^{a_0 t}) E(e^{a_1 X_1 t}) \cdots E(e^{a_N X_N t}) \\
&= e^{a_0 t} e^{a_1 m_1 t + a_1{}^2 \sigma_1{}^2 t^2/2} \cdots e^{a_N m_N t + a_N{}^2 \sigma_N{}^2 t^2/2} \\
&= e^{(a_0 + a_1 m_1 + \cdots + a_N m_N) t + (a_1{}^2 \sigma_1{}^2 + \cdots + a_N{}^2 \sigma_N{}^2) t^2/2}
\end{aligned}
$$

This is, however, precisely the form of the moment-generating function of the random variable whose CDF is

$$\Phi(x; a_0 + \Sigma a_i m_i, \Sigma a_i{}^2 \sigma_i{}^2)$$

as was to be shown.

When considering a random variable X which is normally distributed with mean m and variance σ^2, it is usually more convenient to work with the *standardized* variable X^*, where

$$X^* = \frac{X - m}{\sigma}$$

It easily follows from Theorem 5.1 that X^* has CDF $\Phi(x;0,1)$. The importance of this result rests on the fact that *the distribution of the standardized random variable X^* does not depend on m or σ^2.* Furthermore, it follows that probability calculations for X can be made in terms of X^*. Thus

$$\text{Prob } (a \leq X \leq b) = \text{Prob } \left(\frac{a - m}{\sigma} \leq X^* \leq \frac{b - m}{\sigma} \right)$$

$$= \Phi \left(\frac{b - m}{\sigma}; 0, 1 \right) - \Phi \left(\frac{a - m}{\sigma}; 0, 1 \right)$$

Instead of requiring tables of $\Phi(x;m;\sigma^2)$ for a great many values of m and σ^2, one table only, $\Phi(x;0,1)$, is needed. Instead of writing $\Phi(x;0,1)$, we shall, from now on, write $\Phi(x)$. Thus, if X has CDF $\Phi(x;m,\sigma^2)$,

$$\text{Prob } (a \leq X \leq b) = \Phi \left(\frac{b - m}{\sigma} \right) - \Phi \left(\frac{a - m}{\sigma} \right)$$

Tables for $\Phi(x)$ are given in the Appendix. From the symmetrical character of the normal distribution we also have that

$$\Phi(x) = 1 - \Phi(-x)$$

Another property of the normal distribution, resulting from the previous remark, is that *probabilities of deviations from the mean depend only on the their magnitude as a multiple of* σ. Thus, if X is normally distributed with mean m and variance σ^2, we have

$$\text{Prob } (|X - m| > a) = \text{Prob } \left(\frac{|X - m|}{\sigma} > \frac{a}{\sigma}\right)$$
$$= \text{Prob } \left(|X^*| > \frac{a}{\sigma}\right) = 2\Phi\left(-\frac{a}{\sigma}\right)$$

The probability depends only on a/σ. It follows also that the percentiles of X can be written in terms of the percentiles of $\Phi(x;0,1)$. This is summarized in the following theorem.

Theorem 5.2 If X has *CDF* $\Phi(x;m,\sigma^2)$ and Z has *CDF* $\Phi(x;0,1)$ then the α percentiles X_α and Z_α of X and Z, respectively, are related as follows:

$$X_\alpha = m + Z_\alpha\sigma$$

This results from the fact that for X_α

$$\text{Prob } (X \leq X_\alpha) = \alpha$$

whence

$$\alpha = \text{Prob } (X \leq X_\alpha) = \text{Prob } \left(X^* \leq \frac{X_\alpha - m}{\sigma}\right) = \text{Prob } \left(Z \leq \frac{X_\alpha - m}{\sigma}\right)$$

Therefore $(X_\alpha - m)/\sigma$ is equal to Z_α.

A simple example will illustrate a common use of the foregoing properties of the normal distribution.

Example 5.3 A product consists of an assembly of three components. The overall length of the product, Z, is equal to the sum of the lengths X_1, X_2, and X_3 of its components. Because of variability in production, they are independent random variables, each normally distributed with *PDF*s

$$\phi_1(x;1,0.002), \quad \phi_2(x;2,0.010), \quad \phi_3(x;3,0.010)$$

What is the probability that Z will meet the overall specification 6.00 ± 0.20 inches?

The question is tantamount to asking for Prob $(6.00 - 0.20 \leq Z \leq 6.00 + 0.20)$, and for the answer one needs the distribution of Z. From Theorem 5.1 it follows that the *CDF* of Z is $\Phi(z; 6, 0.002 + 0.01 + 0.01)$ since Z is normally distributed with $m_Z = m_1 + m_2 + m_3$ and $\sigma_Z^2 = \sigma_1^2 + \sigma_2^2 + \sigma_3^2$. We require then to find this probability from tables, in particular from the table of the cumulative distribution of the standard normal variate. But $\sigma_Z^2 = 0.002 + 0.01 + 0.01$ and $\sigma_Z = 0.148$.

We are seeking, then,

$$\text{Prob } (5.80 \leq Z \leq 6.20) = \text{Prob } \left(\frac{5.80 - 6.00}{0.148} \leq \frac{Z - 6.00}{0.148} \leq \frac{6.20 - 6.00}{0.148} \right)$$

$$= \text{Prob } (-1.3 \leq Z^* \leq +1.3)$$

where Z^* is the standard normal variate. This is precisely $\Phi(1.3) - \Phi(-1.3) = 0.8064$. Roughly, then, out of 100 items of the product (in the long run), we may expect 81 within specifications.

5.2.2 Sampling and sampling distributions

We have been developing a number of distributions in the hope that their properties can be used to make inferences about experiments and to make probability calculations. In many problems we may know the form of the distribution of a random variable of interest. In order, however, to make probability calculations, we need knowledge of parameter values. For example, while we may know that the distribution of male adult foot size is normal, in order to plan shoe production, we require knowledge concerning the mean and variance of this normal population. Obviously, this knowledge must be obtained from observation, which must be limited to a sample of a reasonable number of feet. Again, an insurance company desiring to set premiums on accident policies must know not only the form of the distribution of accidents, but also the pertinent parameters. This information can come only from a sample of accident occurrence. Practically all magnitudes that are used in engineering industry and science are the result of repeated measurements which can be viewed as samples of observations on random variables. In general, much of statistical inference deals with the results of sampling from populations and thus leads to the study of sample distributions.

Let us consider a random variable with a normal distribution with mean m and variance σ^2. Suppose we observe this random variable n times, obtaining the results $x_1, x_2, \ldots, x_n$. One way of looking at this is as n points on a line. If we wish to study how this sample compares with other possible samples, it is more convenient to think of the sample as an entity which can be represented by a point $(x_1, x_2, \ldots, x_n)$ in n-dimensional space. An intuitive way of looking at a sample of n can be obtained from consideration of a simple case of a random variable X which takes on three possible values a_1, a_2, and a_3, with probabilities 0.5, 0.25, and 0.25, respectively. Consider a bowl containing a thousand chips, where each chip has one of the labels a_1, a_2, or a_3. Suppose, further, that 500 chips are labeled a_1, 250 a_2, and 250 a_3. An observation on X can be thought of as equivalent to a random drawing from this bowl and reading of the label. A sample of n independent observations on X is obtained by random drawing *with replacement* of n chips. We may look at the sample as n individual chips, and each sample can be represented as an n-tuple $(x_1, x_2, \ldots, x_n)$, where the x's can take on the value a_1, a_2, or a_3. In fact, the number of possible distinct samples is 3^n. We can compute the probability of each of the 3^n outcomes by using the multiplication rule for independent events. For example, the probability of obtaining (a_1, a_2, a_3, a_2), for a sample of size 4 is $(0.5)(0.25)(0.25)(0.25)$. This conceptualization can be generalized to n independent observations of a continuous random variable X with PDF $f(x)$. The joint probability density function of a random independent sample of n observations on X is given by $f(x_1)f(x_2) \cdots f(x_n)$. In the case where X is normally distributed with mean m and variance σ^2, the joint distribution $f_n(x_1, x_2, \ldots, x_n)$ is

$$f_n(x_1, x_2, \ldots, x_n) = \left(\frac{1}{\sigma \sqrt{2\pi}} \right)^n \exp \left[-\frac{1}{2\sigma^2} \sum_{i=1}^{n} (x_i - m)^2 \right]$$

Suppose we are interested in making inferences concerning m. How can we use the sample information? One way is to estimate m by the arithmetic average $\bar{x}_n$. But $\bar{x}_n$ is itself a random variable, since it is a function of the sample $(x_1, x_2, \ldots, x_n)$, which resulted from repeated observation on x. This random variable $\bar{x}_n$ is a *sample function*. How good is $\bar{x}_n$ as an estimate? To answer this, we may consider how likely it is for $\bar{x}_n$ to be "close" to m. This involves studying the distribution of the sample function $\bar{x}_n$.

Related to estimating the mean m is estimating σ^2. In accordance with the definition of σ^2 it seems natural to use the sample function

$$\hat{s}^2 = \frac{1}{n} \sum_{i=1}^{n} (x_i - \bar{x}_n)^2$$

Of course, it is desirable that the expected value of an estimate equal the parameter being estimated. In the case of $\bar{x}_n$ it is obvious that $E(\bar{x}_n)$, for all n, equals m, the population mean. This is not obvious for $\hat{s}^2$. In fact, we leave it as an exercise for the reader to show that

$$E(\hat{s}^2) = \frac{n-1}{n} \sigma^2$$

This means that, even on repeated sampling, $\hat{s}^2$ underestimates σ^2 for small n. In order to overcome this bias we use

$$\frac{n}{n-1} \hat{s}^2 = \frac{1}{n-1} \sum_{i=1}^{n} (x_i - \bar{x}_n)^2 \equiv s^2$$

where $E(s^2) = \sigma^2$. This estimate s^2 is called the unbiased estimate of σ^2.

In order to study the adequacy of s^2 as an estimate for σ^2, we must examine its distribution.   As the problems indicate, one can form a variety of sample functions which may prove useful in statistical inference.

We shall study a number of sample functions related to the normal distribution which arise quite naturally in a great variety of problems. In this study, the gamma function arises quite frequently, and will therefore be reviewed briefly in the next section.

5.2.3   Gamma function

In a number of problems dealing with the distribution of a sample function from the normal distribution, the following integral appears:

$$\int_0^\infty e^{-u} u^{x-1}\, du \qquad 0 < x < +\infty$$

This function of x is called the gamma function, denoted by $\Gamma(x)$.   One cannot express the value of $\Gamma(x)$ in simple form in terms of familiar functions.   When, however, x is an integer, it follows readily, from repeated integration by parts, that

$$\Gamma(n) = (n-1)! \qquad n = 1, 2, \ldots$$

A property which holds for all x is

$$\Gamma(x) = (x-1)\Gamma(x-1)$$

as can be verified by one integration by parts.   This property of the gamma function, which holds for all values of x, leads to a natural generalization of the concept of factorial n.   It further follows that $0! = 1$, since

$$0! = \Gamma(1) = \int_0^\infty e^{-u}\, du = 1$$

(For the present purpose x is restricted to be positive.   A more general definition is required for the rest of the number domain.)

5.2.4   The χ^2 distribution

In sampling problems, the sum of squares of m independent observations from the normal distribution with mean zero and unit variance is frequently needed.   We shall look for the distribution of this random variable.

$$U = X_1^2 + X_2^2 + \cdots + X_m^2$$

where $X_1, X_2, \ldots, X_m$ are independently standard normal variables. Hereafter, we shall call this random variable chi square, denoted by χ^2, with m degrees of freedom.   It is simpler to derive the moment-generating function than the PDF directly. It then can be shown that a certain function, which will be given later, has this moment-generating function and is therefore, by the uniqueness property of moment-generating functions, the χ^2 distribution.

First, the joint PDF of X_1, X_2, . . . , X_m is

$$f(x_1, x_2, \ldots, x_m) = \left(\frac{1}{\sqrt{2\pi}}\right)^m e^{-\frac{1}{2}\Sigma x_i^2}$$

The moment-generating function $M_U(t)$ of U is the expected value of e^{tU}. Thus

$$M_U(t) = E(e^{tU}) = E(e^{t\Sigma x_i^2})$$
$$= \left(\frac{1}{\sqrt{2\pi}}\right)^m \int_{-\infty}^{\infty} \int_{-\infty}^{\infty} \cdots \int_{-\infty}^{\infty} e^{-\frac{1}{2}\Sigma x_i^2 + t\Sigma x_i^2} \, dx_1 \, dx_2 \ldots dx_m$$
$$= \left(\frac{1}{\sqrt{2\pi}}\right)^m \int_{-\infty}^{\infty} \int_{-\infty}^{\infty} \cdots \int_{-\infty}^{\infty} e^{-\frac{1}{2}(1-2t)\Sigma x_i^2} \, dx_1 \, dx_2 \ldots dx_m$$

This integral can be separated in the product of m integrals of the form

$$\int_{-\infty}^{\infty} \frac{1}{\sqrt{2\pi}} e^{-\frac{1}{2}(1-2t)x_i^2} \, dx_i \qquad i = 1, 2, \ldots, m$$

By the transformation $Z_i = x_i \sqrt{1-2t}$ the above integral becomes

$$\frac{1}{\sqrt{1-2t}} \frac{1}{\sqrt{2\pi}} \int_{-\infty}^{\infty} e^{-Z_i^2/2} \, dZ_i = \frac{1}{\sqrt{1-2t}}$$

Therefore

$$M_U(t) = \left(\frac{1}{\sqrt{1-2t}}\right)^m = (1-2t)^{-m/2} \qquad t < \frac{1}{2}$$

There are some general approaches for finding the PDF of a random variable from its moment-generating function, but the techniques required are mathematically beyond the scope of this text. We shall show, however, that

$$f_m(u) = \frac{(u/2)^{m/2-1}}{2\Gamma(m/2)} e^{-u/2} \qquad 0 \le u \le +\infty$$

is a PDF and has the moment-generating function $(1-2t)^{-m/2}$. It will be left as an exercise to the reader to show that $f_m(u)$ is, in fact, a PDF. We now set up

$$M(t) = \int_0^{\infty} e^{tu} f_m(u) \, du = \int_0^{\infty} \frac{(u/2)^{m/2-1}}{2\Gamma(m/2)} e^{-u/2+tu} \, du$$

A natural transformation of variable is $(u/2)(1 - 2t) = v$, which yields

$$M(t) = \frac{1}{2\Gamma(m/2)} \int_0^\infty \frac{v^{m/2-1}e^{-v}2 \, dv}{(1 - 2t)^{m/2-1}(1 - 2t)}$$

$$= \frac{1}{(1 - 2t)^{m/2}\Gamma(m/2)} \int_0^\infty v^{m/2-1}e^{-v} \, dv = (1 - 2t)^{-m/2}$$

from the definition of the gamma function, noting that m is the degree of freedom in the χ^2 distribution.

We call the reader's attention to the fact that $U = X_1{}^2 + X_2{}^2 + \cdots + X_m{}^2$, where $X_1, X_2, \ldots, X_m$ are independently and indentically distributed standard normal variates, has been shown to have $PDF \, f_m(u)$.

The mean and variance of χ^2 with m degrees of freedom, which can be computed from the moment-generating function by successive differentiation and evaluation at $t = 0$, are

$$E(\chi^2) = m \qquad \text{and} \qquad V(\chi^2) = 2m$$

An interesting special case of χ^2, namely, for $m = 2$, has the PDF of the exponential with mean equal to 2.

A very important property of χ^2 is its *additivity*, which we shall express as a theorem.

Theorem 5.3   Given $\chi_1{}^2, \chi_2{}^2, \ldots, \chi_1{}^2$ independently distributed with $m_1, m_2, \ldots, m_k$ degrees of freedom, respectively, then their sum

$$\chi_1{}^2 + \chi_2{}^2 + \cdots + \chi_k{}^2$$

has the χ^2 distribution with $m_1 + m_2 + \cdots + m_k$ degrees of freedom.

This property follows directly from the definition. We shall now show an important use of the χ^2 distribution in connection with properties of the sample function s^2. Suppose that we have n independent observations on a normal random variable with mean m and variance σ^2. What can we say about the distribution of s^2, the sample variance? We must bear in mind that we rarely know the values of m and σ^2, but must make inference on the basis of sample functions. Consider, then, $(n - 1)s^2 = \Sigma(x_i - \bar{x})^2$, which, as a sum of squares, suggests a possible relation to χ^2. Since the x_i result from observations on a normal variable, it seems natural to standardize the original random variables. Hence we consider

$$\sum_{i=1}^n \left(\frac{x_i - m}{\sigma}\right)^2$$

which clearly has the χ^2 distribution with n degrees of freedom and satisfies the identity

$$\sum_{i=1}^{n} \left(\frac{x_i - m}{\sigma}\right)^2 = \frac{(n-1)s^2}{\sigma^2} + \left(\frac{\bar{x} - m}{\sigma/\sqrt{n}}\right)^2$$

The last term in the identity is precisely the square of a standard normal variate and therefore has the χ^2 distribution with 1 degree of freedom. If $\bar{x}$ and s^2 were independent, then it would follow from the additivity property that $(n-1)s^2/\sigma^2$ has a χ^2 distribution with $n-1$ degrees of freedom. It can be proved, *for samples from the normal distribution,* that in fact $\bar{x}$ *and* s^2 *are independently distributed.* This is an important property of the normal distribution, as is the fact that, *for samples from a normal distribution, the sample function* $(n-1)s^2/\sigma^2$ *has the* χ^2 *distribution with* $n-1$ *degrees of freedom.*

A simple practical use of this result is in the bounding of s^2/σ^2. For example, if one has made n observations on a normal variate, then one can select two values of χ^2, depending on n, such that, for any specified probability $1 - \beta$,

$$\text{Prob}\left(\chi_1{}^2 \le \frac{(n-1)s^2}{\sigma^2} \le \chi_2{}^2\right) = 1 - \beta$$

where the χ^2 has $n-1$ degrees of freedom. The constants which depend on n and β can be selected in a variety of ways. Furthermore, it follows that

$$\text{Prob}\left(\frac{\chi_1{}^2}{n-1} \le \frac{s^2}{\sigma^2} \le \frac{\chi_2{}^2}{n-1}\right) = 1 - \beta$$

whence it appears that s^2/σ^2 can be hemmed in as narrowly as desired for any specified odds. As an example, let $1 - \beta = 0.90$ (for simplicity using equal tails of the χ^2 distribution) and $n = 11$; we obtain, then,

$$\text{Prob}\left(\frac{3.94}{10} \le \frac{s^2}{\sigma^2} \le \frac{18.3}{10}\right) = 0.90$$

(The values 18.3 and 3.94 are the 95 and 5 percentiles, respectively, of χ^2 with 10 degrees of freedom.) If this interval seems rather wide, consider $n = 21$, which gives

$$\text{Prob}\left(\frac{10.9}{20} \le \frac{s^2}{\sigma^2} \le \frac{31.4}{20}\right) = 0.90$$

This property is extensively applied in statistical inference and will be used in later chapters.

5.2.5   Student's t distribution

We shall introduce a type of problem that arises frequently in practice which illustrates the use of some of the sample concepts previously developed and which is, as well, one of the most important sample distributions. A prototype problem is that of estimating process output. Suppose, for example, that the variable output of a chemical plant is normally distributed. In this case, there should be a physically determinable mean value m of the output. How shall we go about estimating m? The statement that the output has a distribution implies that we may consider this to be a stable process. Hence we may denote output by a random variable X with PDF which we assume to be $\phi(x;m,\sigma^2)$. Furthermore, let us assume that each day's output is independent of previous outputs. In this case, we may look upon any day's output as a normal random variable X_i with mean m and variance σ^2. The particular outcomes for n days constitute a sample of n observations on X and can be represented as a sample point $(x_1,x_2, \ldots ,x_n)$ in n-dimensional space. How can we use this observed sample?

The obvious thing to do first is to consider the random variable $\bar{X}_n$ as an estimate of m. Nevertheless, an obvious question arises as to how "good" this estimate is. We are not presently undertaking to develop any statistical theory of estimation. We are merely approaching a typical problem, which naturally leads to an important sample function. The general question of estimation will be taken up, in some detail, in Chap. 8.

One criterion for the "goodness" of an estimate is how "close" the estimate is to the true mean m. One way of doing this is to attempt to hem in $\bar{X}_n - m$ within a specified interval. For example, if σ^2 is assumed to be known, as is reasonable in many situations, we can find a constant a, depending on n and σ^2 and for any specified odds $1 - \beta$, such that

$$\text{Prob}\ (-a \leq \bar{X}_n - m \leq +a) = 1 - \beta$$

In order to obtain a one must convert $\bar{X}_n$ to its standard normal form, which is readily done by dividing through the above equality by $\sigma/\sqrt{n}$, the standard deviation of $\bar{X}_n$. Thus

$$\text{Prob}\left(\frac{-a\sqrt{n}}{\sigma} \leq \frac{\bar{X}_n - m}{\sigma/\sqrt{n}} \leq \frac{+a\sqrt{n}}{\sigma}\right) = 1 - \beta$$

From the tables of the standard normal distribution one can find a. For example, for $1 - \beta = 0.99$,

$$\text{Prob}\left(-2.6 \leq \frac{\bar{X}_n - m}{\sigma/\sqrt{n}} \leq +2.6\right) = 0.99$$

whence $a\sqrt{n}/\sigma = 2.6$. For a given n, a can be determined, or given a, one can choose the appropriate n.

This procedure can be systematized by noting that

$$Z = \frac{\sqrt{n}\,(\bar{X}_n - m)}{\sigma}$$

has a standard normal distribution (independent of m or σ^2). Then bounds on Z, for any β, can be expressed in the form

$$\text{Prob }(Z_{\beta/2} \leq Z \leq Z_{1-\beta/2}) = 1 - \beta$$

where $Z_{1-\beta/2}$ and $Z_{\beta/2}$ are the $1 - \beta/2$ and the $\beta/2$ percentiles of the standard normal variate. In order to get back to our original concern with m, substitute $\sqrt{n}\,(\bar{X}_n - m)/\sigma$ for Z, obtaining

$$\text{Prob}\left(Z_{\beta/2} \leq \frac{\bar{X}_n - m}{\sigma/\sqrt{n}} \leq Z_{1-\beta/2}\right) = 1 - \beta$$

Note that the inequality in the above expression is equivalent to

$$\bar{X}_n - Z_{1-\beta/2}\frac{\sigma}{\sqrt{n}} \leq m \leq \bar{X}_n - Z_{\beta/2}\frac{\sigma}{\sqrt{n}}$$

It should be emphasized that m is an unknown constant, which is, however, covered by the interval with end points $\bar{X}_n - Z_{1-\beta/2}\sigma/\sqrt{n}$ and $\bar{X}_n - Z_{\beta/2}\sigma/\sqrt{n}$, which themselves depend on the sample. For different samples these end points will have different values since the end points are in fact random variables. Because of the equivalence of the two inequalities, their probabilities of occurrence are equal. We can express this relation in the following form:

$$\text{Prob}\left[\left(\bar{X}_n - Z_{1-\beta/2}\frac{\sigma}{\sqrt{n}};\, \bar{X}_n - Z_{\beta/2}\frac{\sigma}{\sqrt{n}}\right) \text{ covers } m\right] = 1 - \beta$$

This probability statement holds regardless of the value of m. The frequency interpretation of this probability statement is: in the long run, for repeated samples of size n, the proportion of times that the interval, bounded by the specified random end points, includes m is $1 - \beta$. This interval is usually called a *confidence interval* with *confidence coefficient* $1 - \beta$. Confidence-interval concepts will be taken up in detail in Chap. 8.

The foregoing result rests essentially on the fact that $Z = \sqrt{n}\,(\bar{X}_n - m)/\sigma$ has a distribution *not depending* on m and σ^2. The use made of this property of Z required, however, knowledge of σ^2. In many cases σ^2, as well as m, must be determined from experiment. Can we also bound m when σ^2 is unknown? The first natural step is to find an equivalent to Z. Suppose we try, then, to replace σ^2 by s^2, a natural sample estimate, and examine the properties of

$$\frac{\bar{X}_n - m}{s/\sqrt{n}} = Z'$$

If Z' has a distribution not depending on m and σ^2, we can proceed, as previously, to find a covering interval for m. In fact, this turns out to be the case, as we shall show. Consider, then, a sample of n observations described by n identical independent normal random variables X_1, $X_2, \ldots, X_n$, with mean m and variance σ^2. We can express each X_i in terms of m, σ^2, and X_i^*, its standardized form, by

$$X_i = m + X_i^* \sigma$$

where X_i^* is normal with mean zero and unit variance. Let us substitute this representation into the sample function Z' and see what happens. First,

$$\bar{X}_n = m + \bar{X}_n^* \sigma$$

where
$$\bar{X}_n^* = \frac{X_1^* + X_2^* + \cdots + X_n^*}{n}$$

Furthermore, by direct substitution,

$$s^2 = \frac{\sigma^2}{n-1} \sum_{i=1}^{N} (X_i^* - \bar{X}_n^*)^2$$

As a result,

$$Z' = \frac{\sigma \bar{X}_n^*}{\dfrac{\sigma}{\sqrt{n}} \sqrt{\dfrac{\Sigma(X_i^* - \bar{X}_n^*)^2}{n-1}}} = \frac{\sqrt{n}\, \bar{X}_n^* \sqrt{n-1}}{\sqrt{\Sigma(X_i^* - \bar{X}_u^*)^2}}$$

Since Z' depends only on X_1^*, X_2^*, $\ldots$, X_n^* and n, it *does not* depend on m and σ^2.

In order to study the distribution of Z' we note that $\sqrt{n}\, \bar{X}_n^*$ is a standard normal variate and that the square of the denominator is χ^2 with $n-1$ degrees of freedom. Furthermore, the numerator and the denominator are independent. Let X be a standard normal variate, and let U be independent of X with a χ^2 distribution with $n-1$ degrees of freedom. Then Z' has the same distribution as $\sqrt{n-1}\, X/\sqrt{U}$, which has Student's t distribution, the distribution of the quantity (a random variable)

$$\frac{X \sqrt{n-1}}{\sqrt{U}}$$

The *PDF* of the t distribution with m degrees of freedom is

$$f(t) = \frac{\Gamma\left(\dfrac{m+1}{2}\right)}{\sqrt{m\pi}\, \Gamma(m/2)} \left(1 + \frac{t^2}{m}\right)^{-\frac{1}{2}(m+1)} \qquad -\infty \leq t \leq +\infty$$

whence Z' has the t distribution with $n-1$ degrees of freedom.

We found the present distribution in order to put bounds on $\bar{X}_n - m$, when σ^2 is unknown. Since Z' has the t distribution with $n - 1$ degrees of freedom, we can find a constant a, depending on n and a specified $1 - \beta$, such that Prob $(-a \leq Z' \leq +a) = 1 - \beta$. Substituting for Z', we have

$$\text{Prob}\left(-a \leq \frac{\bar{X}_n - m}{s/\sqrt{n}} \leq +a\right) = 1 - \beta$$

The inequality can, in turn, be expressed as bounds on m as follows:

$$\bar{X}_n - \frac{as}{\sqrt{n}} \leq m \leq \bar{X}_n + \frac{as}{\sqrt{n}}$$

We can then state that the random interval with end points $\bar{X}_n - as/\sqrt{n}$ and $\bar{X}_n + as/\sqrt{n}$ covers m with probability $1 - \beta$.

Note that, whereas with σ^2 known, the length of the random covering interval is fixed and can be computed in advance, when σ^2 is unknown, the length of the covering interval is also a random variable.

5.2.6   The F distribution

Another problem of frequent interest is the comparison of the variability of a newly designed product with the former product. It seems natural to compare differences and ratios of the sample estimates s_1^2 and s_2^2 of the respective variances. We do know that $(n_1 - 1)s_1^2/\sigma_1^2$ and $(n_2 - 1)s_2^2/\sigma_2^2$ have χ^2 distributions, with $n_1 - 1$ and $n_2 - 1$ degrees of freedom. The study of the ratio seems indicated, since in many problems we are primarily interested in the relative degree of variation rather than in the absolute difference in variation. We are led to studying the following ratio of χ^2 variates:

$$\frac{[(n_1 - 1)s_1^2]/\sigma_1^2}{[(n_2 - 1)s_2^2]/\sigma_2^2}$$

While we shall not go into a formal derivation of the distribution of this random variable, we must take cognizance of the fact that it is much simpler to study the above ratio when the numerators are independent. It can be shown that *if U is χ^2 with m_1 degrees of freedom and W is χ^2 with m_2 degrees of freedom, where U and W are independent, then*

$$\frac{V/m_1}{W/m_2} = F_{m_1, m_2}$$

has the following PDF:

$$f_{m_1,m_2}(t) = \frac{\Gamma\left(\dfrac{m_1 + m_2}{2}\right)}{\Gamma\left(\dfrac{m_1}{2}\right)\Gamma\left(\dfrac{m_2}{2}\right)}\left(\frac{m_1}{m_2}\right)^{\frac{m_1}{2}} t^{\frac{m_1}{2} - 1}\left(1 + \frac{m_1}{m_2}t\right)^{-\frac{1}{2}(m_1+m_2)} \qquad -\infty \leq t \leq \infty$$

which is called the F distribution, with m_1 and m_2 degrees of freedom. The mean and variance are

$$E(F) = \frac{m_2}{m_2 - 2} \quad (m_2 > 2) \quad V(F) = \frac{m_2{}^2(2m_2 + 2m_1 + 4)}{m_1(m_2 - 2)^2(m_2 - 4)}$$

$$(m_2 > 4)$$

A useful property is the reciprocal property of the percentiles, where

$$F_{1-\alpha,m_1,m_2} = \frac{1}{F_{\alpha,m_2,m_1}}$$

While we shall not go further into the development of the F distribution, we shall make extensive use of it in later chapters.

5.3   Central limit theorem and applications

This section is devoted to a discussion of one of the most celebrated theorems in probability.   The central limit theorem has important implications, practical as well as theoretical.

In the previous section we have shown that if $X_1, X_2, \ldots, X_n$ are independent normal random variables, then the arithmetic average $\bar{X}_n$ is also normally distributed.   The central limit theorem implies, essentially, that *under very general conditions, $\bar{X}_n$ is normally distributed, for n large,* even if $X_1, \ldots, X_n$ are not normal.

In many applications we are concerned with probability calculations involving sums of many independent random variables.   Often, in these cases, we may know something about the mean and variances but very little about the distributions.   The central limit theorem provides a way of making these calculations without having to specify the distributions in great detail.   Incidentally, this fact again emphasizes the importance of the concept of the mean and variance.

5.3.1   Central limit theorem

We shall now demonstrate a special case of the central limit theorem with the use of the moment-generating function.

Theorem 5.4   Let $X_1, X_2, \ldots, X_N$ be independent and identically distributed random variables with mean m and variance σ^2. Assume, also, that all moments exist.   If $\bar{X}_N$ denotes the arithmetic average, then, for N large, the standardized random variable $\bar{X}_N^*$ is approximately normally distributed with mean zero and unit variance.

The argument is as follows.   Consider the random variable $\bar{X}_N^*$, which we shall write as a sum of random variables as follows:

$$\bar{X}_N^* = \frac{\bar{X}_N - m}{\sigma/\sqrt{N}} = \left(\frac{X_1 - m}{\sigma\sqrt{N}}\right) + \left(\frac{X_2 - m}{\sigma\sqrt{N}}\right) + \cdots + \left(\frac{X_N - m}{\sigma\sqrt{N}}\right)$$

For any i ($i = 1, \ldots, N$) we have, for the moment-generating function $M_{X_i-m}(t)$ for $X_i - m$, that

$$M_{X_i-m}(t) = 1 + \frac{1}{2!} t^2\sigma^2 + \frac{1}{3!} t^3\mu_3 + \frac{1}{4!} t^4\mu_4 + \cdots$$

Thus

$$M_{\frac{X_i-m}{\sigma\sqrt{N}}}(t) = M_{X_i-m}\left(\frac{t}{\sigma\sqrt{N}}\right) = 1 + \frac{t^2}{2N} + \frac{t^3}{3!N^{3/2}}\left(\frac{\mu_3}{\sigma^3}\right) + \cdots$$

$$= 1 + \frac{t^2}{2N} + R_N$$

where R_N is the remainder in the series beyond the term $t^2/2N$. We note that $N R_N \to 0$ as $N \to \infty$. From the multiplication rule for moment-generating functions,

$$M_{\frac{\sqrt{N}(\bar{X}_N-m)}{\sigma}}(t) = M_{\frac{X_1-m}{\sigma\sqrt{N}}}(t)\ M_{\frac{X_2-m}{\sigma\sqrt{N}}}(t)\ \cdots\ M_{\frac{X_N-m}{\sigma\sqrt{N}}}(t)$$

$$= \left[1 + \frac{1}{2}\left(\frac{t^2 + 2NR_N}{N}\right)\right]^N$$

It can be shown that the last term approaches $e^{t^2/2}$ as $N \to \infty$. This is recognized as the moment-generating function of a normal random variable with zero mean and unit variance.

In the above, we have assumed that all the moments existed. This was done to utilize the moment-generating function. However, the result is true if only the mean m and the variance σ^2 are assumed to be finite. Furthermore, a more general central limit theorem can be proved. In this formulation the restriction that $X_1, X_2, \ldots, X_N$ all have the same distribution is dropped. The theorem requires some conditions which we shall not elaborate on in this text. Very generally, however, this condition holds when each X_i contributes a small amount relative to the sum $X_1 + X_2 + \cdots + X_N$.

Suppose $X_1, \ldots, X_N$ are independently distributed with means $m_1, m_2, m_3, \ldots, m_N$ and variances $\sigma_1^2, \sigma_2^2, \ldots, \sigma_N^2$. Let

$$M_N = m_1 + m_2 + \cdots + m_N$$
$$V_N = \sigma_1^2 + \sigma_2^2 + \cdots + \sigma_N^2$$
$$S_N = X_1 + X_2 + \cdots + X_N$$

It is clear that $E(S_N) = M_N$ and $V(S_N) = V_N$. Then, *under quite general conditions, the standardized random variable S_N^* tends to a normal distribution with zero mean and unit variance.* That is, for N large and any $b > a$,

$$\text{Prob } (a \le S_N^* \le b) \cong \frac{1}{\sqrt{2\pi}} \int_a^b e^{-t^2/2}\, dt = \Phi(b) - \Phi(a)$$

The above theorem indicates why the normal distribution plays such a central role.

In the light of the central limit theorem, it is quite clear that many of the results, in previous examples, are true for more general conditions than indicated in those examples. For instance, in Example 4.8, we studied the random variable D_N. It is seen that $E|D_N|$ increases proportionally as $\sqrt{N}$, with X_1, X_2, . . . , X_N having some general distribution. Also, for N large, we can make an approximate probability calculation. Suppose X_1, . . . , X_N are independent with mean 0 and variance σ^2. Then $V(D_N) = N\sigma^2$. Thus, for N large and any t, we have

$$\text{Prob } (|D_N| > t) = \text{Prob } \left(|D_N^*| > \frac{t}{\sigma\sqrt{N}}\right) \cong 2\Phi\left(-\frac{t}{\sigma\sqrt{N}}\right)$$

We note that the result depends on t as a multiple of $\sigma\sqrt{N}$. In Example 4.8 we had σ^2 equal to 1. Let $N = 100$. Then we calculate that $E|D_{100}| \cong 8$. What is the probability that $|D_{100}|$ is as large as 10 or 20? From the above we find

$$\text{Prob } (|D_{100}| \geq 10) \cong 2\Phi(-1) = 31.73\%$$
$$\text{Prob } (|D_{100}| \geq 20) \cong 2\Phi(-2) = 4.55\%$$

Another instance, when the result does not depend much on the distribution, for N large, is in Sec. 5.2.5. The confidence interval for the mean m, for σ^2 known, was based only on the distribution of X_N^*. Thus the argument carries through with the use of the central limit theorem. Therefore, for large N,

$$\text{Prob }\left[\left(\bar{X}_N - Z_{1-\beta/2}\frac{\sigma}{\sqrt{N}}; \bar{X}_N - Z_{\beta/2}\frac{\sigma}{\sqrt{N}}\right) \text{ covers } m\right] \cong 1 - \beta$$

In the application of the central limit theorem we require that N be large. However, the approximations are often adequate for N equal to 5 or 10. The adequacy of the approximation, as a function of N, depends on the detailed nature of the distributions.

5.3.2 Approximations

The central limit theorem can be used to approximate various distributions. In the following we demonstrate this for the binomial and Poisson distributions. The argument, in the following, usually rests on expressing the relevant random variable as a sum of independent random variables.

Normal Approximation to the Binomial From previous results we have that the number of successes S_N in N independent binomial trials can be expressed as a sum, where

$$S_N = X_1 + X_2 + \cdots + X_N$$

and X_i $(i = 1, \ldots, N)$ are independently distributed and take on two values, 1 and 0, with probability p and q. Also, $E(S_N) = Np$ and $V(S_N) = Npq$, and the standardized random variable S_N^* is

$$S_N^* = \frac{S_N - Np}{\sqrt{Npq}}$$

Thus, from the central limit theorem, S_N^*, for large N, has CDF $\Phi(x;0,1)$. The approximation is quite adequate when p is not close to 0 or 1. When p (or $1 - p$) is small, then, from Sec. 5.1, we have that S_N is approximately Poisson.

Example 5.4   A problem of frequent occurrence calls for decision on the magnitude of service facilities for the accommodation of N customers.   Examples of this are demand for telephone trunk lines, demand for seats on a bus, and demand for power at a power station.   Let there be k facilities.   On the one hand, we can ensure that customers will always be served by choosing $k = N$.   On the other hand, we know that customers, in most practical cases, are very unlikely to demand service all at the same time.   Thus, when $k = N$, we can expect much idle time on the facilities.   However, if k is made very small, we can expect that we often will have demand for facilities which cannot be met.   The choice of k is determined by *balancing* the consequences of building and maintaining idle facilities as compared with not satisfying demand for service.

Consider the following model.   We have N customers, each acting independently and having probability p of demanding the use of a facility at any time.   Empirically, p can be interpreted as the fraction of the time that a customer uses a facility.   We assume that p is constant for all the customers.   The case when this is not so can be handled by a generalization of the subsequent development.   The demand, at an arbitrary time, can be considered in terms of the binomial distribution.   Let us find the probability that there is more demand, S_N, than facilities. From the binomial distribution, we have

$$\text{Prob}\,(S_N > k) = \sum_{j=k+1}^{N} \binom{N}{j} p^j q^{N-j}$$

Consider finding k such that the above probability is a specified level α.   The value $1 - \alpha$ is often called the *service level*.   Let the necessary value of k be denoted by $k(\alpha,N)$.   Thus we require the solution, for $k(\alpha,N)$, of

$$\sum_{j=k(\alpha,N)+1}^{N} \binom{N}{j} p^j q^{N-j} = \alpha$$

The above computation, aside from being quite tedious, does not shed much light on the dependence of $k(\alpha,N)$ on α and N. The use of the central limit theorem is quite revealing in this case. For N large (usually the situation in cases of this kind), we have

$$\text{Prob } (S_N > k) = \text{Prob} \left(\frac{S_N - Np}{\sqrt{Npq}} > \frac{k - Np}{\sqrt{Npq}} \right) = \text{Prob} \left(S_N^* > \frac{k - Np}{\sqrt{Npq}} \right)$$

$$\cong 1 - \Phi \left(\frac{k - Np}{\sqrt{Npq}} \right)$$

Recall that S_N^* is approximately distributed with CDF $\Phi(x;0,1)$. Therefore, for $k(\alpha,N)$, we need the solution of

$$1 - \Phi \left(\frac{k(\alpha,N) - Np}{\sqrt{Npq}} \right) = \alpha$$

The solution is obtained from the well-tabulated percentiles of the standard normal. Thus, for $Z_{1-\alpha}$ denoting the $(1 - \alpha)$ percentile,

$$\frac{k(\alpha,N) - Np}{\sqrt{Npq}} = Z_{1-\alpha}$$

Thus $$k(\alpha,N) \cong Np + Z_{1-\alpha} \sqrt{Npq}$$

We note that for N large and p small we have $Npq \cong Np$ and $k(\alpha,N) \cong Np + Z_{1-\alpha} \sqrt{Np}$. That is, $k(\alpha,N) - Np$ increases approximately as the square root of the average demand.

In general, to have probability $1 - \alpha$ of accommodating service, we need some facilities above the average demand Np. The extra, usually called the buffer, is the payment for the unpredictability of demand. We note that *the required buffer increases as* $\sqrt{N}$. For example, let $N = 10,000$, $p = 0.01$, and $\alpha = 5$ per cent (service level is 95 per cent). The average number of facilities required is 100. How many facilities are needed to accommodate 95 per cent of demand? The calculation based on the above development gives an answer 116, which is 16 per cent above the average. When $N = 1,000,000$, the required number is 10,160, which is only 1.6 per cent above the average demand. Note the advantage of "bigness," which holds for such other situations as safety stock for inventory and reserve cash ratio at banks and insurance companies.

Normal Approximation to Poisson Consider N independent Poisson random variables $Y_1, Y_2, \ldots, Y_N$, each with parameter λ.

Then the sum $Y_1 + Y_2 + \cdots + Y_N$ is also Poisson with parameter $N\lambda$. Thus a Poisson random variable Y, with parameter m, approaches normality as m increases. That is, the standardized variate $Y^* = (Y - m)/\sqrt{m}$ has, for m large, a CDF $\Phi(x;0,1)$. For most practical purposes the approximation is adequate for $m > 10$. For example, if the intensity of events, occurring according to the Poisson process, is θ, then the number of events occurring in an interval of length T is approximately normal when $T > 10/\theta$. That is, T is larger than ten times the average interval between events.

Example 5.5   Continuing with Example 5.1, we derive an expression for the CDF of $Z_{k,N}$, the time until the kth failure out of N items. The normal distribution is then used to obtain a convenient approximation. Consider the interval from time 0 to t. How can $Z_{k,N} > t$? This can happen in k mutually exclusive ways, namely, E_0, E_1, $\ldots$, E_{k-1}, where E_0 is the event where exactly zero failures occur in $[0,t]$, E_1 is the event where exactly one failure occurs in $[0,t]$, etc. That is,

$$E_i: \quad (\text{exactly } i \text{ failures in } [0,t]) \qquad i = 0, \ldots, k-1$$

Thus

$$\text{Prob } (Z_{k,N} > t) = P(E_0) + P(E_1) + \cdots + P(E_{k-1})$$

The number of failures in $[0,t]$ has a binomial distribution with probability $F(t)$, where $F(t)$ is the CDF of time to failure of the items. Thus

$$P(E_i) = \binom{N}{i} [F(t)]^i [1 - F(t)]^{N-i}$$

Thus

$$\text{Prob } (Z_{k,N} > t) = \sum_{i=0}^{k-1} \binom{N}{i} [F(t)]^i [1 - F(t)]^{N-i}$$

The special case $k = 1$ checks with the previous result in Example 5.1. The CDF of $Z_{k,N}$ is obtained from the previous expression by subtracting from 1.

The normal approximation to the binomial can be used to obtain a simpler expression for the CDF of $Z_{k,N}$. The probability that $Z_{k,N} > t$ is seen to be equal to the probability that the number of successes S_N out of N trials does not exceed $k - 1$, where S_N has a binomial distribution with probability of success $F(t)$. Thus

$$\text{Prob } (Z_{k,N} > t) = \text{Prob } (S_N \leq k - 1)$$

Furthermore

$$\text{Prob } (S_N \leq k - 1) = \text{Prob } \left\{ \frac{S_N - NF(t)}{\sqrt{NF(t)[1 - F(t)]}} \leq \frac{k - 1 - NF(t)}{\sqrt{NF(t)[1 - F(t)]}} \right\}$$

$$\cong \Phi \left\{ \frac{k - 1 - NF(t)}{\sqrt{NF(t)[1 - F(t)]}} \right\}$$

Thus

$$\text{Prob} \ (Z_{k,N} \le t) \cong 1 - \Phi \left\{ \frac{k - 1 - NF(t)}{\sqrt{NF(t)[1 - F(t)]}} \right\}$$

Consider the special case where t is chosen t_β and t_β is the β percentile; that is, $F(t_\beta) = \beta$. Then

$$\text{Prob} \ (Z_{k,N} \le t_\beta) \cong 1 - \Phi \left[\frac{k - 1 - N\beta}{\sqrt{N\beta(1 - \beta)}} \right]$$

For example, the probability that at least $1 - \beta$ per cent of the population is larger than $Z_{k,N}$ is given by the right-hand side of the above expression. If we wish to set this probability equal to P, we can, for any N, find the appropriate k. To obtain, approximately, the required k, we set

$$1 - \Phi \left[\frac{k - 1 - N\beta}{\sqrt{N\beta(1 - \beta)}} \right] = P$$

Thus

$$\frac{k - 1 - N\beta}{\sqrt{N\beta(1 - \beta)}} = Z_{1-P}$$

where Z_{1-P} is the $1 - P$ percentile of the standardized normal distribution. Solving for k, we obtain

$$k \cong 1 + N\beta + Z_{1-P} \sqrt{N\beta(1 - \beta)}$$

For instance, let $N = 200$, $\beta = 0.10$, $P = 0.90$; then $k = 16$. That is,

$$\text{Prob} \ (\text{at least } 90\% \text{ of population is larger than } Z_{16,200}) \cong 0.90$$

It is important to note that this result does not depend on any knowledge about the CDF $F(t)$.

Example 5.6 We consider a situation with S systems, each requiring the same critical component. These components are produced according to a schedule: N_1 in the first month, N_2 in the second month, etc. The components are, however, subject to failures described by a random variable, time to failure, having a CDF $F(t)$. We assume that each time a component of a system fails, it is replaced by a good one, if available, from the production. Also, we assume, for the purposes of this example, that the failure characteristic of a component is the same whether it is in the system or in storage. What is the probability that at least α per cent of the S systems be operational at the end of month k?

Consider the random variables $U_{k,i}$, denoting the number of components produced in ith month still operational at the end of month k. Any particular component produced in month i must survive $k - i$ months to be operational at the end of month k. The probability of surviving $k - i$ months is obtained from $1 - F(t)$ evaluated at $k - i$, that is, $1 - F(k - i)$.   Since N_i components were produced in month i, we have that $U_{k,i}$ has a binomial distribution with N_i trials and probability of success $1 - F(k - i)$.   Thus

$$E(U_{k,i}) = N_i[1 - F(k - i)]$$
$$V(U_{k,i}) = N_i[1 - F(k - i)]\, F(k - i)$$

The number of operational components at the end of month k, U_k is clearly the sum of $U_{k,i}$ from i equal 1 to k.   That is,

$$U_k = U_{k,1} + U_{k,2} + \cdots + U_{k,k}$$

Thus

$$E_k = E(U_k) = \sum_{i=1}^{k} N_i[1 - F(k - i)]$$

$$V_k = V(U_k) = \sum_{i=1}^{k} N_i[1 - F(k - i)]\, F(k - i)$$

Since U_k can be written as a sum of independent random variables, an application of the central limit theorem allows us to make approximate probability calculations involving U_k.   What is the probability that there will be a sufficient number of operational components to support at least αS of the systems?   In other words, what is Prob $(U_k \geq \alpha S)$?

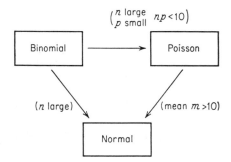

Figure 5.3

From the previous remarks we have that U_k is approximately normally distributed, with mean E_k and variance V_k.   Thus

$$\text{Prob } (U_k \geq \alpha S) = \text{Prob } \left(\frac{U_k - E_k}{\sqrt{V_k}} \geq \frac{\alpha S - E_k}{\sqrt{V_k}}\right) \cong 1 - \Phi\left(\frac{\alpha S - E_k}{\sqrt{V_k}}\right)$$

Calculations of the kind given above, in conjunction with knowledge of $F(t)$, can be used to obtain reasonable decisions concerning the choice of a production schedule.   The optimum choices of the N's must balance the cost of producing and storing the components, with the loss resulting when systems do not operate because of unavailability of critical components.

The various approximations can be summarized in terms of Fig. 5.3.

Correction for Continuity When using a continuous distribution to approximate a discrete one, we obtain a better approximation by the use of a correction for continuity. To illustrate this, consider the *PF* of the Poisson distribution with parameter $m = 10$, at values 7, 8, 9, and 10 as shown in Fig. 5.4.

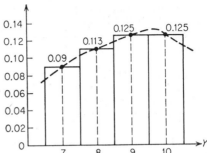

Figure 5.4

Thus, to find the probability that the random variable is 8, 9, or 10, we should integrate from 7.5 to 10.5. Then

$$\text{Prob } (Y = 8) + \text{Prob } (Y = 9) + \text{Prob } (Y = 10)$$

$$\cong \frac{1}{\sqrt{10}\,\sqrt{2\pi}} \int_{7.5}^{10.5} e^{-\frac{1}{2}\left(\frac{t-10}{\sqrt{10}}\right)^2} dt = \Phi\left(\frac{0.5}{\sqrt{10}}\right) - \Phi\left(-\frac{0.5}{\sqrt{10}}\right) = 34.8\%$$

while the actual value is 36.3 per cent. Similarly, prob $(Y = 9) \cong \Phi(-0.5/\sqrt{10}) - \Phi(-1.5/\sqrt{10}) = 12$ per cent, while the actual value is 12.5 per cent. Similarly, for the binomial case,

$$\text{Prob } (a \leq S_N \leq b) \cong \Phi\left(\frac{b + \frac{1}{2} - Np}{\sqrt{Npq}}\right) - \Phi\left(\frac{a - \frac{1}{2} - Np}{\sqrt{Npq}}\right)$$

The use of $\frac{1}{2}$ on both sides is an effective improvement of the approximation. The extent of improvement will be illustrated in subsequent exercises.

EXERCISES

5.1. The life of a certain type of electron tube is normally distributed with mean 95 hours and standard deviation 6 hours. Five tubes are used in a circuit. Assume that these tubes alone determine the operating life of the circuit and that, if any one fails, the circuit is inoperative.

a. What is the probability of a tube living at least 100 hours?
b. What is the probability that the circuit will operate for more than 90 hours?

5.2. A switchboard gets 500 calls on the average per hour. Furthermore, no more than 12 connections per minute can be made.

   a. What is the probability that the switchboard will get more calls than it can handle during any minute? (Use the Poisson distribution.)

   b. What is the answer in (*a*) for a period of 3 minutes?

   c. Do (*a*) and (*b*), using normal approximation.

5.3. An insurance company finds that 0.02 per cent of a population dies from a certain cause each year.   Find the probability that the company will pay more than 3 out of the 10,000 insured risks in a given year.

5.4. Suppose that $X_1, X_2, \ldots, X_n$ are independently, identically distributed normal random variables with mean μ and variance σ^2.

   a. Prove that $(n - 1)s^2/\sigma^2$ has a distribution not depending on μ or σ^2.

   b. Prove that $[\max (X_1, X_2, \ldots, X_n) - \min (X_1, X_2, \ldots, X_n)]/\sigma = R/\sigma$ (R is the range) has a distribution not depending on μ or σ^2.

   c. Use the Monte Carlo method to estimate $E(R/\sigma)$ for $n = 5$.

5.5. The random variable X is normally distributed with mean equal to 2 and variance equal to 4.

   a. Find an expression for the *CDF* of the absolute value Y of X ($Y = |X|$).

   b. What is the probability that Y exceeds the value 2?

5.6. The quantity of demand in pounds (D_i) on the ith day ($i = 1, 2, \ldots, 5$) for a certain stock item has been found to have a χ^2 distribution with 4 degrees of freedom.   Assume that the quantity of demand on each day is independent of that for every other day.

   a. What is the probability of having a demand greater than 4.878 pounds on any day?

   b. What is the distribution of total demand in the 5-day period?

   c. Company policy is to stock a quantity at the beginning of each 5-day period sufficient to allow shortages on the average in only 1 per cent of the 5-day periods.   How many pounds should be stocked to meet policy requirements?

   d. For the amount computed in (*c*), what is the expected number of pounds short for periods where shortage occurs?

   e. For the amount computed in (*c*), what is the expected number of pounds remaining for periods with no shortage?

5.7. Suppose the distribution of the length of life Y of an electronic tube is

$$f(t) = \begin{cases} 0 & t < 0 \\ 2te^{-t^2} & t \geq 0 \end{cases}$$

   a. Find Prob $(Y \geq y + x \mid Y > y)$, where $x > 0$.

   b. Compare the expression obtained in (*a*) with a similar expression if Y had the exponential distribution $f(t) = e^{-t}$ for $t \geq 0$.

5.8. An experimenter takes n independent observations on a normal random variable with unknown mean μ and variance $\sigma^2 = 4$.   After taking these observations, he will estimate μ by taking the arithmetic average $\bar{X}$ of his observations.   He wants the chance that $\bar{X}$ will differ from μ by more than 0.05 to be less than 1 per cent.   How many observations must be made to achieve this aim?

5.9. Suppose X has an exponential distribution with mean m.

    a. Show that $2X/m$ has a χ^2 distribution. Find its degrees of freedom.

    b. Let $U_k = X_1 + X_2 + \cdots + X_k$, where $X_1, X_2, \ldots, X_k$ are k independent observations on X. That is, U_k has an Erlang distribution with parameters k and $1/m$. Find the distribution of $2U_k/m$.

    c. Let $k = 5$ and $m = 2.5$. What is the probability that $U_5 > 20.00$?

5.10. Suppose a particle starts its random motion at the origin. At each trial, it moves one unit to the right or stays in the same position with probabilities p and $1 - p$, respectively. The decision at each stage is assumed to be independent of the previous decisions and its present position. Let N_r denote the number of steps until the particle reaches position r for the first time.

    a. Find $E(N_r)$ and $V(N_r)$.

    b. Using the central limit theorem, find an approximate expression for Prob $(N_r > n)$.

5.11. The functioning of a machine depends on a critical component. Suppose a component is in the machine and $r - 1$ spares are available. As soon as a component fails, a spare is chosen to replace it and the machine continues to function. Suppose the lifetimes of the components are independent, each with mean m and variance σ^2. Let T_r be the lifetime of a machine with the spares.

    a. Use central limit to find an approximate expression for the probability that $T_r > t$.

    b. Using the result in (*a*), find Prob $(T_r > 100)$ when $m = 6$, $\sigma = 1$, and $r = 16$ (units in weeks).

The operation of the machine is required for 100 weeks. If the machine plus spares fails before 100 weeks, there is a loss of C_F. Assume that the cost of a component (or spares) is C_S.

    c. Let C_r denote the total cost with $r - 1$ spares. Find $E(C_r)$, as a function of r, when $m = 6$, $\sigma = 1$, $C_S = \$1$, and $C_F = \$50$. [Use approximate expression in (*a*).]

    d. What is best r under the conditions specified in (*c*)?

5.12. A particle at each step can move one unit to the right or one unit to the left with probabilities p and $1 - p$, respectively. The starting position is assumed to be the origin. The decision at each step is made independently of the previous steps and on the present position. The motion ends either when the particle reaches $B > 0$ or the value $A < 0$. Use the Monte Carlo method to find:

    a. The probability of reaching B before A when $A = -3$, $B = 6$, and $p = \frac{3}{4}$.

    b. Same as (*a*), when $A = -2$, $B = 4$, and $p = \frac{3}{4}$.

    c. Expected duration of motion (number of steps until either A or B is reached).

5.13. A particle moves one unit to the right or to the left at each stage as in Exercise 5.12, except that the probabilities at each stage depend on its position. Denote by $P_{r,r+1}$ and $P_{r,r-1}$ the probabilities of going from r to $r + 1$ and from r to $r - 1$, respectively. Let $P_{r,r+1} = 1/r$ when $r > 0$ and $1 - 1/|r|$ when $r < 0$. Assume that when $r = 0$ the chances of going to the right or to the left are equal. Use the

Monte Carlo procedure to answer questions (a) to (c) of Exercise 5.12 for the present process.

5.14. In relation to Example 5.2, find the probability that $Z > 8$ when $\theta_1 = 0.50$, $\theta_2 = 0.10$, and $p = 0.50$.

5.15. An item consists of an assembly of 10 components. The overall length of the assembly L is the sum of the lengths $L_1, L_2, \ldots, L_{10}$ of the components. Assume that $L_1, L_2, \ldots, L_{10}$ are independently and normally distributed with mean equal to 3 and variance σ^2 equal to 0.016.

  a. What is the probability that the overall assembly has length within 30 ± 0.50?
  b. What is the maximum value of σ^2 so that the probability in (a) is at least 99 per cent?

5.16. A circular ground target has a radius equal to 5 yards. In trying to hit this target, it is found that the vertical and horizontal deviations X and Y from the target center are independently and normally distributed with zero mean and variance $\sigma^2 = 5.42$.

  a. What is the probability of hitting the target with one bomb?
  b. How many bombs must be dropped to make the probability of at least one hit 99 per cent?
  c. What is the maximum value of σ^2 so that the probability in (a) is 99 per cent?

5.17. X and Y are two independent normal random variables with variances σ_x^2 and σ_y^2, respectively. It is decided to take n independent observations from X and Y. How large must n be so that the probability that $(s_x^2/s_y^2)/(\sigma_x^2/\sigma_y^2)$ be within the range from 0.63 to 1.6 is 90 per cent?

5.18. Let the random variable X have a Poisson distribution with mean λ. Show that Prob $(X \leq c) = 1 - $ Prob $(\chi^2 \leq 2\lambda)$, where the χ^2 variate has $2(c + 1)$ degrees of freedom. (HINT: Use repeated integration by parts.)

5.19. A common procedure in industry for the sampling of a lot is specified by the numbers n and c. The procedure is to take a random sample of n items from the lot and compute the number of defectives d. If $d \leq c$, the lot is accepted, and if $d > c$, the lot is rejected. Let N denote the number of items in the lot and p the proportion defective in the lot. Assume that N is a large and that d may be approximated by the Poisson distribution.

  a. Find the probability of accepting a lot as a function of p when $n = 50$ and $c = 3$. Plot this function, which is called the operating characteristic (OC) curve of the plan.
  b. Using the result in Exercise 5.18, find n and c such that:

  (i) Prob (accepting lot when $p = 0.01$) ≥ 0.90.
  (ii) Prob (accepting lot when $p = 0.04$) ≤ 0.10.

5.20. Suppose that, in conjunction with a sampling plan specified by n and c, a screening procedure is used as follows. When the lot is accepted, it is sent out unscreened. On the other hand, when a lot is rejected, it is fully screened and all defective items are replaced by good ones. Let z denote the proportion of defectives in the outgoing lot. Find $E(z)$ as a function of p, the proportion defective in the incoming lot. The function $E(z)$ is called the AOQ (average outgoing quality) curve associated with the plan. Plot $E(z)$ as a function of p when $n = 50$ and $c = 3$.

5.21. Consider a series of independent random variables $Y_1, Y_2, Y_3, \ldots$, each with mean zero and variance σ^2. A new set of random variables $X_1, X_2, X_3, \ldots$ is defined from the relationship

$$X_j = \alpha X_{j-1} + Y_j \qquad j = 1, 2, \ldots$$

and X_0 is defined to be zero. Let $-1 < \alpha < +1$.

a. Find $E(X_n)$ and $V(X_n)$.

b. Use the central limit theorem to obtain an approximate expression for large n for Prob $(X_n \leq t)$.

5.22. The successive intervals between accidents in a certain plant has been found to be independently distributed. From past data, the probabilities of various interval lengths have been estimated to be as follows:

Interval, weeks	1	2	3	4	5	6	7	8	9
Probability	0.07	0.10	0.12	0.25	0.25	0.14	0.03	0.02	0.02

Assume the chance of two or more accidents per week to be negligible. Let N_w denote the number of accidents in a period of w weeks.

a. Use the Monte Carlo technique to estimate the probability function of N_{20} and N_{10}.

5.23. A piece of equipment is operating. Every once in a while it fails and is immediately repaired and begins operating again until the next failure. Assume that the machine is as new after it is repaired. Let the time to failure be described by a random variable L with mean m_L and variance $\sigma_L{}^2$. Furthermore, let the length of time for repair be described by another random variable, R, independent of L, with mean m_R and variance $\sigma_R{}^2$. Assume the successive life intervals and repair intervals to be independent. Let N_T denote the number of failures in the time interval $[0,T]$. Use the central limit theorem to get an approximate expression for Prob $(N_T \geq S)$ for large S (large enough for the central limit theorem to apply). (HINT: First show that $L_1 + L_2 + \cdots + L_S + R_1 + R_2 + \cdots + R_{S-1} > T$ is equivalent to $N_T < S$.)

5.24. Show that the χ^2 distribution with n degrees of freedom can be approximated by the normal distribution when n is large. How would you approximate Prob $(\chi^2 > a)$?

5.25. Demonstrate the formula (from Sec. 5.2.6)

$$F_{1-\alpha, m_1, m_2} = \frac{1}{F_{\alpha, m_2, m_1}}$$

$\left(\text{HINT: Compare the distribution of } \dfrac{U}{m_1} \Big/ \dfrac{W}{m_2} \text{ and } \dfrac{W}{m_2} \Big/ \dfrac{U}{m_1}.\right)$

5.26. Let X be normally distributed with mean m and variance σ^2. Find an expression for the CDF and PDF of X^2.

5.27. If Y is a random variable such that ln Y has a normal distribution with mean m and variance σ^2, then Y is said to have a log normal distribution. Plot the CDF of Y with $m = 2.0$ and $\sigma = 0.1$ and 1.0.

5.28. Let X have a Poisson distribution with parameter λ.

a. Calculate directly from the definition the mean and variance of X.
b. Using the moment-generating function, find $E(X^3)$ and $E(X^4)$.

5.29. Using the moment-generating function of the exponential random variable X, compute $E(X^3)$ and $E(X^4)$.

5.30. Let $X_1, X_2, \ldots, X_N$ be N independent exponentially distributed random variables with parameter θ. Show that:

a. $E\left[\min (X_1, X_2, \ldots, X_N)\right] = 1/N\theta$.

b. $E\left[\max (X_1, X_2, \ldots, X_N)\right] = \dfrac{1}{\theta}\left(\dfrac{1}{N} + \dfrac{1}{N-1} + \dfrac{1}{N-2} + \cdots + \dfrac{1}{2} + 1\right)$.
   (HINT: Write $\max (X_1, X_2, \ldots, X_N)$ in terms of $I_1 + I_2 + \cdots + I_N$, where I_j equals the interval between the $(j-1)$st largest to the jth largest value of $X_1, X_2, \ldots, X_N$.)

5.31. Find the moment-generating function of the hyperexponential distribution. Use the result to find the mean and variance of this distribution.

5.32. Let X be normally distributed with mean m and variance σ^2. Find the third and fourth moments, using the moment-generating function.

5.33. Let $X_1, X_2, \ldots, X_n$ be n independent observations of a random variable X with variance σ^2. Let $s^2 = \Sigma(X_i - \bar{X})/(n-1)$. Show that $E(s^2) = \sigma^2$.

5.34. Show that $f_m(u)$ is a PDF, where

$$f_m(u) = \frac{(u/2)^{m/2-1}}{2\Gamma(m/2)}\, e^{-u/2} \qquad 0 \leq u \leq \infty$$

5.35. Find an expression for the moments of the χ^2 distribution with m degrees of freedom.

5.36. Suppose 100 items are in storage. Let the lifetimes of the items be $L_1, L_2, \ldots, L_{100}$ independent and each normally distributed with mean $m = 150$ weeks and $\sigma = 30$. What is the approximate probability that 45 per cent of the stockpile will still be operative after 160 weeks? (HINT: Use the approximation in Example 5.6.)

5.37. Use the normal approximation to find the probability of obtaining more than 215 heads in 400 independent tosses of a fair coin. Compare the results using and not using the correction for continuity.

5.38. Suppose X has a uniform distribution over interval $[0,1]$, and N independent observations $X_1, X_2, \ldots, X_N$ are taken on X. Let these be ordered $X_{[1]} \leq X_{[2]} \leq \cdots \leq X_{[N]}$. Let $\bar{X}$ be the arithmetic average. Denote by $P_N(i,j)$ the probability that $X_{[i]} \leq \bar{X} \leq X_{[j]}$ ($i \leq j$). That is,

$$P_N(i,j) = \text{Prob}\ (X_{[i]} \leq \bar{X} \leq X_{[j]})$$

Use the Monte Carlo method to estimate $P_{10}(3,6)$.

5.39. Let X have a normal distribution with mean m and variance σ^2. Let $P_N(i,j)$ be defined as in (5.38).

a. Show that $P_N(i,j)$ does not depend on m and σ^2.
b. Use the Monte Carlo method to estimate $P_{10}(3,6)$. Compare with Exercise 5.38.

5.40. Suppose Y_1 and Y_2 are independent random variables such that $E(Y_1) = E(Y_2) = 1$ and $V(Y_1) = V(Y_2) = 1$.

a. Using Tchebycheff's inequality, give a bound on the probability that $|Y_1 - Y_2| > 6$.

b. Using Tchebycheff's inequality, find a bound for the probability that $|Y_1 - 1| > \frac{1}{2}$.

c. Compare the bound found in (b) with exact values in the cases when Y_1 is known to be exponentially and normally distributed.

5.41. Suppose the number of accidents $N(t)$ in time interval $[0,t]$ is Poisson-distributed with mean λt. Furthermore, each time an event occurs, there is a chance p that it is recorded. If $R(t)$ is the number of recorded accidents in $[0,t]$, what is the distribution of $R(t)$? [HINT: Use the concept of conditional expectations and find the moment-generating function of $R(t)$.]

5.42. Show that $t_{\alpha,m}^2 = F_{\alpha,1,m}$.

5.43. Prove the relationship $\sum_{j=0}^{N} \binom{N}{j} = 2^N$. [HINT: Expand $(p + q)^N$.]

5.44. In relation to Example 5.4, let $N = 100{,}000$, $p = 0.05$, and $\alpha = 1$ per cent (service level is 99 per cent). How many facilities are required? Plot the required number of facilities versus N.

5.45. In relation to Example 5.5, assume that $F(t) = 1 - e^{-t/2}$. Find approximately Prob $(Z_{55,100} > 2)$.

5.46. In relation to Example 5.6, let $N_i = N$ for all i; $F(t) = (t/10)$ $(0 \le t \le 10)$, $S = 100$. Find minimum N such that Prob $(U_{20} > 99) \ge 95$ per cent.

5.47. Let Y be uniformly distributed over interval $[0,1]$.

a. Show that $-2 \ln Y$ has a χ^2 distribution with 2 degrees of freedom.

b. Find Prob $(Y_1 Y_2 \cdots Y_{10} \le 0.8)$, where $Y_1, Y_2, \ldots, Y_{10}$ are independently and uniformly distributed over $[0,1]$.

5.48. Consider a random variable X which takes on values 0, 1, 2, . . . , with probabilities p_0, p_1, p_2, . . . , respectively. If $E(X)$ and $V(X)$ denote the mean and variance of X, show that, when $E(X)$ and $V(X)$ are finite, $p_i \le E(X)/i$ and $p_i \le V(X)/[i - E(X)]^2$.

5.49. Let X_1, X_2, . . . , X_n be independent normal random variables with variance σ^2. Using properties of the moment-generating function, show that $(n - 1)s^2/\sigma^2$ has a χ^2 distribution with $n - 1$ degrees of freedom.

6

DECISION MAKING

Introduction Much has been written, both formal and non-formal, about decision making. Industrial and business executives, as well as the government official and the military commander, have been singled out for special attention with respect to their role as "decision makers." There is no argument about the fact that the principal occupation of persons in these categories is that of making decisions on a variety of problems. Lest one assume that all problems confronting these decision makers are always of major importance, the reader is reminded that military commanders of high rank, even under combat circumstances, may be responsible for determining the magnitude of shipments of supplies of relatively minor importance. The delegation of decisions which the manager or executive considers of minor importance is in itself a decision of some importance. Let us not pass over the fact that, as well as the scientist, engineer, and physician, the housewife, with her many concerns, and all of us humble human beings are making decisions that are important (to us, at least) every day.

At the moment we are not assessing the importance of decision making as a general function nor the relative importance of various categories of decisions. We hope merely to explore the nature of decision making, the demands it makes upon probability and statistical inference, and the roles which these disciplines can play in contributing to effective decisions. Since this discussion is not intended to be comprehensive, we believe that the best way to examine the process and structure of decision making, from the perspective of this text, is to look at some specific problems. Selection of problems can be made for various reasons. Here they are made primarily to show the operational and formal differences in decision situations which may arise. In respect to obtaining relevant evidence, stable observations and verifiability and differences between internal manipulatable variables and external nonmanipulatable variables are quite pertinent. There may be circumstances for repetitive-corrective decisions, reversible decisions, or nonrepetitive and irreversible decisions.

Again, problems may differ markedly in the consequences of decision, where gains and penalties may differ widely. In some situations intuitive decision is all that can be hoped for, in contrast with those situations where the process of decision can be advantageously formally structured.

6.1   Some problems for decision

6.1.1   Capacity of auto gasoline tank

A national automobile manufacturer has made the decision to introduce a small car to compete with the imported cars. Among many technical problems, one holding his interest at the moment is that of determining the gasoline-tank capacity. How can he go about arriving at this decision? Let us not make any attempt here at an organized or formal procedure, but merely bring forth some intuitive suggestions. One might, for example, decide that the tank should be the same as the smallest now used by the manufacturer. This selection has some practical advantages since it involves no new design, except, perhaps, for connections; it minimizes the number of new drawings; and it involves little new tooling. Obviously, for the first few years this tank may be the least costly to introduce, or at least its cost is well established. There may, however, be difficulties militating against its use. Another possibility is to pick a number out of the air, a new number, in the firm belief (without any substantiating evidence) that it is inherently suited to the size and character of the new car. The reader's first reaction may be to dismiss this approach, but let him stop and consider the means by which he and his colleagues arrived at the last dozen important decisions which they made.

Some other suggestions are as follows:

1. Examine the data on gasoline-tank capacity of existing popular small cars competitive to the one to be introduced.
2. Canvass the company distributors who are to handle the new car.
3. Survey "potential" customers of the new car.
4. Canvass the factory personnel where the company's smallest car is being manufactured.
5. Study daily mileage records of present users of the company's smaller models. Using an engineering estimate of gasoline consumption for the new car, compute expected tank capacity sufficient to satisfy 90 per cent of the daily mileage requirements.

One might propose a number of other approaches, which would merely emphasize the numerous elements that seem to have bearing on making the most effective choice of gasoline capacity. It is hardly necessary to argue that some consistently applicable approach involving quantitative techniques for decision making may be useful.

Note that in this industrial problem there is nonrepetitive decision and high penalty for wrong decision, which is also nonreversible. Furthermore, neither relevant evidence nor decision maker's utilities are readily assessable.

6.1.2 Scientific measurement

An investigation is being made on the simultaneous stress effects on a structure in three directions. Measurements are required continuously over a number of minutes of operation. The available measuring instruments are very expensive, and the investigator is confronted with the choice between two available types. On one instrument one can measure the stress in only one direction at a time; on the other one can measure the stresses simultaneously in three directions. The latter equipment costs five times as much as the single-stress instrument. Which instrument should be purchased? We shall not suggest approaches here, for the reader no doubt already recognizes the various factors bearing upon the decision, not the least of which involve observation and statistical inference.

Here an engineering research problem has been chosen in which decision is hardly reversible, but repetitive observations are possible and the variables to be measured are likely to come from a stable system. The penalties are not as great as in the preceding problem, and the criteria for decision are more clearly expressible.

6.1.3 Safety programs and risk taking

For many years considerable effort has been made to reduce incidence of injuries resulting from industrial accidents. Innumerable studies are still being made to bring to light the principal causes leading to accidents. Much progress has been made on what has been referred to as the environmental and engineering factors which have contributed to accident occurrence. These are essentially physical factors which have been engineered away; the motivation for their removal has frequently been initiated by legislation. The general climate of opinion among safety authorities is that, in the well-established industries, progress in environmental accident control has reached the point of marginal return. Much of the recent effort has been directed toward the training of working personnel in good safety practice. Toward this end a variety of safety-training programs have been devised, whose yearly cost runs into many millions of dollars. A serious question has been raised as to whether or not to continue one or another phase of this program. A hypothesis that has been offered in connection with safety training is that individuals of certain work groups have a certain propensity for "taking risks" in

performance of their jobs.   If the training programs do indeed have a
mitigating effect, there should be measurable evidence of a reduction in
risk taking after a certain "measured quantity" of safety training.   In
one very large organization, a decision problem was raised as to whether
or not to continue the use of safety-training films among other aspects
of their safety-training program.   One may look upon this problem as
demanding the choice of one of two alternatives, namely, continue the
use of safety-training films or discontinue their use.   One may also pose
three alternatives: (1) continue use of the presently available stock of
films, (2) discontinue use of these films but develop new films, (3) discontinue use of all safety-training films.   One may offer other sets of
alternatives, and as a matter of fact, the formulation of alternatives is
one of the major aspects of decision making.

It is apparent that necessary information regarding the consequences
entailed by these alternatives is definitely of a statistical nature since it
involves that of an individual's behavior over time, as well as the differences among different members of a work group.

The study of safety programs and risk taking involves difficulties of
quantification—difficulties in the choice of what to measure.   Although
in such programs there is reversibility of decision, there remain serious
questions of stability of the whole system under study and of pertinent
alternatives.

6.1.4   Packing problem

We have discussed various aspects of the packing problem in the preceding chapters, not without good reason.   The problem itself may seem
to be specialized; in fact, however, it is typical of the general problem of
tolerances.   As such, it is a prototype of a wide class of industrial problems, which of necessity requires probabilistic and statistical treatment.
Here we examine this problem further in the light of its decision-making
aspects (see Exercise 1.6).

One might begin with the question, what are the essential decision
aspects of this problem?   These elements become apparent when one
considers how the problem came about.   In the early stages of the manufacture of this product little thought was given to the specification of the
container or to the costs involved in packing, except that the container
be "large enough" and sturdy.   No serious thought was given to variation in container size until complaints of damage to the part began to
mount up.   Furthermore, a number of the packers complained, to the
surprise of the designer, that some containers had to be set aside because
of insufficient length.   Some of these difficulties led to a closer scrutiny
of the problem of safe and economic packing.

The first attempt to overcome these difficulties centered on the
dimensions of the container, in particular, of the container length.   The

design engineer, on making some observations on the part length, noted the variation actually occurring in part and container length and decided to use the following decision procedure: design the nominal container length so that the nominal minus the tolerance for variation below the nominal is at least as great as the upper tolerance limit of the part.   In symbols, this may be stated as follows:

$$L_c \geq U_p + \delta$$

where L_c is the nominal container length, U_p is the upper specification for the part (this value has been set on the basis that it has been exceeded by not more than 1 per cent of the parts inspected during the past 3 months), and δ is a measure of the variation of container lengths such that 2δ included 99 per cent of the inspected container lengths during the past 3 months.

The reasoning underlying this "play-safe" decision procedure is that the present process is designed with a setting for container length called the nominal and with a symmetric variation such that the nominal $\pm \delta$ includes 99 per cent of the observed container length variations of the past 3 months.

The implication is that since very few containers will be shorter than $L_c - \delta$ and since very few parts will be greater than U_p, very few parts will not fit into any container.   Hence packing should be possible without selection and with rare interference.   The inspection procedure was set up to meet the requirements of this decision rule.   We shall examine the foregoing from the point of view of its implications and consequences.

In previous sections we considered the distribution of gap length E in connection with computing various probabilities relating to interference and the use of felt pads.   These probabilities have obvious bearing on the cost of packing.   As in Chap. 3, where the manager raised questions of overall costs, the design engineer offered the above play-safe decision rule in order to reduce packing costs.   However we look at this problem, we center attention upon costs.   Hence the general decision problem here, as elsewhere, involves the selection of one among many feasible alternatives so as to minimize the costs.   The play-safe rule, which in effect selects an alternative (namely, a particular nominal container length), actually does not take into account costs other than those resulting from interference—obviously the costs of necessary felt-pad fillers may be increased by the use of the play-safe rule.   Thus our task is to recognize all feasible alternatives, to have them incorporated into a cost function, and to select that alternative which minimizes the cost function.   As a matter of fact, a more comprehensive, but still not complete, formulation of the packing decision problem is given as Exercise 1.6; we actually stated a number of decision stages culminating in what is equivalent to a choice of the optimal nominal container length.   Obviously, a more comprehensive formulation of the problem entails consideration of a wider range of alternatives and many other cost factors.   For example, sets of alternatives could include the choice of a nominal, the choice of an inspection procedure, and the modes of selection of containers to match part length.   Again, other costs that arise in maintaining stability in the production process (quality control), inspection, and selection procedure could be incorporated into a total cost function.

One feature pervading this discussion is that of relating the choice of an alternative to its consequences.   Evidence of this relationship is statistical, and we can expect that arriving at effective decisions will involve probabilistic and statistical methods.

This problem in production engineering entails interaction between process and consequent effect on decisions as to design of the product and its manufacturing control.   Here there is repetitiveness, reversibility, means for attaining statistical stability, and availability of relevant evidence.

6.1.5   Surgery and choice of a surgeon

At one time or another in one's life, one may be faced with the likelihood of surgical therapy—to be or not to be operated upon.   One need hardly state that such decisions are grave ones, not to be made lightly.   It would be reassuring if there were systematic procedures for making such decisions with confidence.   We shall not discuss the various approaches now commonly used, but we shall point out some of the difficulties in decision making when the consequences cannot be measured in monetary terms alone.   We shall illustrate by a discussion of a particular case.

A rather vigorous man in his early fifties suffered a severe abdominal spasm—so distressing that he had visions of dying during the eight hours of its duration.   Upon recovering from the acute symptoms he was subject to comprehensive medical examinations, whose findings indicated a diseased gall bladder.   Repeated X rays seemed to lend conviction to this diagnosis.   The physician suggested surgical treatment—this ailment is usually chronic and recurrent—without much delay, since after fifty, the risks involved in the operation become markedly greater.

How would the reader go about making a decision in this case?   Can one offer a procedure for such decision making that can be followed with conviction?   Suppose that many of one's friends had followed one such procedure successfully: would the reader consider this a basis for his own action?   Suppose that there were considerable statistical data as to the "success" and consequences of such operations as the one discussed: would this be relevant to your own decision?   Are data giving "odds on success" relevant to this decision?   Would the sense of the relevance of these odds be different in the cases 9 to 1 and 99 to 1?

Can one assess the consequences of nonoperation meaningfully? Can one properly evaluate the consequences of the failure of an operation? In short, can one apply probabilistic and statistical methods, with conviction, to such decision problems?

It is evident that there are many difficulties to be overcome in framing a policy for *individual* decision making in such questions. In the first place, the decision is essentially made once for an individual and may be irrevocable. The factual basis of probability of success or failure of the operation is, under the best circumstances, subject to different interpretations. The criteria of success or failure are, in many cases, far from universal. Evaluating the consequences of foregoing surgical action as compared with the range of consequences resulting from surgery is hardly an established procedure. At present, it is doubtful that we have reliable means for quantifying the relevant factors.

Circumstances for decisions affecting surgery do arise, however, which lend themselves to statistical treatment. Decisions are made by executives of hospitals, army commanders, and, in general, persons responsible for the health of large sectors of the population, with authority for action. In effect, these authorities either formulate or are responsible for the execution of policy which may result in surgery, where the effectiveness of surgery is evaluated on a statistical basis. Here, of course, the repetition of action in many cases makes meaningful the use of probability, at least in the evaluation of consequences, where in the case of an individual "one-time" decision the meaningfulness of probability considerations may be in question.

We have discussed so-called individualized decisions of great consequence in order to emphasize the difficulties which can be involved. Fortunately, many important decisions in our daily affairs are not irrevocable, and many apply to repetitive action where probability and statistical inference are highly effective.

No attempt is being made here to make a comprehensive coverage of varieties of decision problems—this could be the subject of a treatise by itself. We refer below to a few more problems to establish a broader feeling for the nuances of decision making and to indicate the scope for implementation of probabilistic and statistical methods.

6.1.6   Inventory and scheduling

A ship is going on a cruise: what quantities of its various required items should it stock? A mens' club cashes checks for its members: what limit should it put on the size of check it will cash, and how much cash should it have on hand daily? A factory is producing a consumer product which it distributes nationwide: what production schedule should it establish, and what quantities should it stock in the various warehouses? A mail-order house sells 6,000 items: what ordering and stocking policy should it follow?   There are innumerable problems of this type, which have in common the feature of making policy decisions in the face of varying degrees of uncertainty regarding the future.   Since these uncertainties can often be formulated statistically, they are a fruitful field for treatment by statistical means.

6.1.7   Storm warnings

A wide region along the eastern seaboard of the United States is subject to severe damage from hurricanes.   The United States Weather Bureau is repeatedly faced with the decision as to broadcasting storm warnings. When a warning is issued, considerable expenditure is required in preparations for mitigating the effects of the storm.   On the other hand, should a storm strike without warning, the consequences can be devastating. At present any forecast of the approach and intensity of a storm can be made with only a degree of reliability.   Arriving at a decision to give storm warnings or not calls for a considerable degree of statistical insight.

This problem will be dealt with at some length later in the chapter. It entails all the difficulties of nonrepetitiveness, nonreversibility, questions of stability, high penalty, uncertainties of measurement, among others.   Yet the role of statistical inference is quite important here, and some of the nuances of problem solving and decision making can be touched on in the discussion.

6.1.8   Determining rates of industrial productivity

Economic decisions in mass production require the establishment of productivity targets for specific manufacturing operations.   The rates of production for the same individual are highly variable over a long run, and different individuals differ from one another in their average rates. Nevertheless, the maintenance of "optimum" cost of production is essentially dependent on setting a target of the productivity level to be achieved by each worker.   The consequences of setting the target too high or too low can be very costly.   The decision as to the appropriate rate of production has recently been recognized as being amenable to statistical analysis.

6.1.9   Telegraph code

When S. F. B. Morse invented the telegraph in 1832 he was confronted with the problem of deciding on a suitable code for transmission.   The criterion he used for determining the code representation for a letter was that of the expected economy in the time for transmission.   In a sense, he intuitively undertook optimizing channel capacity.   He was aware of the difference of the frequencies of occurrence of the different letters of the English alphabet.   He therefore conceived a table of relative frequency of occurrence of the letters.   His procedure was both simple and ingenious. In order to obtain evidence of these frequencies Mr. Morse visited a print shop for a number of days, during which he tallied the letter frequencies of the material set in type. He arranged these frequencies in descending order and assigned the shortest code to the most frequent letter, the next shortest to the next frequent letter, and so on. The letter *e* occurred most frequently. The letter *e* was assigned a dot, and *t* was assigned a dash. Subsequent letters were assigned different sequences of dots, dashes, and spaces. The idea underlying the assignment was that the code length should increase inversely with the frequency of letter occurrence. In a very rough sense, this assignment tends to minimize the expected length of transmission.

There are many presuppositions underlying Morse's choice of code. The first, and perhaps most important, is that there is a stable probability of occurrence of any letter in the English alphabet. The second is that, in the long run, the expected value of the relative frequencies of the letter occurrence will be in the same order as that of the frequencies that Morse observed. In other words, Morse assumed stability, took a sample, and called his sample representative. It is interesting that Morse quite intuitively, and without thought of formal validity, hit upon some of the essentials of statistical method which apply to the coding problem.

There are, of course, other important considerations which influence the effective transmission of information. Some of these factors are related to redundancy in language, signal-transmission errors, and channel characteristics. In the last decade, the technical problems of information transmittal have received considerable attention. These studies, as was anticipated by the example of the Morse code, rely heavily on probability and statistical inference.

6.1.10   Product range and variety

A manufacturer produces 10 different items. For each item he offers a choice of 20 different models. The controller of the company is concerned about the high inventory maintained in order to have a sufficient variety on hand to meet expected sales demand. He feels that the number of different models for the individual items can be cut in half, with resulting great savings in inventory costs. The sales manager wants a larger product line and more models per product, in order to step up sales. The production manager favors decreasing the number of varieties and increasing the size of manufacturing runs, in order to reduce manufacturing costs. The general manager is concerned with making some decision as to the optimum selection of items and models. Among the many relevant factors to be considered is the consumer demand by product and model. Such data may be available from past records on the present product-model mix. On the other hand, information on the nature of consumer demand for a given product, were fewer models available, would require sample surveys.   Data collected over many years have indicated that more than half of the company's sales volume derives from only 20 per cent of the product-model mix.   It is not to be assumed, however, that the sales volume of these 20 per cent will hold up when the consumer has a smaller variety to choose from.   Making profitable decisions, in such problems, invites considerable ingenuity in planning investigations, as well as in the statistical interpretation of the results.

The foregoing problems provide considerable opportunity for examining the principles of decision-making procedures and the role of probability and statistical inference.   We consider some of them in this light.

6.2   Considerations in the structure of decisions

Introductory Discussion   In exploring the nature of decision making we shall focus on certain features which seem essential to any discussion on the subject.   The obvious is often honored by neglect, and this occurs in decision making as well, where formulation of overall *goals* and *values* of the decision maker and specification of the *objectives* aimed at in a problem are all too infrequently explicitly formulated.   The very posing of a decision problem implies the existence of choice among *alternative courses of action*, for if there were no choice, there would be no decision problem.   Preferences among these alternatives are certainly related to the *consequences* of the alternatives considered.   The degree of knowledge relating consequences to courses of action is fundamental in making a choice between alternatives.   This knowledge can be incorporated, in more specifically quantitative form, by setting up *measures of effectiveness*. Measures of effectiveness should, if possible, reflect unambiguously the degree of attainment of objectives, values, and overall goals.   Usually the above elements are incorporated into symbolic form, often called *models*, which provide means for computing consequences of courses of action and measures of effectiveness.   Since many decisions are effective over substantial periods of time, during which modification may be possible, and since many decisions on problems of a similar nature are made repeatedly, much of decision making is essentially of a continuing self-corrective nature.   Hence evaluation of effectiveness of decision is essential.

Much attention has been given in the statistical literature to making a choice of alternatives.   Statistical inference has been presented as a formal theory of decision.   We have used the expression decision making in a broader sense than the one commonly in use and should emphasize that the basic task is problem solving.   In problem solving (and all decision making is a stage in problem solving) the structuring of a decision process is an early and exploratory stage.   When one comes to the use of a selected formal decision procedure, much of the infighting, intuitive grappling with alternatives, utilities, criteria of choice, and measures of

effectiveness has been gone through, for better or worse.   Our discussion
in this chapter, it is hoped, will indicate some of the operational constraints encountered in problem solving in general and in the use of statistical inference in particular at the later stage of decisions.

We shall discuss these selected elements in respect to their utilization
of probability and statistics in the decision process.

6.2.1   Goals, values, and objectives

What are the objectives to be achieved in the "small auto gas tank"
problem?   Is one of the objectives the largest capacity possible?   Is
another the lowest-cost tank?   Are these obviously acceptable objectives?   Do they conflict with our goals?   Before answering these questions, let us look at our other suggested problems.

Can we clearly enunciate goals and values in the "safety program"
problem?   Suppose we agree that there is but a single objective, namely,
to reduce accidents.   Can the study of training-film effectiveness achieve
this objective?   In fact, is not the objective to measure the effect of
training films on risk taking?   Is risk taking a suitable predictor of
accidents?   Is not accident reduction rather a general goal?   Is not the
objective the reduction in risk-taking behavior?   What values underlie
our objective?   This problem may seem a bit confusing, but it is for this
reason that it is considered.   For one of the virtues of an organized decision procedure, employing statistical methods, lies in its ability to reduce
questions of goals, values, and objectives to tractable quantitative form.
In actual experience, it has been found necessary to observe an industrial
environment over periods of a year or more in order to make decisions
on the effects of safety programs on accident incidence.   The difficulty
confronting the decision maker in this problem lies in the conflict between
the serious consequences to the individual injured in an industrial accident
and the low incidence of accident occurrence, factors which are difficult to
evaluate statistically.   Meaningful translation of goals and values into
specific   objectives,   for   experimentation   and   observation,   must   be
expressed in tractable quantitative terms.   While accidents can be very
easily counted, investigations concerning accident incidence are much
more costly and time-consuming than are investigations on risk taking.
Here, clearly, determining specific objectives cannot be considered apart
from the possibility of meaningful measurement and statistical analysis.

Now we ask, is the reduction of accidents the true unqualified goal?
Apparently cost considerations enter the decision maker's plans.   Is the
expenditure on accident reduction a worthwhile investment?   Clearly,
cost considerations are among the limiting factors affecting our goals
and objectives.   Although only a few of our values may be expressible
in material costs, we cannot escape their consideration in the framing of
goals and objectives.

The foregoing discussion has illustrated some of the intangibles connected with the meaningful, measurable, and statistically interpretable objectives. In the gas-tank problem, where no such profound issues arise, there remains the issue between reduction of production costs and overall effectiveness. It is also to be recognized that an objective may be effective for a short period and yet be detrimental to the long-range goals of the decision maker. Undoubtedly, the production manager and the sales manager will be at odds concerning the principal objective, and neither may be close to meeting the overall requirements. It is not a large gas tank (which the sales manager wants for promotional reasons) nor the lowest-cost gas tank (which will show the production manager in the best light), but a combination of optimizing profit, providing for long-range stability of the company, and possible prestige factors, which is likely to lead to a satisfactory framing of objectives.

In inventory problems, reducing the size of inventory is not necessarily the desirable objective, but rather an inventory which *balances* various losses such as cost of maintaining inventory at a certain level and the loss resulting from shortages. The framing of objectives bears directly on the loss function, with which the decision maker must work.

In the "storm-warning" problem, there again is the conflict between loss of both life and property and the cost to the community for storm preparations.

This brief discussion on goals, values, and objectives has been offered to indicate the possible misdirection which may be the outcome of inappropriate framing of objectives. This often results in decisions which do not realize the true goals of the decision maker. No degree of acuteness in the formulation of alternatives and their consequences can make up for "wrong" objectives. In fact, the evaluation stage should show the degree to which the decision made departs not only from the achievement of objectives, but even more, from the attainment of goals. Furthermore, even in cases where objectives are not erroneous, the evaluation procedure may lead to modification of objectives.

6.2.2   Formulation of alternative courses of action

A decision is but a selection of a course of action—every decision can be translated into this form. In the gas-tank problem the decision is the selection of one design from among a class of feasible designs. What is a class of feasible designs, or rather, how does one "think up" a feasible design? We shall not go into this aspect of decision making, which covers an infinite variety of specialized techniques. But alternatives must be offered, and they must relate to attainment of the objectives. This is a crucial step in any decision problem. The final decision, after all, is one of the alternatives. The framing of alternatives often requires resort to technical knowledge. Yet there may be some pitfalls we can avoid.   In the initial stages it is advisable to consider as wide a range of alternatives as one can conceive, independent of preconceptions concerning their feasibility.   One need not, in the first instance, be restricted by concern with difficulties of measurement.   Too strong a preconception as to a few possible alternatives may leave out of initial consideration that alternative which provides the most effective realization of objectives.   In the packing problem, the alternatives considered by the engineer in framing the play-safe decision rule actually excluded a class of alternatives.   In fact, among the alternatives of nominal container lengths which result in some interference may have been the most economical choice.   In inventory problems there is often the tendency to limit the alternatives in one direction.   For example, the decision question is often framed in terms of making longer runs rather than the optimum lengths of runs.   Similarly, in respect to purchase policy, the decision question is often expressed in terms of a reduced inventory rather than of the optimum inventory.

Alternatives are more readily assessable when stated in operational terms.   In the case of storm warnings one may simply express the alternatives verbally as: give storm warnings, do not give storm warnings. These alternatives are both empirically and logically exhaustive.   The implication is that there is but one type of storm warning, which is carried out in a unique set of steps.   If, however, storm warnings can be carried out in various degrees of preparation, then one should formulate a set of alternative warnings.   As a matter of fact, there are different storm warnings which are based on a classification into ranges of wind velocity.

6.2.3 Consequences

Alternatives are chosen because of the consequences to which they lead. The particular consequences resulting from a course of action depend upon the state of environment prevailing.   Hence, a consequence is specified by a pair consisting of alternative and state.   We know the possible states of the environment with varying degrees from complete ignorance to certainty.

The intermediate stages entail varying degrees of knowledge of the probabilities with which the various states of the environment can occur. This knowledge is usually derived from both past experience and current experimentation.   It is here that probability and statistical inference are intrinsic to the quantification of the problem in a form amenable to analysis.   In Sec. 6.3, we shall classify decision problems in terms of degrees of knowledge of the relationship between consequences of alternatives and the states of the environment.

To illustrate, consider the storm-warning problem in terms of the two alternatives: give warning, do not give warning.   We further con sider two states of the environment: state of storm, no storm. These states are logically exhaustive and mutually exclusive. We can represent the various alternative-state combinations as in Table 6.1. Each alternative leads to two consequences which are determined by the prevailing state of the environment. The value of this formulation lies in its focus on the elements which must be evaluated and on the state of our knowledge.

As was previously pointed out, storms can be classified into several categories, yielding a wider range of alternatives as well as states. The resulting consequence matrix is therefore larger. The problems of evaluation of the consequences may, however, become more manageable. This refinement may make the final decision more effective in the attainment of objectives.

TABLE 6.1

	State	
Alternative	Storm (S_1)	No storm (S_2)
Storm warning (a_1)	C_{11}	C_{12}
No storm warning (a_2)	C_{21}	C_{22}

Note that we have here considered a problem where the states of the environment are essentially distinct. The problem of rolling steel bars (example in Sec. 1.1) may appear to differ essentially from the storm-warning problem since a single state of the environment represented prevails there, namely, the distribution of the mass of the billets. For a given setting of the bar-rolling machine, a distribution of bar lengths results, dependent principally on the distribution of the mass of the billets. One can look upon the masses of the billets as constituting a great many different states of environment or as one state of environment represented by a distribution. It is not fruitful, in this case, to use the many-state characterization. We shall discuss in the next section some of the differences between the steel-bars problem and the storm-warning problem.

6.2.4 Measures of effectiveness and evaluation

The test of any decision lies in the degree to which it reflects realization of the decision maker's goals and values. In order to make a choice we must have some measure of the degree to which the consequences of the choice represent attainment of objectives. A choice among alternatives must reflect the decision maker's preferences among consequences (denoted by C_{ij}). A basic task, therefore, is to express these preferences in a form which will make the problem of selection amenable to unambiguous rules of choice.   This is most effectively done when numerical assignments can be made.   Admittedly, this is a big task.   Nevertheless, it is fruitful to attempt this numericalization.   The result of this procedure, then, is a set of numbers U_{ij} (sometimes called *utilities*) corresponding to the consequences C_{ij}.   The scale is so chosen that the greater the U_{ij}, the greater the preference for the C_{ij}.

Let us attempt to try this out on the storm-warning problem, which we now explicitly formulate as follows.   Given a certain quantity of meteorological knowledge about the state of the region 1,000-mile radius, centered at St. Petersburg, Fla., the decision problem is, shall we give storm warnings for sections of the eastern seaboard from Florida to Norfolk, Va.?   Let us examine the consequences in Table 6.1.   Consequence C_{11}, storm warning–storm occurrence, on the basis of previous experience, will entail preparation costs of \$370,000, expected property damage of \$110,000, and expectation of 15 personal injuries and no loss of life.   Consequence C_{12}, storm warning–no storm, entails the preparation cost of \$370,000.   Consequence C_{21}, no storm warning–storm occurrence, entails zero preparation costs, expected property damage of \$2,500,000, and 150 personal injuries and 10 deaths.   Consequence C_{22}, no storm warning–no storm, entails zero cost.   Let us point out that we could hardly approach this problem systematically if we did not have data on previous storms and statistical means of estimating expected consequences.

How shall we proceed to find the U_{ij}?   Were there no injuries or loss of life, we could simply add up the costs, yielding

$$U_{11} = -480,000 \qquad U_{12} = -370,000$$
$$U_{21} = -2,500,000 \qquad U_{22} = 0$$

Since the higher the utility, the greater the preference, costs have been represented negatively, and the preferred consequence is C_{22}.   It might seem from this that a_2, no storm warning, is the choice.   On the other hand, it is obvious that C_{21} is by far the worst consequence. Preference among consequences does not necessarily provide a choice of alternative.   And let us bear in mind that we have simplified the problem of choice considerably by omitting the significance of human loss, which presents even more perplexing questions of value.

Without some form of knowledge we are stymied.   Our difficulty seems to arise from the fact that the different states lead to different U_{ij}'s.   If both $U_{11} > U_{21}$ and $U_{12} > U_{22}$ prevailed, alternative a_1 would be preferred.   In such a case, knowledge of the state is not necessary, but in most practical cases uniform preference rarely occurs.

How shall we resolve this dilemma?   Where shall the new knowledge come from?   It seems that it is knowledge about the states that we need. For if we knew whether or not a storm would occur, the decision problem would disappear. Thus our *knowledge of the states of environment is vital.* Next to certainty, we can have knowledge of the probabilities of the states. We shall examine this further in the next section.

The nature of the analysis in this problem is predicated upon the existence of several distinct states of environment. Nevertheless, each distinct state of environment may be, in itself, representable by a distribution. For example, when we considered the C_{ij}, we used expected utilities, since each C_{ij} in fact represented a whole range of consequences.

The steel-bar problem can be looked upon in the same framework as the storm-warning problem, but it would not be a fruitful endeavor, since one would require some hundreds of individual states of billets. A more practically effective approach to this problem is to look upon the state of environment as a distribution. Then the consequence of an alternative (namely, setting for a nominal bar length) yields a distribution with an expected utility which represents the composite evaluation of the distribution of bar lengths and their utilities. This, of course, includes the values that we place upon short bars, trimming, scrap, etc. In point of fact, the setting chosen is the one which gives the maximum expected utility (in this case, minimum expected cost).

6.3 Classification of decision situations

Introductory Discussion Our discussion so far has brought to light the varying degrees with which consequences as well as states of environment are known. There are situations in which choice of an alternative can be made in a determinate formulation of the problem. That is to say, in these situations, an action leads to a unique consequence. We call this the case of *deterministic certainty.* A common variant of this situation is one in which an action leads to a set of consequences with known probabilities. In other words, we cannot specify beforehand which consequence will result from a course of action, but we can state the probability with which each can occur. We call this *probabilistic certainty.*

6.3.1 Degrees of uncertainty and decision

In some situations, as we have already indicated, there is an even lesser degree of knowledge relating action to consequence than in the situations mentioned above. In such cases, even though probabilities may be assumed to exist, they are not fully known. Here experiments and statistical inference play a central role. This type of situation is called *stable uncertainty.*

An even more uncertain decision situation exists when the assumption of stability cannot be made. We are not only uncertain as to which consequence will occur as a result of a given course of action, but more distressing is the fact that we have no conviction that definite probabilities can be meaningfully ascribed to the various occurrences. It may be little consolation to many stock-market speculators to learn that they are in this unfortunate decision situation. We call these situations *unstable uncertainty*. In fact, one of the predominant tasks in many important decision situations is converting unstable uncertainty to stable uncertainty.

The classification of decision situations into four categories, (1) deterministic certainty, (2) probabilistic certainty, (3) stable uncertainty, and (4) unstable uncertainty, has been made in order to remove some of the confusion inherent in decision making. This classification is not absolute, but rather suggestive; it represents a progressive order of lack of required knowledge. Some may argue that no decision is made with adequate knowledge. Nevertheless, there is the conviction that criteria for decision can be formulated, and more fruitfully by taking cognizance of different degrees of adequacy of knowledge. In passing, we might mention the fact that situation 2 may be considered as a special case of situation 3, where the decision maker has elected to accept his probability estimates as unchanging. Again, situation 1 is a special case of situation 2, where the decision maker has the conviction that his probabilities assume only the values 1 or 0. Hence one can look upon all decision situations as basically falling into situation 3 or 4. We may repeat this statement in other words by emphasizing the view that one of the central problems in every decision situation is that of establishing its stability. Having said this, we must add that categorizing a situation as stable or not is itself a fundamental decision implementing the decision maker's primary values. A further consequence of this line of thought leads to decision making as a continuing self-corrective procedure. The remaining chapters of this book will be mainly devoted to the study of statistical control and inference and the interrelationship of these two in treating situations 3 and 4.

We wish, however, to emphasize categories 1 and 2, since many situations are fruitfully resolved when treated as belonging to these categories. Many decision problems go through a gradual metamorphosis from category 4 to 3. After having attained stability for a long period, considerable knowledge having been obtained about the probabilities, the decision situation may, without fear of loss, be treated as a situation of probabilistic certainty. Occasionally, a situation treated as category 2 may have to be reevaluated and put back into category 3.

An added categorization of decision situations is to consider type 3 as consisting of a range of decreasing uncertainty whose limiting situation is type 2. The decreasing uncertainty comes from increasing evidence. It must not be assumed, however, that it is always possible or practical to convert decision situations from type 3 to 2.   In many cases, it is either too costly or time-consuming to gather enough evidence necessary to treat the problem as in category 2.   The problem then is properly framed as in stable uncertainty in the light of evidence at hand.   These problems are often treated in terms of *statistical decision rules*, which will be emphasized in the treatment of statistical inference.

In the preceding chapters we have developed a considerable body of techniques pertinent to problems in category 2, illustrated by a number of examples.   For purposes of distinguishing between problems of categories 1 and 2, we now present a few more simple examples.

6.3.2   Problems of deterministic certainty

There is a wide choice of problems exemplifying this area of decision making.   Many problems of industry and engineering, business and governmental activity, and various scientific disciplines have been formulated in deterministic form.   The choice of alternative is usually found by various analytical maximization (minimization) techniques.   We have selected two simple problems of common industrial interest, as well as one classical problem with which the readers are likely to be familiar.

1.   The yearly demand for a given product is known.   The variable costs of procurement include the cost of the product, the cost of a purchase order, and the cost of holding inventory.   It is known that merely to issue a purchase order, whether for one or a thousand items, incurs a cost that cannot be ignored.   Keeping items in stock, for whatever reason, entails such costs as interest on capital tied up, rental on storage space, and handling costs, among others.   The holding cost is a composite figure expressed as a percentage, or fraction, of the unit product cost.   The decision to be made calls for determining the number of items of product to procure at each order, or equivalently, how many times per year to order so as to fulfill yearly demand.   The approach is apparently to formulate a cost function which will be minimized at one choice of order quantity.   The procedure follows.   Let

Q = number of pieces per order—order quantity
Y = yearly demand
C = cost of one item
P = cost per purchase order—procurement cost
I = holding cost
TVC = total variable cost

The cost equation is made up of two parts, the ordering cost and the holding cost.   Two assumptions are used in forming the cost equation: that orders are available instantaneously and that consumption of product is uniform.   On this basis, the annual holding cost is equal to one-half the quantity ordered times the cost of a unit times the holding cost. The annual ordering cost is the cost per purchase order times the number of orders per year. The sum yields the equation

$$TVC = \underset{\text{annual holding cost}}{\tfrac{1}{2}QCI} + \underset{\text{annual ordering cost}}{PY/Q} \tag{6.3.1}$$

Minimizing TVC with respect to Q gives the optimum order quantity:

$$Q_0 = \sqrt{\frac{2YP}{IC}} \tag{6.3.2}$$

The minimum variable annual cost is

$$(TVC)_0 = \sqrt{2CIPY} \tag{6.3.3}$$

The expression for Q is the classical square-root formula for *economic lot size*. Note further that $(TVC)_0$ is proportional to the square root of Y.

2. A certain shop, having machine time available, wished to schedule most profitably two types of tapered fastening pins. The question was, how many lots of each to schedule. Three machine tools were used: lathe A for rough turn and cutoff, lathe B for finish turn, and grinder G for finish grind. Spare time available on each machine was $A - 20$ hours, $B - 16$ hours, and $G - 60$ hours. The lot manufacturing times are given below:

	Machine		
	A	B	G
Taper pin type 1	5	8	5
Taper pin type 2	2	2	20

Profit on these pins was $10 per lot for type 1 taper pins and $5 per lot for type 2 taper pins.

Denote by x and y the number of lots of type 1 and type 2 pins, respectively. The restrictions on x and y are represented by the following equations:

$$\begin{aligned}
x \geq 0 \quad & y \geq 0 \\
5x + 2y & \leq 20 \\
8x + 2y & \leq 16 \\
5x + 20y & \leq 60
\end{aligned} \tag{6.3.4}$$

The profit P is given by

$$P = 10x + 5y \tag{6.3.5}$$

The problem, then, is to find x and y satisfying the restrictions of Eq. (6.3.4) and maximizing the profit P given by Eq. (6.3.5).

This is a decision problem where a pair of values (x_0, y_0) is to be chosen among a set of alternatives (x, y). We shall represent the set of possible alternatives graphically as in Fig. 6.1.

The set of feasible alternatives are all the points in the polygon bounded by the axes and lines AB and CD. The feasible optimum must be a point of this region which makes P a maximum. Recall that

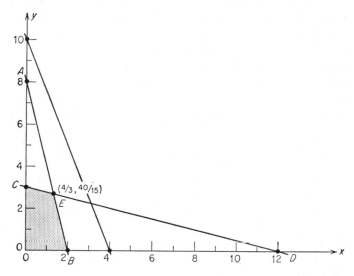

Figure 6.1

for P constant, Eq. (6.3.5) is a straight line. Hence a graphical solution can be obtained by determining this line for various increasing values of P until one hits a vertex of the polygon. The optimum point (x, y) is $(\frac{4}{3}, \frac{40}{15})$, that is, point E.

Although this example is quite simple and can be "solved" graphically, other problems of this type, called programming problems, can be quite complex and require rather sophisticated mathematical techniques for solution.

3. Two towns are located on the same side of a straight river. They agree to construct a pumping station at the river's edge to be used jointly in order to supply the two towns with water. Where along the river's edge should the pumping station be located so as to minimize the length of pipeline installation?

It is obvious that the set of alternatives consists of all the points along the river's edge and that the measure of effectiveness, which serves as the criterion for decision, is the total length of pipeline. Most readers are familiar with this problem as one which frequently appears in chapters on maxima and minima in elementary calculus texts.

6.3.3   Problems of probabilistic certainty

We have already treated a number of problems of this type, such as the packing problem and the steel-bar problem. These problems initially were not formulated as probabilistically certain; they were later modified so as to belong to this category when we assumed stability and accepted the sample estimates as providing the "true" probabilities. In all these cases we set up an expected cost (effectiveness function) which expressed the dependence of the objective sought on the choice of alternative. The function was in a form which theoretically permitted minimization (maximization) with respect to the alternative. In these cases the choice of optimum alternative was dependent upon effecting a balance among a number of costs. Note that these costs represent essentially our choice of utilities. Hence the optimum alternative is in a real sense a reflection of our preferences. Again, let us note that, in contrast with deterministic certainty, our measure of effectiveness is *expected* cost. We shall illustrate this again by two simple examples.

Example 6.1   Reconsider the storm-warning problem as formulated in Table 6.1. Assume now, however, that we know the probabilities with which states S_1 and states S_2 occur. (This, of course, presupposes stability.) Let the probability of occurrence S_1 be p; whence the probability of occurrence of S_2 is $1 - p$.

Utilizing the U_{ij}, we compute the expected utilities resulting from alternatives S_1 and S_2.

$$EU_1 = U_{11}p + U_{12}(1 - p) \qquad EU_2 = U_{21}p + U_{22}(1 - p) \quad (6.3.6)$$

Alternative a_1 is preferred to a_2 if $EU_1 > EU_2$:

$$U_{11}p + U_{12}(1 - p) > U_{21}p + U_{22}(1 - p) \tag{6.3.7}$$

Solving for p we obtain

$$p > \cfrac{1}{1 + \cfrac{U_{11} - U_{21}}{U_{22} - U_{12}}} \tag{6.3.8}$$

which shows the interrelationship between p and our utilities on the optimal alternative. Using the utilities represented by the financial costs only (refer to page 216), we obtain that storm warning a_1 should be called if p, the probability of a storm, is 0.15 or greater. This probability can only become lower when injury and loss of life are considered. In fact, we seem to be led to the conclusion that storm warnings should be called "on slight suspicion of storm," given the present utilities. The choice of expected utility as a measure of effectiveness can be supported, but requires discussion beyond the scope of this book.

Example 6.2 One of the decision problems which frequently arises in the inventory category is determining an optimum order quantity where the demand is known only in terms of a distribution function. There are many forms of this problem, and we select one to illustrate the role of the distribution function and the decision maker's values. Given:

C = cost of one item
S = selling price of one item
T = penalty per item short
X = random variable demand for a given fixed time period
$F(t) = \text{Prob}\ (X \leq t) = \int_0^t f(x)\ dx,\ CDF$ of demand
Q = order quantity
$f(x)$ = probability density of X

Find that value of Q which maximizes expected profit, where the quantity Q is chosen for one fixed time period. We first set up the profit function P, itself a random variable:

$$P = \begin{cases} Sx - CQ & x \leq Q \\ (S - C)Q - T(x - Q) & x > Q \end{cases} \quad (6.3.9)$$

We are maximizing expected profit because we do not know what the actual demand will be, but merely the probabilities. We may be asked, why maximize expected profit when we are making a decision for a single period? Essentially, in a business, these single periods are repeated, even though there may be no carry-over from one order period to the next. Hence, if many such orders are made, it is the accumulated effect in which the decision maker is interested, namely, the total profit resulting from many order periods. It is assumed that this is a stable situation and that the lack of carry-over is realistic in that stock remaining over is lost and back orders cannot be filled; this assumption is approximated in a number of selling situations, in particular in the case of seasonal goods. Experience has shown that this model does not do violence to these situations. This model should be used, however, with one further caution. The probability of low demand must be small, and the expectation of loss must be small enough to "eliminate" fears of bankruptcy. It is possible to set a measure of effectiveness in terms of bankruptcy (as defined by the decision maker), but we shall limit ourselves to the present model. The expected profit is

$$E(P) = S \int_0^Q xf(x)\ dx - CQF(Q) + (S - C)Q[1 - F(Q)]$$
$$- T \int_Q^\infty xf(x)\ dx + TQ[1 - F(Q)] \quad (6.3.10)$$

Maximization of this function with respect to Q yields

$$1 - F(Q_0) = \frac{C}{S + T} \qquad (6.3.11)$$

for the optimum value of Q denoted by Q_0.

The expression on the left side of Eq. (6.3.11) is the probability of a shortage evaluated at the optimum order quantity Q_0. It is apparent that this equation is reasonable since the greater C, the smaller Q_0, the greater S and T, the greater Q_0. The optimum order quantity Q_0 balances the effect of C against that of T in accordance with selling price S. The penalty T does not have the definiteness of C and S, but reflects to a larger degree the individual decision maker's evaluation of such non-tangibles as good will and the satisfaction of maintaining service and sales standards.

6.4   Evidence, experiments, and samples

Most of us believe that we make our decisions on the basis of evidence. This is a truism which hardly warrants repeating. A question of primary importance is, however, just what constitutes evidence? Another vital question is, how can we use evidence to the best effect?

In our formulation of the decision tasks we are dependent upon knowledge of consequences of courses of action and knowledge of the prevailing states of the environment at a time of implementing a decision. It is to be expected that we have some knowledge of the conceivable consequences of courses of action and that we may not be troubled with gathering extensive evidence on this score. In any case, questions of such evidence will be of the same sort as those arising in obtaining evidence of states of environment. Hence our principal concern in determining what is evidence is with the relevance of our information (however obtained) to predicting the state of environment prevailing. In the case of stable uncertainty we must procure evidence *relevant* to our decision. The usefulness of the concept of distinction among states of environment depends upon the existence of experiments (recall that experiment may be synonymous with observation), the distribution of whose outcomes varies with the state of environment prevailing. For example, observations of pressure, temperature, wind velocity, humidity, etc., are used to anticipate the occurrence of storms. Were it not possible to make such observations and were their distributions not dependent upon the intensity of impending storm, observation of these variables would not yield relevant evidence. Where our experience indicates that an impending storm influences the distribution of pressure (and other) readings, we consider pressure (and the other variables) as providing relevant data (evidence) for the decision. It is an important function of statistical inference to provide an analytic procedure for interpreting these distributions in terms of prevailing states of environment which produced them. In other words, from observation of pressure readings, with knowledge of what pressure readings are likely under storm conditions, we hope to infer something about the prevalence or nonprevalence of a storm.

Suppose we are faced with making a choice between two machines: what constitutes relevant evidence? We wish to choose the machine with highest expected productivity, and clearly, expected productivity is the state of environment to be inferred. Shall we seek relevant evidence in terms of the physical properties of the components directly or from productivity measurements? This problem becomes analogous with the storm problem if we choose to base our decision in large part on measurements related to productivity, namely, hardness of cutting edges, tolerances of moving parts, bearing friction, and the like. In this case, in contrast with the storm problem, we can *sample* the state of environment directly, running each machine under specified conditions and observing the productivity. Methods of statistical inference provide us with a basis for inferring from a *sample* to a *population*, that is to say, from a limited set of data to expected long-run behavior. Here relevance of evidence is quite clear, yet there remains the fact that inference was made. Statistical methods provide us with a measure of the confidence which we can place in such inferences.

The relevant evidence has been gathered to contribute both to intermediate decisions on states of environment and ultimately to the choice of alternative. A *decision rule* prescribes the random variables to observe, the number of observations to take, and which alternative course of action to choose as a function of the observations. In this process errors of inference can be made concerning the state of environment, and the relative importance of these errors is appraised in terms of our utilities. The cost of gathering relevant stable evidence should be balanced against the increased expected utility resulting from reduced error of inference. Toward this end statistical methods provide criteria for the choice of sample size.

We have indicated the significance of the gathering of evidence in the translation of data into probabilistic terms amenable to statistical inference on states of environment, and ultimately, in the study of decision rules which provide for the choice among alternatives.

6.5 Aspects of decision making under stable uncertainty

Here we shall discuss, somewhat informally, a number of concepts basic to effective formulation of problems entailing the use of statistical methods.

In succeeding chapters we shall develop formally a variety of techniques that have been found useful in decision making. In order to highlight some of the difficulties involved in statistical aspects of decision making, we shall develop our discussion in terms of specific problems.

6.5.1 A decision problem on equipment purchase

In the weaving of cloth, for example, the assembly of TV sets, and in many other production processes, the resulting unit of product is subject to a variety of defects. It is customary to weave certain grades of wool suiting in bolt lengths. Such bolts are rarely "perfect" or totally unacceptable. In most cases there will be such defects as broken fibers, protruding knots, loose ends, and the like. In TV sets there may be holes in the screen, scratches on a cabinet surface, a loose binding post, a poor solder joint, and the like. In either case the whole unit is usually not rejected, although no defects are ever welcome. It is hoped that machinery design and maintenance under standard operating performance will yield an economically low number of defects per unit of product. It is beyond our present needs to discuss the specific nature of defects and associated technical problems in detail. It is sufficient to emphasize that defects imply losses which can be measured in terms of the number of defects per unit. Furthermore, the "expected" loss from outgoing product is an important parameter in assessing the merit of a particular piece of manufacturing equipment.

It is not uncommon for a manufacturer, from time to time, to question the effectiveness of some equipment. His doubts may have been raised by the more restrictive demands of prospective customers, or perhaps the promise of newly designed equipment. It is a fact, in any case, that frequently the manufacturer is confronted with the question, to buy or not to buy? We shall consider some of the statistical implications of this question.

We now formulate the problem in such terms that the fundamental decision question is clear and the relevant statistical questions become apparent. The practical situation is that present equipment A is functioning under conditions of stability, namely, the rate of production, the material consumption, the labor cost, and other associated costs, and that the number of defects per unit are random variables having distributions known or not. The existence of such stability and the ability to maintain such stability are based on considerable past experience with this type of equipment. The newly designed equipment B, which is under consideration, has been sufficiently tested to give assurance that it can be operated so as to be stable. The manufacturer is interested in equipment B because the designer claims that it produces with a lower level of defects per unit of product. The manufacturer is looking for an adequate criterion to decide whether or not to replace equipment A with equipment B.   Intuitively, it seems that the total cost per unit of product should provide the criterion of choice.   It would seem that if the unit cost of using equipment B were less than that for equipment A, the manufacturer would choose equipment B.   A little reflection will show, however, that were the rates of production quite different, the expected profit per unit time might be a more meaningful criterion.   There may be other factors, such as difficulties of equipment change-over, which will influence the manufacturer's choice of a decision criterion.   It is not the purpose of this book to investigate all the ramifications involved in criteria choice.   We are concerned with choice of courses of action, given certain criteria, hopefully, sensible criteria.

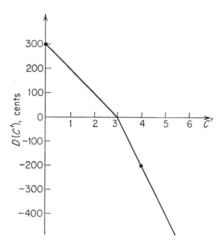

Figure 6.2 $D(C')$ versus C'.

The specific criterion that will be used in this illustration is in terms of the profit that can be expected from the sale of a product made on equipment A or B for different values of the mean number of defects C' per unit of product.   Assume that the profit function is contingent on the value of C', however it may be calculated.   To be sure, the profit function is an expectation over the variation of C, the number of defects for any unit, for a fixed C'.   Furthermore, the profit function includes a whole host of costs such as production rate, change-over costs, equipment life, material consumption, and the like.   We have, however, specified that, for the present problem, we shall consider the variation of the profit function as it is affected by C'.   For machine A we are concerned with only one value of the profit function, $P_A(4)$, where $C' = 4$ is the actual present operating mean number of defects per unit.   For machine B the profit function $P_B(C')$ may indeed be different from $P_A(4)$.   Clearly, the decision whether or not to purchase B depends on the difference, $D(C') = P_B(C') - P_A(4)$, which is represented in Fig. 6.2.

The specific function $D(C')$ has value zero for $C' = 3$ and is greater than zero for $C' < 3$.   Hence the number 3 is the break-even point with respect to the machine under the specific circumstances considered.   For $C' < 3$, choose the new machine, whereas for $C' \geq 3$, continue with the old machine.   In the present case the costs which were applied yielded the value $C' = 3$ as the break-even point.   It should be borne in mind that different costs might have resulted in other cutoff points.   For example, were the new machine more productive, a break-even point larger than $C' = 4$ would be conceivable.   Again, note that for $D(3) = 0$ the criterion is indifferent as to the problem of choice.   It is customary, however, to make no change for no gain, although the choice is at the discretion of the decision maker.

The present decision criterion clearly hinges on the numerical value of C'.   There are essentially two different circumstances in the state of knowledge of C'.   There may have been a considerable amount of previous testing of C', on the basis of which we are convinced that a substantially stable value of C' has been obtained in the previous experience of the users of the machine.   Although one may raise questions as to the relevance of the evidence on which this value of C' is based, for the purposes of this discussion, let us assume that it is known.   Under these circumstances the decision we have offered can be carried out without seeking further evidence.   Usually, however, C' must be estimated by the decision maker, raising questions of relevant evidence and pertinent inference.

What constitutes *relevant evidence* for C'?   Since C' is an expected value, we need some evidence of a distribution of C, the number of defects per unit of product made with the new equipment.   Of course, it is essential that any observations we take, if they are to constitute relevant evidence, be made under circumstances representative of operating conditions.   For example, one would not carry out these observations in the equipment-manufacturing plant unless the decision maker could control the operating conditions.   More specifically, one would not use especially skilled workers nor provide for exceptionally efficient flow of materials if this were not consistent with one's own operating conditions.   Regular production runs of product will be made and the values of C obtained by routine inspection procedures.   These observations are used in the computation of a statistical decision function which is to be formulated.   We further require that these observations satisfy the requirements of stability as discussed nonformally in Chap. 1.   We shall treat the concept of statistical stability and control in Chap. 11.   In summary, then, we require that (1) the observations be representative of regular operating conditions, and (2) that they be statistically stable. If these requirements are satisfied, we say that we have a *representative random sample*, in the present case, of C numbers, which can be used for prediction.

We are now in a position to consider the statistical character of a decision procedure.   The essential features of such a procedure are:

1. The choice of what to observe
2. The choice of the number of observations
3. The choice of the relationship between the observation results and the decision

In the previous discussion we have indicated that the observations chosen should constitute relevant evidence.   A representative random sample of the process under operating conditions provides relevant evidence.   A specifically statistical question is raised in point 2, for which we suggest possible plausible procedures.   It is important to note that the choices required in points 1, 2, and 3 essentially reflect the decision maker's objectives, which entail the costs of gathering relevant evidence and of the consequences of the decision.   Here, then, arises the question of evaluating the decision function in terms of possible losses and gains.

We shall proceed with our example, making computations to illustrate the essential points involved, and then suggest plausible decision procedures.   We shall proceed on the basis that we have a method of observation giving representative random samples, even though this is difficult to verify in practice.   We shall defer consideration of sample size until we have examined a number of procedures.   Some of the procedures that readily come to mind are:

1. Take no observations, $N = 0$; buy machine B.
2. Take no observations, $N = 0$; keep machine A.
3. Take no observations, $N = 0$; toss a coin, choose machine B if coin turns up head and keep A otherwise.
4. Take N independent observations, compute the average number of defects per item, $\bar{C}_N$; buy machine B if $\bar{C}_N < a$, keep machine A otherwise.

This set of procedures will be designated by $S(N,a)$.

We shall consider procedures 1 to 3 first.   According to procedure 1, we buy machine B without any observations.   Is this a "good" procedure?   How do we evaluate it?   Apparently we must consider the long-run consequences of this decision.   Obviously, this depends on what we could have gotten from machine A, had we kept it, and what we shall get from machine B.   We can evalute the expected performance of machine A on the basis of past relevant experience.   We have an estimate of C' for machine A; under conditions of statistical stability this value should persist until the machine becomes inoperative.   We have made the assumption, for purposes of illustration, of no deterioration in quality of output.   We cannot estimate the value of C' at which machine B will perform, since $N = 0$, but we can calculate the consequences of using machine B for different values of C'.   In fact, we have already calculated the expected gain from decision procedure 1 in function $D(C')$ given in Fig. 6.2.   All that this tells us is that when C' for machine B is low, the gain is high, and that when C' is high, the gain is in fact negative.

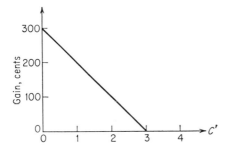

Figure 6.3   Gain function of standard.

This statement contains nothing that is not quite obvious for procedure 1. On the other hand, function $D(C')$ can be used for comparing different procedures where their consequences are not obvious.   For this purpose, it will be convenient to introduce the notion of a *regret function* which will make the comparison of the different procedures more transparent. What, then, is a good criterion for comparing the merits of different

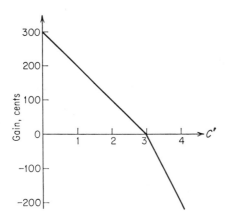

Figure 6.4   Gain function for procedure 1.

procedures?   Clearly, the best circumstance for decision is one in which C' is known, for then one can accurately evaluate the consequence of decision, as indicated in Fig. 6.2.   We shall use the criterion of gain expressed by $D(C')$ when C' is known as a standard against which to compare the gain for any other procedure.   Thus the gain function for known C' is precisely $D(C')$ when $C' \leq 3$ and zero when $C' > 3$.

Clearly, the gain function for procedure 1 is precisely $D(C')$ as given in Fig. 6.2.

Let us now make the following interpretation of the merit of a decision procedure. For any value of C' the greatest possible gain (attained for C' known) minus the gain for the given procedure is a measure of the merit of a decision procedure for that value of C'. This is the regret

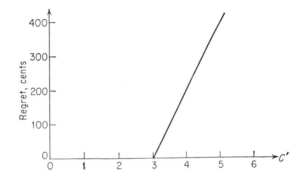

Figure 6.5 Regret function for procedure 1.

function introduced by L. J. Savage. This seems to be entirely reasonable intuitively since it is the measure of the amount by which a procedure falls short of the best possible gain. Specifically, the gain functions for the standard and procedure 1 are given in Figs. 6.3 and 6.4, respectively. The regret function for procedure 1 is then obtained by subtracting for each C' the value of the gain function for the standard (Fig. 6.3) from

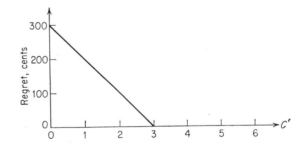

Figure 6.6 Regret function for procedure 2.

the gain function of procedure 1 (Fig. 6.4). The resulting regret function for procedure 1 is given in Fig. 6.5.

For procedure 2 the gain function is identically zero, since no change from *status quo* is made. The regret function is as given in Fig. 6.6.

In procedure 3, by flipping a coin, which falls with equal probability head or tail, we buy machine B half the time and stick with machine A half the time, on the average, regardless of C'. Hence the regret function for procedure 3 is the average of the regret functions for procedures

1 and 2.   The resulting function lies halfway between regret functions for procedures 1 and 2, as given in Fig. 6.7.

It is quite obvious that the first three procedures do not use any information about the performance of machine B.   On the other hand, procedure 4 seems to characterize a whole class of reasonable procedures which make use of relevant data about machine B's performance.   Intuitively, it appears that $\bar{C}_N$ is a natural estimator of C' for machine B.   Certainly, the smaller C', the more likely we are to buy machine B.   One can justify the use of the class of procedure 4 on deeper grounds in the realm of statistical decision theory, which, however, is beyond the scope of this book.   We can nevertheless readily show, by means of the regret function, the preference for procedure 4 over the other three procedures.

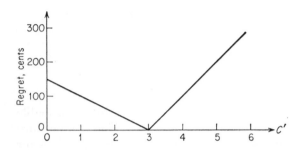

Figure 6.7   Regret function for procedure 3.

On the other hand, observations on the performance of machine B involve some knowledge of the distribution of random variable C, the number of defects per unit produced.   For the purpose of discussion we shall assume (not unreasonably) that C has a Poisson distribution with mean C'.   This assumption can be tested in practice.   The distribution $P(c)$ is

$$P(c) = \text{Prob (number of defects } C = c) = \frac{e^{-C'}(C')^c}{c!} \qquad c = 0, 1, 2, \ldots$$

$$(6.5.1)$$

The parameter C' is $E(C)$, the expected value of the random variable C.

Let us now indicate how the calculations of the regret functions for the class of procedures $S(N,a)$ are performed.   In order to obtain the regret function we must obtain the gain function.   For a fixed N and a, and given C' for machine B, the expected gain $G_{N,a}(C')$ is

$$G_{N,a}(C') = G \text{ (buying } B \mid C') \text{ Prob (buying } B \mid C')$$
$$+ G \text{ (keeping } A \mid C') \text{ Prob (keeping } A \mid C') \quad (6.5.2)$$

This follows directly from the property of expectations as given in Sec. 4.2.3.   It has been shown above, as is quite clear, that the gain in keeping machine A is zero; hence the second term in Eq. (6.5.2) drops out.

If, actually, the mean number of defects per unit for machine B is C', then buying B results in a gain denoted by G (buying $B \mid C'$), as given in Fig. 6.4. For different values of C' we may get different values of gain. In order to get the regret, we subtract $G_{N,a}(C')$ from the standard gain given in Fig. 6.3. The probability of buying B when the mean number of defects per unit equals C' is

$$\text{Prob (buying } B \mid C') = \text{Prob } (\bar{C}_N < a \mid C')$$

$$= \text{Prob } (C_1 + C_2 + \cdots + C_N < Na \mid C') = \sum_{i=0}^{Na-1} \frac{e^{-NC'}(NC')^i}{i!} \quad (6.5.3)$$

According to procedure $S(N,a)$, we buy machine B when $\bar{C}_N < a$. Since C is a Poisson variate with mean C', $C_1 + C_2 + \cdots + C_N$ is a Poisson variate with mean NC'. This fact justifies the last step in the previous equation. We now illustrate the calculation of values of the regret function and give, in Table 6.2, regret values for $N = 9$ and $a = 2$ in $S(N,a)$. We shall do this calculation for $C' = 2.5$. Then the first step is to determine

$$G(\text{buying } B \mid C' = 2.5)$$

which, from Fig. 6.4, we note to be 50. Next we determine

$$\text{Prob (buying } B \mid C' = 2.5) = \sum_{i=0}^{17} e^{-22.5} \frac{(22.5)^i}{i!} \quad (6.5.4)$$

This value can be obtained from tables of the cumulative Poisson function.[1] The value obtained is 0.146. Hence

$$G_{9,2}(2.5) = 50 \times 0.146 = 7.3 \quad (6.5.5)$$

The regret, then, is obtained by subtracting 7.3 from the standard gain, which, as given in Fig. 6.3, is 50 (again, for $C' = 2.5$). Thus the regret equals $50 - 7.3 = 42.7$ per unit of product. The dimensions of this number are in the scale in which the product is evaluated. This could be pounds of material, square feet of material, cents or dollars, etc. In this illustration, assuming that a unit is a bolt of cloth and the dimension of the regret function is in cents, we interpret the regret as 42.7 per bolt of cloth produced as missing by almost 43 cents on the average per bolt of cloth the gain we could get if we had complete knowledge of C'. This appears to be a poor decision procedure on the surface, but we can better understand the full implication of this procedure by examining the regret table and graphs which follow.

[1] E. C. Molina, "Poisson Exponential Binomial Limit," D. Van Nostrand Company, Princeton, N.J., 1943. See also Appendix, Table A.2.

We have computed the regret function from decision procedure $S(N,a)$ for a number of values of a at a fixed value of N equal to 9.   The graphs of these results are given in Fig. 6.8.   We have also the numerical

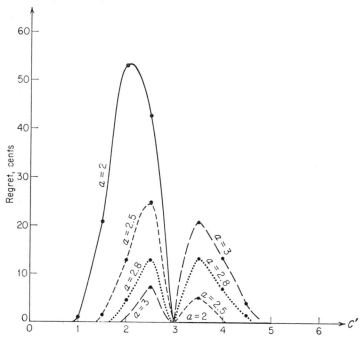

Figure 6.8   Regret values of $S(9,a)$ for a = 2, 2.5, 2.8, 3.

results for $S(9,2)$, in Table 6.2.   An overall look at the graph of the regret for $S(9,2)$ suggests that when $C' > 3$, this procedure is effective, for we have zero regret.   We could not have done better, apparently, since for large C', this procedure will almost never result in buying machine B.

TABLE 6.2
Regret Values of $S(9,2)$ versus C'

C'	G (buying $B \mid C'$)	Prob (buying $B \mid C'$)	$G \times P$	*Standard*	*Regret, cents*
1.0	200	0.995	199.0	200	1.0
1.5	150	0.861	129.2	150	21.0
2.0	100	0.469	46.9	100	53.0
2.5	50	0.146	7.3	50	42.7
3.0	0	0.030	0.0	0	0.0
3.5	−100	. . . . .	. . . . .	. . .	0.0
4.0	−200	. . . . .	. . . . .	. . .	0.0
4.5	−300	. . . . .	. . . . .	. . .	0.0
5.0	−400	. . . . .	. . . . .	. . .	0.0

This occurs because a equal to 2 is quite low.   On the other hand, we pay a price when C' is relatively low.   For example, the regret function at even $C' = 2$ is 53 cents.   A large regret results mainly from the fact that the decision to buy machine B occurs less than 50 per cent of the time and also from the loss of an opportunity to gain \$1 per unit of product.   Then again, for C' equal to 1 the regret disappears, quite obviously because for such a low C' almost any "reasonable" procedure leads to buying machine B.   Thus we may call this procedure $S(9,2)$ rather conservative.   Nevertheless, it is somewhat sensitive to the data and less conservative than procedure 2, where one never buys machine B.   Procedure 2 is ultraconservative, but unwise in the sense that it forgoes opportunities for gain.

Now suppose we select a equal to 3, the break-even point.   Note (Fig. 6.8) that the regret curve for $S(9,3)$ is low for $C' < 3$ and high for $C' > 3$, in contrast with $S(9,2)$.   Is this situation more desirable than the preceding?   If we expect machine B to perform well, we ought to have a decision procedure where the probability of deciding to buy machine B is reasonably high; on the other hand, we should hope that at the same time the probability of deciding to buy B is substantially low in the event C' is high.   It seems, however, that $S(9,3)$ does not yield both these desired characteristics.   Obviously, an a greater than 3 offers no choice. On scanning the regret curves we note that all but one of them are unbalanced and that $S(9,2.8)$ yields an approximately balanced regret function.   Observe that we may characterize the regret functions in three categories:

1. High regret on left and low regret on right ($a < 2.8$)
2. Low regret on left and high regret on right ($a > 2.8$)
3. Balanced regret ($a = 2.8$)

A priori, one cannot say that one of this class of regret functions is better or worse than another.   The choice among the regret functions is based entirely on the decision maker's outlook.   One decision maker may want to minimize the maximum regret over the whole range of C' (this leads to $a \cong 2.8$).   Another decision maker, rather optimistic, seeks to do well when C' is low and would therefore choose $a > 2.8$.   Similarly, a very conservative decision maker will buy machine B only if the evidence is very strongly in favor of its superiority.   He would choose $a < 2.8$ and therefore would accept a high regret when C' is low and only a small regret when C' is high, that is, when the functioning of the machine is bad. The moral of this test procedure is that you cannot have your cake and eat it too.   The merit of this type of analysis is that it warns you when you are eating your cake.

A perceptive decision maker, somewhat disappointed in this analysis, seeks greater assurance for lower regret.   What can one change in the

$S(N,a)$ procedure?   Obviously, by increasing N and getting more information, one may gain these ends.   In order to illustrate the effect of N, we shall fix a at the balanced value 2.8 and compute the regret function of $S(N,2.8)$ for $N = 2$ and $N = 4$.   The regret curves for these values, as well as for $N = 9$ (Fig. 6.9), emphatically indicate that the regrets decrease with increasing N.   But bear in mind that one must pay for added observations.   We have not included the effect of the cost of observations in the formulation of the regret function used here, and so

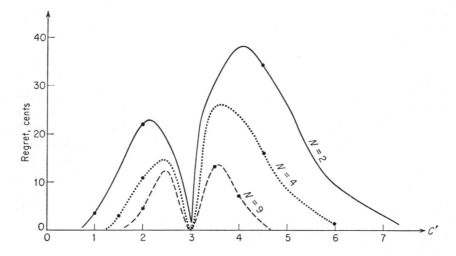

Figure 6.9   Regret values for $S(N,2.8)$ for $N = 2, 4, 9$.

our comparisons for different N's are not strictly correct.   Nevertheless, the essential significance is properly shown, and the cost of observations can be incorporated very simply.

It would be nice if we could systematically compare the merits of the four procedures which we have discussed.   The best we can do for the present and within the scope of this text is to compare the regret functions of the different procedures.

There are times when it is difficult to evaluate accurately either gain functions or regret functions, for often accurate cost figures are not readily available.   In spite of this limitation one factor in the regret function, namely, the probability of buying machine B for given values of C', reveals considerable insight into the effectiveness of the decision procedure. Ideally, we should want to buy machine B when $C' < 3$ and keep machine A when $C' \geq 3$.   Such a procedure is equivalent to

$$\text{Prob (buying } B \mid C') = \begin{cases} 1 & C' < 3 \\ 0 & C' \geq 3 \end{cases} \qquad (6.5.6)$$

Clearly, this is not possible as the result of sampling. Suppose now that we consider $S(N,2.8)$ for $N = 2$, 4, and 9. Recall that the probability of buying machine B for various values of C' is given in Eq. (6.5.3). The results of these computations for the three values of N and the ideal case are given in Fig. 6.10. In the language of sampling inspection, these curves are called *operating characteristics*, or *OC* curves. It is apparent that the discrimination with respect to buying machine B improves with increasing N. When $N = 2$ and $C' = 2.5$, we buy machine B only 61.6

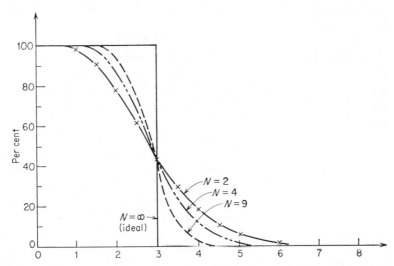

Figure 6.10 Operating characteristic (*OC*) curve for $S(N,2.8)$ for $N = 2$, 4, 9, and ∞.

per cent of the time, while when $N = 4$ and $C' = 2.5$ we buy machine B 69.7 per cent of the time, and for $N = 9$, 74 per cent of the time. Even for $C' = 2$ we take a correct action only 88.8 per cent of the time when $N = 4$ and 95.5 per cent of the time when $N = 9$. It is not possible to get ideal discrimination. These *OC* curves tell us what to expect and how much we have to pay in order to get a desired degree of discrimination.

A procedure based on the regret function provides decision on an evaluation of gain and losses in terms of regret. The procedures provided by the *OC* curves merely give a basis of decision in terms of probabilities of making errors. Much of statistical decision is based on the selection of *OC* curves which meet certain practical requirements. Subsequent developments will deal, to a large extent, with the use of *OC* curves in a variety of statistical problems. Where, however, it is possible to express the aims of our decision in terms of gain functions, then decision procedures based on the regret functions (or similar criteria) yield the basis for decision which is more closely representative of the decision maker's objectives.

6.5.2 Some decision aspects of the storm-warning problem

Let us recall the storm-warning problem previously discussed in Secs. 6.1.7, 6.2.3, and 6.2.4. We indicated the framing of alternatives, the specification of states of environment, and the choice of utility measures. Also, a utility matrix was set up. As we presented the problem, no uniform preference emerged, and relevant information was needed. We shall now carry the discussion further, going more deeply into the bearing of relevant evidence.

It is best to make clear at the outset the liberties we are taking in simplifying the real problem for purposes of emphasizing the role of evidence and statistical inference in decision procedures. For one, we are assuming only two states of environment, storm impending (S_1) and no storm impending (S_2). Obviously, such a presumed clear-cut dichotomy in environmental conditions is far from realistic. Yet, to specify a continuum of environmental states would so complicate the formal aspects as to obscure the essentials. Again, to limit ourselves to only two alternative courses of action, namely, call storm warning (a_1) and do not call storm warning (a_2), is to deprive ourselves of the most effective decision over a wide range of conditions by a choice among intermediate degrees of storm warning. Beyond this, the very physical nature of the problem has been restricted to one pertinent measurable independent variable, namely, sea-level barometric reading of pressure in inches. It is well known that many other variables, in particular the rate of pressure change and wind direction, have significant bearing on the likelihood of storm. Furthermore, we are tacitly assuming that we are in a state of stable uncertainty regarding pressure readings.

We are considering the storm-warning problem since it is a genuine example where the decision maker has only environmental variables, over which he has no control, to provide him with relevant evidence. Even with the present simplifications, this problem presents a nontrivial generic decision situation. For a large variety of situations can be viewed in a framework of two states of nature and two action alternatives.

It is well known that storms occur under conditions of low pressure whereas fair weather is associated with relatively high pressures. We shall assume that pressure is a chance variable and that the distribution of pressure over a limited region is normal (normality is assumed for illustrative convenience) with standard deviation of approximately 0.30. Furthermore, when the mean value is 29.8 inches, state of environment S_1 prevails, and on the other hand, a mean pressure of 30.1 inches is associated with fair weather, condition S_2.

Let us consider the following possible decision rules.

Rule 1: Call storm warning without taking pressure observations (a_1).

Rule 2: Never call storm warnings (a_2).

Rule 3: Take N pressure readings; compute the average $\bar{X}_N$ and call a storm warning when $\bar{X}_N \leq b$ and do nothing otherwise. We designate such a rule by $R(N,b)$, where N is the number of observations and b is a constant. It should be noted that the likelihood of calling a storm warning increases with b.

Any rule for decision in the type of situation under discussion is subject to two types of error. Specifically, in the present example, there may be decision a_1 when condition S_2 prevails and there may be decision a_2 when S_1 prevails. Let us designate the chance of the first type of error by $P(a_1 \mid S_2)$ and the chance of the second type of error by $P(a_2 \mid S_1)$. Under stable uncertainty we can evaluate these two probabilities for any given decision rule. This leads to assessing the consequence of decision in terms of the probabilities of error in conjunction with their importance expressed as utilities.

We shall now compute $P(a_1 \mid S_2)$ and $P(a_2 \mid S_1)$ for the different decision rules.

Rule 1: Since this rule calls for a_1, we have

$$P(a_1 \mid S_2) = 1 \qquad \text{and} \qquad P(a_2 \mid S_1) = 0$$

Rule 2: Since this rule calls for a_2, we have

$$P(a_1 \mid S_2) = 0 \qquad \text{and} \qquad P(a_2 \mid S_1) = 1$$

Rule 3: Since the decision between a_1 and a_2 depends on the outcome of observations, we must compute the probabilities of their occurrence under S_1 and S_2. Recall that we are assuming a normal distribution of pressure readings with standard deviation 0.30, mean of 29.8 under S_1, and mean of 30.1 under S_2.

Therefore

$$P(a_1 \mid S_2) = \text{Prob} \ (\bar{X}_N \leq b; \ 30.1, \ 0.09)$$

Making the usual transformation to the standard normal variate, we have

$$P(a_1 \mid S_2) = \text{Prob} \left[\frac{\sqrt{N} \ (\bar{X}_N - 30.1)}{0.3} \leq \frac{\sqrt{N} \ (b - 30.1)}{0.3} \right]$$
$$= \Phi \left(\sqrt{N} \ \frac{b - 30.1}{0.3} \right)$$

where $\Phi(u)$ is the cumulative normal distribution function. Similarly,

$$P(a_2 \mid S_1) = \text{Prob} \ (\bar{X}_N > b; \ 29.8, \ 0.09)$$
$$= 1 - \Phi \left(\sqrt{N} \ \frac{b - 29.8}{0.9} \right)$$

The computation of these probabilities for values $N = 4$, 9, and 16 and $b = -\infty$, 29.9, 29.95, 30.0, 30.1, and $+\infty$ is given in Table 6.3. For convenience of interpretation we devise the following graphical presentation.   Let $P(a_2 \mid S_1)$ and $P(a_1 \mid S_2)$ correspond to points in a two-dimensional cartesian space.   Thus, to each $R(N,b)$ there corresponds a point in that space.   To each rule, for a fixed N, there corresponds a curve, as b varies.   Figure 6.11 represents the error curves for rules $R(4,b)$, $R(9,b)$, and $R(16,b)$ for $-\infty \le b \le +\infty$.   Let us examine the curve for $R(4,b)$ for different values of b.   For example, for $b = 29.90$ the error of the first kind $P(a_2 \mid S_1) = 25.46$ per cent and the error of the second kind

TABLE 6.3

N	b	$P(a_2 \mid S_1)$	$P(a_1 \mid S_2)$
4	29.90	0.2546	0.0934
4	29.95	0.1587	0.1587
4	30.00	0.0934	0.2546
4	30.10	0.0239	0.5000
9	29.90	0.1611	0.0239
9	29.95	0.0668	0.0668
9	30.00	0.0239	0.1611
9	30.10	0.0015	0.5000
16	29.90	0.0934	0.0041
16	29.95	0.0228	0.0228
16	30.00	0.0041	0.0934
16	30.10	0.00004	0.5000

$P(a_1 \mid S_2) = 9.34$ per cent.   Again, for $b = 30.0$, the errors are reversed, so that $P(a_1 \mid S_2) = 25.46$ per cent and $P(a_2 \mid S_1) = 9.34$ per cent.   Note that as b increases for $-\infty$ to $+\infty$, the error of the first kind decreases while the error of the second kind increases.   At the extremes, note that rule 3 becomes equivalent to rule 2 for $b = -\infty$ and to rule 1 for $b = +\infty$.

Now consider variation of N.   In Fig. 6.11 note that the error curve for $R(16,b)$ lies between the curve for $R(4,b)$ and the axis passing through the points $(0,1.00)$ and $(1.00,0)$.   For any rule $R(4,b)$ one can find a rule $R(16,b')$ such that the errors of both kinds are less than those for $R(4,b)$. Obviously, b' need not necessarily be equal to b.

In ultimate value we are not interested in the errors themselves, but the losses resulting from them.   Hence we should like to determine the losses associated with the decision procedures as a result of error.   We shall compute some of these losses in terms of utilities.   We refer back to Table 6.1 and compute the expected utilities under the various decision procedures.   We shall first express the expected utilities in general terms

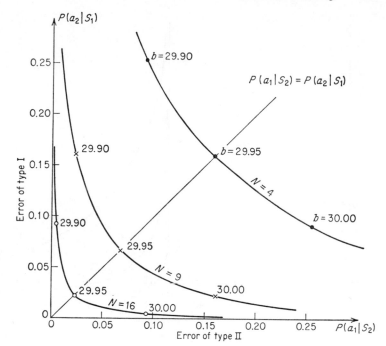

Figure 6.11

and then determine the expected utilities for values given in Sec. 6.2.4. The expected utility for S_1 is as follows:

$$E(\text{utility} \mid S_1) = U_{11}[1 - P(a_2 \mid S_1)] + U_{21}P(a_2 \mid S_1)$$
$$= U_{11} + P(a_2 \mid S_1)(U_{21} - U_{11}) \quad (6.5.7)$$

For S_2 the formula is symmetric in symbols 1 and 2, whence we have

$$E(\text{utility} \mid S_2) = U_{22} + P(a_1 \mid S_2)(U_{12} - U_{22}) \quad (6.5.8)$$

In particular, for the utilities given in Sec. 6.2.4, we obtain

$$\begin{aligned} E(\text{utility} \mid S_1) &= -480,000 + P(a_2 \mid S_1)(-2,020,000) \\ E(\text{utility} \mid S_2) &= 0 + P(a_1 \mid S_2)(-370,000) \end{aligned} \quad (6.5.9)$$

Note that the major part of the calculation has already been carried out in obtaining $P(a_2 \mid S_1)$ and $P(a_1 \mid S_2)$, the errors of decision. A typical computation for $R(16,30.0)$ follows:

$$E(\text{utility} \mid S_1) = -480,000 + (0.0041)(-2,020,000) = -480,282$$
$$(6.5.10)$$
$$E(\text{utility} \mid S_2) = 0 + (0.0934)(-370,000) = -34,558$$

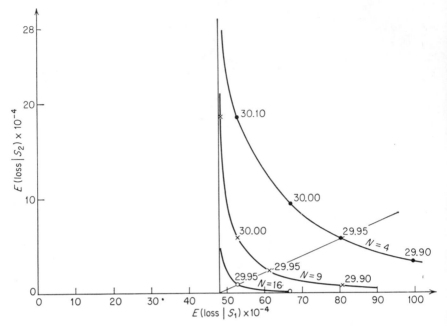

Figure 6.12

We can compute these pairs of values for other choices of b and N, and they may be plotted as in Fig. 6.12. We note that one cannot simultaneously increase both expected utilities without increasing N. This indicates that, in order to assure ourselves of greater utility resulting from decision on relevant evidence, we must increase the amount of

TABLE 6.4

N	b	$E(\text{loss} \mid S_1)$	$E(\text{loss} \mid S_2)$
4	29.90	994,292	34,558
4	29.95	800,574	58,719
4	30.00	668,668	94,202
4	30.10	528,278	185,000
9	29.90	805,422	8,843
9	29.95	614,936	24,716
9	30.00	528,278	59,607
9	30.10	483,030	185,800
16	29.90	668,668	1,517
16	29.95	526,056	8,436
16	30.00	488,282	34,558
16	30.10	480,081	185,000

evidence.   This analysis can be made so as to include the cost of gathering relevant evidence.   We note that, whereas we have expressed the consequences of decision in terms of utilities in this example, by merely taking the negative of the utilities we have the losses and expected losses. Although the present discussion has shown us how to assess the consequences of different decision rules, we need other conditions as a basis for selection among decision rules.   For example, we may wish to minimize maximum loss (maximize minimum utility), or we may specify $E(\text{utility} \mid S_1)$ and attempt to find a procedure which maximizes $E(\text{utility} \mid S_2)$.

We have devoted considerable attention to showing how to determine the consequences of decision procedures in connection with relevant evidence.   Essential to this analysis has been the role of errors of inference.   Whatever decision procedures are used, assessing errors of inference is fundamental.   We are here concerned with the statistical aspect of inference as it relates to decision making, and the remainder of this book will be devoted to developing methods of statistics which have been found useful in engineering, science, and industry.

7

STATISTICAL HYPOTHESIS TESTING

Let us consider again the question of whether or not to purchase a new machine, presented in the preceding chapter. In effect, the practical problem is, will the manufacturer make more money over some period of time with the new machine? We approached this situation as one of "optimal decision," where the optimality was expressed as maximizing a profit function. While our operational goal was the maximization of profit, our formulation of the problem led to the question of whether the mean number of defects per unit was larger than 3 or not. In a sense, our decision problem entailed a test of a statistical hypothesis. In this chapter we shall develop a number of aspects of statistical hypothesis testing and relate these principles to practical decision problems.

7.1 Introductory examples

We shall illustrate some practical problems which can be viewed in terms of statistical hypothesis testing.

1. Again referring to the textile-machine purchase, we can formulate one of the essential aspects of the problem in the following way: The mean number of defects per unit is less than 3 or is not. It appears obvious that we should be able to propose an experiment relevant to answering this question, as in fact we did. Explicitly, then, our statistical hypothesis is $H: m \geq 3$. The symbol H is universally used to designate a hypothesis. We must now provide a procedure for accepting or rejecting this hypothesis.

A pertinent observation about this hypothesis is that it places the mean in a one-sided region bounded from below by 3. We also may ask, if m is not greater than or equal to 3, what are practical alternative values? An important historical development in statistical inference is the appreciation of the fact that the practical alternative to a hypothesis is important in the framing of effective hypothesis-testing procedures. This point will be thoroughly developed as the chapter proceeds.

Another question the reader may ask is, why test a hypothesis on m, why not estimate m? There is an essential correspondence between hypothesis testing and estimation, but in many practical situations it is more effective to provide the decision maker with a hypothesis which he can accept or reject. The manufacturer is, in the main, not so much interested in the magnitude of m as in whether it is larger or smaller than a certain number. As a matter of fact, so long as $m \geq 3$, the manufacturer prefers not to buy the new machine.

A reasonable alternative to $m \geq 3$ is $m < 3$. To be sure, if m were equal to 2.9, some manufacturers might weaken in their decision. To examine this weakness further, suppose m were equal to 2.8 or 2.7: when does one's decision become firm? A definite alternative is essential if one is to make decisions where the probability of error or the magnitude of loss and gain is to be assessed. Hence we can express the hypothesis to be tested in this form:

$$H_0: \quad m \geq 3 \quad \text{against} \quad H_1: \quad m < 3$$

The hypothesis with subscript zero is called the null hypothesis, and H_1 is referred to as the alternative hypothesis.

2. Consider the problem of filling jars with some kind of fluid for sale to the retail consumer. Governmental divisions which have jurisdiction over "weights and measures" usually specify that a quart jar, for example, shall contain no less than a specified number, v', of fluid ounces. No upper specification is usually given since the government is concerned primarily with protecting the consumer against short measure. On the other hand, the producer is concerned not only with meeting government specification, but with protecting himself against overfill. Here is a case where the statistical hypothesis may be formulated as one-sided or two-sided. The hypotheses are expressed as follows:

Government test:

$$H_0: \quad m \geq v \quad \text{against} \quad H_1: \quad m < v \quad v > v'$$

Manufacturer's test:

$$H_0: \quad v \leq m \leq w \quad \text{against} \quad H_1: \quad m < v \quad \text{or} \quad m > w$$

Here $w > v$ has been selected as an economically tolerable upper specification. Again, m is the mean volume of fluid per bottle of a given batch of bottles.

3. An important industrial problem is that of accepting or rejecting lots of manufactured product. A manufacturer usually forms what are

called production lots as the result of circumstances inherent in the production process. For example, a lot may be formed from the production resulting from a given batch of raw material. Sometimes it is necessary to adjust the process or to make another setup, thereby, naturally, starting a new lot. However, before releasing each lot for shipment, the manufacturer usually performs some tests to determine whether the lot conforms to acceptable standards. A customary criterion for acceptability is that of the fraction defective p of the lot. The big question, however, is how to make inferences concerning p and the associated acceptability of the lot. Furthermore, it is desirable to do this economically.

In practice, it is customary to specify a fraction defective p_1 such that, for all practical purposes, if $p \leq p_1$, we consider the lot acceptable. Of course, the value p_1 is a matter of choice by agreement between producer and consumer and varies from product to product, depending on the consequences of using nonacceptable lots. It is not economically practical to designate every lot whose fraction defective p is greater than p_1 as unacceptable, but we do want a procedure such that the greater p, the smaller the chance of accepting the lot, and for some designated $p_2 > p_1$, the chance of acceptance of a lot with $p > p_2$ is very small. This description of desirable characteristics of an acceptance procedure captures the essential elements. The suggested procedure can be formulated more precisely in terms of statistical hypothesis testing.

A possible formulation of a statistical hypothesis incorporating our objectives is

$$H_0: \quad p \leq p_1 \qquad \text{against} \qquad H_1: \quad p > p_1$$

A little reflection shows that this formulation is not quite satisfactory since it does not explicitly incorporate what happens when $p \geq p_2$. Nevertheless, from the point of view of the consumer, the foregoing may be a reasonable formulation. On the other hand, from the point of view of the producer, it might be desirable to have as many of his lots acceptable as possible. Hence he might select as the cutoff value of p some value above p_1, say, p'. His statistical hypothesis could be

$$H_0: \quad p \leq p' \qquad \text{against} \qquad H_1: \quad p > p'$$

Let us consider how this would work out in practice. Assume that the consumer has a test procedure designed to accept lots whose fraction defective $p = p_1$. Since any statistical procedure is subject to error, the consumer might reject 10 per cent of lots whose fraction defective $p \leq p_1$ and ship them back to the producer. The producer discovers this fact upon reexamining the returned lots and complains to his customer that he is being unfairly treated. The customer, in the meantime, sees that the consequences of accepting lots somewhat worse than p_1 are not so serious. If the customer insisted on an acceptance procedure which rejected practically all lots with $p > p_1$, the producer's price would increase considerably. Hence the customer agrees to modify his procedure. He does not change his statistical hypothesis, but his procedure permits acceptance of a higher percentage of lots with $p > p_1$. Now the shoe is on the other foot, for the customer discovers that he is accepting too high a percentage of lots with $p \geq p_2$. His complaint to the producer results in an agreement that the producer will try to obtain better control of his process at an average level $p \leq p_1$ such that only a small percentage of his lots will have $p \geq p_1$. The customer realizes that he must restrict his statistical procedure so that the chance of accepting lots with $p \geq p_2$ is less than or equal to some specified per cent. He still must guarantee the producer that his rejection of lots with $p \leq p_1$ will be less than some specified per cent.

In practice, it has been found that the desired objectives can be achieved by formulating what is called a *simple hypothesis* against a *simple alternative* as follows:

$$H_0: \quad p = p_1 \qquad \text{against} \qquad H_1: \quad p = p_2$$

where the procedure makes the following promises:

$$\text{Prob (rejection when } p = p_1) = \alpha$$
$$\text{Prob (acceptance when } p = p_2) = \beta$$

The values of α and β are the errors of the first and second kind, respectively, as described in Chap. 6. It can be shown, for the procedures to be considered, that if these values hold, then

$$\text{Prob (rejection when } p \leq p_1) \leq \alpha$$
$$\text{Prob (acceptance when } p \geq p_2) \leq \beta$$

This monotonicity property is typical of many situations formulated as a simple hypothesis against a simple alternative, and it lends merit to the use of this form of statistical hypothesis.

7.2 Some basic concepts

7.2.1 Errors and mistakes

The term *error* is used frequently in technical and scientific discourse, with, however, various meanings. The Oxford Universal Dictionary (1955) gives as one meaning the action of wandering, and one meaning given for *erroneous* is moving aimlessly. These notions are suggestive of random variation. Other dictionaries also offer numerous alternative usages, including the notion of *mistake*. In statistical practice a distinction between the two terms is usually made. For example, if a cutting machine is set to cut rods into 10-inch pieces, the resulting pieces will vary in length.   The variation about the mean value of the pieces, provided the setting is unchanged, may be regarded as error, that is, as random variation.   No "mistake" has been made, for the observed variation is inherent in the cutting process.   If the mean length of many pieces turns out to be 10 inches, we can say that the setting was made without *mistake*, or as is sometimes said, without *bias*.   On the other hand, if the mean value were $10\frac{1}{4}$ inches, we should be inclined to say there was a mistake in setting.   We believe that the mean value could not be so far off "by chance."   Small error is not a guarantee of correctness, for one can be a sharpshooter and yet aim at the wrong target. One can carry this discussion to great lengths, but for our purposes, error implies sampling variation, inherent in the process by means of which the observations are made.   One of the primary aims of statistical analysis is to assess and possibly reduce errors.   One implication of these remarks is that, in any statistical investigation, we must guard against mistakes.   A famous illustration of this point is the *Literary Digest* poll of 1932.   This fiasco of polling of the order of a million voters was quite precise for the universe of telephone subscribers, but not for the universe of American voters.   The mistake was to sample from telephone books rather than from the population of actual interest.

7.2.2   Type I and type II errors, operating characteristic curve, and power curve

We introduced the notion of two types of errors somewhat informally in previous discussions.   We now wish to state these notions more precisely. Let us consider a simple hypothesis against a simple alternative.   Note that a simple hypothesis completely specifies the population under study. For example, the chance variable number defective for large lots and small p can be closely approximated by a Poisson distribution.   Thus, when we formulate a simple hypothesis against a simple alternative as follows,

$$H_0: \quad p = p_1 \quad \text{against} \quad H_1: \quad p = p_2$$

we are dealing with a Poisson distribution which is completely specified when values of p are assumed.   We shall consider this case from the point of view of the errors which can be made as a result of sampling variation.   Suppose

$$\begin{aligned} p_1 &= 0.04 \quad \text{and} \quad p_2 = 0.135 \\ \alpha &= 0.035 \quad \text{and} \quad \beta = 0.13 \end{aligned} \qquad (7.2.1)$$

Consider a lot where $p = 0.04$ and where, as the result of our testing procedure, we reject the lot.   This is called an error of the first kind. In repeated uses of this procedure under these conditions, we can expect, as a result of sampling variation, to make this type of error 3.5 per cent of the time.   Suppose, on the other hand, that we were dealing with a lot with $p = 0.135$.   As the result of sampling variation we could decide to accept the lot, making an error of the second kind, which could be expected in 13 per cent of the cases where lots with $p = 0.135$ are presented.   In general, an error of type I is committed when H_0 is rejected although true, and an error of type II is committed when H_0 is accepted although H_1 is true.   Statistical hypothesis testing is largely concerned with the relationship of testing procedures with errors of types I and II.

To illustrate these concepts we consider the simple-vs.-simple hypothesis stated above.   A common procedure for testing this hypothesis is to draw a random independent sample of n items from the lot, to classify each item in the sample as defective or nondefective as the result of inspection, and then to compare the number of defectives d in the sample with a specified number c.   The hypothesis H_0 is rejected if

$$d > c \qquad (7.2.2)$$

This single-sample inspection plan which provides a test of simple hypothesis vs. a simple alternative is usually labeled $S(n,c)$, to indicate its specification by the two numbers n and c.   This procedure, on repeated application, should accept H_0 when it is true 96.5 per cent of the time and therefore reject H_0 3.5 per cent of the time.   Again, when p is 13.5 per cent, we should reject the lot 87 per cent of the time, making the error of the second kind 13 per cent of the time.   Bear in mind that rejecting H_1, when it is true, is an error of the second kind.   Furthermore, this plan has the property that when $p < 4$ per cent, the error of the first kind is less than $\alpha = 0.035$ and when $p > 13.5$ per cent the error of the second kind is less than $\beta = 0.13$.   A specific plan $S(n,c)$ which will accomplish these objectives is given by $S(75,6)$.   This can readily be verified by application of properties of the Poisson distribution. For if $p = 0.04$, then the number of defectives d in a sample of 75 has a Poisson distribution with mean $np = (75)(0.04) = 3$.   When the mean value of d is 3 ($p = 0.04$), the probability that $d > 6$ (the rejection region) is given by

$$\text{Prob} \ (d > 6 \mid np = np_1 = 3) = \sum_{i=7}^{\infty} \frac{e^{-3}3^i}{i!} = 0.0335$$

The actual error of the first kind is 0.0335, and for all practical purposes close enough to our specification.   The error of the second kind is given by

$$\text{Prob} \ (d \leq 6 \mid np = np_2 = 10.125) = \sum_{i=0}^{6} \frac{e^{-10.125}(10.125)^i}{i!} = 0.123$$

It is well to note here that, because of the discrete nature of the Poisson distribution, it may not be possible to meet the exact specification of the magnitude of errors of the first and second type.

It may have occurred to the reader that specifying errors for only two values of p may not be adequate for making decisions in real situations. The selection of "appropriate" inspection sampling plans is in itself a subject, involving a good deal more than statistical hypothesis testing. Nevertheless, it is entirely appropriate to consider the consequence of plan $S(75,6)$ for lots with p other than p_1 and p_2. One can

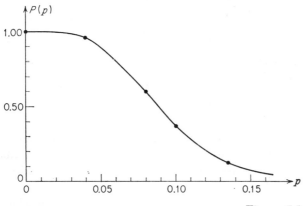

Figure 7.1

compute $P(p)$, the probability of accepting a lot whose proportion defective is p, as follows:

$$P(p) = \text{Prob}\ (d \le 6 \mid np = 75p) = \sum_{i=0}^{6} \frac{e^{-75p}(75p)^i}{i!} \qquad (7.2.3)$$

The result is represented by the curve in Fig. 7.1, which was plotted from Table 7.1.

TABLE 7.1

p	$P(p)$
0.00	1.00
0.04	0.965
0.08	0.60
0.10	0.36
0.135	0.123
0.20	0.008

As can be seen from Table 7.1, $P(p) > 0.965$ when $p < 0.04$ and $P(p) < 0.123$ when $p > 0.135$. Although sample plan $S(75,6)$ was designed to test hypothesis (7.2.1), the curve $P(p)$ tells us much more about the consequences of using such a test procedure.   The curve $P(p)$ is called the *operating characteristic* (*OC*) of the test procedure $S(n,c)$.   It is commonly used in industrial sampling practice.   A historically earlier form for expressing the consequences of testing a statistical hypothesis under various alternatives is contained in the *power function*, which is equal to $1 - P(p)$.   This function was designed in order to give the probability of rejecting H_0 when in fact some alternative hypothesis is true.   Further consideration of the operating characteristic curve and of the power function might lead one to ask whether $S(75,6)$ might be "improved upon."   This question will be considered specifically in connection with the Neyman-Pearson theory of statistical hypothesis testing.

7.2.3   Loss function

By what criteria can we assess and compare tests of statistical hypothesis?   Can we sensibly evaluate $S(75,6)$?   How can we compare $S(75,6)$ with other procedures, such as $S(150,10)$?   These are the types of questions that arise in practice and are of concern in the theory of statistical hypothesis testing.   Basic elements involved in the answers to these questions are the *OC* curve and the *loss function*, already touched upon in Chap. 6.   We shall first examine a loss function applied to testing Eq. (7.2.1) with $S(75,6)$.   For this purpose we require a loss function which consists of the costs associated with the test procedure.   In the present case three costs seem to be relevant.   First, there is the cost of performing the inspection tests, which is assumed to be proportional to the number of items inspected.   The second is the penalty resulting from accepting lots in which there are defectives.   The larger the proportion of defectives, the greater the penalty for accepting such lots.   We assume, for illustrative purposes, that function $f_a(p)$, given in Table 7.2, describes a set of penalties which can occur in practice.   The third loss is that associated with the rejection of basically satisfactory lots.   Were there no such loss, the optimal procedure would be to reject all lots.   We assume, again for illustrative purposes, that function $f_r(p)$, given in the table, in Fig. 7.2 describes the relevant penalties.   The total expected loss $L(p)$ is, for any p,

$$L(p) = Cn + f_a(p)P(p) + f_r(p)[1 - P(p)] \qquad (7.2.4)$$

where C is the cost of one inspection and will be assumed to be equal to 0.05.

One can analyze the loss functions quite simply by inspection (Fig. 7.3).   For example, when $0.085 \leq p \leq 0.17$, $L_2 \leq L_1$.   Thus, were p usually in this range, we should prefer plan $S(150,10)$ to $S(75,6)$.   On the other hand, were p usually outside this range, we should prefer $S(75,6)$.

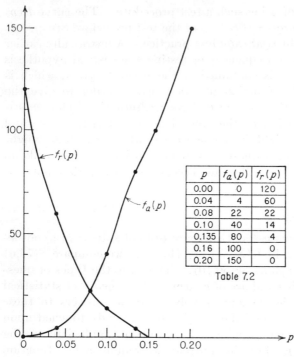

p	$f_a(p)$	$f_r(p)$
0.00	0	120
0.04	4	60
0.08	22	22
0.10	40	14
0.135	80	4
0.16	100	0
0.20	150	0

Table 7.2

Figure 7.2

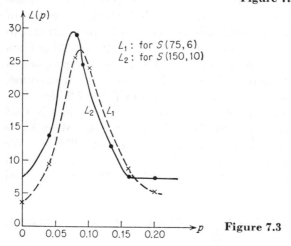

L_1: for $S(75,6)$
L_2: for $S(150,10)$

Figure 7.3

In case rejected lots are fully screened and all defective items replaced by good ones, $f_r(p)$ may be interpreted as a loss due to the screening process.

Ideally, it is preferred that one $L(p)$ curve among a whole class of procedures under consideration lie everywhere below any of the other $L(p)$ curves. This rarely occurs in practical situations. Often, choice between procedures can be based on the OC curves. Among many methods used to compare procedures, one that is sometimes used involves comparing the maxima of the $L(p)$ curves. This method leads to the *minimax criterion* (related to balanced regret, Sec. 6.5.1). Accordingly, L_1 is preferred to L_2. It has been customary to compare procedures on the basis of OC curves or power functions, and we shall consider them in detail. Furthermore, the OC curve is needed for calculating any practical loss function. Our focus of attention will be on the errors of decision in the theory of statistical hypothesis testing. However, it must be realized that a more comprehensive analysis must include the relevant losses associated with the consequences of our decisions.

7.3 The likelihood function and statistical-testing procedures

Modern statistical practice makes considerable use of the likelihood function introduced by Gauss and developed by R. A. Fisher. This function arises naturally in the following way. Assume one is attempting to characterize the diameter of ball bearings manufactured to a specification of $\frac{1}{4}$ inch. One might set up the hypothesis concerning the mean diameter M_d.

$$H_0: \quad M_d = 0.25 \text{ inch} \qquad \text{against} \qquad H_1: \quad M_d > 0.25 \text{ inch} \quad (7.3.1)$$

In order to test this, one takes a random sample of size n and measures the diameters of the spheres in the sample. Let the results be d_1, $d_2, \ldots, d_n$. It seems relevant to ask how "likely" it is to obtain such measurements if in fact H_0 is true. In order to discuss this question more explicitly, let us assume that the manufacturing process yields a normal distribution of the spheres. Under these circumstances the density function $f(d)$ of the random variable D (diameter of sphere) is

$$f(d) = \frac{1}{\sigma \sqrt{2\pi}} \exp\left[\frac{-(d - M_d)^2}{2\sigma^2}\right] \quad (7.3.2)$$

where σ is assumed a known finite quantity. Since the individual measurements are assumed to be independent, the likelihood of the given measurements is

$$L(d_1,d_2, \ldots ,d_n \mid M_d) = f(d_1 \mid M_d)f(d_2 \mid M_d) \cdots f(d_n \mid M_d)$$
$$= \left(\frac{1}{\sigma \sqrt{2\pi}}\right)^n \exp\left[-\frac{1}{2\sigma^2} \sum_{i=1}^{n} (d_i - M_d)^2\right] \quad (7.3.3)$$

The likelihood function is the joint multivariate density function of $(d_1,d_2, \ldots ,d_n)$, which can be thought of as a point in n-dimensional space. It is apparent that, given M_d, σ, and the measurements d_1,

$d_2, \ldots, d_n$, one can compute the value of the likelihood function. Under the hypothesis H_0 (usually called the null hypothesis)

$$L(d_1, d_2, \ldots, d_n \mid 0.25) = \left(\frac{1}{\sigma \sqrt{2\pi}}\right)^n \exp\left[-\frac{1}{2\sigma^2} \sum_{i=1}^{n} (d_i - 0.25)^2\right]$$

The maximum value of $L(d_1, \ldots, d_n \mid 0.25)$ is taken on when $d_1 = d_2 = \cdots = d_n = 0.25$ and is equal to L^*, where $L^* = (1/\sigma \sqrt{2\pi})^n$. Obviously, as the deviations $(d_i - 0.25)^2$ increase, L decreases. We should be more inclined to H_0, the greater L. What we need, however, is a sharp criterion separating acceptance from rejection. A reasonable criterion might be a number k between 0 and L^* (the range of L) such that H_0 is rejected when $L \leq k$ and accepted otherwise. The question still remains, however, is this a "satisfactory" procedure?

We shall try this procedure in a situation where a decision seems intuitively obvious but where the merits and demerits of this approach become apparent. Consider the familiar case of tossing a coin 100 times and obtaining x heads. On the basis of this evidence is it reasonable to assume that the probability p of a head is one-half (i.e., is the coin unbiased)? Recall that the procedure requires rejecting the null hypothesis H_0: $p = 0.5$ when the likelihood is "too small." Now we must determine precisely a value k such that the likelihood less than that is too small. In order to do this we must specify a probability α such that if $p = 0.5$, then probability of getting $L_0 \leq k$ is less than or equal to α. This value α is called the *significance level* of the test and corresponds to the error of the first kind. This makes explicit the notion of "too small" in this case as we use it. Other values of α can be chosen, and reflect the experimenter's views as well as the nature of the situation. The region of outcomes where the likelihood $L_0 \leq k$ is called the *rejection region*. Hence, if the outcome is in the rejection region, we reject H_0. Our next step should be to calculate the value k corresponding to the required significance level. If we choose a level of significance $\alpha = 0.05$, it can be shown that the required rejection region $L_0 \leq k$ is equivalent to rejecting when $|x - 50| \geq 10$, where x denotes the number of heads in 100 tosses. Suppose that the experiment yielded a value $x = 38$. Then $|x - 50| = 12 > 10$ and calls for rejection of H_0: $p = 0.50$.

The rejection region was determined here only by considering H_0 and made no reference to alternatives. Suppose that we considered

$$H_0: \quad p = 0.50 \qquad \text{against} \qquad H_1: \quad p = 0.60$$

Would it follow that the alternative is to be preferred to H_0? Should we not reconsider whether or not to reject H_0 by first examining the likelihood L_1 of the alternative H_1? For in truth, rejecting H_0 implies, in many situations, the acceptance of the alternative. It is obvious, without recourse to statistical analysis, that if $x = 38$ is unlikely under H_0, it is certainly *less likely* under H_1. We should then be more strongly inclined to reject H_1 than we were to reject H_0. It seems clear, even from such a simple example, that the magnitude of L_0 alone may not be a satisfactory basis for choosing between H_0 and some alternative H_1. In some manner, satisfying our intuition about choice among alternatives, we must introduce a comparison of L_1 with L_0.

It seems reasonable, then, to reformulate the problem of choice in terms of the *likelihood ratio*

$$\frac{L_0}{L_1} \qquad (7.3.4)$$

This approach has been developed in the Neyman-Pearson theory, where justification for the use of the likelihood ratio has been established. Basic principles of this theory are presented in the next section.

It is apparent that the rejection region $|x - 50| \geq 10$ may not be satisfactory in all situations. For the same significance level α we can suggest a number of other possible rejection regions, as for example:

$$x > 58 \qquad \alpha = 0.05$$
$$x < 42 \qquad \alpha = 0.05$$
$$x = 50 \qquad \alpha = 0.08$$

The merits of these rejection regions depend on the alternatives, which must be seriously considered. The Neyman-Pearson theory attempts to resolve the issue of choosing the appropriate rejection region.

At this point, however, it is desirable to consider briefly whether statistical inference must be formulated only in the light of an alternative hypothesis. In experimental work we often pursue a "hunch." After a certain amount of evidence has been collected, the experimenter takes stock and asks whether the data support his hunch. Bear in mind, however, that the experimenter may have no alternative to his hunch. Given a level of significance, which in development work may be quite high, the experimenter will usually continue following his hunch if L_0 is greater than the significance level. In such exploratory work investigators pursue, so to speak, "reasonable chances" of success and are not bound to follow only highly probable courses of action. The formulation of such situations, in terms of alternative hypotheses, may not necessarily be useful at that stage. Hence the concept that one really can reject only a null hypothesis, without necessarily being committed to an alternative, may have genuine merit in some situations. The question of an appropriate formulation of the relevance of evidence in relation to testing statistical hypotheses is still an open one.

7.4   Neyman-Pearson approach

Recapitulating the discussion in the previous section, it is apparent that a test of statistical hypothesis resolves itself into the determination of a rejection region.   For the test procedure is completely specified once a rejection region is fixed.   It should be emphasized that any subset of the possible outcomes of the experiment is a possible rejection region.   A few examples were given.   The important question remaining is how to choose among the possible regions to best serve the purpose for which the statistical test is being performed.   The following discussion deals with the way the Neyman-Pearson approach attempts to resolve this issue.

Before beginning the discussion it is best to classify problems in statistical hypothesis testing.   One broad class of problems arises in situations where the form of the distribution of a random variable is known and we are concerned with the possible values of characterizing parameters.   Suppose, for example, that we are dealing with a normal distribution and wish to make inferences concerning the mean m and standard deviation σ.   We know that the range of m can be $-\infty \le m \le +\infty$, and that of σ, $0 \le \sigma \le +\infty$.   Hence we can think of all possible combinations (m,σ) as points in a *parameter space*, which is the upper half plane.   Of course, we may know a priori, from the empirical nature of the problem, that m cannot be negative, in which case the parameter space is the first quadrant.   In general, one can specify the set of possible values of the parameters that is under consideration.   If we designate this set by Ω, hypotheses become statements about that specific portion of the parameter space wherein the true value lies.

A statement of the type $(m,\sigma) = (2,3)$ is called a *simple hypothesis* since one point of the space is specified.   This condition completely specifies the distribution, a fact which is made use of.   A statement of the type (m,σ) lies in the region where $m = 2$ is called a *composite hypothesis*, since $m = 2$ does not completely specify the distribution, for σ is still unspecified.   Another illustration of these concepts is the following.   A random variable has a Poisson distribution with mean λ.   The parameter space is the half line $\lambda \ge 0$.   A simple hypothesis is $\lambda = 2$, whereas the statement $\lambda > 2$ is a composite hypothesis.

The study of statistical hypothesis testing is usually classified in terms of the following combinations of null (H_0) and alternate (H_1) hypotheses: simple against simple, simple against composite, composite against simple, and composite against composite.

The first step is to limit rejection regions, for any particular case, to those having an error of the first kind $\le \alpha$, specified before taking observations.   Assume that H_0 is true and that we take n observations, $X_1, X_2, \ldots, X_n$.   Since H_0, in the case of a simple hypothesis vs. a simple alternative which we are considering, completely specifies the probability distribution of X_1, X_2, . . . , X_n, we can write the joint probability distribution function under H_0, which is in fact the likelihood function $L_0(x_1, x_2, . . . , x_n)$. For a given rejection region R (in n dimensions there are n observations), α is equal to the probability that the sample $(X_1, X_2, . . . , X_n)$ falls in R under the null hypothesis. But this is precisely

$$\iint_R \cdots \int L_0(x_1, x_2, . . . , x_n) \, dx_1 \, dx_2 \cdots dx_n \leq \alpha \qquad (7.4.1)$$

where the integration is taken over the n-dimensional region R. Given a fixed value of α, we shall consider only such regions as satisfy Eq. (7.4.1). For example, in the coin-tossing example in Sec. 7.3, the rejection region $|X - 50| \geq 10$ corresponds to α approximately 0.05.

Now that we have a whole class of possible rejection regions, on what basis should we select one among them? The Neyman-Pearson theory suggests making this selection in the light of what happens when the alternative H_1 is true. The particular criterion suggested is that of maximizing the probability of $(X_1, X_2, . . . , X_n)$ falling in R when, in fact, H_1 is true. This seems like a reasonable criterion to adopt when definite alternatives are seriously under consideration. This criterion is equivalent to minimizing the error of the second kind. Formally, we wish to find a region R such that

$$\text{Prob } [(X_1, X_2, . . . , X_n) \text{ in } R \mid H_0] \leq \alpha \qquad (7.4.2)$$

and for which

$$\text{Prob } [(X_1, X_2, . . . , X_n) \text{ in } R \mid H_1] \qquad (7.4.3)$$

is maximized among all regions R satisfying (7.4.2). The Neyman-Pearson lemma, stated and proved in the next section, shows how to obtain the optimum rejection region.

7.4.1 Neyman-Pearson lemma

It may be helpful to devise an intuitive picture suggestive of the reasoning behind the construction of the optimum rejection region. Consider, then, an experiment which has a set of possible outcomes. Under H_0, each of these outcomes can occur with a specified probability of occurrence. Similarly, under H_1, each of these same outcomes is possible, but with another set of associated probabilities of occurrence. One can view this simply as though each outcome has attached to it two numbers, one the probability of occurrence under H_0 and the other the probability of occurrence under H_1. Suppose we picture this in nerms of chips, each of which corresponds to a possible outcome and on each of which are the two numbers described above. For any given significance level α, a rejection region, in this model, corresponds to a set of chips, the sum of whose associated H_0 numbers is less than or equal to α. Now the task is to select among all possible such rejection sets one for which the sum of the associated H_1 numbers is as large as possible. An obvious method for constructing this set is as follows:

1. Select that chip for which the ratio of the associated H_0 to the H_1 number is the smallest.

2. Proceed in the same way, selecting again from the remaining chips that one for which the ratio of the H_0 to H_1 numbers is a minimum.

3. Continue in this manner until the sum of the H_0 numbers is such that to add one more chip would make this sum greater than α.

By this means we obtain a set of chips, corresponding to possible outcomes, whose probability $\leq \alpha$ under H_0 and whose probability of occurrence under H_1 is greater than for any other acceptable set of chips. We can state this intuitively expressed rejection region R formally as

$$R = \left[(x_1, x_2, \ \ldots \ , x_n) \left| \frac{L_0(x_1, x_2, \ \ldots \ , x_n)}{L_1(x_1, x_2, \ \ldots \ , x_n)} \leq k \right. \right] \qquad (7.4.4)$$

The expression $(x_1, \ \ldots \ , x_n)$ represents a possible outcome of the experiment where the experiment prescribes n observations. For example, an experiment consisting of making two measurements of the diameter of a rod results in outcomes (x_1, x_2), which can be represented by points in the plane. Thus an experiment requiring n observations can be looked upon as having an n-dimensional sample space of outcomes.

Let us try our intuitive procedure for finding k in the problem of tossing a coin three times independently and testing $H_0: p = 0.50$ against $H_1: p = 0.6$. Table 7.2 contains the eight possible outcomes and the associated probabilities under H_0, H_1, and $H_1': p = 0.4$.

TABLE 7.2

Outcome	L_0 $H_0: \quad p = 0.50$	L_1 $H_1: \quad p = 0.60$	L_1' $H_1': \quad p = 0.40$
TTT	0.125	0.064	0.216
TTH	0.125	0.096	0.144
THT	0.125	0.096	0.144
THH	0.125	0.144	0.096
HTT	0.125	0.096	0.144
HTH	0.125	0.144	0.096
HHT	0.125	0.144	0.096
HHH	0.125	0.216	0.064

First consider H_0 against H_1 and $\alpha = 0.15$ the procedure for finding the outcome for which the likelihood ratio L_0/L_1 is a minimum. This yields HHH, where $L_0/L_1 = 0.125/0.216 = 0.5787$. The chip (outcome)

HHH is marked with the two numbers 0.125 and 0.216. Since 0.125 is less than $\alpha = 0.15$, we look for another chip among the remaining seven. Regardless of which one is chosen, the sum of the H_0 numbers becomes 0.25. Hence our rejection region under the present conditions is the set of chips consisting of the outcome HHH. This means H_0 is rejected if the outcome of the experiment is HHH. The error of the first kind is only 0.125. The error of the second kind is the probability of accepting H_0 (outcome not HHH) when H_1 is true and is equal to $1 - 0.216 = 0.784$. It is obvious that this test, tossing a coin three times, does not discriminate well between H_0: $p = 0.5$ and H_1: $p = 0.6$. Any other rejection region with $\alpha \leq 0.15$ yields a greater error of the second kind. The reader may try to test H_0 against H_1' and convince himself that the optimum rejection region depends on the alternative under consideration.

We now proceed to the Neyman-Pearson lemma formalizing the procedure which was suggested above with the use of chips. To simplify the presentation, we assume continuous distributions.

Theorem 7.1 *Neyman-Pearson lemma* Suppose we are given an n-dimensional sample space, each possible outcome being represented by an n-tuple $(x_1, x_2, \ldots, x_n)$. Let $L_0(x_1, \ldots, x_n)$ and $L_1(x_1, \ldots, x_n)$ be the likelihoods of $(x_1, \ldots, x_n)$ under H_0 and H_1, respectively. We can consider rejection regions R for which the error of the first kind

$$\int \cdots \int_R L_0(x_1, x_2, \ldots, x_n) \, dx_1 \, dx_2 \ldots dx_n = \alpha \qquad (7.4.5)$$

Consider the region R_0 defined by

$$R_0 = \left[(x_1, x_2, \ldots, x_n) \,\middle|\, \frac{L_0(x_1, x_2, \ldots, x_n)}{L_1(x_1, x_2, \ldots, x_n)} \leq k \right]$$

where k is chosen to satisfy (7.4.5). For any rejection region R the power (1 minus the error of the second kind) is

$$\int \cdots \int_R L_1(x_1, x_2, \ldots, x_n) \, dx_1 \, dx_2 \ldots dx_n \qquad (7.4.6)$$

For the region R_0 and *any* region R satisfying (7.4.5), we have

$$\int \cdots \int_{R_0} L_1(x_1, x_2, \ldots, x_n) \, dx_1 \, dx_2 \ldots dx_n$$

$$\geq \int \cdots \int_R L_1(x_1, x_2, \ldots, x_n) \, dx_1 \, dx_2 \ldots dx_n \qquad (7.4.7)$$

Note that the integral in (7.4.7) is the probability of rejecting H_0 when H_1 is true since the integration is over the rejection region. In order to facilitate proof we shall use Fig. 7.4. Note that (7.4.7) is a comparison of the integral of $L_1(x_1, x_2, \ldots, x_n)$ over R and R_0. But they have in common region II if they overlap, and proving the inequality

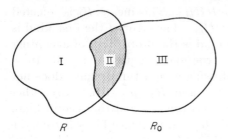

R R_0 **Figure 7.4**

in (7.4.7) over regions I and III is equivalent to proving the theorem. We wish to show that

$$\int \cdots \int_{\text{III}} L_1(x_1, x_2, \ldots, x_n) \, dx_1 \, dx_2 \ldots dx_n$$

$$\geq \int \cdots \int_{\text{I}} L_1(x_1, x_2, \ldots, x_n) \, dx_1 \, dx_2 \ldots dx_n \quad (7.4.8)$$

Since in region III (a subregion of R_0) we have given the inequality

$$\frac{L_0(x_1, x_2, \ldots, x_n)}{L_1(x_1, x_2, \ldots, x_n)} \leq k \quad (7.4.9)$$

we have

$$\int \cdots \int_{\text{III}} L_1(x_1, x_2, \ldots, x_n) \, dx_1 \, dx_2 \ldots dx_n$$

$$\geq \frac{1}{k} \int \cdots \int_{\text{III}} L_0(x_1, x_2, \ldots, x_n) \, dx_1 \, dx_2 \ldots dx_n$$

Now, by virtue of (7.4.5), we also have

$$\frac{1}{k} \int \cdots \int_{\text{III}} L_0(x_1, x_2, \ldots, x_n) \, dx_1 \, dx_2 \ldots dx_n$$

$$= \frac{1}{k} \int \cdots \int_{\text{I}} L_0(x_1, x_2, \ldots, x_n) \, dx_1 \, dx_2 \ldots dx_n$$

Again, since region I is outside R_0, we get the reverse of the inequality of (7.4.9) for points in region I. Thus

$$\frac{L_0(x_1, x_2, \ldots, x_n)}{L_1(x_1, x_2, \ldots, x_n)} > k$$

which yields

$$\frac{1}{k} \int \cdots \int_I L_0(x_1,x_2,\ldots,x_n)\,dx_1\,dx_2\ldots dx_n$$

$$\geq k\left(\frac{1}{k}\right)\int \cdots \int_I L_1(x_1,x_2,\ldots,x_n)\,dx_1\,dx_2\ldots dx_n$$

Putting this chain of inequalities together yields the relation in (7.4.8), which is equivalent to (7.4.7), as was to be shown.

The significance of the Neyman-Pearson lemma will be brought out in the following sequence of examples. (In some cases certain formal niceties are required, in particular, a randomization procedure, which, however, are beyond the scope of this work.)

7.4.2 Applications of the Neyman-Pearson lemma

Example 7.1 Industrial accidents are measured in terms of the incidents of accidents per million man-hours. The accident rate is, of course, a chance variable, and often, under conditions of statistical control, can be represented by a Poisson distribution with parameter λ, which is the mean number of accidents per million man-hours. The probability $P(a)$ of a accidents in h million man-hours is

$$P(a) = \frac{e^{-\lambda h}(\lambda h)^a}{a!} \qquad a = 0, 1, 2, \ldots$$

Suppose we denote the current value of λ by λ_0. If we were to institute a safety program, how should we assess its effectiveness? We propose to test the hope that the λ obtained after the program has been in effect is less than λ_0. Calling this new value λ_1, we make the following test of hypothesis:

$$H_0: \quad \lambda = \lambda_0 \qquad \text{against} \qquad H_1: \quad \lambda = \lambda_1 \qquad (\lambda_1 < \lambda_0)$$

where α has been specified.

The experiment consists of observing the number of accidents a during the test period consisting of h million man-hours. Following the procedure previously specified, we form

$$L_0(a) = \frac{e^{-\lambda_0 h}(\lambda_0 h)^a}{a!} \qquad \text{and} \qquad L_1(a) = \frac{e^{-\lambda_1 h}(\lambda_1 h)^a}{a!}$$

and the ratio

$$R(a) = \frac{L_0(a)}{L_1(a)} = e^{-h(\lambda_0-\lambda_1)}\left(\frac{\lambda_0}{\lambda_1}\right)^a$$

The rejection region is of the form $R(a) \leq k$.

We need, then, to find the set of values of a comprising the rejection region. In this case we can take advantage of the fact that $\lambda_1 < \lambda_0$

implies that $R(a)$ is an increasing function of a. This implies that the set of values $R(a) \leq k$ is equivalent to the set of values of a less than or equal to some other constant k'. Our job is to find k' for the given significance level α, say, $\alpha = 0.02$. The value k' must be such that the error of the first kind is $\alpha = 0.02$, namely,

$$\text{Prob} \ (a \leq k' \mid H_0) = \sum_{a=0}^{k'} \frac{e^{-\lambda_0 h}(\lambda_0 h)^a}{a!} = 0.02 = \alpha$$

The value of k' can, of course, be obtained from tables such as Molina's.[1]

It is important to note that in the present instance k' does not depend on the specific value of the alternative λ_1, but merely on the fact that $\lambda_1 \leq \lambda_0$. Hence the present rejection region minimizes the error of the second kind for *all* one-sided alternatives $\lambda_1 \leq \lambda_0$. This situation is not necessarily to be expected; it is, however, a very desirable condition. This condition, where the rejection region minimizes the error of the second kind for a whole range of alternatives, is called a *uniformly most powerful* test over the range of alternatives.

Example 7.2 Suppose that a component in a piece of complex equipment has an operating life which can be represented by an exponential distribution with parameter θ. A design change has been introduced, and it is desired to determine whether the change has increased the mean operating life of the component.

In order to test this conjecture we undertake to observe the length of life of n components under customary operating conditions following the design change. The experiment yields outcomes $x_1, x_2, \ldots, x_n$. Before the design change the mean life was $1/\theta_0$ time units; that is, the value of the parameter $\theta = \theta_0$. Hence, if the new mean life is $1/\theta_1$, we wish to test

$$H_0: \quad \theta = \theta_0 \quad \text{against} \quad H_1: \quad \theta = \theta_1 \quad (\theta_1 < \theta_0)$$

Following the procedure established, we form the likelihoods under H_0 and H_1:

$$L_0(x_1, x_2, \ldots, x_n) = \theta_0{}^n e^{-\theta_0(x_1 + x_2 + \cdots + x_n)}$$
$$L_1(x_1, x_2, \ldots, x_n) = \theta_1{}^n e^{-\theta_1(x_1 + x_2 + \cdots + x_n)}$$

Then the ratio $R(x_1, x_2, \ldots, x_n)$ is

$$R(x_1, x_2, \ldots, x_n) = \left(\frac{\theta_0}{\theta_1}\right)^n e^{-(\theta_0 - \theta_1)(x_1 + x_2 + \cdots + x_n)} \tag{7.4.10}$$

The optimum rejection region for any specified significance level α is of the form

$$R(x_1, x_2, \ldots, x_n) \leq k \tag{7.4.11}$$

[1] "Poisson Exponential Binomial Limit," D. Van Nostrand Company, Inc., Princeton, N.J., 1943. See also Appendix Table A.2.

where again, since the exponent in (7.4.10) is negative $(1/\theta_1 > 1/\theta_0)$, $R(x_1, x_2, \ldots, x_n)$ is a monotonically decreasing function of $x_1 + x_2 + \cdots + x_n$. Therefore (7.4.11) will hold when $x + x_2 + \cdots + x_n \geq k'$. In words, this states that when the sum of the observed lifetimes is greater than some appropriate constant k', we prefer to reject the null hypothesis in the light of the chosen error of the first kind α. This result is consistent with our intuitive feeling about life testing, although finding k' may at times prove difficult.

In order to find the value of k' the following condition must be satisfied:

$$P(X_1 + X_2 + \cdots + X_n \geq k' \mid \theta = \theta_0) = \alpha$$

It was shown in Sec. 5.1.6 that under the present assumptions $X_1 + X_2 + \cdots + X_n$ has an Erlang distribution. Therefore the value k' can be obtained from the following relation:

$$\int_{k'}^{\infty} \frac{\theta_0(\theta_0 t)^{n-1} e^{-\theta_0 t}}{(n-1)!} \, dt = \alpha$$

where the integrand is an Erlang distribution. This integral is related to the χ^2 distribution, and the appropriate value of k' can be found from χ^2 tables (see Exercise 5.9).

Example 7.3 Continuing with the same problem we propose another experiment: again using n components under customary conditions after design change, at some selected time T, count the number of components X which have failed. Again, test

$$H_0: \quad \theta = \theta_0 \qquad \text{against} \qquad H_1: \quad \theta = \theta_1 \qquad (\theta_1 < \theta_0)$$

How shall we proceed? We may first ask for the probability of failure in the time interval $[0, T]$, under the null hypothesis. This is equivalent to the probability that a component's lifetime is not larger than T, but this is, under the null hypothesis, given by the CDF of the exponential distribution with parameter θ_0 at T. This is equal to $1 - e^{-\theta_0 T}$, and consequently the probability of survival past T is $e^{-\theta_0 T}$. Since n components are under test, the random variable X has a binomial distribution and the respective likelihoods and their ratios are

$$L_0(x) = \frac{n!}{x!(n-x)!} (1 - e^{-\theta_0 T})^x e^{-\theta_0 T(n-x)}$$

$$L_1(x) = \frac{n!}{x!(n-x)!} (1 - e^{-\theta_1 T})^x e^{-\theta_1 T(n-x)}$$

$$R(x) = \left(\frac{1 - e^{-\theta_0 T}}{1 - e^{-\theta_1 T}} \right)^x e^{-T(n-x)(\theta_0 - \theta_1)}$$

The optimum rejection region is $R(x) \leq k$. It turns out that $R(x)$ is monotonically increasing, and therefore the rejection region is equivalent to $x \le k'$. The value of k', for any significance level α, can be obtained from tables of the cumulative binomial distribution, where k' satisfies

$$\alpha = \sum_{i=0}^{k'} \frac{n!}{i!(n-i)!} \, (1 - e^{-\theta_0 T})^i e^{-\theta_0 T(n-i)}$$

In this example and the previous one we have been testing the same statistical hypothesis with outcomes of different experiments. The theory of design of statistical experiments is concerned with the choice among different possible experiments. Here the difference lies in observing actual times to failure of each of the n items as compared with counting the number of failures during a specific time interval. Some of the differences between the experiments which can influence the choice of experiment are: (1) the time to perform the first experiment may be much

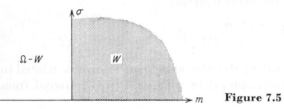

Figure 7.5

greater than a selected T; (2) when a component is operating it is reasonable to monitor the lifetime, while for equipment which is in storage and deteriorates under storage conditions, it may not be practical or economically feasible to monitor lifetime; (3) the error of the second kind may differ considerably between the two experimental procedures.

7.4.3 The likelihood-ratio test

From the foregoing discussions it is apparent that the statement of a statistical hypothesis concerning the parameter point θ (θ can be in a multidimensional space) in the parameter space Ω can be expressed in the following general form:

$$H_0: \quad \theta \text{ in } W \qquad \text{against} \qquad H_1: \quad \theta \text{ in } \Omega - W$$

where W is a subset of Ω. For example, in the case of the simple against the simple, Ω consists of two parameter points $\theta = \theta_0$ and $\theta = \theta_1$ and W is $\theta = \theta_0$. In a case which frequently arises, for the normal distribution with mean m and standard deviation σ, we wish to test $H_0: m \ge 0$ against $H_1: m < 0$. Here the problem is composite against composite, and Ω is the upper half plane and W is the first quadrant (Fig. 7.5).

In the simple against simple we were led to a rejection region involving the likelihood ratio L_0/L_1, less than or equal to a constant (depending on significance level α). In this case the likelihood ratio is computed for given particular parameter points, where L_0 (L at θ_0) is the explanation of how the sample could have been obtained under H_0, while L_1 (L at θ_1) is the explanation under H_1. Furthermore, the Neyman-Pearson lemma shows that this procedure has desirable properties. When, however, there is a composite hypothesis (say, H_0) under consideration, one requires a criterion for the most appropriate explanation of how the observations came about. To "explain" the likelihood of the observations when the composite hypothesis (H_0) is true requires evaluating the likelihood $L(x,\theta)$ for all θ in W. Which of these to use is to be resolved. A reasonable criterion, in many instances, is to maximize $L(x,\theta)$ for θ in W. This maximum gives the sample which did occur the maximum chance of occurrence when θ is restricted to W. A natural generalization of the Neyman-Pearson method for finding a rejection region in the simple against the simple is to reject when the following ratio is sufficiently small:

$$\max_{\theta \text{ in } W} L(x,\theta) / \max_{\theta \text{ in } \Omega - W} L(x,\theta) \leq k$$

This ratio reduces to the ratio considered in the simple-against-simple case previously developed. In the general case, the numerator offers the "best explanation" of the observations (X) under H_0, while the denominator does similarly under H_1. In the literature it is usual, however, to express this rejection region in the following equivalent form:

$$\text{Reject when} \quad \lambda(x) = \max_{\theta \text{ in } W} L(x,\theta) / \max_{\theta \text{ in } \Omega} L(x,\theta) \leq k \qquad k < 1$$

(The proof of the equivalence of the regions is left as an exercise to the reader.) If the maximum does not exist, use the supremum.

Example 7.4 Consider n independent observations on a normal random variable with known $\sigma = \sigma_0$. Suppose we wish to test the hypothesis that the mean $m = m_0$ against the alternative $m \neq m_0$. The parameter space is the line $\sigma = \sigma_0$, $-\infty \leq m \leq +\infty$. The null hypothesis H_0 states that the parameter point is (m_0, σ_0). The alternative hypothesis H_1 states that the parameter point is on the line $\sigma = \sigma_0$, excluding the point (m_0, σ_0). The present alternative H_1 is two-sided, while in some of our previous examples the composite alternatives were one-sided.

The likelihood function L of the observation for any parameter point (m, σ_0) is

$$L(x_1, x_2, \ldots, x_n; m, \sigma_0) = \left(\frac{1}{\sigma_0 \sqrt{2\pi}}\right)^n e^{-\frac{1}{2\sigma_0^2} \sum_{i=1}^{n} (x_i - m)^2} \tag{7.4.12}$$

In order to evaluate the likelihood ratio we must first determine the maximum of L, given in (7.4.12), at (m_0, σ_0) and then for (m, σ_0), $-\infty \leq m \leq +\infty$. Clearly, then, the first evaluation which gives the numerator of the likelihood ratio is

$$\left(\frac{1}{\sigma_0 \sqrt{2\pi}}\right)^n e^{-\frac{1}{2\sigma_0^2}\sum\limits_{i=1}^{n}(x_i-m_0)^2}$$

The denominator of the likelihood ratio is found by evaluating (7.4.12) for the value of m which minimizes $\sum\limits_{i=1}^{N}(x_1 - m)^2$. As an exercise the reader may verify that this minimum occurs for $m = \bar{x}$, the arithmetic average of the observations. Thus the likelihood ratio is

$$\lambda(x_1, x_2, \ldots , x_n) = \exp\left\{-\frac{1}{2\sigma_0^2}\left[\sum_i (x_i - m_0)^2 - \sum_i (x_i - \bar{x})^2\right]\right\}$$

$$= \exp\left[-\frac{n}{2\sigma_0^2}(\bar{x} - m_0)^2\right] \quad (7.4.13)$$

The rejection region then consists of those values of $(x_1, x_2, \ldots , x_n)$ which yield a likelihood ratio $\lambda(x_1, x_2, \ldots , x_n)$ sufficiently small, that is, less than some k, depending on the selected value of α. Since $\lambda(x_1, x_2, \ldots , x_n)$, in this case, is a decreasing function of $|\bar{x} - m_0|$, the rejection is equivalent to those values of $|\bar{x} - m_0| \geq k'$. We shall illustrate the details of determining k' with specific numbers. Let $\alpha = 0.10$. Then

$$\alpha = \text{Prob}\,(|\bar{X} - m_0| \geq k' \mid m_0, \sigma_0)$$

$$= \text{Prob}\left(\frac{|\bar{X} - m_0|}{\sigma_0/\sqrt{n}} \geq \frac{k'}{\sigma_0/\sqrt{n}}\right) = 2\Phi\left(\frac{-k'}{\sigma_0/\sqrt{n}}\right)$$

From the table of the cumulative standard normal distribution the appropriate value of k' can be found. For $\alpha = 0.10$,

$$\frac{k'}{\sigma_0/\sqrt{n}} = 1.64 \quad \text{and} \quad k' = \frac{1.64\sigma_0}{\sqrt{n}}$$

The rejection region for $\alpha = 0.10$ is therefore

$$|\bar{x} - m_0| \geq \frac{1.64\sigma_0}{\sqrt{n}}$$

It is natural to ask how well this test performs for different alternative values of m, as well as for different values of σ_0 and n. The essential effects are expressed in the power function $\pi(m)$ for given alternatives. The power is equal to 1 minus the error of the second kind. By definition $\pi(m)$ is

$$\text{Prob [rejection} \mid (m, \sigma_0)] = \text{Prob}\left[|\bar{X} - m_0| \geq \frac{1.64\sigma_0}{\sqrt{n}} \mid (m, \sigma_0)\right]$$

It is more convenient, in this case, to find the error of the second kind, $1 - \pi(m)$, which is

$$1 - \pi(m) = \text{Prob} \left[-\frac{1.64\sigma_0}{\sqrt{n}} \leq \bar{X} - m_0 \leq +\frac{1.64\sigma_0}{\sqrt{n}} \bigg| (m, \sigma_0) \right]$$

In order to evaluate $1 - \pi(m)$, we make use of tables of the standard normal variate,

$$\frac{\bar{X} - m}{\sigma_0/\sqrt{n}}$$

This is obtained from $\bar{X} - m_0$ by adding $m_0 - m$ and dividing the result by $\sigma_0/\sqrt{n}$. On performing this standard normal transformation to all terms in the inequality, we obtain

$$1 - \pi(m) = \text{Prob} \left(\frac{m_0 - m}{\sigma_0/\sqrt{n}} - \frac{1.64\sigma_0/\sqrt{n}}{\sigma_0/\sqrt{n}} \right.$$
$$\left. \leq \frac{\bar{X} - m}{\sigma_0/\sqrt{n}} \leq \frac{m_0 - m}{\sigma_0/\sqrt{n}} + \frac{1.64\sigma_0/\sqrt{n}}{\sigma_0/\sqrt{n}} \right)$$

On simplifying with the notation δ and the standard normal variate Z, the error of the second kind becomes

$$1 - \pi(m) = \text{Prob} (\delta - 1.64 \leq Z \leq \delta + 1.64)$$
$$= \Phi(+1.64 + \delta) - \Phi(-1.64 + \delta)$$

where $\Phi(\ )$ is the CDF of the standard normal distribution. Returning to the power function $\pi(m)$, we have

$$\pi(m) = 1 - \Phi(+1.64 + \delta) + \Phi(-1.64 + \delta)$$
$$= \Phi(-1.64 - \delta) + \Phi(-1.64 + \delta) \quad (7.4.14)$$

since $\Phi(-u) = 1 - \Phi(u)$. Note first that $\pi(m)$ depends only on the parameter δ, and second, that it is symmetric in δ. Of special interest is the fact that the power is an increasing function of δ for $\delta > 0$ as well as for $\delta < 0$. At $\delta = 0$, the value of the power is a minimum and is, in fact, equal to the significance level α, which in the present case was chosen to be 0.10. Figure 7.6 gives a representation of the power function for the present example with $\alpha = 0.10$. It seems intuitively satisfactory that the power should increase as the alternative departs from H_0. For any sample size n, the power $\pi(m)$ can also be plotted against $\delta/\sqrt{n} = (m - m_0)/\sigma_0$ and gives a convenient representation of what the procedure does under various alternatives.

The practical dictates, in many situations, require that when $|m - m_0| \geq \Delta$, where Δ is specified by the situation, the probability of rejecting H_0 be at least some particular level, usually denoted by $1 - \beta$.

Given this requirement, α and σ_0, what minimum n will meet it? The procedure for doing this is to set $\pi(m) = 1 - \beta$ in Eq. (7.4.14) and solve for δ. Setting this value of δ, denoted by δ^*, equal to $\sqrt{n}\,\Delta/\sigma_0$ and solving for n, one obtains a solution n^*, where

$$n^* = \left(\frac{\sigma_0\delta^*}{\Delta}\right)^2$$

The requirement will be met, then, for any $n \geq n^*$. It may be quite difficult to solve (7.4.14) for δ^*, whereas the plot of $\pi(m)$ provides a simple graphical procedure for doing this. For example, when $\alpha = 0.10$,

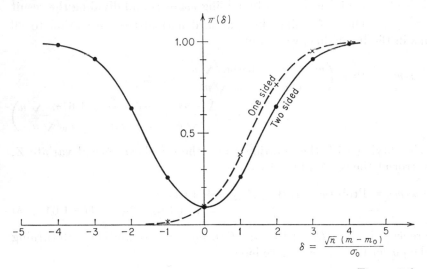

Figure 7.6

$\sigma_0 = 2$, $\Delta = 1$, and $1 - \beta = 0.80$, we have, from Fig. 7.6, that $\delta^* \approx 2.5$; whence $n^* \approx 25$.

We worked out the example just completed in order to show how the likelihood-ratio test can be applied in an important case. It turned out that the mathematical details were not formidable. In general, however, application of the likelihood-ratio test may lead to considerable mathematical difficulties in finding the rejection region. In particular, if H_0 is composite, there is the added difficulty of interpreting the error of the first kind. For Prob (rejection of $H_0 \mid \theta$) is not unique when θ can be one of a set of values in W, specified by H_0. A plausible interpretation is that Prob (rejection of $H_0 \mid \theta) \leq \alpha$, for all θ in W. This of course entails added mathematical difficulty over that experienced in the example given.

Let us look again at Eq. (7.4.13), which is the likelihood ratio $\lambda(X_1, X_2, \ldots, X_n)$ in Example 7.4. A thoughtful look at the exponent

$-n(\bar{x} - m_0)^2/2\sigma_0^2$ shows that it is related to the χ^2 distribution with 1 degree of freedom. In fact,

$$-2 \ln \lambda(X_1, X_2, \ldots, X_n) = \left(\frac{\bar{X} - m_0}{\sigma_0/\sqrt{n}}\right)^2$$

has a χ^2 distribution with 1 degree of freedom. An advantage of this form lies in the fact that the rejection region λ sufficiently small is equivalent to $-2 \ln \lambda$ sufficiently large since $-2 \ln \lambda$ is monotonically decreasing with λ and $0 \leq \lambda \leq 1$. The rejection region can be written in the form

$$\left(\frac{\bar{x} - m_0}{\sigma_0/\sqrt{n}}\right)^2 \geq k'$$

and k' can be found from tables of the χ^2 distribution. We may wonder whether this sort of relation holds more generally. It turns out, in fact, that *under rather general conditions, given H_0, the distribution of*

$$-2 \ln \lambda(X_1, X_2, \ldots, X_n)$$

converges to that of χ^2 with $d_1 - d_2$ degrees of freedom as $n \to \infty$, where d_1 is the dimensionality of Ω and d_2 is the dimensionality of W. This fact will be used in simplifying the application of the likelihood-ratio test when n is large. The proof of this result is rather intricate. It should be noted expressly that this result resolves, for large sample size, the difficulty of interpreting the error of the first kind for composite H_0. For the rejection region can be determined, for any significance level α, independent of the parameter θ in W.

One can summarize the merits of the likelihood-ratio test in terms of the following. In many cases, it leads to intuitively reasonable procedures; if a uniformly most powerful test exists, it is given by the likelihood-ratio test; for large n it has optimum properties as was shown by A. Wald; for large n the rejection region, for any α, can be found by use of the χ^2 tables.

7.5   Design and analysis of simple comparative experiments involving the normal distribution

In previous discussions we have considered a number of problems involving a comparison of the mean values of physical dimensions of items as well as of rates of accident occurrence. The common nature of these problems involves the comparison of mean values between populations where one of these mean values may be known. More precisely, we consider comparisons of a mean m against a specified value m_0, or a comparison of the mean of one population m_1 with the mean of another, m_2.

There can be many forms of these comparisons, depending on the alternatives and whether σ^2 is known or unknown.   We shall consider a variety of these cases.

7.5.1   Comparing a mean against a specified alternative value

Two-sided Alternative   In Example 7.4 we discussed at length the comparison

$$H_0: \quad m = m_0 \qquad \text{against} \qquad H_1: \quad m \neq m_0$$

where $\sigma^2 = \sigma_0^2$ is known.   This is a two-sided alternative, and the reject region for a significance level α is found to be of the form $|\bar{x} - m_0| \geq Z_{1-\alpha/2}\sigma_0/\sqrt{n}$ (in particular for $\alpha = 0.10$, $Z_{1-\alpha/2} = 1.64$).

How is the procedure affected when σ^2 is unknown?   As for σ^2 known, we shall try to find a rejection region of the form $|\bar{x} - m_0| \geq k'$, where, as before, k' must be chosen so that the error of the first kind is some specified value α.   Intuitively, we reject m_0 if $\bar{x}$ deviates from m_0 by "too much."   We shall try to find k' following the method used in Example 7.4.   We must find k' such that

$$\text{Prob } (|\bar{X} - m_0| \geq k' \mid m = m_0) = \alpha$$

In Example 7.4, when σ^2 was a known value σ_0^2, we standardized by dividing both sides of the inequality by $\sigma_0/\sqrt{n}$.   In the present case, however, σ^2 is unknown, and it is natural to try our luck with an estimate of σ^2.   Recall that in Chap. 5 we discussed the consequences of standardizing with an estimate $s^2 = \Sigma(X_i - \bar{X})^2/(n - 1)$ for σ^2.   The resulting random variable has the t distribution with $n - 1$ degrees of freedom and does not depend on m or σ^2.   Let us consider, then,

$$t = \frac{\bar{X} - m_0}{s/\sqrt{n}}$$

and find k', satisfying

$$\alpha = \text{Prob}\left(\frac{|\bar{X} - m_0|}{s/\sqrt{n}} \geq \frac{k'}{s/\sqrt{n}}\right) = \text{Prob}\left(|t| \geq \frac{k'}{s/\sqrt{n}}\right)$$

From tables of the t distribution we find $k'/(s/\sqrt{n}) = t_{1-\alpha/2}$, for $n - 1$ degrees of freedom.   Then it follows that the rejection region is $|\bar{x} - m_0| \geq t_{1-\alpha/2}s/\sqrt{n}$.   It is important to recognize that k' is not a constant for a given n.   Note the parallel with the case σ^2 known, where the rejection region is $|\bar{x} - m_0| \geq Z_{1-\alpha/2}\sigma_0/\sqrt{n}$.   The analogy between the cases is more apparent when the rejection regions are viewed in the standardized and "Studentized" forms

$$\frac{|\bar{x} - m_0|}{\sigma_0/\sqrt{n}} \geq Z_{1-\alpha/2} \qquad \sigma^2 = \sigma_0{}^2 \text{ known}$$

$$\frac{|\bar{x} - m_0|}{s/\sqrt{n}} \geq t_{1-\alpha/2} \qquad \sigma^2 \text{ unknown}$$

It turns out that these tests are, in fact, likelihood-ratio tests.

It is often not enough to know the error of the first kind since the error of the second kind may have serious consequences. In any case, we wish to understand how the test behaves for a variety of prevailing circumstances other than those specified by H_0. The power function $\pi(m)$, for the case σ^2 known, was found, in Example 7.4, for significance level $\alpha = 0.10$; for any α,

$$\pi(m) = \Phi(Z_{\alpha/2} - \delta) + \Phi(Z_{\alpha/2} + \delta)$$

where $\delta = (m - m_0)\sqrt{n}/\sigma$.

When σ^2 is unknown, the power at $m \neq m_0$ and σ^2 is

$$\text{Prob}\left(\frac{|\bar{X} - m_0|}{s/\sqrt{n}} \geq t_{1-\alpha/2} \,\bigg|\, m, \sigma^2\right)$$

The result hinges on the distribution of $\sqrt{n}\,(\bar{X} - m_0)/s$ and depends on m and σ^2. This random variable has a noncentral t distribution with $n - 1$ degrees of freedom and depending on a parameter of noncentrality $\delta = (m - m_0)\sqrt{n}/\sigma$, which is a measure of deviation from H_0. The noncentral t distribution is tabulated. Again, for any n, the power can be plotted against $(m - m_0)/\sigma$. Figures 7.7 and 7.8 give the operating characteristic curves $1 - \pi(m)$ versus $d = \delta/\sqrt{n} = (m - m_0)/\sigma$, for various values of n, $\alpha = 0.01$, and $\alpha = 0.05$.

In Example 7.4 we also found the smallest value of sample size n such that the odds for rejection of $m = m_0$ when $|m - m_0| \geq \Delta$ is larger than $1 - \beta$, having specified β. We should like to do the same for the case σ^2 unknown. We can plot the power, for any n, as a function of $\delta/\sqrt{n} = (m - m_0)/\sigma$ by means of tables of the noncentral t distribution with $n - 1$ degrees of freedom, and this is presented in Figs. 7.7 and 7.8. Since σ^2 is unknown, we cannot find n by specifying Δ alone, but must specify Δ as a multiple of σ. Thus, for a given "deviation from H_0," in terms of Δ/σ (regardless of σ's value), we can find the desired n graphically from the plot of $1 - \pi(m)$ versus $(m - m_0)/\sigma$ from looking at $\pi(\Delta/\sigma)$ for various n and noting the smallest n for which this value is $\geq 1 - \beta$. For example, when $\alpha = 0.01$, $\beta = 0.10$, and $\Delta/\sigma = 0.60$, we can see from Fig. 7.7 that the minimum n is approximately equal to 48.

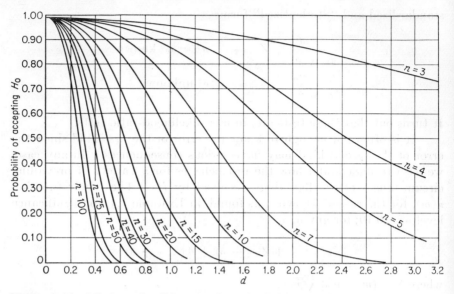

Figure 7.7* *OC* curves for different values of n for the two-sided t test for a level of significance $a = 0.01$.

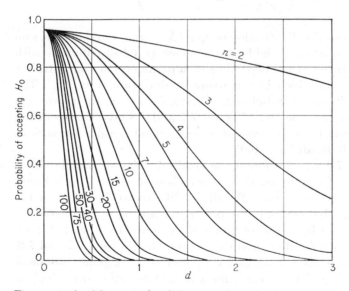

Figure 7.8* *OC* curves for different values of n for the two-sided t test for a level of significance $a = 0.05$.

* Figures 7.7 and 7.8 are reproduced by permission from Charles L. Ferris, Frank E. Grubbs, Chalmer L. Weaver, Operating Characteristics for the Common Statistical Tests of Significance, *Annals of Mathematical Statistics*, June, 1946.

We have presented the case of a comparison of the mean against a standard for σ^2 unknown without detailed derivations and have also made use of the noncentral t distribution without mathematical treatment in order to enable the reader to treat these problems, which are common in practice.

One-sided Alternative In many cases where we are interested in testing $H_0: m = m_0$, we are basically concerned with a one-sided alternative $m < m_0$. For example, suppose a cement manufacturer distributes his product in bags to various builders who use large numbers of bags of cement for any batch. Under these circumstances, the customer, wishing to protect himself against short weight, is primarily concerned with the mean weight per bag, and therefore with testing $H_0: m = m_0$ against $H_1: m < m_0$. On the other hand, the manufacturer may test $H_0: m = m_0$ against $m > m_0$. (A very conscientious manufacturer will be interested in the two-sided alternative $m \neq m_0$.) In either case we have a comparison of a mean with a standard against a one-sided alternative. Again, the variance σ^2 may or may not be known.

We shall now formulate systematically each of the two different cases, σ^2 known and σ^2 unknown, for the one-sided alternative $m > m_0$. Let us first consider the case $\sigma^2 = \sigma_0^2$ known. This is a simple-against-composite hypothesis. We have a procedure for constructing the test statistic and the rejection region for the simple-against-simple case by means of the Neyman-Pearson lemma. Let us first consider the case of testing $H_0: m = m_0$ against $H_1: m = m_1$, where $m_1 > m_0$. If it turns out that the rejection region is independent of the choice of m_1, so long as it is greater than m_0, then we have in fact a procedure for the original problem $H_0: m = m_0$ against $m > m_0$. We apply the Neyman-Pearson lemma as follows:

$$L_0(x_1, x_2, \ldots, x_n) = \left(\frac{1}{\sigma_0\sqrt{2\pi}}\right)^n \exp\left[-\frac{1}{2\sigma_0^2}\sum_i (x_i - m_0)^2\right]$$

$$L_1(x_1, x_2, \ldots, x_n) = \left(\frac{1}{\sigma_0\sqrt{2\pi}}\right)^n \exp\left[-\frac{1}{2\sigma_0^2}\sum_i (x_i - m_1)^2\right]$$

Then the ratio $R(x_1, x_2, \ldots, x_n)$ is

$$R(x_1, x_2, \ldots, x_n) = \exp\left[-\frac{n(m_0^2 - m_1^2)}{2\sigma_0^2}\right] \exp\left[-\frac{n\bar{x}(m_1 - m_0)}{\sigma_0^2}\right]$$

The Neyman-Pearson lemma calls for rejecting when R is sufficiently small (depending on the significance level α). Since R is a decreasing function of $\bar{x}$ (since $m_1 - m_0 > 0$), this region is equivalent to rejection when $\bar{x}$ is sufficiently large. Therefore $\bar{x}$ is the test statistic, and the rejection region is of the form $\bar{x} > k$, where k is to be determined from α.

The value of k is found by the usual standardization procedure,

$$\alpha = \text{Prob } (\bar{X} > k \mid m = m_0) = \text{Prob } \left(\frac{\bar{X} - m_0}{\sigma_0/\sqrt{n}} > \frac{k - m_0}{\sigma_0/\sqrt{n}}\right)$$

$$= 1 - \Phi\left(\frac{k - m_0}{\sigma_0/\sqrt{n}}\right)$$

Therefore $(k - m_0)\sqrt{n}/\sigma_0 = Z_{1-\alpha}$, where $Z_{1-\alpha}$ is the $1 - \alpha$ percentile of the standard normal variate, and thus $k = m_0 + Z_{1-\alpha}\sigma_0/\sqrt{n}$. The rejection region, for any specified α, is $\bar{x} > m_0 + Z_{1-\alpha}\sigma_0/\sqrt{n}$. Note that the rejection is independent of m_1 so long as $m_1 \geq m_0$. The Neyman-Pearson lemma provides, for any α, a rejection region which minimizes the error of the second kind, or maximizes power. Therefore, for any $m_1 \geq m_0$ and the specified α, the power of the procedure evaluated at m_1, $\pi(m_1)$, is not smaller than the power at m_1, $\pi'(m_1)$, for any other procedure with the same α. That is, for $m_1 > m_0$, $\pi(m_1) \geq \pi'(m_1)$. Since the rejection does not depend on $m_1(m_1 > m_0)$, we have, in fact, a *uniformly most powerful* (*UMP*) procedure for the original problem $H_0: m = m_0$ against $m > m_0$.

Let us proceed to find an expression for the power function $\pi(m)$. By definition,

$$\pi(m) = \text{Prob (rejection} \mid m, \sigma_0^2) = \text{Prob } (\bar{X} > m_0 + Z_{1-\alpha}\sigma_0/\sqrt{n} \mid m, \sigma_0^2)$$

By the usual procedure of standardization of the normal variate $\bar{X}$, we obtain

$$\pi(m) = \text{Prob } \left(\frac{\bar{X} - m}{\sigma_0/\sqrt{n}} \geq \frac{m_0 - m}{\sigma_0/\sqrt{n}} + Z_{1-\alpha}\right)$$

Denoting $\sqrt{n}\,(\bar{X} - m)/\sigma_0$ by Z and again letting $\delta = \sqrt{n}\,(m - m_0)/\sigma_0$, the power becomes

$$\pi(m) = \text{Prob } (Z \geq -\delta + Z_{1-\alpha}) = 1 - \Phi(Z_{1-\alpha} - \delta) \qquad (7.5.1)$$

where $\Phi(\ )$ is the *CDF* of the standard normal variate. The determination of $\pi(m)$, for $\alpha = 0.10$, is illustrated in Fig. 7.6. Comparing this power function with that of the two-sided alternative (Fig. 7.6), it is readily apparent that the one-sided test is superior when $m > m_0$ but inferior when $m < m_0$.

Recall that in most real situations, where a one-sided alternative applies, one is particularly interested in detecting a practically significant difference, $\Delta = m - m_0$, with a given degree of assurance $1 - \beta$. This, of course, depends on n, and we wish to find the smallest n for which $\pi(m) \geq 1 - \beta$, when $m - m_0 \geq \Delta$. This is equivalent to solving Eq. (7.5.1) for δ, which depends on n, when $\pi(m)$ is set equal to $1 - \beta$. Denote this value of δ as $\delta_{1-\beta}$; whence $1 - \beta = 1 - \Phi(Z_{1-\alpha} - \delta_{1-\beta})$.

Therefore $\beta = \Phi(Z_{1-\alpha} - \delta_{1-\beta})$, and in consequence, $Z_{1-\alpha} - \delta_{1-\beta} = Z_{\beta}$, yielding $-\delta_{1-\beta} = Z_{\beta} - Z_{1-\alpha}$. Since $\delta = \sqrt{n}\,(m - m_0)/\sigma_0$, we can find the appropriate n as the smallest integer larger than n^* by setting $m - m_0 = \Delta$ in $\delta_{1-\beta}$ and solving for n^* in $\delta_{1-\beta} = \Delta \sqrt{n^*}/\sigma_0$. Therefore

$$n^* = \left(\frac{\sigma_0 \delta_{1-\beta}}{\Delta}\right)^2 = \left[\frac{\sigma_0(Z_{\beta} - Z_{1-\alpha})}{\Delta}\right]^2$$

For example, letting $\Delta/\sigma_0 = 1$ and $\alpha = 0.10$, $\beta = 0.05$. Then, since $Z_{0.05} = -1.64$, $Z_{0.90} = 1.28$, we obtain $n^* = 8.526$. Hence, when $n \geq 8.526$, the probability of rejecting H_0 when $m - m_0 \geq \sigma_0$ is at least 95 per cent.

We shall now present briefly the one-sided case when σ^2 is unknown, giving essential steps without rigorous argument. Recall, for σ^2 known, that the rejecting region, for a specified α, is

$$\frac{\bar{X} - m_0}{\sigma_0/\sqrt{n}} > Z_{1-\alpha}$$

The likelihood-ratio test, for σ^2 unknown, leads to a similar rejection region where σ_0 is replaced by its estimate s and $Z_{1-\alpha}$ by $t_{1-\alpha}$ with $n - 1$ degrees of freedom. This is $(\bar{X} - m)/(s/\sqrt{n}) > t_{1-\alpha}$.

The power function of the procedure involves the distribution of $\sqrt{n}\,(\bar{X} - m_0)/s$ when the mean and variance are m and σ^2, respectively. Again, this distribution depends only on $\delta = \sqrt{n}\,(m - m_0)/\sigma$, and its percentiles, as a function of δ, can be found in the tables of the non-central t distribution.

The operating characteristic curve can be plotted as a function $(m - m_0)/\sigma$ for various values of n. In Figs. 7.9 and 7.10, these functions are given for $\alpha = 0.01$ and $\alpha = 0.05$.

When we are interested in rejecting H_0 when $m - m_0 \geq \Delta$, some specified important difference, with given odds $1 - \beta$, the smallest sample size which gives this protection can be found by analogy with the two-sided cases. For example, when $\alpha = 0.01$, $\beta = 0.10$, and $\Delta/\sigma = 0.60$, we find, from Fig. 7.9, that the minimum n is approximately 40. It is interesting to compare this with the two-sided cases, which yielded approximately 48 under these circumstances. Note again that it is not sufficient to specify only Δ, but it is necessary to give the alternative as a multiple of σ; namely, Δ/σ must be given.

The importance of determining the minimum n is not merely the economy that can be gained, but the protection it gives us against conducting inconclusive experiments. Where enough means are available to provide for conducting enough replications to assure decision with the desired discriminating power, the investigation can be conducted with economy of experimental effort. In addition, one is protected against performing too many replications, which are not only excessively costly, but also can lead to too fine a discrimination, which may be less than practically significant. A further advantage is gained when the minimum n is so great that means are not available to perform the required number of replications. Then one is protected against conducting an

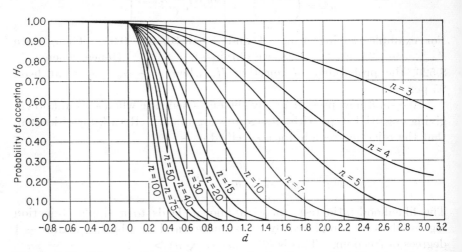

Figure 7.9* *OC* curves for different values of n for the one-sided t test for a level of significance $a = 0.01$.

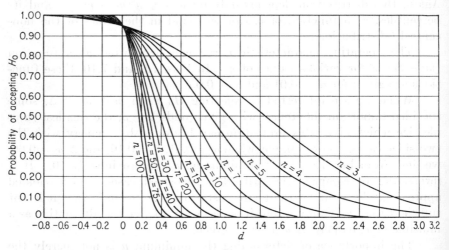

Figure 7.10* *OC* curves for different values of n for the one-sided t test for a level of significance $a = 0.05$.

* Figures 7.9 and 7.10 are reproduced by permission from Charles L. Ferris, Frank E. Grubbs, Chalmer L. Weaver, Operating Characteristics for the Common Statistical Tests of Significance, *Annals of Mathematical Statistics*, June, 1946.

investigation which cannot give the desired discrimination and which, as a result, remains inconclusive.

It should be remarked that not rejecting H_0 does not necessarily imply that H_0 is true; it merely implies that the evidence at hand does not warrant rejecting H_0. In practice, what often seems to happen is that H_0 is accepted when the sample size n is small and is rejected when n is large. This occurs because, when n is small, H_0 will be rejected with reasonable odds only when Δ is large, and similarly, when n is large, H_0 will usually be rejected when Δ is small. These facts reemphasize the importance of the OC curve and the proper choice of sample size. As will be seen in Chap. 8, more light will be shed on the present issues when estimation problems are discussed.

7.5.2 Some empirical aspects of sampling in experimentation

We have considered a number of aspects of experimentation in connection with the use of statistical inference. Now, in approaching more complex comparisons, it is well to take a closer look at the nature of these comparisons and the possibly different experimental situations and procedures which influence the basis of the decisions to be made. In particular, we shall examine different ways of making comparisons. We shall introduce some of the pertinent factors underlying experimentation by considering some common problems.

Occasionally, one is called upon to purchase a new machine where there is a choice between two manufacturers. What is involved in making a "good" choice? Examination of available information does not provide a clear-cut choice between the two manufacturers. We have decided to make some experimental runs. But how?

A little reflection makes us wonder: how many machines to test; how to select the machines to be tested; whether the machines are to be run for a particular job only or for a variety of jobs; whether to use only our most skilled workers in the test; whether to limit the test to one type of raw material or to use a variety of types. In fact, we begin to wonder what it is we should be comparing. Decisions as to all these queries are part of the specification of the total experiment. We shall expand on these issues after considering other examples.

A problem which regularly arises in scientific work is the comparison of different means for measuring various quantities. For example, the question of color measurement in many applications is still a touchy problem. The accurate measurement of small distances, high speeds, or accelerations presents real problems in the comparison of the effectiveness of different measuring procedures. Among the questions that can be raised are, how are accuracy and precision of the procedures influenced by the variability among the things being measured, by differences among observers, by environmental influences, such as temperature and humidity, and by differences among the same types of measuring instruments?

Comparing the merits of various types of medical treatments has always raised intricate problems. Specifically, how would one go about comparing the effectiveness of two serums? It would appear quite simple to give each of the serums to a large sample of the population and note the effects. Are there different ways of administering the serum? Does the serum affect adults differently than children? What side effects must be accounted for? How is effectiveness to be assessed? Again, what specifically are we comparing? These questions are all relevant to precise specification of the experiment and the appropriateness of different ways of administering the tests and selecting the sample.

Can one characterize an experiment? To be sure, there is the observer, the things being compared, the things acted upon, and the outcomes. Referring to the comparison between the two machines, the observer is assumed not to influence the experiment. There are, however, many situations where observer interaction raises touchy questions, which we shall not consider here. The things being compared are the two makes of machine under consideration. If, however, we were interested in two specific machines only, these machines would constitute the things being compared. In the case of the serums, we may focus attention on the types of serum or on the conjunction of the serum type and the method of administration. We should like to find a better expression than "things being compared." They can be not only things such as machines, but also policies of action, manufacturing methods, magnitudes of variables, and the like. Another characteristic of the "things to be compared" is that they can be manipulated by the experimenter. Hereafter we shall call the things being compared *strategies*. (In agricultural experimentation the term *treatment* has been used for this purpose, and this usage has carried over into other fields. The term strategy seems more appropriate in most contexts.)

An experiment involves many aspects of the environment, and we find it desirable in describing and analyzing an experiment to identify those elements, other than the experimenter and the strategies, which are collectively called the *experimental environment*. Again, as a result of usage in agriculture, the term *experimental unit* has been used for this purpose. In the problem of the machine selection, the workers operating the machines under test, the machines chosen for test, the materials worked on, the production method used, and perhaps other variables, such as temperature and humidity, which may influence the outcomes are part of the experimental environment. Whereas the strategies must be wholly manipulatable by the experimenter, the experimental environment need not be, and often cannot be, manipulated. In the serum problem the experimental environment includes the persons given the serum, the method of administering the serum, and a variety of conditions of the natural environment.   Actually, the condition of the person receiving the serum is an essential element of the experimental environment.   In the case where the method of administration is included in the specification of strategy, it is not a part of the experimental environment.

What is the nature of the outcomes of experiment?   Given a strategy and an experimental environment, there results, presumably, a particular set of outcomes with which we are concerned.   One of the tasks of the experimenter is to choose from among the variety of outcomes occurring those which are pertinent to the comparison under consideration.   In the machine-selection problem we may count the number of units produced in a specified time interval.   On the other hand, we may want to exclude defective units.   We may also observe metal scrap, heating of the machine, and the like.   The experimenter must determine what specifically among the outcomes will be included in his observation.   The serum problem raises similar questions, for in addition to positive or negative reaction to the serum, there may be side effects, difficulties in administering the serum, and other consequences.   In fact, the question of side effects can create considerable confusion in the interpretation of experimental investigations of this type.

For the purposes of our subsequent discussion, we have suggested characterizing an experiment in terms of the experimenter, the strategies under comparison, the experimental environment, and the outcomes. We have indicated that in spite of the apparent obviousness of this characterization, there can be confusion in implementing it in particular experiments.   Furthermore, it is quite necessary to make some such characterization before one can fruitfully plan and analyze the statistical questions involved in experimentation.

In spite of the fact that we have offered a characterization of an experiment, we have yet to specify explicitly what is meant by comparing strategies.   Of course, a comparison of strategies involves the outcomes.   In our characterization a single outcome is determined by the combined effect of the strategy and a single instance of the experimental environment.   Thus the totality of outcomes which will be considered in any comparison constitutes a population which is a consequence of the conjunction of the strategy replicated with "all relevant" experimental environments.   In the case of the machine selection one strategy is to use machine A, the alternative is to use machine B.   We agree that it would be best to observe the machines under experimental environments similar to those of usual operation of the machine, since these are the circumstances for which we wish to make inferences.   As stated above, workers, materials, time of day, material flow, and the like contribute to the experiment.   Hence we should compare the machines under a sampling of various relevant manifestations of the possible environments.   Again, in the comparison of serums the individual treated is part of the environment, so that a serum intended for persons of all ages, all walks of life, both sexes, a broad range of physical constitutions, etc., should be tested on a sample of the human population reflecting its various strata.

In summary, then, we focus attention on the relevant population of experimental environments and measure the outcomes of a strategy, in effect, on a "fair sample" of this population.   Inference, then, can be made about the strategy by statistical analyses of these outcomes.   Most often, we shall be concerned with inferences about the population means of outcomes.   It should be emphasized that the mean (about which we are making inference) is the mean of outcomes over the whole of the population of relevant experimental environments.   We must bear in mind that since we usually can measure only a sampling of this population, the machinery of probability and statistical method becomes essential to this inferential procedure.   Different possible modes of sampling remain to be considered.

We shall find it useful to consider rather different types of experimental environment population (hereafter *EEP*).   There are populations of which we have no prior knowledge for differentiating manifestations of the experimental environment.   In such cases, there is no way of subdividing the population into more homogeneous subgroups with respect to the possible outcomes.   We have no alternative but to enact strategy *A* on one random sample of the *EEP* and enact strategy *B* on another random sample of the *EEP*, and so on, for the other conceivable strategies.   The outcomes resulting from these samples will provide the basis for inference about the strategies.   Again, for another type of *EEP* we may have some basis for subdividing the *EEP* into differentiable subgroups.   Nevertheless, we may have no knowledge as to the way the outcomes are affected by the different subgroups, so that in this case there seems to be no reason for taking other than random samples over the *EEP*.

In many important situations, however, prior knowledge provides a basis for differentiating among subgroups of the *EEP*, which have greater homogeneity relative to the possible outcomes than does the *EEP* itself. For example, we know that an expert machine operator can produce appreciably more acceptable parts per hour (of a given part on a given machine) than can an ordinary operator.   Again, it frequently happens that raw materials from different suppliers affect the output of a worker in measurably distinct ways.   This knowledge can be used to provide more homogeneous subgroups of the *EEP* upon which to test different machines.   In the serum problem, homogeneous subgrouping can be affected by differentiations of sex, age, occupation, condition of health, and the like.

Under these circumstances it is usually not advantageous to take two random samples from the whole of the *EEP*.[1] Instead, we take random pairs from the homogeneous subgroups and study the differences of the outcomes for these pairs. This mode of sampling is called *stratified sampling*, and this mode of comparison is called *paired comparison*. The previous mode of comparison, for nonstratified comparison, is called *unpaired comparison*. The method of paired comparison can also be applied to more than two strategies.

The notion behind paired comparisons is that, within homogeneous subgroups, the difference between outcomes of two different strategies is not affected by the differences between the subgroups. Hence the comparison of different strategies will be less affected by the differences between subgroups than in unpaired comparison.

For example, in the comparison of the two machines, unpaired comparison would involve testing each of the machines on two separate random samplings of the total experimental environments, which include a variety of raw materials, different workers, and the like. On the other hand, paired comparison in this case involves classifying the raw materials into relatively homogeneous strata, grading workers into various levels of skill, specifying different working and operating conditions, and selecting a representative number of different operations to be performed. The various combinations of these factors form relatively homogeneous subgroups of the *EEP*. It may not be feasible to test both machines on each of the strata thus formed. A random sample of strata may first be selected, and then each machine tested on a random sample selected from these strata. A detailed discussion of the relative merits of paired and unpaired comparisons will be given in a later section.

7.5.3 Comparison of two means

The discussion in this section will be based on the assumption that the outcomes of the experiment over the *EEP* can be considered as a normal variate. Hence, in comparing two strategies A and B, the outcomes for these strategies will be designated, respectively, by the random variables X and Y. The means and variances of X and Y will be denoted by m_A and m_B, σ_A^2 and σ_B^2, respectively. The possible comparisons with which we are concerned are

$$H_0:\quad m_A - m_B = \Delta = 0 \qquad \text{against} \qquad H_1:\quad m_A - m_B = \Delta > 0$$

a one-sided alternative, and for a two-sided alternative,

$$H_0 \qquad \text{against} \qquad H_1':\quad m_A - m_B = \Delta \neq 0$$

[1] The *EEP* is related to the notion sample space.

Again, there are the cases where both $\sigma_A{}^2$ and $\sigma_B{}^2$ are known and also where they are not known. Subsidiary to these conditions, the two variances $\sigma_A{}^2$ and $\sigma_B{}^2$ may be equal. We shall study both paired and unpaired comparisons in a selected number of cases.

1 Variances Known and Equal, Two-sided Alternatives, Unpaired The explicit hypothesis to be tested is

$$H_0: \quad m_A - m_B = \Delta = 0 \quad \text{against} \quad H_1: \quad \Delta \neq 0$$

under the conditions that the variances $\sigma_A{}^2$ and $\sigma_B{}^2$ are equal to a known common value $\sigma_0{}^2$.

The experiment consists of $2n$ random independent choices of states of the experimental environment divided randomly into equal sample sizes n. This procedure yields two sets of observations, $x_1, x_2, \ldots, x_n$ and $y_1, y_2, \ldots, y_n$, from their respective normal populations.

It should be noted that both H_0 and H_1 are composite hypotheses since neither H_0 nor H_1 completely specifies the distribution of $x_1, x_2, \ldots, x_n$ and $y_1, y_2, \ldots, y_n$. This fact precludes a straightforward use of the Neyman-Pearson lemma in seeking to construct a satisfactory test. As we have indicated in (7.4.3), the likelihood-ratio test can generally be used to find a test procedure which has satisfactory properties. The likelihood function for the data is

$$L(x_1, x_2, \ldots, x_n; y_1, \ldots, y_n)$$

$$= \left(\frac{1}{\sigma_0 \sqrt{2\pi}}\right)^{2n} \exp\left\{-\frac{1}{2\sigma_0{}^2}\left[\sum_{i=1}^{n}(x_i - m_A)^2 + \sum_{i=1}^{n}(y_i - m_B)^2\right]\right\} \quad (7.5.2)$$

The likelihood-ratio procedure then calls for forming the ratio of the maximum of L under H_0 to the maximum of L under all conditions specified by both H_0 and H_1 (the parameter space). The parameter space Ω in this case consists of all values of m_A and m_B with the variance equal to $\sigma_0{}^2$, whereas for the null hypothesis, the set W is restricted to those values in Ω for which $m_A = m_B$.

It is sufficient, in order to maximize L, with respect to m_A and m_B, to minimize the expression in brackets in (7.5.2). Since both terms in the expression to be minimized are positive and since each sum of squares can be minimized separately and independently of the other, the desired minimum can be obtained by minimizing

$$\sum_{i=1}^{n}(x_i - m_A)^2 \quad \text{and} \quad \sum_{i=1}^{n}(y_i - m_B)^2$$

with respect to m_A and m_B, respectively. This yields, by standard procedures, $m_A = \bar{x}$ and $m_B = \bar{y}$. Similarly, under $H_0: m_A = m_B = m$, L is maximized for $m = (\bar{x} + \bar{y})/2$. The likelihood ratio is then

$$\lambda(x_1, x_2, \ldots, x_n; y_1, y_2, \ldots, y_n)$$
$$= \exp\left\{\frac{1}{2\sigma_0^2}\left[\sum_i (x_i - \bar{x})^2 + \sum_i (y_i - \bar{y})^2 \right.\right.$$
$$\left.\left. - \sum_i \left(x_i - \frac{\bar{x} + \bar{y}}{2}\right)^2 - \sum_i \left(y_i - \frac{\bar{x} + \bar{y}}{2}\right)^2\right]\right\}$$

which simplifies to

$$\lambda = \exp\left[-\frac{n}{4\sigma_0^2}(\bar{x} - \bar{y})^2\right] \tag{7.5.3}$$

The likelihood-ratio procedure calls for rejecting H_0 when λ is sufficiently small, which in this case is equivalent to rejecting when $(\bar{x} - \bar{y})^2$ is too large. This, in turn, is equivalent to $|\bar{x} - \bar{y}|$ too large. The rejection region, therefore, takes the form

$$|\bar{x} - \bar{y}| \geq k$$

where k is determined when a significance level is specified. In order to determine k, we use the fact that, under present assumptions,

$$Z = \frac{\bar{x} - \bar{y} - \Delta}{\sigma_0 \sqrt{2/n}} \tag{7.5.4}$$

has a normal distribution with zero mean and unit variance. Under H_0, when $\Delta = 0$, we seek the appropriate k such that Prob $(|\bar{x} - \bar{y}| \geq k) = \alpha$, which is equivalent to

$$\text{Prob}\left(\frac{|\bar{x} - \bar{y}|}{\sigma_0 \sqrt{2/n}} \geq \frac{k}{\sigma_0 \sqrt{2/n}}\right) = 2\left[1 - \Phi\left(\frac{k}{\sigma_0 \sqrt{2/n}}\right)\right] = \alpha \tag{7.5.5}$$

As a result,

$$\frac{k}{\sigma_0 \sqrt{2/n}} = Z_{1-\alpha/2}$$

The rejection region for any specified significance level is therefore

$$|\bar{x} - \bar{y}| \geq Z_{1-\alpha/2}\sigma_0 \sqrt{\frac{2}{n}} \tag{7.5.6}$$

This test procedure seems intuitively reasonable. It has, furthermore, optimal properties, the demonstration of which is, however, beyond the scope of this text. It turns out, in many cases, as in this one, that the test procedures derived from the likelihood ratio have certain optimum properties, even though this is not a general consequence of the likelihood-ratio procedure for arbitrary n.

We shall now find the power function for this test. As previously defined, the power function $\pi(\Delta)$ is the probability of rejecting H_0 for any alternative Δ. An obvious consequence is that the power at $\Delta = 0$ is the significance level α. It is to be hoped that as the alternative increasingly deviates from H_0, $\pi(\Delta)$ increases, and, in fact, this will be demonstrated. Explicitly, using the rejection region in (7.5.6),

$$\pi(\Delta) = \text{Prob}\left(|\bar{x} - \bar{y}| \geq Z_{1-\alpha/2}\sigma_0 \sqrt{\frac{2}{n}}\ \Big|\ \Delta, \sigma_0{}^2\right)$$

$$= 1 - \text{Prob}\left(-Z_{1-\alpha/2}\sigma_0 \sqrt{\frac{2}{n}} \leq \bar{x} - \bar{y} \leq Z_{1-\alpha/2}\sigma_0 \sqrt{\frac{2}{n}}\right) \quad (7.5.7)$$

Standardizing [as in (7.5.4)], we obtain

$$\pi(\Delta) = 1 - \text{Prob}\left(\frac{-Z_{1-\alpha/2}\sigma_0 \sqrt{2/n} - \Delta}{\sigma_0 \sqrt{2/n}} \leq \frac{\bar{x} - \bar{y} - \Delta}{\sigma_0 \sqrt{2/n}}\right.$$
$$\left. \leq \frac{Z_{1-\alpha/2}\sigma_0 \sqrt{2/n} - \Delta}{\sigma_0 \sqrt{2/n}}\right)$$

Now, using standard normal notation,

$$\pi(\Delta) = 1 - \left[\Phi\left(Z_{1-\alpha/2} - \frac{\Delta}{\sigma_0}\sqrt{\frac{n}{2}}\right) - \Phi\left(-Z_{1-\alpha/2} - \frac{\Delta}{\sigma_0}\sqrt{\frac{n}{2}}\right)\right] \quad (7.5.8)$$

In order to put (7.5.8) into more symmetrical form, we make use of the fact that $\Phi(-u) = 1 - \Phi(u)$; whence, letting $\delta = \dfrac{\Delta}{\sigma_0}\sqrt{\dfrac{n}{2}}$, (7.5.8) becomes

$$\pi(\Delta) = \Phi(-Z_{1-\alpha/2} + \delta) + \Phi(-Z_{1-\alpha/2} - \delta)$$

Again, noting that $-Z_{1-\alpha/2} = Z_{\alpha/2}$, we have

$$\pi(\Delta) = \Phi(Z_{\alpha/2} + \delta) + \Phi(Z_{\alpha/2} - \delta) \quad (7.5.9)$$

The form of $\pi(\Delta)$ in (7.5.9) clearly indicates that, for $\delta = 0$, $\pi(0) = \alpha$. Furthermore, $\pi(\Delta)$ is symmetrical in Δ about $\delta = 0$ and, as can be seen from the power function, depends on Δ, n, and σ_0 in the relationship

$$\delta = \frac{\Delta}{\sigma_0}\sqrt{\frac{n}{2}}$$

We now examine the power function. In particular, we want to find the minimum of n, n^*, such that the power $\pi(\Delta_0)$ at Δ_0 is not less than $1 - \beta$, where β is the error of the second kind for alternative Δ_0. A natural way to determine n^* is to solve for n^* in

$$1 - \beta = \Phi\left(Z_{\alpha/2} + \frac{\Delta_0}{\sigma_0}\sqrt{\frac{n^*}{2}}\right) + \Phi\left(Z_{\alpha/2} - \frac{\Delta_0}{\sigma_0}\sqrt{\frac{n^*}{2}}\right) \quad (7.5.10)$$

There is, however, no direct analytical method for solving (7.5.10). We can resort to graphical means, plotting the power function in terms of δ

and determining graphically a value δ^* corresponding to $1 - \beta$. Thus the value of $\delta^* = \dfrac{\Delta_0}{\sigma_0} \sqrt{\dfrac{n^*}{2}}$ so obtained yields the desired

$$n^* = 2 \left(\frac{\sigma_0 \delta^*}{\Delta_0} \right)^2 \qquad (7.5.11)$$

Since the power function is increasing in $|\delta|$, the value of n^* is a minimum for the desired power. Obviously, n^* may not be an integer, so that one is obliged to take the integer succeeding n^*.

One can approximate δ^* by means of a modification of (7.5.9). In general, α is a small quantity, usually less than 0.10. Therefore $Z_{\alpha/2}$ is negative and of the order of -2. It follows, then, that either $Z_{\alpha/2} - \delta$ or $Z_{\alpha/2} + \delta$ is even "more negative" than $Z_{\alpha/2}$. Hence, for positive δ, $\Phi(Z_{\alpha/2} - \delta) \leq \alpha/2$ and contributes very little to the expression for the power function. For example, when $\delta = 1.00$ and $\alpha = 0.05$,

$$\Phi(Z_{0.025} - 1.00) = \Phi(-1.96 - 1.00) = 0.0015$$

and $\Phi(-1.96 + 1.00) = 0.1685$. The value of δ^* (assumed positive) can be approximated by dropping $\Phi(Z_{\alpha/2} - \delta)$ from (7.5.10) and solving $\Phi(Z_{\alpha/2} + \delta^*) = 1 - \beta$, which gives $\delta^* = Z_{1-\beta} - Z_{\alpha/2}$. From (7.5.11), on substitution of this approximation of δ^*, the following approximation to n^* is obtained:

$$n^* \cong 2 \left(\frac{\sigma_0}{\Delta_0} \right)^2 (Z_{1-\beta} - Z_{\alpha/2})^2 \qquad (7.5.12)$$

(The same result follows for δ assumed negative, since only δ^{*2} is involved in the expression for n^*.)

As a very simple illustration of the above test procedure, consider the following sample averages obtained from an experiment for testing the difference of two means:

$$\bar{x} = 21.50 \qquad \bar{y} = 20.00 \qquad n = 32$$

Suppose, further, that from prior experience, it is reasonable to assume $\sigma_0^2 = 25$. Can we conclude from this experiment that the two population means are different? A way to approach this question is to test

$$H_0: \quad \Delta = 0 \qquad \text{against} \qquad H_1: \quad \Delta \neq 0$$

where Δ is the difference of the two population means. The rejection region given in (7.5.6) is

$$|\bar{x} - \bar{y}| \geq (Z_{1-\alpha/2})(5) \sqrt{(2/32)} \qquad (7.5.13)$$

where, for $\alpha = 0.05$,

$$|\bar{x} - \bar{y}| \geq (1.96)(5)(0.25) = 2.45 \qquad (7.5.14)$$

In the present case $\bar{x} - \bar{y} = 1.50$; whence H_0 *is not rejected*. The interpretation placed on this result is that the evidence of this experiment does not warrant rejection of H_0.

It is reasonable to ask ourselves whether this conclusion is sound. We do not necessarily accept H_0; we merely do not reject H_0. Is it not possible that there is an actual difference between the means of two populations? In fact, we may inquire as to what size difference we can reasonably expect to detect. From a practical point of view, we are interested in the detection of a certain minimum difference Δ_0 and also in the probability that we shall not reject H_0 when in fact $\Delta \geq \Delta_0$. Suppose that $\Delta_0 = 2$, what is the error of the second kind? The answer to this question is given by the value of 1 minus the power function at $\Delta = 2$, which can be obtained from (7.5.9) and becomes, for $\Delta = 2$,

$$1 - \pi(2) = 1 - \Phi(-1.96 + \tfrac{2}{5}\sqrt{16}) - \Phi(-1.96 - \tfrac{2}{5}\sqrt{16}) = 0.64$$
$$(7.5.15)$$

This result implies that, for $\Delta = \Delta_0 = 2$, H_0 is not rejected 64 per cent of the time. Such an error of the second kind seems much too great. It seems more reasonable that, when the difference of these sample averages is as large as two units, H_0 should be rejected at least 95 per cent of the time. In other words, for $\Delta = \Delta_0 = 2$, we prefer not to tolerate an error of the second kind which is greater than 5 per cent. What is the smallest n which will yield this result? We can find the approximate minimum value of n for this purpose from (7.5.12):

$$n^* \cong 2(\tfrac{5}{2})^2[1.65 - (-1.96)]^2 = 162.9$$

It might be pointed out that n^* varies directly as σ_0^2 and inversely as Δ_0^2, as can be seen from (7.5.12). For a reduction of Δ_0 from 2 to 1, the minimum sample size is to be quadrupled. On the other hand, if σ_0 can be reduced by one-half, the necessary n^*, for the same discrimination, is reduced fourfold.

2   *Variances Known and Equal, Two-sided Alternative, Paired*   The explicit hypothesis to be treated is

$$H_0: \quad m_A - m_B = \Delta = 0 \qquad \text{against} \qquad H_1: \quad \Delta \neq 0$$

This is the same problem as that posed in section 1 above, except that the method of paired sampling will be used.

The experiment in this case requires first that the *EEP* be divided into a number of relatively homogeneous strata with respect to the factors influencing the two strategies being compared. Let us assume, for the moment, that a particular sample size n is required for each strategy. Then, if there are s strata and $s = n$, we may proceed by selecting randomly two conditions of the *EEP* within each stratum. For n greater than s such that $n = as + b$, sample a pairs randomly within each strata;

then, from among the s strata, select b strata at random and choose a pair at random from each of these strata. If $n < s$, select n strata at random from all the strata and then a pair at random from each of these n strata. The experiment yields n pairs of observations (x_1, y_1), (x_2, y_2), . . . , (x_n, y_n), whose differences $d_i = x_i - y_i$ $(i = 1, 2, \ldots, n)$ are of interest to us, since, under suitable conditions, by the mode of sampling, $E(d_i) = m_A - m_B = \Delta$. We assume that the variance of d, σ_d^2, is known. The underlying idea of paired sampling is that σ_d^2 is due only to variations within strata and is not affected by variation between strata. We also assume that the variations within strata are constant for all strata. In order to test H_0 we can test

$$\Delta = E(d) = 0 \qquad \text{against} \qquad \Delta = E(d) \neq 0 \qquad (\sigma_d^2 \text{ known})$$

This formulation is equivalent to testing a mean against a standard equal to zero, variance known, for a two-sided alternative. This problem was treated in Example 7.4. For a significance level α, applying this result, we have rejection region

$$|\bar{d}| \geq Z_{1-\alpha/2} \frac{\sigma_d}{\sqrt{n}} \tag{7.5.16}$$

where $\bar{d}$ is the arithmetic average of the d_i. The power $\pi(\Delta)$ of this test procedure is given in Sec. 7.5.1 with $m = \Delta$ and $\delta = (\Delta \sqrt{n})/\sigma_d$. Therefore, for the present case,

$$\pi(\Delta) = \Phi(Z_{\alpha/2} - \delta) + \Phi(Z_{\alpha/2} + \delta) \tag{7.5.17}$$

The minimal n, n^* required to detect a difference $\Delta = \Delta_0$ with probability $1 - \beta$ can be approximated, as in Sec. 7.5.3, by

$$n^* \cong \left(\frac{\sigma_d}{\Delta_0}\right)^2 (Z_{1-\beta} - Z_{\alpha/2})^2 \tag{7.5.18}$$

This is almost identical with (7.5.12) except that σ_d^2 replaces $2\sigma_0^2$. In evaluating the relative merits of paired and unpaired sampling, consideration must be given to a comparison of σ_d^2 with $2\sigma_0^2$. This question will be studied in section 3 below.

3   *Comparative Evaluation of Paired and Unpaired Sampling Procedures*   It is evident by now that the magnitudes of the variances involved in experimentation are of fundamental importance in determining the effectiveness—discriminatory power—of a test procedure. In particular, the merits of paired and unpaired comparisons depend upon variances σ_0^2 and σ_d^2. The relation of these two variances can be better assessed by decomposing the chance variables X and Y into their essential components. Suppose we consider the chance variable X as consisting of its population mean m_A and an error term reflecting its variation over the *EEP*. X, then, can be written as $m_A + \epsilon$, where m_A is the population mean, and therefore a constant, and ϵ a chance variable over the *EEP*. Similarly for Y, and we denote this by

$$X = m_A + \epsilon \qquad \text{and} \qquad Y = m_B + \epsilon' \qquad (7.5.19)$$

The basic assumption of normality and variances known and equal can be formulated as

$$\text{var } (X) = \text{var } (\epsilon) = \sigma_0^2 \qquad (7.5.20)$$

and

$$\text{var } (Y) = \text{var } (\epsilon') = \sigma_0^2 \qquad (7.5.21)$$

In this representation, σ_0^2 is a measure of the total variation of X or Y over the *whole EEP*.

We have, however, made a further diagnosis of the experimental situation and divided the *EEP* into a number of distinguishable strata. Within each stratum the effect of the differences of the *EEP* on the strategies X and Y is assumed to be relatively small. Between strata the effects on either X or Y may be large. We can represent this condition by decomposing ϵ and ϵ' into a source of variation *within* strata and a source of variation *between* strata. Hence we shall distinguish the chance variables by strata and represent them as follows:

$$X_s = m_{As} + \epsilon_s \qquad \text{and} \qquad Y_s = m_{Bs} + \epsilon'_s \qquad (7.5.22)$$

The chance variables X_s and Y_s are defined with respect to strata s. Furthermore, ϵ_s and ϵ'_s are defined for strata s and are measures of variability *within* strata. On the other hand, m_{As} and m_{Bs} can vary between strata and can be represented as a population mean and a strategy effect varying between strata as follows:

$$\begin{aligned} m_{As} &= m_A + (m_{As} - m_A) = m_A + t_{As} \\ m_{Bs} &= m_B + (m_{Bs} - m_B) = m_B + t_{Bs} \end{aligned} \qquad (7.5.23)$$

Thus the general representation becomes

$$\begin{aligned} X_s &= m_A + t_{As} + \epsilon_s \\ Y_s &= m_B + t_{Bs} + \epsilon'_s \end{aligned} \qquad (7.5.24)$$

The difference chance variable $X - Y$ is represented within a stratum by

$$\begin{aligned} d_s &= X_s - Y_s = (m_A - m_B) + (t_{As} - t_{Bs}) + (\epsilon_s - \epsilon'_s) \\ &= \Delta + (t_{As} - t_{Bs}) + (\epsilon_s - \epsilon'_s) \end{aligned}$$

It is not unreasonable to suppose that in many situations $t_{As} - t_{Bs}$, within any stratum, is relatively small.

The implication of this condition is that $m_{As} - m_{Bs}$ is relatively constant for different strata, even though m_{As} and m_{Bs}, individually, may change considerably with s. This is readily evident from the difference $m_{As} - m_{Bs}$, as expressed in Eqs. (7.5.23). It is further evident that this difference is approximately $m_A - m_B$, independent of strata. When this condition prevails, it can be said that the effect of the strategies among strata is additive.   This condition is often referred to in the literature as one of *noninteraction* between strategies and strata.   For example, in comparing two industrial processes, the *EEP* may be in part stratified by taking different batches of raw materials where the batches may differ with respect to some quality characteristic.   The condition of noninteraction between processes and batches implies that a "good" batch results in approximately equally good effects from both processes.   Similarly, for "bad" batches, equally bad effects result from both processes.   In the light of the above discussion, in those situations where $t_{As} - t_{Bs}$ is small,

$$E(d_s) = \Delta \qquad \text{and} \qquad V(d_s) \cong 2\sigma_{\epsilon_s}^2$$

For purposes of simplicity in exposition, let us assume that $2\sigma_{\epsilon_s}^2 = 2\sigma_w^2$, for all s, where σ_w^2 is a measure of intrinsic variability *within* strata. Under these conditions, it is apparent that σ_d^2 is "essentially" equal to $2\sigma_w^2$.

In studying the unpaired case, let us reconsider the individual observations.   We must bear in mind that the observations were made under conditions of the *EEP* that were selected without regard to strata. Hence, each observation can be thought of as consisting of its population mean and its random part, as in Eq. (7.5.19).   Again, we may view the random part as due to a difference between strata and to a random part within a stratum, where, of course, the random part within a stratum has variance σ_w^2.   On the other hand, the between-strata variability component is due to the variation of t_{As} and t_{Bs} between strata. Since X and Y are not paired in the formulation of $\bar{x}$ and $\bar{y}$ separately, the t_{As} and t_{Bs} remain random variables whose variances are assumed equal and denoted by σ_t^2 (usually called the *between* variation).   Under these conditions, then,

$$V(X) = V(t_{As}) + V(\epsilon_s)$$
and
$$V(Y) = V(t_{Bs}) + V(\epsilon_s')$$

where t_{As} and t_{Bs} vary over the strata.   Denoting their common variance by σ_t^2, we have

$$V(X) = V(Y) = \sigma_t^2 + \sigma_w^2 = \sigma_0^2 \qquad (7.5.25)$$

In the paired case, however, we have

$$V(d) = 2\sigma_w^2 = \sigma_d^2 \qquad (7.5.26)$$

The foregoing analysis of the variance components of the unpaired and paired procedures has been restricted by a number of simplifications. It was assumed that $t_{As} - t_{Bs}$ is relatively small for strata in the paired case.   This assumption need not always be made when the number of strata s equals the sample size n.   Again, even where stratification can be clearly made, it may be quite apparent that the distribution of conditions in the EEP is not necessarily uniform; therefore, weighting of the strata, when $t_{As} - t_{Bs}$ is not small, may be required.   These points will not be further examined here since they are beyond the scope of this work.

The efficiency of the paired and unpaired comparisons can be considered in terms of the ratios of the n^*.   For instance, for both the two-sided and one-sided cases,

$$\frac{n_U^*}{n_P^*} = \frac{2\sigma_0^2}{\sigma_d^2} \simeq \frac{2\sigma_t^2 + 2\sigma_w^2}{2\sigma_w^2} = 1 + \left(\frac{\sigma_t}{\sigma_w}\right)^2 \qquad (7.5.27)$$

where n_U^* and n_P^* are the required n^*, for the unpaired and paired cases, respectively.   The advantage from pairing obviously depends on the ratio $(\sigma_t/\sigma_w)^2$, which, in turn, implies that the strata should be so chosen that within strata there is the greatest possible homogeneity, whereas between strata the difference is as great as possible.   This seems to be intuitively apparent.   Accomplishing such stratification may, however, be a difficult task.

4   Variances Unknown and Equal, Two-sided Alternatives, Unpaired   The explicit hypothesis to be tested is

$$H_0: \quad m_A - m_R = \Delta = 0 \qquad \text{against} \qquad H_1: \quad \Delta \neq 0$$

on condition that the variances are unknown and equal to σ_0^2.   The experimental procedure here is as described in section 1, where σ^2 was assumed known.

In section 1 the rejection region, as found by means of the likelihood-ratio procedure, is

$$\frac{|\bar{x} - \bar{y}|}{\sigma_0 \sqrt{2/n}} \geq Z_{1-\alpha/2}$$

Analogously, by means of the likelihood-ratio procedure, the following rejection region can be obtained:

$$\frac{|\bar{x} - \bar{y}|}{s \sqrt{2/n}} \geq t_{1-\alpha/2} \qquad (7.5.28)$$

where $t_{1-\alpha/2}$ is the upper $1 - \alpha/2$ percentile of the t distribution with $2(n - 1)$ degrees of freedom, and s^2 is an unbiased estimate of σ_0^2.   This region seems reasonable, since it provides for rejection of H_0 when $|\bar{x} - \bar{y}|$ is too large.   It remains to show that the rejection region as given in (7.5.28) is, in fact, of size α.   This will clearly be the case if

$$\frac{\bar{x} - \bar{y}}{s \sqrt{2/n}} \qquad (7.5.29)$$

has the t distribution with $2n - 2$ degrees of freedom.

A natural way to demonstrate that the expression in (7.5.29) has the t distribution is to build it up from the definition of t given in Sec. 5.2.5. Recall that

$$t = \frac{Z \sqrt{v}}{\sqrt{\chi_v^2}} \tag{7.5.30}$$

where Z has the standard normal distribution, and χ_v^2 has v degrees of freedom and is independent of Z. The first step is to standardize $\bar{x} - \bar{y}$ by forming

$$Z = \frac{\bar{x} - \bar{y}}{\sigma_0 \sqrt{2/n}} \tag{7.5.31}$$

Then it seems necessary to define s in such a way as to be expressed in terms of χ^2. This is ready at hand if we consider the usual estimates of σ_0^2 both from the observations on X and those on Y and combine them appropriately. Denoting these estimates by s_x^2 and s_y^2, respectively, we consider $(n-1)s_x^2/\sigma_0^2$ and $(n-1)s_y^2/\sigma_0^2$, which have the χ^2 distribution, each with $n-1$ degrees of freedom, and are statistically independent since the x and y values have been obtained independently. Hence the sum

$$\frac{(n-1)s_x^2}{\sigma_0^2} + \frac{(n-1)s_y^2}{\sigma_0^2} \tag{7.5.32}$$

has the χ^2 distribution with $2(n-1)$ degrees of freedom. Now substituting for Z the expression (7.5.31) and for $\chi_{2(n-1)}^2$ the expression (7.5.32) in Eq. (7.5.30), we obtain

$$t = \frac{\left(\dfrac{\bar{x} - \bar{y}}{\sigma_0 \sqrt{2/n}}\right) \sqrt{2(n-1)}}{\sqrt{\dfrac{(n-1)s_x^2 + (n-1)s_y^2}{\sigma_0^2}}} = \frac{\bar{x} - \bar{y}}{\sqrt{\dfrac{s_x^2 + s_y^2}{2}} \sqrt{\dfrac{2}{n}}} \tag{7.5.33}$$

But $(s_x^2 + s_y^2)/2$ is a natural estimate of σ_0^2 and will be denoted by s^2. We thus have shown that the expression in (7.5.29) has the t distribution with $2(n-1)$ degrees of freedom, where s^2 is defined as above.

It might be noted in passing that when the number of observations on X, n_x differs from n_y, the rejection region, for variance σ_0^2 known, is

$$\frac{|\bar{x} - \bar{y}|}{\sigma_0 \sqrt{1/n_x + 1/n_y}} \geq Z_{1-\alpha/2} \tag{7.5.34}$$

Similarly, for σ_0^2 unknown, the rejection region is

$$\frac{|\bar{x} - \bar{y}|}{s \sqrt{1/n_x + 1/n_y}} \geq t_{1-\alpha/2} \qquad n_x + n_y - 2 \text{ degrees of freedom} \tag{7.5.35}$$

where

$$s^2 = \frac{(n_x - 1)s_x^2 + (n_y - 1)s_y^2}{n_x + n_y - 2} \tag{7.5.36}$$

The power of the test, $\pi(\Delta)$, depends on $m_x - m_y = \Delta$ and $\sigma_0{}^2$ and is

$$\pi(\Delta) = \text{Prob}\left(\frac{|\bar{x} - \bar{y}|}{s\sqrt{2/n}} \geq t_{1-\alpha/2} \mid \Delta, \sigma_0{}^2\right)$$

The result hinges on the distribution of $\sqrt{n/2}\,(\bar{x} - \bar{y})/s$ and depends on Δ and $\sigma_0{}^2$. This random variable has a noncentral t distribution with $2(n - 1)$ degrees of freedom and with a parameter of noncentrality

$$\delta' = \frac{m_A - m_B}{\sigma_0}\sqrt{\frac{n}{2}}$$

which is a measure of deviation from H_0. For any n, as in Sec. 7.5.1, the power can be plotted against Δ/σ_0. Figures 7.7 and 7.8 can be utilized for this purpose and give $1 - \pi(\Delta)$ versus $\Delta/2\sigma_0$ on the abscissa for various values of n', $\alpha = 0.01$ and $\alpha = 0.05$. The curves in Figs. 7.7 and 7.8 can be used as an approximation when the abscissa scale is defined as $\Delta/2\sigma_0$ and $n = (n' + 1)/2$.

Again, as in Sec. 7.5.1, we can find the smallest n', such that the odds for rejecting $\Delta = 0$ when $|\Delta| \geq \Delta_0$ is larger than $1 - \beta$, β specified in advance. For $\sigma_0{}^2$ unknown, we can utilize the graphs of $1 - \pi(\Delta)$, as given in Figs. 7.7 and 7.8. For example, if $\alpha = 0.01$, $\beta = 0.20$, and $\Delta/2\sigma_0 = 0.40$, we can see from Fig. 7.7 that the minimum n' is approximately equal to 75. The required $n_x = n_y = (n' + 1)/2 = 76/2 = 38$.

5 *Variances Unknown and Equal, One-sided Alternatives, Unpaired*

$$H_0: \quad m_A - m_B = \Delta = 0 \qquad \text{against} \qquad H_1: \quad \Delta > 0$$

under the conditions that the variances are unknown but equal, denoted by $\sigma_0{}^2$. The experimental procedure is as in section 1, where $\sigma_0{}^2$ was assumed known.

The rejection region for the case σ^2 known is

$$\frac{\bar{x} - \bar{y}}{\sigma_0\sqrt{2/n}} \geq Z_{1-\alpha} \tag{7.5.37}$$

Similarly, it can be shown for $\sigma_0{}^2$ unknown that the optimum procedure is to use the rejection region

$$\frac{\bar{x} - \bar{y}}{s\sqrt{2/n}} \geq t_{1-\alpha} \tag{7.5.38}$$

where $t_{1-\alpha}$ is the upper $1 - \alpha$ percentile of the t distribution with $2(n - 1)$ degrees of freedom, and s^2, as in section 4, is the pooled estimate of $\sigma_0{}^2$. This region calls for rejection when $\bar{x} - \bar{y}$ is too large. The region in (7.5.38) is, in fact, of size α, since, as shown in section 4, $\sqrt{n/2}\,(\bar{x} - \bar{y})/s$ has the t distribution with $2(n - 1)$ degrees of freedom.

The power of the test, $\pi(\Delta)$, depends on $m_x - m_y = \Delta$ and σ_0^2. The result again depends on the distribution of $\sqrt{n/2}\,(\bar{x} - \bar{y})/s$. This random variable has a noncentral t distribution with $2(n - 1)$ degrees of freedom and noncentrality parameter $\delta' = \dfrac{\Delta}{\sigma_0}\sqrt{\dfrac{n}{2}}$.

In Figs. 7.9 and 7.10, $1 - \pi(\Delta)$ is given as a function of $\Delta/2\sigma_0$. The smallest n' for which the odds of detecting a difference $\Delta \geq \Delta_0$ is $100(1 - \beta)$ to 100β can be found with the aid of Figs. 7.9 and 7.10. For the conditions $\alpha = 0.01$, $\beta = 0.20$, and $\Delta/2\sigma_0 = 0.40$, the minimum value of n', with the aid of Fig. 7.9, is found to be approximately 59 and $n_x = n_y = 30$. The use of Figs. 7.7, 7.8, 7.9, and 7.10 to approximate the power functions for the comparison of means when σ_0^2 is unknown by suitable redefinition of the abscissa is quite satisfactory but assumes $n_x = n_y$.

6 Variances Unknown and Equal, Two-sided Alternatives, Paired The explicit hypothesis to be tested is

$$H_0: \quad m_A - m_B = \Delta = 0 \qquad \text{against} \qquad H_1: \quad \Delta \neq 0$$

This is the same problem as posed in section 1, except that the method of paired sampling, as described in section 2, is used. The experiment yields n pairs of observations (x_1,y_1), (x_2,y_2), $\ldots$, (x_n,y_n), whose differences $d_i = x_i - y_i$ are used, since, by the sampling procedure, $E(d_i) = \Delta$. We assume that the variance of d, σ_d^2, is unknown. In order to test H_0, we can test

$$\Delta = E(d) = 0 \qquad \text{against} \qquad \Delta = E(d) \neq 0 \qquad (\sigma_d^2 \text{ unknown})$$

This formulation is the same as in section 2, except that σ_d^2 is not assumed known; it is equivalent to testing a mean against a standard equal to zero with variance unknown. This test is treated in Sec. 7.5.1. For a significance level α, the rejection region is

$$\frac{|\bar{d}|}{s_d/\sqrt{n}} \geq t_{1-\alpha/2} \qquad n - 1 \text{ degrees of freedom}$$

where $\bar{d}$ is the arithmetic average of the d_i, and s_d is given by

$$s_d^2 = \frac{1}{n - 1} \sum_{i=1}^{n} (d_i - \bar{d})^2$$

which is an unbiased estimate of σ_d^2.

The power of the test at $\Delta \neq 0$ and σ_d^2 is

$$\text{Prob}\left(\frac{|\bar{d}|}{s_d/\sqrt{n}} \geq t_{1-\alpha/2} \mid \Delta, \sigma_d^2\right)$$

The result hinges on the distribution of $\sqrt{n}\,\bar{d}/\sigma_d$, which is non-central t with $n-1$ degrees of freedom and noncentrality parameter $\sqrt{n}\,\Delta/\sigma_d$. For any n, the power can be plotted against Δ/σ_d. Figures 7.7 and 7.8 give the power as a function of Δ/σ_d.

The minimum value of n necessary to detect differences $|\Delta| \geq \Delta_0$ with odds $100(1-\beta)$ to 100β can be obtained from Figs. 7.7 and 7.8. For the case $\alpha = 0.01$, $\beta = 0.10$, and $\Delta/\sigma_d = 0.60$, we see, from Fig. 7.7, that the minimum n is approximately 48.

It is worthwhile at this point to contrast the paired and unpaired methods of sampling for the case of two-sided alternatives, where variances are unknown. The rejection regions are, unpaired,

$$\frac{\bar{x} - \bar{y}}{s\sqrt{2/n}} \geq t_{1-\alpha/2} \qquad 2(n-1) \text{ degrees of freedom}$$

and paired,

$$\frac{\bar{x} - \bar{y}}{s_d/\sqrt{n}} \geq t_{1-\alpha/2} \qquad n-1 \text{ degrees of freedom}$$

One difference readily apparent is that the test statistic utilized in the unpaired procedure has twice as many degrees of freedom as that of the paired procedure. On the other hand, the parameters of noncentrality as expressed by the abscissas in Figs. 7.7 and 7.8 are $\Delta/2\sigma_0$, unpaired, and Δ/σ_d, paired. This is clearly advantageous to paired sampling when $(\sigma_d/\sigma_0)^2$ is small. This aspect of the comparison between paired and unpaired sampling is discussed in section 3.

Example 7.5 In order to illustrate the comparative merits of paired and unpaired sampling procedures, consider two methods, A and B, of measuring the per cent insoluble residue in cement. A batch of material was sent to 29 laboratories, in each of which both procedures, A and B, were used to obtain the measurements. The data reported by the 29 laboratories are given in Table 7.3. The sampling procedure used here is that of paired comparison where the strata consist of laboratories. Consider the hypothesis

$$H_0: \quad m_A - m_B = 0 \qquad \text{against} \qquad H_1: \quad m_A - m_B = \Delta > 0$$

with $\sigma_d{}^2$ unknown. The rejection region is

$$t = \frac{\bar{d}}{s_d/\sqrt{n}} \geq t_{1-\alpha}$$

The value of $\bar{x} = 0.259$, $\bar{y} = 0.163$, and $s_d = 0.08$. Using $\alpha = 0.05$, we obtain

$$t = \frac{\bar{d}}{s_d/\sqrt{n}} = \frac{0.096}{0.08}\sqrt{29} = 6.4$$

TABLE 7.3

Data and Calculations on Per Cent Insoluble Residue in Cement Reported by 29 Laboratories

| Laboratory | Per cent residue | | $A - B$ |
	A	B	
1	0.31	0.22	0.09
2	0.08	0.12	−0.04
3	0.24	0.14	0.10
4	0.14	0.07	0.07
5	0.52	0.37	0.15
6	0.38	0.19	0.19
7	0.22	0.14	0.08
8	0.46	0.23	0.23
9	0.26	0.05	0.21
10	0.28	0.14	0.14
11	0.10	0.18	−0.08
12	0.20	0.09	0.11
13	0.26	0.10	0.16
14	0.28	0.14	0.14
15	0.25	0.13	0.12
16	0.25	0.11	0.14
17	0.26	0.17	0.09
18	0.26	0.18	0.08
19	0.12	0.05	0.07
20	0.29	0.14	0.15
21	0.22	0.11	0.11
22	0.13	0.10	0.03
23	0.56	0.42	0.14
24	0.30	0.30	0.00
25	0.24	0.06	0.18
26	0.25	0.35	−0.10
27	0.24	0.09	0.15
28	0.28	0.23	0.05
29	0.14	0.10	0.04
Average	0.259	0.163	0.096

Since $t_{1-\alpha} = t_{0.95} = 1.70$ for 28 degrees of freedom, H_0 is to be rejected. In fact, since $t_{0.9995} = 3.674$ (for 28 degrees of freedom), we should reject even at a significance level of $\alpha = 0.0005$. Thus the data give very significant evidence against H_0. The power $\pi(\Delta)$ of the test can be obtained from Fig. 7.10. Since the abscissa is Δ/σ_d, we can represent $\pi(\Delta)$ versus Δ only approximately, using estimate s_d for σ_d, with the result shown in Fig. 7.11.

What happens when the sampling procedure is unpaired? Assuming that $\sigma_A^2 = \sigma_B^2 = \sigma_0^2$, the test procedure leads to the t distribution with $2(n-1) = 56$ degrees of freedom and a power function, as given in Fig. 7.10, with abscissa $\Delta/2\sigma_0$. If we can estimate σ_0, we can approxi-

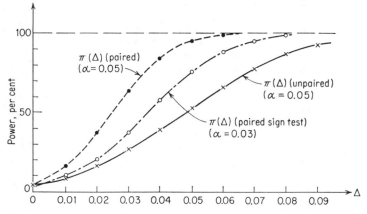

Figure 7.11 Approximate comparison of paired, unpaired, and paired sign test ($\alpha = 0.05$) for H_0: $m_A - m_B = \Delta = 0$ against H_1: $\Delta > 0$.

mate the power function against Δ and compare it with the paired procedure. How can we estimate σ_0? It is apparent that the variations among the x's and those among the y's both form estimates of σ_0^2. From the data in Table 7.3, pooling the estimates s_A^2 and s_B^2, we obtain for σ_0^2 an estimate $s_0^2 = 0.0125$. With this estimate, the approximate power curve, as a function of Δ, can be obtained from Fig. 7.10, using 56 degrees of freedom. The result is shown in Fig. 7.11 and is a graphic illustration of the advantage of paired over unpaired comparisons. The respective efficiencies of paired and unpaired tests can also be studied in terms of the ratios of the minimum values of n required to detect a specified practical difference Δ_0, with given odds $1 - \beta$. From Eq. (7.5.27), it is seen that the ratio of the minimal n values depends on $2\sigma_0^2/\sigma_d^2$. From the data in Table 7.3 we can estimate this as being of an order of magnitude equal to 4. The interpretation of this result is that it takes about four times as much sampling for the unpaired procedure as is required in the paired procedure to have the same odds of detecting any practical difference Δ_0.

7   The Sign Test for Nonparametric Paired Comparisons   The procedures studied in the previous sections of this chapter are valid when the observations come from normal populations and are only approximately valid otherwise.   The sign test, to be discussed in this section, is a procedure whose validity does not depend on the normality of the observations.   In fact, only the continuity and symmetry of the distributions are assumed.   Procedures which do not depend on the form of distribution of the observations are called *nonparametric* procedures.

Consider again the one-sided hypothesis treated in section 5, namely,

$$H_0: \quad m_A - m_B = \Delta = 0 \qquad \text{against} \qquad H_1: \quad \Delta > 0 \quad (7.5.39)$$

It is assumed that the paired sampling procedure is used.   Thus we have n pairs (x_1, y_1), (x_2, y_2), . . . , (x_n, y_n) and their differences $d_1, d_2, \ldots ,$ d_n.   Under hypothesis H_0, we expect that there is approximately an equal number of positive and negative d's.   In fact, when H_0 is true, Prob $(d > 0) = $ Prob $(d \leq 0) = \frac{1}{2}$.   On the other hand, under alternative $\Delta = \Delta_1 > 0$, we have Prob $(d > 0) > \frac{1}{2}$.   As a consequence, H_0 can be tested in terms of the signs of $d_1, d_2, \ldots , d_n$.   Letting $p = $ Prob $(d > 0)$, we can reformulate the problem of testing $H_0: \Delta = 0$ against $H_1: \Delta > 0$ in terms of p as follows:

$$H_0: \quad p = \frac{1}{2} \qquad \text{against} \qquad H_1: \quad p > \frac{1}{2} \qquad (7.5.40)$$

This is a problem of testing a simple hypothesis concerning the binomial distribution against a one-sided composite alternative.   In order to find the rejection region, we can consider the simple-against-simple case:

$$H_0: \quad p = \frac{1}{2} \qquad \text{against} \qquad H_1: \quad p = p_1 > \frac{1}{2} \qquad (7.5.41)$$

Let u equal the number of positive d's; then, for the likelihood functions $L_0(u)$ (under H_0) and $L_1(u)$ (under H_1) and their ratio $L(u)$, we obtain

$$L_0(u) = \frac{n!}{u!(n-u)!} \left(\frac{1}{2} \right)^n$$

$$L_1(u) = \frac{n!}{u!(n-u)!} p_1{}^u (1 - p_1)^{n-u}$$

$$L(u) = \frac{L_0(u)}{L_1(u)} = \left(\frac{1}{2} \right)^n \left(\frac{1}{1 - p_1} \right)^n \left(\frac{1 - p_1}{p_1} \right)^u$$

According to the Neyman-Pearson lemma the optimum rejection region is of the form

$$L(u) \leq k$$

Since $L(u)$ is a decreasing function as u increases (for $p_1 > \frac{1}{2}$), the optimum rejection region $L(u) \leq k$ is equivalent to $u \geq k'$, where k' is to be determined by choice of the significance level α. The value k', for any level, is determined by the relationship

$$\text{Prob (rejection} \mid p = \tfrac{1}{2}) = \text{Prob } (u \geq k' \mid p = \tfrac{1}{2})$$

$$= \sum_{s=k'}^{n} \frac{n!}{s!(n-s)!} \left(\frac{1}{2}\right)^{n} \quad (7.5.42)$$

Actual evaluations can be made with the aid of tables of the cumulative binomial distribution.[1] Since the binomial is a discrete distribution, all α values cannot be attained.

It is important to note that the optimum rejection region for testing the hypothesis given in (7.5.41) does *not* depend upon the value of p_1, but only on the condition that $p_1 > \frac{1}{2}$. As a result, we have, in fact, an optimum rejection region for testing the hypothesis as expressed in (7.5.40) and, consequently, as originally posed in (7.5.39).

The power function $\pi(p)$ for various alternatives p is

$$\pi(p) = \text{Prob (rejection} \mid p) = \text{Prob } (u \geq k' \mid p)$$

$$= \sum_{s=k'}^{n} \frac{n!}{s!(n-s)!} p^{s}(1-p)^{n-s} \quad (7.5.43)$$

which again can be determined by means of tables of the cumulative binomial probability distribution.

In comparing the sign-test procedure with that of the paired comparison, several aspects must be noted. On the one hand, since only the signs, and not the magnitudes, are used for the sign test, it cannot be as informative as the paired comparison, which uses the magnitudes of the d's. On the other hand, the sign test does not depend on making assumptions of normality. We may ask, if in fact the d's are normally distributed, how much power is lost in using only the signs of the d's and ignoring their magnitudes? To answer this question, we compare the two relevant power functions. In the case of the sign test, we shall express $\pi(p)$ in terms of Δ, when in fact the d's are normal variates. Recall that $p = \text{Prob } (d > 0)$ and that consequently, when $m_A - m_B = \Delta$, we have, assuming normality,

$$p = \text{Prob } (d > 0) = \text{Prob } \left(\frac{d - \Delta}{\sigma_d} > \frac{-\Delta}{\sigma_d}\right)$$

$$= \text{Prob } \left(Z > \frac{-\Delta}{\sigma_d}\right) = \Phi\left(\frac{\Delta}{\sigma_d}\right) \quad (7.5.44)$$

---

[1] Tables of the Cumulative Binomial Probability Distribution, Harvard University Press, Cambridge, Mass.

For any Δ, we can compute p from (7.5.44) and substitute the value obtained in the power function of the sign test given in (7.5.43).

Example 7.6 Continuing with Example 7.5, we shall test the hypothesis considered there by means of the sign-test procedure. The rejection region $u \geq k'$, for $\alpha = 0.0307$ and $n = 29$, is found to be $k' = 20$ from the fact that

$$\text{Prob } (u \geq 20 \mid p = \tfrac{1}{2}) = 0.03071$$

A significance level of $\alpha = 0.0307$ will be used instead of 0.05 (as in Example 7.5), since for $k' = 19$,

$$\text{Prob } (u \geq 19 \mid p = \tfrac{1}{2}) = 0.06802$$

which is larger than 0.05. The power function $\pi(p)$ is then

$$\pi(p) = \text{Prob } (u \geq 20 \mid p) = \sum_{s=20}^{29} \frac{(29)!}{s!(29 - s)!} p^s (1 - p)^{29-s} \quad (7.5.45)$$

which can be evaluated from tables of the cumulative binomial probability function. Assuming normal alternatives for comparison with Example 7.5, we express p in terms of Δ and σ_d. From expression (7.5.44) we have $p = \Phi(\Delta/\sigma_d)$. For illustrative purposes we shall use the estimate of σ_d contained in the data of Table 7.3 and obtain an approximate expression for the power function.

For example, when $\Delta = 0.02$, $\Delta/\sigma_d \cong 0.02/0.08 = 0.25$ and $p \cong \Phi(0.25) = 0.5987$. The power is then, from (7.5.45), $\pi(0.5987)$, which equals 0.215. Repetition of this procedure yields the power curve shown in Fig. 7.11.

As expected, since not all the information about the d_i is used, the power of the sign test is weaker than that of the paired-comparison procedure which was considered. On the other hand, in the present example, the power of the sign test is superior to that of the unpaired procedure. This may often be the case, but of course not always.

The sign test has other adaptations, in particular, to answering questions of the type:

1. Is strategy A better than strategy B by fraction P?
2. Is strategy A better than strategy B by amount Q?

The expression "better than" implies that the measure of the outcomes for strategy A is greater than the outcomes for strategy B. Suppose then that strategies A and B, paired, yield outcomes (x_1, y_1), (x_2, y_2), . . . , (x_n, y_n). Question 1 is answered by applying the sign test to the differences

$$x_1 - (1 + P)y_1, \; x_2 - (1 + P)y_2, \; . . . , \; x_n - (1 + P)y_n$$

Question 2, again, requires application of the sign test to

$$x_1 - (y_1 + Q), \ x_2 - (y_2 + Q), \ \ldots, \ x_n - (y_n + Q)$$

Another interesting adaptation of the sign test can be made to test H_0: $\Delta = 0$ against the two-sided alternative H_1: $\Delta \neq 0$, a procedure which leads to a two-part rejection region.

In sum, the sign test can be very effectively used to test a variety of hypotheses, even though it is much less powerful than the corresponding paired-comparison procedure based on the normality assumption. On the other hand, the sign test can have a much broader range of application to situations where the normality assumption is not warranted.

7.5.4 Comparison of variances

In previous sections we considered problems involving comparison of mean values under a variety of conditions. This section deals with comparisons of variances. Explicitly, we consider comparison of a variance σ^2 against a standard value σ_0^2 or a comparison of the variance of one population, σ_1^2, with the variance of another, σ_2^2. A variety of circumstances may arise, depending on whether the alternatives are one-sided or two-sided.

Comparing the Variance against a Specified Value, Two-sided Alternatives   The explicit hypothesis treated is

$$H_0: \quad \sigma^2 = \sigma_0^2 \quad\quad (-\infty \leq m \leq +\infty)$$

against $\quad H_1: \quad \sigma^2 \neq \sigma_0^2 \quad\quad (-\infty \leq m \leq +\infty)$

It should first be noted that both H_0 and H_1 are composite hypotheses. The null hypothesis H_0 is composite, since the mean of the normal population m is not assumed known and can range from $-\infty$ to $+\infty$. The experiment consists of a random choice of n states of the experimental environment. This procedure yields n observations $x_1, x_2, \ldots, x_n$.

As indicated in (7.4.3), the likelihood-ratio test can generally be used and often leads to test procedures having desirable properties. The likelihood function of the data is

$$L(x_1, \ \ldots, x_n; m, \sigma^2) = \left(\frac{1}{\sigma\sqrt{2\pi}}\right)^n \exp\left[-\frac{1}{2\sigma^2}\sum_i (x_i - m)^2\right] \quad (7.5.46)$$

In order to determine the likelihood ratio, we must find the maximum of $L(x_1, x_2, \ldots, x_n; m, \sigma^2)$ first for $\sigma^2 = \sigma_0^2$ ($-\infty \leq m \leq +\infty$) and then for (m, σ^2), where $\sigma^2 \geq 0$ ($-\infty \leq m \leq +\infty$). Under the null hypothesis H_0, the likelihood function is

$$L(x_1, x_2, \ \ldots, x_n; m, \sigma_0^2) = \left(\frac{1}{\sigma_0\sqrt{2\pi}}\right)^n \exp\left[-\frac{1}{2\sigma_0^2}\sum_i (x_i - m)^2\right]$$

$$(7.5.47)$$

and must be maximized under the condition $-\infty \leq m \leq +\infty$ in order to obtain the numerator of the likelihood ratio. Clearly,

$$L(x_1, x_2, \ldots, x_n; m, \sigma_0{}^2)$$

is maximized when $\Sigma(x_i - m)^2$ is minimized with respect to m. This minimum occurs for $m = \bar{x}$, the arithmetic average of the observations. The denominator of the likelihood ratio involves finding m and σ^2, which maximize $L = L(x_1, x_2, \ldots, x_n; m, \sigma^2)$, as given in Eq. (7.5.46), for $\sigma^2 \geq 0$ $(-\infty \leq m \leq +\infty)$. This can be accomplished by the standard procedure of setting the first derivatives of L with respect to m and σ^2 each equal to zero and solving the resulting equations for m and σ^2. It is left as an exercise for the reader to verify that the maximum occurs for $m = \bar{x}$ and $\sigma^2 = (n-1)s^2/n$, where s^2 is the usual unbiased estimate of σ^2. Using these values of m and σ^2 and substituting them into L in Eq. (7.5.46) gives the denominator of the likelihood ratio. Consequently,

$$\max_{(m,\sigma_0{}^2)} L = \left(\frac{1}{\sigma_0 \sqrt{2\pi}}\right)^n \exp\left[-\frac{1}{2\sigma_0{}^2}\sum_i (x_i - \bar{x})^2\right]$$

$$= \left(\frac{1}{\sigma_0 \sqrt{2\pi}}\right)^n \exp\left(-\frac{n-1}{2\sigma_0{}^2}s^2\right)$$

is the numerator of the likelihood ratio,

$$\max_{(m,\sigma^2)} L = \left(\frac{\sqrt{n}}{s\sqrt{2\pi(n-1)}}\right)^n \exp\left(-\frac{n}{2}\right)$$

is the denominator, and

$$\lambda(x_1, \ldots, x_n) = \left[\frac{(n-1)s^2}{n\sigma_0{}^2}\right]^{n/2} \exp\left(\frac{n}{2} - \frac{n-1}{2}\frac{s^2}{\sigma_0{}^2}\right)$$

is the likelihood ratio.

The likelihood ratio depends on the quantity $s^2/\sigma_0{}^2$. The acceptance region is of the form $\lambda(x_1, \ldots, x_n) \geq k$, where k is chosen to satisfy the requirement of the significance level α. A study of λ as a function of $s^2/\sigma_0{}^2$ shows that it is small when $s^2/\sigma_0{}^2$ is small, increases with $s^2/\sigma_0{}^2$ until a maximum is reached, and then decreases with increasing $s^2/\sigma_0{}^2$. As a result, the acceptance region $\lambda \geq k$ is equivalent to $k_1 \leq s^2/\sigma_0{}^2 \leq k_2$, where k_1 and k_2 are constants depending on n and the significance level α.

In order to find the acceptance region for any specified significance level α, we must find k_1 and k_2 such that

$$1 - \alpha = \text{Prob}\left(k_1 \leq \frac{s^2}{\sigma_0{}^2} \leq k_2 \mid m, \sigma_0{}^2\right) \tag{7.5.48}$$

The problem of evaluating the above expression suggests use of the fact that $(n - 1)s^2/\sigma_0^2$ has, under H_0, the χ^2 distribution with $n - 1$ degrees of freedom. Consequently,

$$1 - \alpha = \text{Prob}\left[(n - 1)k_1 \le \frac{(n - 1)s^2}{\sigma_0^2} \le (n - 1)k_2 \right]$$
$$= \text{Prob}\left[(n - 1)k_1 \le \chi^2 \le (n - 1)k_2 \right] \qquad (7.5.49)$$

Values of k_1 and k_2 satisfying this condition can be found from tables of the χ^2 distribution. There are many values k_1 and k_2 satisfying Eq. (7.5.49). The likelihood ratio calls for a particular set, which is difficult to find. An approximately optimum procedure, similar to that called for by the likelihood-ratio procedure, is to choose $(n - 1)k_1$ and $(n - 1)k_2$, using equal tails of the χ^2 distribution. For instance, if the significance level is α, then $(n - 1)k_1 = \chi^2_{\alpha/2}$ and $(n - 1)k_2 = \chi^2_{1-\alpha/2}$, where $\chi^2_{\alpha/2}$, $\chi^2_{1-\alpha/2}$ are the $\alpha/2$ and $1 - \alpha/2$ percentiles of the χ^2 distribution with $n - 1$ degrees of freedom. As a result, the acceptance region, for significance level α, is

$$\frac{1}{n - 1} \chi^2_{\alpha/2, n-1} \le \frac{s^2}{\sigma_0^2} \le \frac{1}{n - 1} \chi^2_{1-\alpha/2, n-1}$$

The power of this test, $\pi(\sigma^2)$, for any alternative σ^2, is

$$\pi(\sigma^2) = \text{Prob (rejection} \mid \sigma) = 1 - \text{Prob (accepting} \mid \sigma^2)$$
$$= 1 - \text{Prob}\left(\chi^2_{\alpha/2, n-1} \le \frac{(n - 1)s^2}{\sigma_0^2} \le \chi^2_{1-\alpha/2, n-1} \mid \sigma^2 \right) \qquad (7.5.50)$$

When the variance is σ^2, we know that $(n - 1)s^2/\sigma^2$ has a χ^2 distribution with $n - 1$ degrees of freedom. This fact can be utilized in computing $\pi(\sigma^2)$ by multiplying all three parts of inequality (7.5.50) by σ_0^2/σ^2, yielding

$$\pi(\sigma^2) = 1 - \text{Prob}\left[\chi^2_{\alpha/2, n-1} \frac{\sigma_0^2}{\sigma^2} \le \frac{(n - 1)s^2}{\sigma_0} \le \chi^2_{1-\alpha/2, n-1} \frac{\sigma_0^2}{\sigma^2} \right]$$
$$= 1 - \text{Prob}\left(\chi^2_{\alpha/2, n-1} \frac{\sigma_0^2}{\sigma^2} \le \chi^2 \le \chi^2_{1-\alpha/2, n-1} \frac{\sigma_0^2}{\sigma^2} \right) \qquad (7.5.51)$$

which can be evaluated with the aid of a table of the percentiles of the χ^2 distribution. It is apparent that $\pi(\sigma^2)$ depends on the deviation from σ_0^2 in terms of the ratio σ^2/σ_0^2.

The minimum n to achieve power $1 - \beta$ at $\sigma^2 = \sigma_1^2$ can be obtained from tables of the percentiles of the χ^2 distribution. In order to do this, let us rewrite $\pi(\sigma^2)$, in Eq. (7.5.51), as

$$\pi(\sigma^2) = \text{Prob (rejecting} \mid \sigma^2) = \text{Prob}\left(\chi^2 \le \chi^2_{\alpha/2, n-1} \frac{\sigma_0^2}{\sigma^2} \right)$$
$$+ \text{Prob}\left(\chi^2 \ge \chi^2_{1-\alpha/2, n-1} \frac{\sigma_0^2}{\sigma^2} \right) \qquad (7.5.52)$$

Suppose for the present that $\sigma_1{}^2 > \sigma_0{}^2$. In that case, $\chi^2_{\alpha/2, n-1}\sigma_0{}^2/\sigma_1{}^2 \leq \chi^2_{\alpha/2, n-1}$. Consequently,

$$\text{Prob}\left(\chi^2 \leq \chi^2_{\alpha/2, n-1}\frac{\sigma_0{}^2}{\sigma_1{}^2}\right) \leq \text{Prob}\,(\chi^2 \leq \chi^2_{\alpha/2, n-1}) = \frac{\alpha}{2}$$

Thus an approximate expression for $\pi(\sigma^2)$, $\sigma^2 > \sigma_0{}^2$, is, by neglecting one term,

$$\pi(\sigma^2) \cong \text{Prob}\left(\chi^2 \geq \chi^2_{1-\alpha/2, n-1}\frac{\sigma_0{}^2}{\sigma_1{}^2}\right) \tag{7.5.53}$$

To find n such that $\pi(\sigma_1{}^2) = 1 - \beta$, we use (7.5.53) to obtain

$$\pi(\sigma_1{}^2) \cong \text{Prob}\left(\chi^2 \geq \chi^2_{1-\alpha/2, n-1}\frac{\sigma_0{}^2}{\sigma_1{}^2}\right) = 1 - \beta$$

For this equation to be satisfied, $\chi^2_{1-\alpha/2, n-1}\sigma_0{}^2/\sigma_1{}^2$ must equal the β percentile of the χ^2 distribution. Thus

$$\chi^2_{1-\alpha/2, n-1}\frac{\sigma_0{}^2}{\sigma_1{}^2} \cong \chi^2_{\beta, n-1} \tag{7.5.54}$$

that is,

$$\frac{\sigma_1{}^2}{\sigma_0{}^2} \cong \frac{\chi^2_{1-\alpha/2, n-1}}{\chi^2_{\beta, n-1}} \tag{7.5.55}$$

The smallest n, to satisfy (7.5.55), is obtained by comparing $\chi^2_{1-\alpha/2, n-1}/\chi^2_{\beta, n-1}$ with $\sigma_1{}^2/\sigma_0{}^2$ for successive values of n. When $\sigma_1{}^2 < \sigma_0{}^2$, a similar procedure can be used.

To illustrate the procedures, consider testing $H_0: \sigma^2 = 4$ against $H_1: \sigma^2 \neq 4$, where the result of 11 observations yields $s^2 = 7$. At a significance level $\alpha = 0.05$, is the evidence against H_0? From tables of the χ^2 we have $\chi^2_{\alpha/2, n-1} = \chi^2_{0.025, 10} = 3.247$ and $\chi^2_{1-\alpha/2, n-1} = \chi^2_{0.975, 10} = 20.483$. The acceptance region is $0.3247 \leq s^2/\sigma_0{}^2 \leq 2.0483$. Since, in our numerical example, $s^2/\sigma_0{}^2 = 7/4 = 1.75$, we do not reject H_0 at a significance level of 0.05. What is the chance, under the present experimental conditions, of detecting a variance $\sigma^2 = \sigma_1{}^2 = 10$? From Eq. (7.5.53), $\pi(10) \cong \text{Prob}\,[\chi^2 \geq (20.483)\,4/10] = \text{Prob}\,(\chi^2 \geq 8.1932) = 0.60$. Consequently, there is (approximately) only a 60 per cent chance, with $n = 11$, of detecting a variance $\sigma_1{}^2 = 10$. How big must n be to raise this probability to 90 per cent? Using (7.5.55), we compare $\chi^2_{0.975, n-1}/\chi^2_{0.10, n-1}$ with $\sigma_1{}^2/\sigma_0{}^2 = 10/4 = 2.5$ for successive values of n. For $n - 1 = 24$, we find $\chi^2_{0.975, 24}/\chi^2_{0.10, 24} = 2.5$. Accordingly, a sample size $n = 25$ will achieve the stated purpose of detecting $\sigma^2 = 10$ with the specified odds 9 to 1.

Comparing Two Variances, One-sided Alternatives The explicit hypothesis considered is

$$H_0: \quad \sigma_1{}^2 = \sigma_2{}^2 \quad (-\infty \leq m_1 \leq +\infty, \, -\infty \leq m_2 \leq +\infty)$$

against

$$H_1: \quad \sigma_1^2 > \sigma_2^2 \qquad (-\infty \leq m_1 \leq +\infty, \; -\infty \leq m_2 \leq +\infty) \tag{7.5.56}$$

The experiment results in observations $x_1, x_2, \ldots, x_n$ and $y_1, y_2, \ldots, y_n$ from their respective normal universes. Again, denote by s_x^2 and s_y^2 the respective sample estimates of the σ_1^2 and σ_2^2. A test procedure having optimum properties can be shown to consist of a rejection region

$$\frac{s_x^2}{s_y^2} \geq k \tag{7.5.57}$$

where k must be found by specifying the significance level α. Thus

$$\alpha = \text{Prob}\left(\frac{s_x^2}{s_y^2} \geq k \mid \sigma_1^2 = \sigma_2^2\right) \tag{7.5.58}$$

Under the null hypothesis, s_x^2/s_y^2 has an F distribution with $(n-1, n-1)$ degrees of freedom, resulting in $k = F_{1-\alpha;n-1,n-1}$ and rejection region

$$\frac{s_x^2}{s_y^2} \geq F_{1-\alpha;n-1,n-1} \tag{7.5.59}$$

The power of the test, $\pi(\sigma_1^2,\sigma_2^2)$, is

$$\pi(\sigma_1^2,\sigma_2^2) = \text{Prob}\left(\frac{s_x^2}{s_y^2} \geq F_{1-\alpha;n-1,n-1} \mid \sigma_1^2,\sigma_2^2\right) \tag{7.5.60}$$

Using the general result stated in Sec. 5.2.6 and multiplying the inequality within the probability statement of (7.5.60) by σ_2^2/σ_1^2, we obtain

$$\pi(\sigma_1^2,\sigma_2^2) = \text{Prob}\left(\frac{s_x^2}{s_y^2} \cdot \frac{\sigma_2^2}{\sigma_1^2} \geq \frac{\sigma_2^2}{\sigma_1^2} F_{1-\alpha;n-1,n-1}\right)$$

$$= \text{Prob}\left(F \geq \frac{\sigma_2^2}{\sigma_1^2} F_{1-\alpha;n-1,n-1}\right) \tag{7.5.61}$$

Again, the power depends on σ_2^2/σ_1^2 and can be evaluated with the aid of F tables.

The minimum n, for any significance level α, to detect a deviation $\theta = \sigma_2^2/\sigma_1^2 < 1$ with specified odds $1 - \beta$ to β, is found by substituting θ into (7.5.61) and setting $\pi(\sigma_1^2,\sigma_2^2) = \pi(\theta)$ equal to $1 - \beta$. That is,

$$\pi(\sigma_1^2,\sigma_2^2) = \pi(\theta) = \text{Prob}\,(F \geq \theta F_{1-\alpha;n-1,n-1}) = 1 - \beta \tag{7.5.62}$$

The condition of (7.5.62) can be satisfied by choosing n such that

$$\theta F_{1-\alpha;n-1,n-1} = F_{\beta;n-1,n-1}$$

Tables of the F distribution can be used to find the minimum n by comparing $F_{\beta;\,n-1,n-1}/F_{1-\alpha;\,n-1,n-1}$ with θ for successive values of n until a suitable sample size is obtained.

Comparing Several Variances An important problem for many applications is testing the homogeneity of variance for several normal populations. Explicitly, the hypothesis to be treated is

$$H_0:\quad \sigma_1^2 = \sigma_2^2 = \cdots = \sigma_k^2 \qquad (-\infty \leq m_i \leq +\infty\,;\, i = 1, 2, \ldots, k)$$

against $\qquad\qquad\qquad H_1:\quad \sigma_1^2, \sigma_2^2, \ldots, \sigma_k^2 \qquad\qquad (7.5.63)$

where the k variances are not all equal. The null hypothesis H_0 and the alternative H_1 are both composite.

The experimental procedure consists of choosing N states of the experimental environment at random and then allocating $n_1, n_2, \ldots, n_k$ of them, at random, to the k populations. This procedure yields k sets of observations: $x_{11}, x_{12}, \ldots, x_{1n_1}; x_{21}, x_{22}, \ldots, x_{2n_2}; \ldots; x_{k1}, x_{k2}, \ldots, x_{kn_k}$ from the k respective normal populations. That is, there are n_i observations from population i and $n_1 + n_2 + \cdots + n_k = N$.

Let s_i^2 be the usual unbiased estimate of the variance σ_i^2 of population i.

$$s_i^2 = \frac{1}{n_i - 1} \sum_j (x_{ij} - \bar{x}_i)^2 \qquad i = 1, 2, \ldots, k \qquad (7.5.64)$$

where $\bar{x}_i$ is the arithmetic average of the observations of population i. In order to obtain a test statistic we apply the likelihood-ratio procedure. The likelihood L of the sample observations occurring under the assumed conditions is

$$L = \left\{ \left(\frac{1}{\sigma_1 \sqrt{2\pi}} \right)^{n_1} \exp\left[-\frac{1}{2\sigma_1^2} \sum_j (x_{1j} - m_1)^2 \right] \right\} \cdot$$
$$\left\{ \left(\frac{1}{\sigma_2 \sqrt{2\pi}} \right)^{n_2} \exp\left[-\frac{1}{2\sigma_2^2} \sum_j (x_{2j} - m_2)^2 \right] \right\} \cdots$$
$$\left\{ \left(\frac{1}{\sigma_k \sqrt{2\pi}} \right)^{n_k} \exp\left[-\frac{1}{2\sigma_k^2} \sum_j (x_{kj} - m_k)^2 \right] \right\} \qquad (7.5.65)$$

The parameter space Ω consists of all points

$$(m_1, m_2, \ldots, m_k, \sigma_1^2, \sigma_2^2, \ldots, \sigma_k^2)$$

with $\sigma_1^2 \geq 0$, $\sigma_2^2 \geq 0$, $\ldots$, $\sigma_k^2 \geq 0$, and has dimension $d = 2k$. The denominator of the likelihood ratio is obtained by maximizing L over Ω. It can be seen from (7.5.65) that each term in the product can be maximized separately. The subset W of Ω, specified by H_0, consists of all points in Ω of the form $(m_1, m_2, \ldots, m_k, \sigma^2, \sigma^2, \ldots, \sigma^2)$ with $\sigma^2 \geq 0$ and has dimension $d_2 = k + 1$. The likelihood function of the data under H_0 is obtained by substituting σ^2 for $\sigma_1^2, \sigma_2^2, \ldots, \sigma_k^2$. The numerator of the likelihood ratio is then formed by maximizing L over the parameter points in W. The result of applying this procedure leads to a likelihood ratio

$$\lambda = \frac{\left[\dfrac{(n_1 - 1)s_1^2}{n_1}\right]^{n_1/2} \left[\dfrac{(n_2 - 1)s_2^2}{n_2}\right]^{n_2/2} \cdots \left[\dfrac{(n_k - 1)s_k^2}{n_k}\right]^{n_k/2}}{\left[\dfrac{(n_1 - 1)s_1^2 + (n_2 - 1)s_2^2 + \cdots + (n_k - 1)s_k^2}{N}\right]^{N/2}} \quad (7.5.66)$$

The rejection region is of the form $\lambda \leq c$. When the number of observations taken on each population is equal to n, $N = nk$ and the likelihood ratio becomes

$$\lambda = \frac{[(s_1^2 s_2^2 \cdots s_k^2)^{1/k}]^{kn/2}}{\left(\dfrac{s_1^2 + s_2^2 + \cdots + s_k^2}{k}\right)^{kn/2}} \quad (7.5.67)$$

This is essentially a ratio of the geometric and arithmetic averages of $s_1^2, s_2^2, \ldots, s_k^2$.

The distribution of λ in (7.5.67) is very difficult to find even under the null hypothesis H_0. When the n_i are large, we can use the asymptotic result quoted in Sec. 7.4.3, wherein the distribution of $-2 \ln \lambda$, under H_0, converges to that of χ^2 with $d_1 - d_2$ degrees of freedom, which in the present case equals $2k - (k + 1) = k - 1$. It turns out, for this particular case, that the χ^2 approximation is adequate for even moderate values of $n_1, n_2, \ldots, n_k$. The rejection region is then of the form $-2 \ln \lambda > c'$, where c' must be evaluated in terms of the specified significance level α. Since $-2 \ln \lambda$ is approximately χ^2, c' is chosen as the upper $1 - \alpha$ percentile of χ^2 with $k - 1$ degrees of freedom. The rejection region is then

$$-2 \ln \lambda = N \ln \left[\sum_i \frac{(n_i - 1)s_i^2}{N}\right] - 2 \sum_i \frac{n_i}{2} \ln \left[\frac{(n_i - 1)s_i^2}{n_i}\right] > \chi^2_{1-\alpha, k-1}$$

$$(7.5.68)$$

7.6 Design and analysis of simple comparative experiments involving the binomial and the Poisson distributions

The binomial and Poisson distributions arise in a variety of problems. In Secs. 7.4.2 and 7.5.3, part 7, we discussed particular examples of testing hypotheses concerning these distributions. We shall here examine, more systematically, a variety of situations.

1 *Comparing a Binomial Distribution with a Standard, One-sided Alternative* The explicit hypothesis to be treated is

$$H_0: \quad p = p_0 \quad \text{against} \quad H_1: \quad p > p_0 \quad (7.6.1)$$

where p is the probability of "success" of a binomial variate. The experiment consists of n trials and results in noting the number x of successes. The null hypothesis H_0 in (7.6.1) is simple, while H_1 is composite. To obtain a suitable rejection region, we study the modified simple-against-simple problem

$$H_0: \quad p = p_0 \quad \text{against} \quad H_1: \quad p = p_1 > p_0 \quad (7.6.2)$$

For this modified problem, an optimum rejection region can be found by means of the Neyman-Pearson lemma. As in a variety of previous sections, it turns out that this region does not depend on p_1, but only on the fact that $p_1 > p_0$, and consequently is a solution to the original problem. The likelihood of x is given by the binomial distribution

$$L(x) = \frac{n!}{x!(n-x)!} p^x (1-p)^{n-x} \quad (7.6.3)$$

Writing $L_0(x)$, $L_1(x)$ for the likelihoods of x under H_0 and H_1, respectively, and $\lambda(x)$ for their ratio, we have

$$L_0(x) = \frac{n!}{x!(n-x)!} p_0^x (1-p_0)^{n-x}$$

$$L_1(x) = \frac{n!}{x!(n-x)!} p_1^x (1-p_1)^{n-x} \quad (7.6.4)$$

$$\lambda(x) = \frac{p_0^x (1-p_0)^{n-x}}{p_1^x (1-p_1)^{n-x}} = \left(\frac{1-p_0}{1-p_1}\right)^n \left[\frac{p_0(1-p_1)}{p_1(1-p_0)}\right]^x$$

Since $p_1 > p_0$, $p_0(1-p_1)/p_1(1-p_0) < 1$ and $\lambda(x)$ is a decreasing function for increasing x. The optimum rejection region is of the form $\lambda(x) < k$, which is equivalent to $x > k'$. Thus H_0 is rejected when the number of successes x is too large. The value of k' is found by specifying the level of significance α as follows:

$$\alpha = \text{Prob (rejecting} \mid p_0) = \text{Prob } (x > k' \mid p_0)$$

$$= \sum_{s=k'+1}^{n} \frac{n!}{s!(n-s)!} p_0^s (1-p_0)^{n-s} = 1 - \sum_{s=0}^{k'} \frac{n!}{s!(n-s)!} p_0^s (1-p_0)^{n-s} \quad (7.6.5)$$

The value k' which satisfies the above can be found from tables of the binomial distribution. The exact value of k' for all α cannot be found since the binomial is a discrete distribution. Letting $B_v(n,p)$ denote the upper v percentile of the binomial distribution with n trials and probability p, we have, from (7.6.5),

$$k' = B_{1-\alpha}(n,p_0) \tag{7.6.6}$$

Since the binomial variate has a discrete distribution, all percentiles do not exist. In that event the required percentile can be set equal to the one closest to it.

The power of this test is

$$\pi(p) = \text{Prob (reject} \mid p) = \text{Prob } (x > k' \mid p)$$

$$= 1 - \sum_{s=0}^{k'} \frac{n!}{s!(n-s)!}\, p^x(1-p)^{n-x} \tag{7.6.7}$$

The minimum n, for significance level α, required to detect a difference $p = p_1 > p_0$, with specified odds $1 - \beta$, is obtained by setting $\pi(p_1) = 1 - \beta$ and solving for n. Thus

$$\pi(p_1) = 1 - \text{Prob } (x \leq k' \mid p_1) = 1 - \beta \tag{7.6.8}$$

For Eq. (7.6.8) to be satisfied, k' must equal the upper β percentile of the binomial with probability p_1 and n trials. Using (7.6.6) and (7.6.8), we obtain as the minimum n the smallest n for which

$$k' = B_{1-\alpha}(n,p_0) = B_{\beta}(n,p_1) \tag{7.6.9}$$

found from tables of the cumulative binomial distribution by trying successive values of n.

Expressions (7.6.6) for k', (7.6.7) for $\pi(p)$, and (7.6.9) for the minimum are not very easy to manipulate or readily revealing of orders of magnitude. For large n, however, the normal approximation to the binomial can be utilized to simplify the above expressions as follows:

$$\text{Prob } (x \leq a \mid p) = \text{Prob}\left(\frac{x-np}{\sqrt{npq}} \leq \frac{a-np}{\sqrt{npq}}\right) \cong \Phi\left(\frac{a-np}{\sqrt{npq}}\right) \tag{7.6.10}$$

Consequently, the upper v percentile can be found approximately by equating Prob $(x \leq a \mid p)$ to v, which is equivalent to specifying that a satisfies

$$\Phi\left(\frac{a-np}{\sqrt{npq}}\right) = v$$

If Z_v is the value of the standard normal variate at the v percentile, $(a - np)/\sqrt{npq} = Z_v$; whence $a = np + \sqrt{npq}\, Z_v$. But $B_v(n,p)$ from (7.6.10) is approximately a, and therefore

$$B_v(n,p) \cong np + Z_v\sqrt{npq} \tag{7.6.11}$$

Making use of this approximation to $B_v(n,p)$ in Eq. (7.6.6), k' can be expressed approximately by $k' \cong np_0 + Z_{1-\alpha}\sqrt{np_0q_0}$. Finally, in view of relations (7.6.10) and (7.6.7), an approximation to the power is

$$\pi(p) \cong 1 - \Phi\left(\frac{k' - np}{\sqrt{npq}}\right) \tag{7.6.12}$$

Relationship (7.6.11) provides an approximate expression for the minimum n required to give specified odds, since this value of n must satisfy both (7.6.11) and (7.6.9), which yields

$$n^* \cong \left(\frac{\sqrt{p_0 q_0}\, Z_{1-\alpha} - \sqrt{p_1 q_1}\, Z_\beta}{p_1 - p_0}\right)^2 \tag{7.6.13}$$

As an illustration, consider testing $H_0: p = 0.20$ against $H_1: p > 0.20$. At significance level α, H_0 is rejected when the number of successes $x > k'$. For $\alpha = 0.02$, $n = 36$, using (7.6.6), $k' = B_{0.98}(36, 0.20) = 12$. From the approximation in (7.6.11),

$$k' = np_0 + Z_{1-\alpha}\sqrt{np_0 q_0} = 7.2 + (2.05)(6)(0.4) = 12.12$$

which compares adequately with the exact result. To find the minimum n to detect an alternative $p_1 = 0.30$ with odds 0.90, we use (7.6.13) and compute $n = 196$, which agrees well with an exact computation carried out in terms of (7.6.9).

2 Comparing Two Binomial Distributions   Suppose there are two different universes 1 and 2 of red and black spheres. The proportions of red spheres in each universe are fixed, and they may be denoted by p_1 and p_2, respectively. Recall that n random drawings (with replacement) of spheres from such a universe will yield a binomial frequency X/n, the proportion of red spheres in a sample. The mean of such a binomial population is p, the fraction of red spheres in the original set (or universe) of spheres, and the variance of this population is $\sigma^2 = p(1 - p)/n$. Let us say, then, that we have, analogously, as the outcome of a given experiment, two classes of events, success and failure, where the expected fraction of successes is p. Specifically, consider two binomial populations 1 and 2, with unknown means p_1 and p_2, and an experiment whereby we wish to test the one-sided hypothesis

$$H_0: \quad p_1 - p_2 = \Delta = 0 \qquad \text{against} \qquad H_1: \quad \Delta > 0 \tag{7.6.14}$$

The experiment, for example, may be to measure the emission of vacuum tubes, designating as failures those tubes whose emission is less than a specified magnitude. For tubes coming from a statistically controlled process, the concept of a mean p has practical significance, and the comparison of different production runs of tubes and, in particular, runs from different sealing machines is often performed. Hence we may consider the existence of two binomial populations resulting from the performance of such an experiment. From process, or population, 1, we obtain x successes out of n trials, and from population 2, y successes out of n trials. Can we conclude from x/n and y/n that $\Delta = 0$ or $\Delta > 0$? Yes, but how? It turns out that there are a number of formal intricacies involved, which are beyond the scope of the present text, and therefore, an exact, detailed treatment of the test of hypothesis stated in (7.6.14) will not be developed. Instead, an approximation will be offered which reduces this test to a test on the normal distribution, developed in Sec. 7.5.3.

We may begin by considering n large enough so that x/n and y/n can be treated as observations from a normal population with means p_1 and p_2, respectively. Hence their variances are $\sigma_1^2 = p_1(1 - p_1)/n$ and $\sigma_2^2 = p_2(1 - p_2)/n$, both unknown. Then we may consider the test

$$H_0: \quad p_1 - p_2 = 0 \qquad \text{against} \qquad H_1: \quad p_1 - p_2 > 0 \quad (7.6.15)$$

for the approximately normal variates X/n and Y/n. The experiment, n random independent trials on each universe, yields x/n and y/n, respectively, as estimate of p_1 and p_2. Were the two variances known, we could consider the comparison expressed in (7.6.15) as that of two means from normal populations, falling back on the procedure in Sec. 7.5.3. Since, however, the variances are unknown, we are in a dilemma, for they may not be equal—p_1 may not equal p_2, and the variances are functions of p_1 and p_2, respectively. If it were possible so to transform X/n and Y/n that the new variables remain approximately normal and, in addition, the new variances are both known and equal, we could then make use of the methods of Sec. 7.5.3.

The mathematical motivation leading to such a transformation is beyond the scope of this work. We shall merely give the form of the transformation and its consequences. *Given that X is a chance variable with a binomial distribution and expected value np,*

$$U = \arcsin \sqrt{\frac{X}{n}} \tag{7.6.16}$$

is approximately normally distributed with mean

$$E(U) = m = \arcsin \sqrt{p} \tag{7.6.17}$$

and variance

$$V\left(\arcsin \sqrt{\frac{X}{n}}\right) \cong 1/4n \tag{7.6.18}$$

The original comparison in (7.6.14) can now be replaced by the comparison

$$H_0: \quad m_1 - m_2 = 0 \qquad \text{against} \qquad H_1: \quad m_1 - m_2 = \Delta > 0 \quad (7.6.19)$$

where m_1 and m_2 represent, respectively, the means of

$$U = \arcsin \sqrt{X/n} \qquad \text{and} \qquad W = \arcsin \sqrt{Y/n}$$

and where the variances of U and W are known and equal to $1/4n$.

Following the procedure in Sec. 7.5.3, the rejection region is of the form $u - w \geq k$, where k is determined by the specified significance level α. As usual,

$$
\begin{aligned}
\alpha &= \text{Prob } (U - W \geq k \mid \Delta = 0) \\
&= \text{Prob} \left(\frac{U - W}{\sqrt{\frac{1}{4n} + \frac{1}{4n}}} \geq \frac{k}{\sqrt{\frac{1}{4n} + \frac{1}{4n}}} \right) = \text{Prob } (Z \geq k\sqrt{2n}) \quad (7.6.20)
\end{aligned}
$$

Consequently,

$$
k = \frac{Z_{1-\alpha}}{\sqrt{2n}} \tag{7.6.21}
$$

The power function $\pi(\Delta)$ with $\Delta = \arcsin \sqrt{p_1} - \arcsin \sqrt{p_2}$ is

$$
\begin{aligned}
\pi(\Delta) &= \text{Prob} \left(U - W \geq \frac{Z_{1-\alpha}}{\sqrt{2n}} \,\middle|\, \Delta \right) \\
&= \text{Prob} \left(\frac{U - W - \Delta}{\sqrt{1/2n}} \geq \frac{Z_{1-\alpha}/\sqrt{2n} - \Delta}{\sqrt{1/2n}} \right) = \Phi(\Delta\sqrt{2n} + Z_\alpha)
\end{aligned}
\tag{7.6.22}
$$

The minimum n necessary to detect a difference Δ_1 with specified odd $1 - \beta$ is obtained by solving

$$
\pi(\Delta_1) = 1 - \beta = \Phi(\Delta_1\sqrt{2n} + Z_\alpha) \tag{7.6.23}
$$

The required n must satisfy $\Delta_1\sqrt{2n} + Z_\alpha = Z_{1-\beta}$. Solving for n, we have

$$
n = \frac{1}{2} \left(\frac{Z_{1-\beta} - Z_\alpha}{\Delta_1} \right)^2 \tag{7.6.24}
$$

which is inversely proportional to the square of the operationally important difference Δ_1. The expressions (7.6.23) and (7.6.24) can be written in terms of p_1, p_2 as follows:

$$
\pi(p_1, p_2) \cong \Phi[(\arcsin \sqrt{p_1} - \arcsin \sqrt{p_2})\sqrt{2n} + Z_\alpha]
$$
$$
n = \frac{1}{2} \left(\frac{Z_{1-\beta} - Z_\alpha}{\arcsin \sqrt{p_1} - \arcsin \sqrt{p_2}} \right)^2 \tag{7.6.25}
$$

As an example, consider comparing two binomial populations at a significance level $\alpha = 0.05$ and $n = 100$. Suppose $x = 35$ and $y = 25$. Is this significant evidence against H_0: $p_1 = p_2$? From tables for $\arcsin \sqrt{x}$, we have (Table A.7)

$$
u = \arcsin \sqrt{\frac{x}{n}} = \arcsin \sqrt{0.35} = 0.6331
$$
$$
w = \arcsin \sqrt{\frac{y}{n}} = \arcsin \sqrt{0.25} = 0.5236
$$
$$\tag{7.6.26}$$

The rejection region is $u - w \geq k$, where, from (7.6.21), $\alpha = 0.05$ and $n = 100$, k is equal to $Z_{0.95}/\sqrt{200} = 1.64/10\sqrt{2} = 0.116$. The value of $u - w$, in the present case, is 0.1095, so that the null hypothesis H_0 is not rejected.

How big a sample size is required to detect a difference with $p_1 = 0.50$ and $p_2 = 0.40$ at odds of 0.90? Applying (7.6.25),

$$n \cong \frac{1}{2} \left(\frac{1.28 + 1.64}{0.7854 - 0.6847} \right)^2 = 425 \tag{7.6.27}$$

The case of testing $H_0: p_1 - p_2 = 0$ against two-sided alternatives $H_1: p_1 - p_2 \neq 0$ is treated, similarly to the one-sided case, in terms of the arcsine transformation. The rejection region in this case, however, is of the form $u - w \leq a$ or $u - w > b$, where a and b must be determined by specifying a significance level α. It is left as an exercise to the reader to determine a, b, the power function, and the minimum n to detect a specified departure from H_0 with given odds $1 - \beta$.

3   *Comparing a Poisson Distribution against a Standard* To study inference problems with respect to the Poisson distribution, it is helpful to think in terms of the physical representation underlying the process as discussed in Sec. 5.1.

In Example 7.1, the case of testing

$$H_0: \quad \lambda = \lambda_0 \qquad \text{against} \qquad H_1: \quad \lambda < \lambda_0 \tag{7.6.28}$$

was studied by applying the Neyman-Pearson lemma for the simple-against-simple case

$$H_0: \quad \lambda = \lambda_1 \qquad \text{versus} \qquad H_1: \quad \lambda = \lambda_1 < \lambda_0$$

noting that the optimum rejection did not depend on λ_1 as long as $\lambda_1 < \lambda_0$.

The experiment in Example 7.1 consisted of observing the number of events occurring in a specified interval h.

The rejection region for the problem in (7.6.28) consists of values $a \leq k'$, where k' is such that, for any specified α,

$$\alpha = \text{Prob}\,(a \leq k' \mid \lambda_0) = \sum_{s=0}^{k'} \frac{e^{-\lambda_0 h}(\lambda_0 h)^s}{s!} \tag{7.6.29}$$

which can be evaluated by means of tables of the cumulative Poisson distribution. When $\lambda_0 h > 10$, the normal approximation can be used. Therefore

$$\alpha = \text{Prob}\,(a \leq k' \mid \lambda_0) = \text{Prob}\left(\frac{a - \lambda_0 h}{\sqrt{\lambda_0 h}} \leq \frac{k' - \lambda_0 h}{\sqrt{\lambda_0 h}} \right) \cong \Phi\left(\frac{k' - \lambda_0 h}{\sqrt{\lambda_0 h}} \right) \tag{7.6.30}$$

Consequently, an approximate expression for k' is

$$k' \cong \lambda_0 h + Z_\alpha \sqrt{\lambda_0 h} \qquad (7.6.31)$$

The power of the test, $\pi(\lambda)$, is

$$\pi(\lambda) = \text{Prob} \ (a \leq k' \mid \lambda) = \sum_{s=0}^{k'} \frac{e^{-\lambda h}(\lambda h)^s}{s!}$$

Again, for $\lambda h > 10$, we may use the normal approximation and obtain

$$\pi(\lambda) = \text{Prob} \left(\frac{a - \lambda h}{\sqrt{\lambda h}} \leq \frac{k' - \lambda h}{\sqrt{\lambda h}} \right) \cong \Phi \left(\frac{k' - \lambda h}{\sqrt{\lambda h}} \right)$$

For the appropriate k' (7.6.31),

$$\pi(\lambda) \cong \Phi \left[\frac{h(\lambda_0 - \lambda)}{\sqrt{\lambda h}} + Z_\alpha \sqrt{\frac{\lambda_0}{\lambda}} \right] \qquad (7.6.32)$$

The minimum interval h within which one can detect a difference $\lambda_1 < \lambda_0$ with odds $1 - \beta$ is found approximately by solving for h in $\pi(\lambda_1) = 1 - \beta$, yielding

$$h \cong \left(\frac{Z_{1-\beta} \sqrt{\lambda_1} - Z_\alpha \sqrt{\lambda_0}}{\lambda_0 - \lambda_1} \right)^2 \qquad (7.6.33)$$

In the foregoing analysis of the problem presented by the test of hypothesis in (7.6.28), the underlying experiment involves observing the number of occurrences of a specified event during a specified time interval h. One can, however, study the same process by observing the length of the time interval during which a specified number k of the events have occurred. The chance variable in this case is time denoted by T. Hence the random variable T can take on values $0 \leq t \leq \infty$, for outcomes of the present form of the experiment are various values t. The random variable T which in the present case is the time during which k accidents occur was discussed in Sec. 5.1 and shown to possess an Erlang distribution with parameters k and λ. The PDF of T is

$$f(t) = \frac{\lambda(\lambda t)^{k-1} e^{-\lambda t}}{(k - 1)!} \qquad (7.6.34)$$

We can set up the same hypothesis for this experiment as was set up in (7.6.28). Before considering this form of the test, however, we shall formulate

$$H_0: \quad \lambda = \lambda_0 \qquad \text{against} \qquad H_1: \quad \lambda = \lambda_1 < \lambda_0$$

since for this test of hypothesis the rejection region does not depend on λ_1 so long as $\lambda_1 < \lambda_0$. In view of this fact, the Neyman-Pearson lemma yields as optimum rejection region $T > c$ when c satisfies

$$\alpha = \text{Prob } (T > c \mid \lambda_0) = \int_c^\infty \frac{\lambda_0(\lambda_0 t)^{k-1} e^{-\lambda_0 t}}{(k-1)!} \, dt \qquad (7.6.35)$$

The integral above need not be evaluated directly, since, if T has an Erlang distribution (k, λ), then $2\lambda T$ has a χ^2 distribution with $2k$ degrees of freedom.[1]

We can now replace (7.6.35) with

$$\alpha = \text{Prob } (T > c \mid \lambda_0) = \text{Prob } (2\lambda_0 T > 2\lambda_0 c) = \text{Prob } (\chi^2 > 2\lambda_0 c)$$

This equation is satisfied when $2\lambda_0 c$ is $\chi^2_{1-\alpha, 2k}$, the upper $1 - \alpha$ percentile of the χ^2 distribution with $2k$ degrees of freedom.   The rejection region is then

$$T > \frac{\chi^2_{1-\alpha, 2k}}{2\lambda_0} \qquad (7.6.36)$$

The power of this test is

$$\pi(\lambda) = \text{Prob}\left(T > \frac{\chi^2_{1-\alpha, 2k}}{2\lambda_0} \,\Big|\, \lambda \right)$$

$$= \text{Prob}\left(2\lambda T > \frac{\lambda}{\lambda_0} \chi^2_{1-\alpha, 2k} \right) = \text{Prob}\left(\chi^2 > \frac{\lambda}{\lambda_0} \chi^2_{1-\alpha, 2k} \right) \qquad (7.6.37)$$

and can be evaluated with the use of χ^2 tables.   Note that the power is a function of the deviation of λ from λ_0 in terms of the ratio λ/λ_0.

The minimum k required to detect a deviation $\lambda_1 < \lambda_0$, with specified odds $1 - \beta$, is obtained by solving for k.   The relation

$$\pi(\lambda_1) = 1 - \beta = \text{Prob}\left(\chi^2 > \frac{\lambda_1}{\lambda_0} \chi^2_{1-\alpha, 2k} \right)$$

which is satisfied when

$$\frac{\lambda_1}{\lambda_0} \chi^2_{1-\alpha, 2k} = \chi^2_{\beta, 2k} \qquad (7.6.38)$$

The required k is found by comparing the ratio $\chi^2_{\beta, 2k}/\chi^2_{1-\alpha, 2k}$ with λ_1/λ_0 for successive values of k.

A simple approximation to the required k follows from the fact that the random variable T is represented by the sum of k independent random variables $X_1 + X_2 + \cdots + X_k$, since for large k, T is approximately normal.   In view of this fact,

$$k \cong \left(\frac{\lambda_0 Z_\beta - \lambda_1 Z_{1-\alpha}}{\lambda_1 - \lambda_0} \right)^2 \qquad (7.6.39)$$

---

[1] The argument for this result will not be developed here.   The interested reader may try Exercise 5.9, where a hint is provided.

We shall give a simple illustration of the determination of h and k, respectively. Suppose that $\lambda_0 = 4$, $\lambda_1 = 1$, $\alpha = 0.05$, and $1 - \beta = 0.90$. The minimum h required, such that the test of hypothesis expressed in (7.6.28) (for the given λ_0 and λ_1) is subject to the specified errors of the first and second, is, in accordance with (7.6.33), $h^* = 2.31$ (expressed in the same unit used to measure T). The minimum number of occurrences of the event (accidents, in our discussion) to be observed in order to test the hypothesis under the conditions specified above is $k^* = 5.20$. Are these two experiments equivalent? How can they be compared? The required time to perform the first experiment is 2.31 time units. How long, on the average, does the second form of the experiment take? The expected value of T, the duration of the experiment, is given by $E(T)$, which is found in Sec. 5.16 to be equal to k/λ. When $\lambda = \lambda_0$, $E(T \mid \lambda_0) = E(T \mid 4) = 5.20/4 = 1.30$ time units, considerably shorter than $h = 2.31$; on the other hand, when $\lambda = \lambda_1 = 1$, $E(T \mid 1) = 5.20/1 = 5.20$ time units, considerably longer than $h = 2.31$. The durations of the respective experiments do not provide a clear-cut basis of comparison of their effectiveness or efficiency. Other factors must be taken into consideration in order to make a meaningful comparison of the two experimental procedures.

In a manner similar to that developed for testing the one-sided alternative, one can test

$$H_0: \quad \lambda = \lambda_0 \qquad \text{against} \qquad H_1: \quad \lambda = \lambda_1 \neq \lambda_0$$

the two-sided alternative. Application of the likelihood-ratio procedure to the experimental procedure of observing the number of occurrences a of the specified event, during a fixed-time period of duration h time units, leads to a two-sided rejection region specified by two numbers k_1, k_2, $k_1 < k_2$ such that $a \leq k_1$ or $a > k_2$. Again, k_1 and k_2 are determined by specifying the significance level α. It will be an interesting exercise for the reader to develop the expression for the power function of this test as well as the expression for h^*, the minimum value of h required for detecting deviations greater than or equal to specified magnitudes, with given odds.

4 Comparing Two Poisson Distributions Suppose we begin by considering a test of a composite hypothesis against one-sided alternatives, namely,

$$H_0: \quad \lambda_1 - \lambda_2 = 0 \qquad \text{against} \qquad H_1: \quad \lambda_1 - \lambda_2 > 0 \qquad (7.6.40)$$

Our experimental procedure may consist in observing the number of specified events occurring during a given interval of h time units in duration for each of the Poisson processes, respectively. The exact treatment of this problem reaches rather beyond the scope of this text. On the other hand, as in section 2, it is possible so to transform the chance variable that in terms of the new chance variable a satisfactory approximation to the sought-after solution is obtained. In the new form the problem is essentially that of comparing means of two normal distributions, each with known variance.

Let us denote the results of observation in the original problem by a_1 and a_2, respectively, the numbers of events occurring for each of the processes during a given period h. We may consider a_1 and a_2 as representations of the chance variables of the original Poisson processes. We seek transformations to two new chance variables, X_1 and X_2, such that they are normally distributed and have a common known variance, independent of λ_1 and λ_2. Following the procedure in section 2, we find the transformations

$$X_1 = \sqrt{a_1} \qquad X_2 = \sqrt{a_2} \qquad (7.6.41)$$

commonly referred to as the square-root transformations. It may be reasonable to expect, since the Poisson distribution is asymptotically normal, and in the light of Theorem 4.7, that *if a has a Poisson distribution with mean λh for period h, then $X = \sqrt{a}$ has an approximately normal distribution with mean $\sqrt{\lambda h}$* and variance

$$V(X) = V(\sqrt{a}) \cong \left(\frac{1}{2\sqrt{a}}\right)^2_{a=\lambda h} V(a) = \frac{1}{4\lambda h}(\lambda h) = \frac{1}{4} \quad (7.6.42)$$

In terms of the new chance variables, the test of hypothesis proposed in (7.6.40) becomes

$$H_0: \quad m_1 - m_2 = \sqrt{\lambda_1} - \sqrt{\lambda_2} = 0$$

against $\qquad H_1: \quad m_1 - m_2 > 0 \qquad\qquad (7.6.43)$

This problem, studied in a previous section, has rejection region $X_1 - X_2 > c$, where c is determined by specifying α. Hence

$$\alpha = \text{Prob }(X_1 - X_2 > c \mid H_0) = \text{Prob}\left(\frac{X_1 - X_2}{\sqrt{\frac{1}{4} + \frac{1}{4}}} > \frac{c}{\sqrt{\frac{1}{4} + \frac{1}{4}}}\right)$$

$$\cong \text{Prob }(Z > c\sqrt{2}) \quad (7.6.44)$$

As a result, $c\sqrt{2} = Z_{1-\alpha}$ and $c = Z_{1-\alpha}/\sqrt{2}$.

The power of the test, $\pi(\lambda_1, \lambda_2)$, is

$$\pi(\lambda_1, \lambda_2) = \text{Prob}\left(X_1 - X_2 > \frac{Z_{1-\alpha}}{\sqrt{2}} \,\middle|\, m_1, m_2\right)$$

$$= \text{Prob}\left[\frac{X_1 - X_2 - (\sqrt{\lambda_1 h} - \sqrt{\lambda_2 h})}{1/\sqrt{2}}\right.$$

$$\left. > \frac{Z_{1-\alpha}/\sqrt{2} - (\sqrt{\lambda_1 h} - \sqrt{\lambda_2 h})}{1/\sqrt{2}}\right]$$

$$= \Phi\left[\sqrt{2h}(\sqrt{\lambda_1} - \sqrt{\lambda_2}) + Z_\alpha\right] \quad (7.6.45)$$

The minimum h to detect a deviation λ_1, λ_2 with odds $1 - \beta$ is obtained by setting $\pi(\lambda_1,\lambda_2)$ in (7.6.45) equal to $1 - \beta$ and solving for h. Carrying out this procedure leads to

$$h \cong \frac{1}{2}\left(\frac{Z_{1-\beta} - Z_\alpha}{\sqrt{\lambda_1} - \sqrt{\lambda_2}}\right)^2 \tag{7.6.46}$$

Had we so chosen, we could have used the alternative experimental procedure, namely, observe each of the processes 1 and 2 until, in each, k of the specified events have occurred, noting the times of occurrence T_1 and T_2 of the kth event in each case. This experimental procedure is quite satisfactory for the test of hypothesis presented in (7.6.40). Under these circumstances (see section 3), the two expressions $2\lambda_1 T_1$ and $2\lambda_2 T_2$ are representations of the essential random variables involved in the experiment. These random variables are independent, and each has a χ^2 distribution with $2k$ degrees of freedom. In view of this fact, the original test of hypotheses in (7.6.40) may be looked upon analogously to that of the comparison of the variances of two normal populations (part 2 of Sec. 7.5.4). The rejection region is then $c > T_1/T_2$, contingent upon significance level α.

Again, the ratio $(2\lambda_1 T_1/2k)/(2\lambda_2 T_2/2k)$ has an F distribution with $(2k,2k)$ degrees of freedom. Under $H_0: \lambda_1 = \lambda_2$, this ratio becomes T_1/T_2; whence, given significance level α, we have

$$\text{Prob}\left(\frac{T_1}{T_2} < c\right) = \alpha \qquad \text{and} \qquad c = F_{\alpha;2k,2k}$$

the upper α percentile of the F distribution with $(2k,2k)$ degrees of freedom.

The power of this test is given by

$$\pi(\lambda_1,\lambda_2) = \text{Prob}\left(\frac{T_1}{T_2} < F_{\alpha;2k,2k} \mid \lambda_1,\lambda_2\right)$$

$$= \text{Prob}\left(\frac{\lambda_1 T_1}{\lambda_2 T_2} < \frac{\lambda_1}{\lambda_2}F_{\alpha;2k,2k}\right) \tag{7.6.47}$$

The minimum value k^* of the rejection region required in order to detect a deviation represented by the ratio λ_1/λ_2 with odds $1 - \beta$ is obtained by solving

$$\frac{\lambda_1}{\lambda_2}F_{\alpha;2k,2k} = F_{1-\beta;2k,2k} \tag{7.6.48}$$

which results from setting $\pi(\lambda_1,\lambda_2) = 1 - \beta$, for k.

Determination of the rejection regions, the power functions, and the minimal h^* and k^* for testing H_0 against two-sided alternatives $H_1: \lambda_1 \neq \lambda_2$, for both experimental procedures, is left as an exercise for the reader.

7.7   Other tests related to χ^2

In the tests of hypothesis considered so far, the entities under test were usually parameters of a known distribution.   The experimental procedures were designed with the presumed distributions in mind.   It happens quite often, however, that in early stages of research, the nature of the distribution for some phenomenon is to be determined.   Or theoretical considerations lead to a distribution, and test of the theory indicates an experiment to determine the frequency distribution associated with the phenomenon being studied.   For example, in the creation of random numbers, the distribution of the integers 0, 1, . . . , 9 is supposedly uniform.   If these random numbers are to be used without incurring serious error, there must be some assurance that the actual numbers do possess a uniform distribution.   A test used is the following.   Select a reasonably long sequence of random digits, and test whether, in the resulting sample, Prob $(X = i) = \frac{1}{10}$ $(i = 0, 1, . . . , 9)$.   Here, in effect, we are to test the degree to which the resulting frequencies of the random digits approximate the theoretical frequencies, or the conformance of the observations to the theoretical distribution, namely, *goodness of fit.*

We shall consider some examples involving these tests which involve the χ^2 distribution.

Tests Involving the Multinomial Distribution   Testing random digits, or the so-called fair die, which requires less calculation, may be represented as follows.   Suppose that an experiment can result in k mutually exclusive outcomes $0_1, 0_2, . . . , 0_k$.   In the selection of random digits, $0_1 = 0, 0_2 = 1, . . . , 0_{10} = 9, k = 10$, and

$$\text{Prob } (X = 0_i) = \frac{1}{k} = \frac{1}{10}$$

For the fair die

$$\text{Prob } (X = 0_i) = \frac{1}{k} = \frac{1}{6}$$

In both cases, denote

$$\text{Prob } (X = 0_i) = p_i \qquad i = 1, 2, . . . , k; p_1 + p_2 + \cdot \cdot \cdot + p_k = 1$$
$$(7.7.1)$$

Suppose now that we consider an experiment, as above, in which there are k mutually exclusive outcomes 0_i, and let the experiment be repeated N times (each repetition independent of the others).   Let the numbers of occurrences of the k outcomes be representative of k independent random variables, namely, X_i = number of occurrences of 0_i $(i = 1, 2, . . . , k)$ among N random independent replications of the experiment.   In order to test the goodness of fit, we require the joint probability distribution of $X_1, X_2, \ldots, X_k$. The k-variate distribution can be built up from intuitively apparent "first principles" by starting with $k = 2$. Suppose now we consider a universe whose probabilities are specified as in (7.7.1), but we concentrate attention on O_1. The probability of an outcome of class O_1 by random independent selection is denoted by p_1; the random variable whose outcome is O_1 is denoted by X_1; the number of occurrences of O_1 in a sampling experiment is denoted by x_1. When we concentrate on O_1, let us consider any other outcomes, $O_2, O_3, \ldots, O_k$, as being all lumped together and denoted by O_0; thus we have chance variable X_0, and the number of occurrences of O_0 in a sampling procedure is denoted by x_0. Hence we can apply the binomial distribution to obtain the joint distribution of X_1, X_0. For the sake of simplicity, we shall express the joint distribution of the chance variables in the notation of their occurrences. Thus

$$p(x_1, x_0) = \frac{N!}{x_1!(N - x_1)!} p_1{}^{x_1}(1 - p_1)^{n - x_1} = \frac{N!}{x_1! x_0!} p_1{}^{x_1} p_0{}^{x_0} \quad (7.7.2)$$

Suppose now that we consider the $N - x_1$ occurrences among the outcomes $O_2, O_3, \ldots, O_k$ and concentrate on O_2, designating the lumped "other" outcomes, $O_3, O_4, \ldots, O_k$, again, by O_0. Following the method and notation used above, the conditional joint distribution of X_2, X_0 in $N - x_1$ independent random trials given $X_1 = x_1$ is

$$p(x_2, x_0 \mid x_1) = \frac{(N - x_1)!}{x_2!(N - x_1 - x_2)!}\left(\frac{p_2}{1 - p_1}\right)^{x_2}\left(\frac{p_0}{1 - p_1}\right)^{N - x_1 - x_2} \quad (7.7.3)$$

Suppose for the moment that $k = 3$; then

$$p(x_2, x_0 \mid x_1) = P(x_2, x_3 \mid x_1) = \frac{(N - x_1)!}{x_2! x_3!} \frac{p_2{}^{x_2} p_3{}^{x_3}}{(1 - p_1)^{N - x_1}} \quad (7.7.4)$$

Hence the joint distribution of X_1, X_2, X_3 is

$$p(x_1, x_2, x_3) = p(x_1)p(x_2, x_3 \mid x_1)$$
$$= \left[\frac{N!}{x_1!(N - x_1)!} p_1{}^{x_1}(1 - p_1)^{N - x_1}\right]\left[\frac{(N - x_1)!}{x_2! x_3!} \frac{p_2{}^{x_2} p_3{}^{x_3}}{(1 - p_1)^{N - x_1}}\right]$$
$$= \frac{N!}{x_1! x_2! x_3!} p_1{}^{x_1} p_2{}^{x_2} p_3{}^{x_3} \quad (7.7.5)$$

This is, of course, the multinomial distribution, and iteration of this procedure leads to the general distribution of possible outcomes,

$$p(x_1, x_2, \ldots, x_k) = \frac{N!}{x_1! x_2! \cdots x_k!} p_1{}^{x_1} p_2{}^{x_2} \cdots p_k{}^{x_k}$$

The coefficient of the probabilities on the right side of (7.7.5) is the number of different permutations of N things taken in groups of size

x_1, x_2, and x_3, where the things within a group are indistinguishable from one another but different from things in the other groups. The generalization to k distinct groups is direct. It may be well to review the derivation of the coefficient in the multinomial distribution, which expresses the number of ways in which a sample of N items can be formed into k groups of x_1, x_2, . . . , x_k items, respectively, in each group, where the items within a group are identical and the items of different groups are different from one another. First consider that each of the N items can be identified, presumably by one among the integers 1 to N. Such a sample could have been drawn in $N!$ different ways, since a particular arrangement of the N items represents a distinct realization of the N items. Hence the drawing of this sample could have occurred in $N!$ different ways. But now let the x_1 items of group 1 become identical and $x_1!$ of the arrangements of these x_1 items become identical, for the rearrangement of identical items in the same positions is indistinguishable. Hence we have only $N!/x_1!$ distinct arrangements. This argument applies to each of the remaining $k - 1$ groups. Hence, by iteration of the argument, we have, for the number of distinct realizations of random samples of N items in k different groups of x_1, x_2, . . . , x_k items, respectively,

$$C^N_{x_1, x_2, \ldots, x_k} = \frac{N!}{x_1! x_2! \ldots x_k!} \tag{7.7.6}$$

The reader will recognize (7.7.6) as the formula for the combination of N things taken x_1, x_2, . . . , x_k at a time.

Before undertaking tests of goodness of fit, we shall try two examples in the use of the multinomial distribution. In the first example we shall consider the "tossing" of the "fair" die, familiar to us from discussion in earlier chapters.

Example 7.7 A fair die has six faces, identified as 1, 2, 3, 4, 5, and 6. A die when tossed has six possible distinct outcomes, namely, faces showing i (i = 1, 2, . . . , 6) dots upward. A fair die is defined as one for which Prob (i) = $\frac{1}{6}$ upon random tossing. Whether or not there exists in reality a fair die is another matter. On the other hand, one may ask whether there is a "tossing" experiment whereby one can test the fairness of the die. It seems reasonable that a test of "fairness" is a test of conformance of outcomes of experiment to a given distribution. The perspective of testing whether or not the outcome of experiment conforms to a given distribution seems to be different from the previous tests we have studied. In those tests, we assumed the existence of a particular distribution (resulting from a specified experimental procedure) and sought procedures for deciding upon characteristics of the distribution such as means and variances. In goodness-of-fit tests, we question the distribution itself. Yet in order to carry out a formal statistical test about the distribution, we do, in fact, introduce the properties of the distribution. Before testing for goodness of fit, namely, the fairness of a die, we shall work out the probability for a number of die-tossing outcomes.

For any outcome i (face up with i dots), denote the number of occurrences of i among N tosses by X_i. Suppose we toss a die 6 times (the tosses are independent of one another) and ask, in how many different ways can the outcome $x_1 = 1$, $x_2 = 1$, $x_3 = 2$, $x_4 = 0$, $x_5 = 0$, $x_6 = 2$ occur? It would be an interesting exercise for the reader to try to enumerate them. We shall calculate this number by applying (7.7.6), namely,

$$C^6_{1,1,2,0,0,2} = \frac{6!}{1!1!2!0!0!2!}$$

Since $0! = 1$, the number we seek is $6 \cdot 5 \cdot 3 \cdot 2 = 180$. Again, in how many ways can two 5s, two 1s, one 6, and one 3 come up? This number is given by

$$C^6_{2,0,1,0,2,1} = \frac{6!}{2!1!2!1!}$$

It is obvious that, in any tossing of a fair die six times, a grouping of two different faces twice each and two different faces once each occurs in the same number of different ways, regardless of which of the faces come up.

Now suppose we ask, what is the probability of getting $X_1 = 1$, $X_2 = 1$, $X_3 = 2$, $X_4 = 0$, $X_5 = 0$, $X_6 = 2$ in a succession of 6 honest tosses of a fair die? From the multiplication theorem for independent events, it follows that any occurrence of six faces resulting from six tosses has the probability $(\frac{1}{6})^6$ of occurring. Since all the different ways of an outcome occurring are mutually exclusive, the probability of any one of them occurring is $(\frac{1}{6})^6$ summed as many times as there are different arrangements of the outcome. Hence, in the honest tossing of six fair dice,

$$p(x_1,x_2,x_3,x_4,x_5,x_6) = \frac{6!(\frac{1}{6})^6}{x_1!x_2!x_3!x_4!x_5!x_6!} \tag{7.7.7}$$

Therefore

Prob $(X_1 = 1, X_2 = 1, X_3 = 2, X_4 = 0, X_5 = 0, X_6 = 2)$
$$= p(1,1,2,0,0,2)$$
$$= \frac{6!}{1!1!2!0!0!2!} \left(\frac{1}{6}\right)^1 \left(\frac{1}{6}\right)^1 \left(\frac{1}{6}\right)^2 \left(\frac{1}{6}\right)^0 \left(\frac{1}{6}\right)^0 \left(\frac{1}{6}\right)^2$$
$$= \frac{6!}{4} \left(\frac{1}{6}\right)^6 = \frac{5}{1,296} \tag{7.7.8}$$

Note that the coefficient is the number of combinations of six things taken in groups of 1, 1, 2, 0, 0, 2 at a time.

Does the most probable outcome have any operational meaning? It is quite obvious that the most probable outcome is one for which the coefficient in (7.7.8) is a maximum and that this occurs when the denominator is its minimum.   But the minimum denominator occurs when each factor in the denominator is 1; this happens when each of the six faces turns up.   It is interesting that although an outcome of (1,1,1,1,1,1) can occur in 6! different arrangements, the probability of its occurrence is only 0.0154.   A most probable event need not be a frequent event.

In many situations, the relevance of the multinomial distribution is not direct, but arises from certain characteristics of the distributions of the phenomena under consideration.   We shall look at an example of such a situation.

Example 7.8   Dealers in electronic equipment seek some guarantee as to the "life" of the equipment.   The quantities of interest are the mean life, half mean life, and the period greater than mean life.   Lifetime is, of course, a random variable (when lifetime is statistically stable), and distributions of life of equipment are arrived at by various theoretical assumptions.   Suppose we have the CDF of the life of a particular item of electronic equipment characterized as follows:

$$\text{Prob } (L \le t) = 1 - e^{-t/6} \qquad (7.7.9)$$

where L is the random variable representing lifetime, and t is measured in months.   It can be readily shown that the mean lifetime is 6 months. We have these facts at our disposal.

The dealer would like some assurance that mean life is 6 months, where lifetime is exponentially distributed.   From a practical point of view, the probability of lifetime less than 3 months is important.   It is also desired to know the probability of a lifetime greater than the mean life.   This leads to characterizing the equipment in three groups:

$$L \le 3 \qquad 3 < L \le 6 \qquad 6 < L$$

The probabilities of the lifetime of a piece of this equipment falling into any of these groups provide a basis for an equipment dealer's decision to purchase this type of equipment.

The three desired probabilities are

$$p_1 = \text{Prob } (L \le 3) = 1 - e^{-3/6} = 0.394$$
$$p_2 = \text{Prob } (3 < L \le 6) = e^{-1/2} - e^{-1} = 0.238$$
$$p_3 = \text{Prob } (6 < L) = e^{-1} = 0.368$$

We can now define three chance variables X_1, X_2, X_3 associated with any lot of N pieces of this equipment such that X_i represents the number of pieces associated with the ith group.   Suppose now that a dealer bought six pieces of this item and found, after they had been sold and put into operation, that two failed before the end of the third month and two more failed before the end of the sixth month. What is the probability that the dealer would get six such pieces of equipment whose lifetimes were distributed two in group 1, two in group 2, and two in group 3? This question is not answerable in definite terms unless we add: provided that the manufacturer's production process was in statistical control and these six pieces were selected randomly. The desired result comes from a direct application of the multinomial distribution with probabilities $p_1 = 0.394$, $p_2 = 0.238$, and $p_3 = 0.368$ given above. Thus

$$\text{Prob } (X_1 = 2, X_2 = 2, X_3 = 2) = \frac{6!}{2!2!2!} (0.394)^2(0.238)^2(0.368)^2 = 0.177$$

The reader may exercise his own judgment as to whether or not the given lot could have come from the source as claimed. The probability of the occurrence of the observed sample may not be an adequate basis for deciding whether the sample came from a universe with distribution of lifetime Prob $(L \leq t) = 1 - e^{-t/6}$.

Goodness of Fit Suppose that, in Example 7.7, the outcomes of six casts resulted in (1,1,0,3,1,0). Should we "suspect" the die? On what basis could we infer that the die used in the experiment is fair or not? Should we examine the die with a magnifying glass, or should we try out the old adage "The proof of the pudding is in the eating"? Our interpretation of this old adage is that the fairness of a die is inferred from the outcomes of casting the die many times. What, then, can we say about the above results of six casts? What characterizes a fair die? As we have specified above, the fair die is one whose outcomes upon N repeated casts have the same probability of occurrence. This is, specifically, the probability that the outcome of any cast is i, where $i = 1$, 2, . . . , 6, is $p_i = \frac{1}{6}$. But this is precisely the probability distribution of the chance variable X_i, where X_i is the number of outcomes with face i upward in N casts. Hence, in order to test whether or not a die is fair is equivalent to testing the hypothesis $H_0 : p_1 = p_2 = \cdots = p_6 = \frac{1}{6}$, under the conditions of the casting experiment. Another way to express this thought is that we wish to test how well the distribution of outcomes fits the multinomial distribution, which is the formal probability distribution of repeated casting of a fair die with k faces. This type of test is called goodness of fit.

In Example 7.8 we measured outcomes in terms of the length of time that an operating item survived. We divided the time scale into three parts: 3 months or less, greater than 3 months but less than or equal to 6 months, and greater than 6 months. Each of these three survival-time categories may be considered to be an event among the outcomes of the experiment of putting an item into operation whose probabilities of survival are determined from a supposed exponential lifetime distribution. Thus, if N "identical" items have been put into operation and the numbers whose survival times fall into each of the three time categories and are denoted, respectively, by (x_1, x_2, x_3), where $x_1 + x_2 + x_3 = N$, we can raise the legitimate and often practical question, shall we (under the conditions and assumptions of the experiment) accept the hypothesis that $p_1 = 0.394$, $p_2 = 0.238$, $p_3 = 0.368$, on the basis of the outcomes of the experiment?   Again, we are testing a hypothesis about whether or not to believe in a given probability distribution of outcomes.

Looking at problems of this type in more general terms, we are making a test of hypothesis

$$H_0: \quad p_i = p_{i0} \quad (i = 1, 2, \ldots, k) \qquad \text{against} \qquad H_1: \quad H_0 \text{ is false}$$
$$(7.7.10)$$

We have as the parameter space Ω all points $(p_1, p_2, \ldots, p_k)$ such that $0 \leq p_i \leq 1$ and $p_1 + p_2 + \cdots + p_k = 1$.   If $k = 3$, it is apparent that

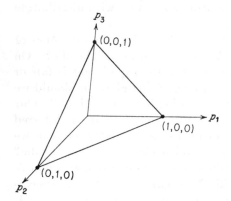

Figure 7.12

Ω is a plane in a Euclidean 3-space, passing through $(1,0,0)$, $(0,1,0)$, and $(0,0,1)$, and that the null hypothesis H_0 asserts that (p_{10}, p_{20}, p_{30}) is a particular point on this plane (Fig. 7.12).   For k any positive integer, Ω is a $(k - 1)$ dimensional hyperplane and the null hypothesis H_0 refers to a point $(p_{10}, p_{20}, \ldots, p_{k0})$ on Ω.   This point is designated by W, which, in general, is some subset of Ω.

In order to derive an effective test, we shall follow the likelihood-ratio procedure, assuming N observations and k categories.   It follows directly, then, if the probability of occurrence in the ith category is denoted by p_i, that the sample $(x_1, x_2, \ldots, x_k)$, where $x_1 + x_2 + \cdots + x_k = N$, has likelihood

$$L(x_1, x_2, \ldots, x_k) = \frac{N!}{x_1! x_1! \cdots x_k!} p_1{}^{x_1} p_2{}^{x_2} \ldots p_k{}^{x_k} \quad (7.7.11)$$

Finding the maximum of L with respect to the probabilities can be done simply with the aid of Lagrange multipliers, but we shall try direct elementary methods.   It is apparent, however, from the multiplicative form of the variables of differentiation in (7.7.11) that some condition on the p_i must be introduced in order to avoid the meaningless result $p_i = \infty$. The p_i are, fortunately, restricted by the relation $p_1 + p_2 + \cdots + p_k = 1$, so that we can let $p_k = 1 - p_1 - p_2 - \cdots - p_k$. Even so, the manipulations are clumsy, and we shall resort to the maximum of $\ln L$, which occurs at the same value of p_i as does the maximum of L. Taking the natural logarithm of (7.7.11), we have

$$\ln L = \sum_{i=1}^{k-1} x_i \ln p_i + x_k \ln (1 - p_1 - p_2 - \cdots - p_{k-1})$$

$$+ \ln N! - \sum_{i=1}^{k} \ln x_i!$$

and

$$\frac{\partial \ln L}{\partial p_i} = \frac{x_i}{p_i} - \frac{x_k}{p_k} \qquad i = 1, 2, \ldots, k-1$$

Setting each partial first derivative of $\ln L$ equal to zero, we obtain

$$\frac{x_i}{p_i} = \frac{x_k}{p_k} \qquad i = 1, 2, \ldots, k \tag{7.7.12}$$

But the solutions given in (7.7.12) say that the frequencies with which the various categories occur in the sample are proportional to their probabilities of occurrence as determined by the universe from which the random sample was drawn. This result for maximum L on Ω is intuitively reasonable.

We can reduce this result to an elegant form by making use of the theorem: the sum of the numerators divided by the sum of the denominators of any number of equal fractions is equal to the value of the original fraction. Hence, given

$$\frac{x_i}{p_i} = \text{constant} \ (i = 1, 2, \ldots, k) \qquad \frac{x_1 + x_2 + \cdots + x_k}{p_1 + p_2 + \cdots + p_k} = \frac{N}{1} = \frac{x_i}{p_i}$$

or

$$p_i = \frac{x_i}{N} \qquad i = 1, 2, \ldots, k$$

Making this substitution in (7.7.11), we obtain

$$\max_{\Omega} L = \frac{N!}{x_1! x_2! \cdots x_k!} \left(\frac{x_1}{N}\right)^{x_1} \left(\frac{x_2}{N}\right)^{x_2} \cdots \left(\frac{x_k}{N}\right)^{x_k} \tag{7.7.13}$$

The maximum of L over W, which consists only of $(p_{10}, p_{20}, \ldots, p_{k0})$, is

$$\max_{W} L = \frac{N!}{x_1! x_2! \cdots x_k!} p_{10}{}^{x_1} p_{20}{}^{x_2} \cdots p_{k0}{}^{x_k}$$

obtained by substituting p_{i0} for p_i. Thus the likelihood ratio is

$$\lambda = \frac{\max\limits_{W} L}{\max\limits_{\Omega} L} = \left(\frac{Np_{10}}{x_1}\right)^{x_1} \left(\frac{Np_{20}}{x_2}\right)^{x_2} \cdots \left(\frac{Np_{k0}}{x_k}\right)^{x_k} \qquad (7.7.14)$$

Recall that the null hypothesis is rejected when λ is too small, or equivalently when $-2 \ln \lambda$ is too large. We require, then, the distribution of

$$-2 \ln \lambda = 2 \sum_{i=1}^{k} x_i \ln \frac{x_i}{Np_{i0}} \qquad (7.7.15)$$

Since, however, the exact distribution of $-2 \ln \lambda$ is very difficult to compute, we resort to the fact that (see Sec. 7.4.3), under H_0, $-2 \ln \lambda$ has asymptotically a χ^2 distribution with degrees of freedom equal in number to the difference between the dimensions of Ω and W, which in the present case is $k - 1$. We use the $1 - \alpha$ percentile of χ^2 with $k - 1$ degrees of freedom, since then, when

$$-2 \ln \lambda = \sum_{i=1}^{k} x_i \ln \frac{x_i}{Np_{i0}} \geq \chi^2_{1-\alpha,k-1} \qquad (7.7.16)$$

the probability of rejecting H_0 when it is true is α per cent or less. As stated before, it seems intuitively reasonable, when H_0 is true, that x_i/N is a "good" estimate of p_{i0}. Hence, when H_0 is true, $\ln (x_i/Np_{i0})$ is small and a lower bounded rejection region on $-2 \ln \lambda$ is reasonable. It might be added that the χ^2 approximation is rather good, even for moderate-size N, so long as $k > 2$.

The test just discussed seems to be an *ad hoc* application of the likelihood-ratio procedure, valid under the conditions obtaining, but yet intuitively suggestive. Karl Pearson suggested measuring the discrepancy between the sample results x_i and the consequences of "true" probabilities p_{i0}, in a rather intuitively direct manner, by taking the differences $x_i - Np_{i0}$. In order to obtain a measure whose distribution was not to be influenced by the size of N, that is to say, in order that N not be a parameter of the distribution which was to reflect departure from H_0, he chose as the element of the measure $(x_i - Np_{i0})/\sqrt{Np_{i0}}$, forming the function

$$Y = \sum_{i=1}^{k} \left(\frac{x_i - Np_{i0}}{\sqrt{Np_{i0}}}\right)^2 = \sum_{i=1}^{k} \frac{(x_i - Np_{i0})^2}{Np_{i0}} \qquad (7.7.17)$$

Intuitively, it seems proper to reject H_0 when Y is too large. Fortunately, when H_0 is true, Y is distributed approximately as χ^2 with $k - 1$

degrees of freedom. In fact, testing the H_0 type of hypothesis—goodness of fit—with function Y is equivalent to testing with $-2 \ln \lambda$ for large N.

In general, the following procedure is used in testing goodness of fit. There is assumed a distribution; there are k events or categories of occurrence; the expected number of occurrence E_i in category i is derived from knowledge of the distribution and the total number of occurrences N. The actual number of occurrences x_i, resulting from experiment, in each category i is observed. Then the random variable

$$Y = \sum_{i=1}^{k} \frac{(x_i - E_i)^2}{E_i}$$

is formed. Under the null hypothesis, for large N, Y has the χ^2 distribution for $k - 1$ degrees of freedom. Reject H_0 when Y is greater than $\chi^2_{1-\alpha, k-1}$.

The equivalence of $-2 \ln \lambda$ and Y can be readily established by making use of the expansion of the natural logarithm about unity. The general term

$$x_i \ln \frac{x_i}{N p_{i0}}$$

can be modified by the device of adding and subtracting the denominator and the numerator, yielding

$$x_i \ln \frac{x_i + N p_{i0} - N p_{i0}}{N p_{i0}} = x_i \ln (1 + \Delta_i) \qquad \text{where } \Delta_i = \frac{x_i - N p_{i0}}{N p_{i0}}$$

$$(7.7.18)$$

whence

$$-2 \ln \lambda = \sum_{i=1}^{k} x_i \ln (1 + \Delta_i) \qquad (7.7.19)$$

But $x_i = N p_{i0}(1 + \Delta_i)$, so that

$$-2 \ln \lambda = \sum_{i=1}^{k} N p_{i0}(1 + \Delta_i) \ln (1 + \Delta_i) \qquad (7.7.20)$$

Since under H_0 we may expect Δ_i to be small for large N, we may develop the sum in (7.7.20) on the assumption that Δ_i is small. But for small Δ_i, $\ln (1 + \Delta_i) \cong \Delta_i$, and therefore

$$-2 \ln \lambda \cong \sum_{i=1}^{k} N p_{i0}(1 + \Delta_i)\Delta_i = \sum_{i=1}^{k} N p_{i0}\Delta_i + \sum_{i=1}^{k} N p_{i0}\Delta_i^2 \quad (7.7.21)$$

Examining each sum in (7.7.21), we find that the second sum is positive but that the first sum is

$$\sum_{i=1}^{k} N p_{i0}\Delta_i = \sum_{i=1}^{k} (x_i - N p_{i0}) = 0$$

Thus (7.7.21) reduces to

$$-2 \ln \lambda \cong \sum_{i=1}^{k} N p_{i0} \Delta_i{}^2 = \sum_{i=1}^{k} \frac{(x_i - N p_{i0})^2}{N p_{i0}} \tag{7.7.22}$$

the equivalence it was desired to establish.

A few examples will help one appreciate the value of the procedure developed for testing goodness of fit.

Example 7.9 We wish to test a die by casting it many times. Suppose that, in an actual experiment consisting of 600 casts, the following distribution of occurrences resulted: (100,100,115,110,90,85). Should we consider this to be evidence of a fair die? (We must, of course, assume some value for α, say, 10 per cent.)

It is apparent that we want to test

$$H_0: \quad p_1 = p_2 = \cdots = p_6 = \tfrac{1}{6} \quad \text{against} \quad H_1: \quad H_0 \text{ is not true}$$

Following the procedure just developed, we form

$$Y = \frac{(100 - 100)^2}{100} + \frac{(100 - 100)^2}{100} + \frac{(115 - 100)^2}{100}$$
$$+ \cdots + \frac{(85 - 100)^2}{110} = 6.50$$

For significance level $\alpha = 0.10$, the rejection region is $Y > \chi^2_{0.90,5} = 9.24$. On the basis of the present evidence, it is not reasonable to reject H_0 at the 0.10 significance level. On the other hand, were the results (100,90,115,120,90,85), Y would equal 10.50 and H_0 should be rejected on this new evidence. An interesting "intuitive" question is, what is less likely, (100,80,115,115,95,95) or (90,90,115,115,95,95)? It is quite obvious that the former is less likely since 20^2 is greater than $10^2 + 10^2$. The meaning of this is that the "likelihood" of deviations in outcomes from expected values is inversely proportional to the square of the deviations.

Example 7.10 A certain type of equipment is supposed to be subject to random failure, and not influenced by wear-out effects. Furthermore, recovery is assumed to be so rapid (circuit breaker reset, broken thread tied, and the like) that the mean failure rate is unaltered over a long period of time. The producer of this equipment claims that for a given battery installation the number of failures per year is 24.

A manufacturer using this equipment decides to test these assumptions by a year's operation. He decides to measure the failure rate by 2-month periods and make a goodness-of-fit test. Assuming that his observed failures X_i during the six 2-month periods are (5,7,4,5,2,1), is it reasonable to assume that the deviations of the actual 2-month failure rates from the expected 2-month failure rates were owing to chance?

Again we test

$$H_0: \quad EX_1 = EX_2 = \cdots = EX_6 = 4 \qquad \text{against} \qquad H_1: \quad H_0 \text{ is not true}$$

at the $\alpha = 0.10$ significance level. As before, form

$$Y = \frac{(5 - 4)^2}{4} + \frac{(7 - 4)^2}{4} + \cdots + \frac{(1 - 4)^2}{4} = 6.00$$

H_0 is not unlikely since $\chi^2_{0.90,5} = 9.24$.

The reader may wish to test the assumptions about this equipment in another way.

Example 7.11 Suppose we try to test at $\alpha = 0.05$ the goodness of fit of the exponential distribution given in Example 7.8 by operating 100 pieces of equipment. Recall that we considered failure before 3 months, between 3 and 6 months, and after 6 months. The probabilities of failure were found to be $p_1 = 0.394$, $p_2 = 0.238$, and $p_3 = 0.368$. If now there were 47 failures during the first 3 months of operation, 28 failures during the next 3 months, and 25 failures thereafter, is it reasonable that the probability of failure should be represented by the assumed exponential distribution?

As before,

$$Y = \frac{(47 - 39.4)^2}{39.4} + \frac{(25 - 23.8)^2}{23.8} + \frac{(28 - 36.8)^2}{36.8} = 3.56$$

which is much less than $\chi^2_{0.95,2} = 5.99$, and the null hypothesis $H_0: p = 0.394$, $p = 0.238$, and $p = 0.368$ is not rejected.

EXERCISES

7.1. The purpose of this experiment was to estimate the change in yield of adenosine triphosphate from rabbit muscle when a certain part of the extraction was carried out at two temperatures, T_1 and T_2. The extraction was carried out at the two temperatures on muscle tissue from each side of each animal. The units of yield have been coded.

Rabbit	Yield	
	T_1	T_2
1	5.1	4.0
2	8.7	7.2
3	6.8	7.2
4	7.0	5.7
5	3.2	2.0
6	10.8	8.9
7	7.8	7.0
8	8.7	7.4
9	9.5	7.2

a. Test for a difference in yield at the two temperatures (use a significance level $\alpha = 0.05$).   Use normal assumption.
b. What is the result in (a) when the sign test is used?
c. Indicate the improvement in the sensitivity of the experiment due to pairing. Express the improvement as the ratio of the number of experiments with no pairing to that required with pairing.
d. Estimate the number of rabbits that will be required in a new experiment (at different temperatures) in order to be 95 per cent certain of detecting a real difference of 0.5 unit.
e. Draw the estimated power curve for paired and unpaired normal test and sign test (under normal alternatives).   (Use estimated σ.)
f. What are the odds for getting a difference in yield as large as that in the experiment where there is no difference in mean yield?

7.2. Suppose that a rule is to be found for testing the hypothesis, for the standard deviation σ of a normal distribution on the basis of n independent observations, $H_0: \sigma = 6$ against alternative $H_1: \sigma = 10$.

If H_0 is accepted when true, a profit of $1 results.
If H_0 is rejected when true, a profit of $-$2 results.
If H_1 is accepted when true, a profit of $3 results.
If H_1 is rejected when true, a profit of $-$1 results.

a. Determine the errors of types I and II so that the expected profit will be at least positive no matter whether H_0 or H_1 is true.
b. Determine a plan that satisfies (a).

7.3. Suppose a random variable X has density function $f(x)$, where

$$f(x) = \begin{cases} \dfrac{1}{b} & 0 \le x \le b \\ 0 & \text{otherwise} \end{cases}$$

The parameter b is unknown, and it is desired to test $H_0: b = 1$ against $H_1: b < 1$. Use the following test.   Take two independent observations X_1 and X_2 and reject H_0 if max $(X_1, X_2) < \frac{3}{4}$.   Derive the power function of the rule.

7.4. A milk distributor claims that the milk sold by his company contains on the average 0.0110 pound of butterfat per quart.   A research laboratory checks this claim by taking random samples.   It is known that the standard deviation of butterfat for this distributor is 0.0012 pound.

a. The laboratory takes a random sample of 16 quarts and finds an arithmetic average of 0.0108 pound of butterfat.   Would you conclude that the distributor's claim was false?   (Use a significance level $\alpha = 0.1$.)
b. What is error of type II if the true mean equals 0.0105?
c. How big a sample is needed to make the answer in (b) equal 0.01?

7.5. A random variable X can take on the values 1, 2, 3, 4, 5, and 6.   We wish to test the hypothesis H_0 against H_1 where:

X	Probability under H_0	Probability under H_1
1	$\frac{1}{6}$	$\frac{1}{12}$
2	$\frac{1}{6}$	$\frac{1}{6}$
3	$\frac{1}{6}$	$\frac{1}{4}$
4	$\frac{1}{6}$	$\frac{1}{4}$
5	$\frac{1}{6}$	$\frac{1}{6}$
6	$\frac{1}{6}$	$\frac{1}{12}$

On the basis of one observation, X, the following test is given. If $X = 1$ or 6, reject H_0; otherwise accept H_0.

    a. What is the error of type I using the test?
    b. What is the power of the test?
    c. Give another test with the same type I error but with greater power.

7.6. It is required to compare the effect of two dyes on cotton fibers. A random sample of 10 pieces of yarn were chosen; 5 pieces were treated with dye A, and 5 with dye B. The results were:

Dye A	4 5 8 8 10
Dye B	6 2 9 4 5

    a. Test the significance of the difference between the two dyes. (Assume normality, common variance, and significance level $\alpha = 0.05$.)
    b. How big a sample do you estimate would be needed to detect a difference equal to 0.5 with probability 99 per cent?
    c. Comment on the choice of sampling procedure for this experiment.
    d. Draw the power curve of the test against the mean difference, using the estimate of σ^2 from the experiment.
    e. What are the odds for getting a difference of at least that of the experiment when H_0 is true?

7.7. An inspector inspects an item. The item is either defective or good. He accepts or rejects the item. The following is a table of appropriate profits.

	Good	Defective
Accepts	10	-20
Rejects	-5	0

Suppose on a single test we have the following probabilities:

	Good	Defective
Probability of item appearing good	0.8	0.3

Consider the following two rules:

>Rule 1: Carry out one test.   Accept if the item appears good and reject otherwise.
>Rule 2: Carry out two tests.   Accept only if the item appears good on both tests.

>*a.* Evaluate rules 1 and 2.
>*b.* Suppose the cost of a test is $C = 3$.   What sort of considerations would be relevant for deciding on the number of tests to make and the acceptance procedure to use?

7.8. Accidental deaths from motor vehicles were 73 in Connecticut in the first quarter of 1955 and 64 over the same period of time in 1956.   A safety campaign was conducted in the last quarter of 1955.   Do the figures give grounds for attributing the decrease to the safety campaign?

7.9. A large corporation has the following accident record for the four quarters of a particular year:

Quarter	No. of disabling injuries	Million man-hours of exposure
1	70	0.528
2	16	0.561
3	23	0.632
4	19	0.606

Would you conclude that accidents were uniformly distributed from quarter to quarter?

7.10. On the basis of two observations (taken at no cost), it must be decided whether a lot of light bulbs contains 5 per cent defectives or 20 per cent defectives.

If it is decided that the lot contains 5 per cent defective bulbs and it actually has 20 per cent, a loss of $1,000 occurs.   On the other hand, if the decision is made that the lot contains 20 per cent defective bulbs when it actually has only 5 per cent, the loss is $500.   For any correct decision assume a zero loss.

>*a.* List several decision rules for this problem, and comment on the relevant questions involved in choosing between these rules.
>*b.* Let E_R (loss | 0.05) and E_R (loss | 0.20) be the expected loss, for any rule R, where the per cent defectives are 0.05 and 0.20, respectively.   What are the values of these expectations for the rules you suggested in (*a*)?
>*c.* It is decided to choose the best rule such that E_R (loss | 0.05) $= E_R$ (loss | 0.20). This is called the minimax criterion.   What is the best rule under this condition?
>*d.* Suppose now that each observation costs $50 and there is no restriction on the number of observations.   We wish to make E_R (loss | 0.05) $= E_R$ (loss | 0.20) [as in (*c*)].   What is the best decision rule?   Find the optimum number of observations and optimum rule.

7.11. Suppose $X_1, X_2, \ldots, X_n$ are independent Poisson random variables with means $\lambda_1, \lambda_2, \ldots, \lambda_n$, respectively.   Let $T = X_1 + X_2 + \cdots + X_n$ and $\lambda = \lambda_1 + \lambda_2 + \cdots + \lambda_n$.   Show that the conditional distribution of $X_1, X_2, \ldots, X_n$ under the condition $T = k$ is multinomial with parameter k and probabilities λ_1/λ, $\lambda_2/\lambda, \ldots, \lambda_n/\lambda$.

7.12. Suppose we have n independent observations each from k populations. Rank the nk observations from 1 to nk. Let $R_1, R_2, \ldots, R_k$ be the sums of the ranks from the k populations.

- *a.* Find $E(R_i)$ $(i = 1, 2, \ldots, k)$ when all the k populations are the same.
- *b.* Use the result of (*a*) to derive a test for the hypothesis that the populations are the same. (HINT: Use goodness-of-fit procedure and asymptotic distribution of $-2 \ln \lambda$.)

7.13. Using a sampling plan $S(n,c)$ with $n = 100$, $c = 3$:

- *a.* Find the operating characteristic curve.
- *b.* Find the expected loss function $L(p)$, using losses as specified in Table 7.2.

7.14. Refer to Example 7.2. Let $\theta_0 = 0.02$, $\theta_1 = 0.01$, $T = 10$ weeks, and $n = 30$ items.

- *a.* Find the rejection region when $\alpha = 0.10$ (use normal approximation to the binomial).
- *b.* Find the error of the second kind for the procedure found in (*a*).
- *c.* Do same as in (*a*) and (*b*) for the experiment in Example 7.3 and compare.
- *d.* Do same as in (*a*) and (*b*) for an experiment where the time until the first failure is observed.

7.15. Consider testing the null hypotheses H_0: $\lambda = \lambda_0$ against the alternative $\lambda < \lambda_0$ for a Poisson distribution, where λ denotes the mean rate per unit time at which events occur.

One experiment for testing H_0 is to observe the number of events a which occur in time interval $[0,h]$. Let $\lambda_0 = 4$, $\alpha = 0.05$.

- *a.* Describe the test procedure when $h = 2$ and 6.
- *b.* Plot the power function for $h = 2$ and 6.

Another experiment for testing H_0 is to observe the time T until k events occur. Again, let $\lambda_0 = 4$ and $\alpha = 0.05$.

- *c.* Find the test procedure where $k = 5$ and 10.
- *d.* Plot the power functions for $k = 5$ and 10.
- *e.* Plot $E(T \mid \lambda)$ as a function of λ for $k = 5$ and 10, where $E(T \mid \lambda)$ denotes the expected duration of the experiment when the true mean equals λ.
- *f.* Compare the two types of experiment.

7.16. An experiment concerning emotionality and perceptual defense was conducted by E. McGinnies (*Psychological Review*, 1949). Sixteen subjects were shown words of two types on a screen. The two types were neutral words and critical words. Examples of neutral words used are "dance," "child," "glass." Examples of critical emotionally toned words are "raped," "whore," "kotex," "penis." Emotionality in this experiment was measured in terms of galvanic skin response by a microammeter. Also, a threshold for recognition was established for each word presented to a subject. These thresholds were determined by exposing the stimulus word at various intervals of time until it was correctly reported by the subject. In the table shown in the article are given results of the experiment in terms of the mean microammeter reading during *prerecognition* exposures and the mean threshold of recognition.

Observer	Mean microammeter reading during prerecognition exposures		Mean threshold of recognition	
	Neutral words	Critical words	Neutral words	Critical words
1	37.80	40.46	0.055	0.184
2	40.96	41.53	0.044	0.094
3	39.31	42.06	0.054	0.080
4	38.34	40.80	0.103	0.126
5	41.48	43.76	0.040	0.064
6	41.41	47.08	0.070	0.130
7	40.75	39.94	0.057	0.104
8	39.98	42.85	0.063	0.076
9	39.44	42.68	0.059	0.130
10	40.02	42.71	0.049	0.223
11	39.88	41.55	0.046	0.077
12	41.27	44.02	0.057	0.091
13	40.56	41.37	0.033	0.037
14	40.19	41.42	0.034	0.054
15	40.85	40.63	0.046	0.056
16	40.83	41.84	0.036	0.046

a. Analyze the results and interpret.   Justify your assumptions.
b. What would be the results using a sign test?
c. Estimate the power functions for paired and unpaired experimentation in this case.
d. What are the odds for getting differences as large as in this experiment when there are no mean differences in response to neutral and critical words?
e. Test for the difference in the variability of response for the subjects with respect to neutral and critical words.   Do this both for microammeter and threshold responses.

7.17. For the data in Exercise 7.6, test the equality of variability of the results for dye A and dye B (assume normality).

7.18. Two machines, A and B, are being compared in terms of their probabilities of turning out defectives.   One hundred items were made with each machine, resulting in eight and three defectives on machine A and B, respectively.   Is their significance evidence that the machines are different?

7.19. A coin is tossed 60 times, resulting in 38 heads.   Is the coin "fair"?

7.20. Prove Eq. (7.6.18).

8

ESTIMATION

In the preceding chapter we were concerned with testing hypotheses involving distributions. In particular, our concern was, typically, with making decisions about parameters of distributions. For example, in Sec. 7.5.1 the problem entailed deciding whether the mean m of a normal distribution was equal to a standard value m_0 or not. In Sec. 7.5.3 the question raised was deciding whether $m_1 - m_2 = 0$ or $m_1 > m_2$ was "true."

In this chapter the concern will be with *estimating* the parameters of distributions. Rather than attempt to decide whether m equals m_0 or not, we shall focus on estimating the value of m. The aim is to construct and study *estimators* of the parameters to learn how "near" we can expect them to be to the parameters being estimated. It will be part of our task to explicate the various interpretations of "nearness" which are possible. This will entail some discussion of the various criteria in terms of which estimators can be compared.

The distinction between hypothesis testing and estimation is not meant to be a rigid one, but is made in part for convenience and in part because the purposes to which they are put are somewhat different. The relationship between estimation and hypothesis testing will be explored.

We distinguish between point and interval estimation. *Point* estimators attempt to estimate, from the data, the value of the parameter. *Interval* estimators, on the other hand, construct intervals, from the data which contain the value of the parameter, with specified odds.

We may further explore the distinction between estimation and hypothesis testing by considering the case of a scientist who has deduced from some theoretical considerations the probability structure of some phenomenon, such as frequency of certain gene combinations in heredity, breaking-strength properties of some material, and the like. He may wish to collect data in order to put the theory to test. On the other hand, another scientist may, in certain circumstances, wish to estimate constants in his theoretical descriptions which he may later use to make deductions concerning some phenomena. It is more convenient to analyze the first of the above two types of circumstances in terms of hypothesis testing, and the latter in terms of estimation.

Another example of the sort of distinction we wish to make is exemplified by the machine-purchase problem in Sec. 6.5.1. We recall that purchase was indicated when the mean number of defects per unit, C', of the new proposed machine was less than 3 ($C' < 3$) and not otherwise. Thus we are basically concerned with *testing* whether the parameter was in one region ($0 \leq C' < 3$) or in another ($C' \geq 3$). Each region implies a suitable decision as to purchase. On the other hand, we might be faced with a problem (e.g., optimum machine utilization, scheduling, etc.) where the concern is primarily to *estimate* the value of C'. In the first case, it does not make any difference to our decision whether $C' = 5$ or 8, since in any case of $C' > 3$ the decision is not to purchase. (If we were concerned about the power of the test, however, we should consider the difference between $C' = 3$ or $C' = 8$.) For other purposes, it may be very important to distinguish between, say, $C' = 5$ or $C' = 8$. Although the two types of problem are related, as will be shown, it is nevertheless advantageous to make a distinction between them, since the focus of interest is quite different.

The two approaches have, in recent years, been more unified by the introduction of the concept of loss functions. The distinctions are then basically indicated by differences in the loss functions reflecting differences in aim. In this chapter we discuss, without extensive detail, some aspects of point and interval estimation.

8.1 Point estimation

In this section we present some methods of constructing point estimators, their properties, and various criteria for evaluating the relative merits of different estimators.

Suppose that the outcome of an experiment can be described in terms of a random variable X with CDF $F(x; \theta_1, \theta_2, \ldots, \theta_k)$, where θ_1, $\theta_2, \ldots, \theta_k$ are unknown parameters, which may, however, be known to lie within a specified region. For example, if X is the number of telephone calls occurring in T seconds, then X may have a Poisson distribution with mean λT (λ is the mean number of calls per second). In this case $\lambda T \geq 0$.

In general, it is desired to make inferences about some or all of the parameters $\theta_1, \theta_2, \ldots, \theta_k$. Again, sometimes a *parametric function* $v(\theta_1, \theta_2, \ldots, \theta_k)$ of the parameters is of interest. For the purpose of making the required inferences we try N-fold independent repetitions of an experiment. The outcomes of these repetitions can be described in terms of N independent random variables $X_1, X_2, \ldots, X_N$, each with the same *CDF*. As in previous chapters, the results of any particular N repetitions, the observations $(x_1, x_2, \ldots, x_N)$, constitute the sample data. On the basis of these N observations, we wish to make inferences about the parameters.

A *point estimator* of $v(\theta_1, \theta_2, \ldots, \theta_k) = \theta$ is a function of the data, represented by $S(X_1, X_2, \ldots, X_N)$. After any particular N repetitions, resulting in sample $(x_1, x_2, \ldots, x_N)$, the point estimate of θ is then given by $S(x_1, x_2, \ldots, x_N)$. It is clear that $S(X_1, X_2, \ldots, X_N)$ is a random variable since it depends on the outcome of the N repetitions of an experiment and is a function of $X_1, X_2, \ldots, X_N$.

The estimator S is sometimes called a *statistic*. In order that $S(X_1, X_2, \ldots, X_N)$ may serve as an estimator of θ, it should yield a value for θ which is "near" to the "true" value of θ. The sense in which the term near is used is to be specified. We shall study some point estimators for parameters of important distributions, such as the normal, binomial, and Poisson, as well as various criteria of "nearness."

8.1.1 Properties of point estimators

Bias, Mean-square Error, Closeness, and Consistency A first question concerning any estimator $S(X_1, X_2, \ldots, X_N)$ for θ is whether it gives, *on the average*, the "true" value of θ. That is, we wish to look at the expected value $E[S(X_1, X_2, \ldots, X_N) \mid \theta_1, \theta_2, \ldots, \theta_k]$ (which naturally depends on $\theta_1, \theta_2, \ldots, \theta_k$) and compare it with θ. Any difference between them, called the bias of the estimator, is denoted by $B(S \mid \theta_1, \theta_2, \ldots, \theta_k)$.

Definition: bias of an estimator The *bias* of an estimator $S(X_1, X_2, \ldots, X_N)$ of θ is given by

$$B[S(X_1, \ldots, X_N) \mid \theta_1, \theta_2, \ldots, \theta_k] \equiv B(S \mid \theta_1, \theta_2, \ldots, \theta_k)$$
$$= E[S(X_1, \ldots, X_N) \mid \theta_1, \theta_2, \ldots, \theta_k] - \theta \quad (8.1.1)$$

When the bias is zero for all $\theta_1, \theta_2, \ldots, \theta_k$, the estimator is said to be unbiased.

Definition: unbiasedness of an estimator The estimator $S(X_1, X_2, \ldots, X_N)$ is said to be *unbiased* when

$$B(S \mid \theta_1, \theta_2, \ldots, \theta_k) = 0 \quad \text{for all } \theta_1, \theta_2, \ldots, \theta_k \quad (8.1.2)$$

This definition is equivalently expressed by

$$E(S \mid \theta_1, \theta_2, \ldots, \theta_k) = \theta \quad \text{for all } \theta_1, \theta_2, \ldots, \theta_k \quad (8.1.3)$$

It is reasonable to ask whether unbiasedness is necessarily a highly desirable characteristic of an estimator. Consider two estimators S_1 and S_2 whose distributions are represented in Fig. 8.1. It is apparent that S_1 is unbiased while S_2 is not. It may happen, however, that S_2 is, in some senses, "nearer" to θ than S_1. Clearly, the variability of an estimator around θ is relevant here since it indicates the degree to which even an unbiased estimator may deviate from the "true" value of θ. In the example given in Fig. 8.1 the biased estimator may be preferred.

The variance of an estimator, S, which measures the variability of the estimator around its mean $E(S)$, is also referred to as a measure of the precision of the estimator. Thus, if an estimator is biased, it is not necessarily desirable to have small variance. On the other hand, small variance is always desirable for unbiased estimators. Thus, what is required in assessing the merits of an estimator is some combination of precision and bias. For this purpose, it is more to the point to examine the variability of the estimator S, not around its mean $E(S)$, but with respect to θ,

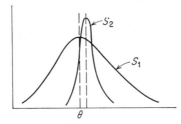

Figure 8.1

the quantity which is being estimated. A practically useful measure resulting from these considerations is the *mean-square error*, which has been in wide use for measuring the effectiveness of electronic control systems.

Definition: mean-square error of estimator, $S(X_1, X_2, \ldots, X_N)$

The *mean square error (MSE)* of estimator $S(X_1, X_2, \ldots, X_N)$ is defined by

$$MSE[S(X_1, X_2, \ldots, X_N) \mid \theta_1, \theta_2, \ldots, \theta_k]$$
$$= E[(S - \theta)^2 \mid \theta_1, \theta_2, \ldots, \theta_k] \quad (8.1.4)$$

The value of MSE is equal to the sum of the variance of S and the square of its bias:

$$MSE(S \mid \theta_1, \theta_2, \ldots, \theta_k)$$
$$= V(S \mid \theta_1, \ldots, \theta_k) + B^2(S \mid \theta_1, \ldots, \theta_k) \quad (8.1.5)$$

This relation can be derived directly from the definition of MSE as given in (8.1.4), as follows:

$$MSE(S) = E(S^2 - 2\theta S + \theta^2) = E(S^2) - 2\theta E(S) + \theta^2$$
$$V(S) = E(S^2) - [E(S)]^2$$
$$B(S) = E(S) - \theta$$

Hence, by adding and subtracting $[E(S)]^2$ to the expanded expression for MSE, Eq. (8.1.5) results.

In comparing two estimators S_1 and S_2, the mean-square error can be used in the following way. If, for all values of $(\theta_1, \ldots, \theta_k)$,

$$MSE(S_2 \mid \theta_1, \ldots, \theta_k) \leq MSE(S_1 \mid \theta_1, \ldots, \theta_k) \qquad (8.1.6)$$

estimator S_2 is at least as good as S_1. And in fact, if the inequality also holds for any values of the parameters, S_2 is preferred to S_1. It should be borne in mind, however, that not all pairs of estimators are comparable in the mean-square-error sense since the MSE relations can reverse signs for different values of the parameters.

In many cases it may be desired to estimate θ within some specified allowable deviation. An estimate of the heat transfer in a certain experimental procedure may be satisfactory if it does not deviate from the true value of the quantity of heat exchanged by more than 10 calories. A measure of "goodness" of an estimator can be expressed, then, by the probability that it does not differ from θ, the parameter estimated, by more than some specified amount (in the same units in which θ is expressed), which may be denoted by t. The magnitude of t of course depends upon the particular problem in which estimation is undertaken and is the result of a value judgment on the part of the experimenter. This measure, then, may be expressed as the probability that the value determined by an estimator falls within $\pm t$ of the "true" parameter value θ. It is obvious, of course, that this measure depends not only on t, but also on the parameter set $(\theta_1, \theta_2, \ldots, \theta_k)$. This measure is called the closeness of an estimator and is now formally defined.

Definition: the closeness of an estimator, $S(X_1, X_2, \ldots, X_N)$ The *closeness* $C[S \mid t; \theta_1, \theta_2, \ldots, \theta_k]$ of an estimator $S(X_1, X_2, \ldots, X_N)$ is

$$C(S \mid t; \theta_1, \theta_2, \ldots, \theta_k)$$
$$= \text{Prob} \left[|S(X_1, X_2, \ldots, X_k) - \theta| \leq t \mid \theta_1, \theta_2, \ldots, \theta_k \right] \qquad (8.1.7)$$

A variant of the closeness measure is proportional closeness, which is defined as follows.

Definition: proportional closeness of an estimator $S(X_1, X_2, \ldots, X_N)$ The *proportional closeness* of an estimator $S(X_1, X_2, \ldots, X_N)$ is

$$PC(S \mid t; \theta_1, \theta_2, \ldots, \theta_k) = \text{Prob} \left(|S - \theta| \leq t\theta \mid \theta_1, \theta_2, \ldots, \theta_k \right) \qquad (8.1.8)$$

It is intuitively desirable that an estimator become more accurate, as well as more precise, as the sample size N increases. That is to say, it is desirable that the bias decrease and approach zero with increasing N. This need not be the case, and in fact there are biased estimators where, as N increases, the bias approaches a limit different from zero. In such cases, since the distribution clusters more closely about an incorrect value, the estimator in this sense becomes "worse" as N increases. There are, of course, a number of possible formulations of the requirement that an estimator improve with increasing N, and one such natural formulation is that, for all the parameters $\theta_1, \theta_2, \ldots, \theta_k$, the mean-square error

$$MSE[S(X_1, X_2, \ldots, X_N) \mid \theta_1, \theta_2, \ldots, \theta_k] \to 0 \text{ as } N \to \infty \quad (8.1.9)$$

The condition expressed in (8.1.9) implies, of course, that the values given by the estimator S cluster closer and closer about θ as N increases. Another interpretation is that the probability that S yields values with specified bounds about θ approaches 1 with increasing θ. This condition, namely, that the closeness approaches 1 for any selected t and for all the parameter values $\theta_1, \theta_2, \ldots, \theta_k$, is called the consistency of an estimator.

Definition: consistency of an estimator, $S(X_1, X_2, \ldots, X_N)$ An estimator $S(X_1, X_2, \ldots, X_N)$ is said to be *consistent* when, for any $t > 0$ and for all $\theta_1, \theta_2, \ldots, \theta_k$,

$$C(S \mid \theta_1, \theta_2, \ldots, \theta_k) = \text{Prob } (|S - \theta| \le t \mid \theta_1, \ldots, \theta_k) \to 1 \quad (8.1.10)$$

Although the consistency condition has been arrived at by an interpretation of (8.1.9), namely, that the mean-square error approaches zero with increasing N, it is not necessarily true that (8.1.9) and (8.1.10) are equivalent. The condition in (8.1.9) can be stated as follows. The convergence of the MSE of an estimator S to 0 with increasing N is equivalent to the statement that the estimator S converges in the mean to θ. This condition implies consistency, and consistency can be stated this way: a consistent estimator S converges in probability to θ. The proof that the convergence in the mean of S to θ implies the convergence in probability of S to θ will not be demonstrated here. Suffice it to say that consistency is a weaker requirement than convergence in the mean (see Exercise 8.19).

Example 8.1 In order to illustrate some of the principles presented above, we shall consider certain estimators of the mean m, the variance σ^2, and the square of the mean m^2 of a normal distribution, based on N independent observations.

a. Estimation of m. A natural estimator is the sample arithmetic average $\bar{X}$, denoted by

$$S(X_1, X_2, \ldots, X_N) = \frac{X_1 + X_2 + \cdots + X_N}{N} \quad (8.1.11)$$

It has been established that $E(\bar{X} \mid m, \sigma^2) = m$ for all m and σ^2; whence S is an unbiased estimator. Furthermore, it follows by definition of the mean-square error that

$$MSE(\bar{X} \mid m, \sigma^2) = V(\bar{X}) = \frac{\sigma^2}{N}$$

For finite σ^2 this measure of error approaches zero as N approaches ∞.

Again, the measure of closeness

$$C(\bar{X} \mid t;m,\sigma^2) = \text{Prob} \left(|\bar{X} - m| \le t\right) = \text{Prob}\left(\frac{|\bar{X} - m|}{\sigma/\sqrt{N}} \le \frac{t}{\sigma}\sqrt{N}\right)$$

$$= 1 - 2\Phi\left(-\frac{t}{\sigma}\sqrt{N}\right)$$

approaches 1 as N approaches ∞, for any $t > 0$. This estimator of m, the sample arithmetic mean $\bar{X}$, is therefore a consistent estimator.

   b. Estimation of σ^2.   In Sec. 5.2, $s^2 = \sum_{i=1}^{N} (X_i - \bar{X})^2/(N - 1)$ was shown to be an unbiased estimator of σ^2. The mean-square error of s^2 can be found by considering $(N - 1)s^2/\sigma^2$, which has been shown to have a χ^2 distribution with $(N - 1)$ degrees of freedom. Since $V(\chi^2)$ equals twice the number of the degrees of freedom of χ^2,

$$V\left[\frac{(N - 1)s^2}{\sigma^2}\right] = 2(N - 1)$$

and

$$V(s^2) = 2(N - 1)\left(\frac{\sigma^2}{N - 1}\right)^2 = \frac{2\sigma^4}{N - 1} \qquad (8.1.12)$$

   It is natural to ask whether s^2 is the "best" estimator of σ^2. It is further indicated that $(X_i - \bar{X})^2$, summed over all N sample observations, is essentially an estimator of σ^2, but that the divisor may be other than N or $N - 1$. Suppose, then, that we consider

$$S_R(X_1,X_2, \ldots ,X_N) = \sum_{i=1}^{N} \frac{(X_i - X)^2}{R} = \frac{N - 1}{R} s^2 \qquad (8.1.13)$$

For $R = N - 1$, S_R is unbiased, but for any $R \ne N - 1$, there is bias, which can be measured by

$$B(S_R \mid m,\sigma^2) = E\left(\frac{N - 1}{R} s^2\right) - \sigma^2 = \sigma^2\left(\frac{N - 1}{R}\right) - \sigma^2 \qquad (8.1.14)$$

   The mean-square error of S_R is

$$MSE(S_R) = V(S_R) + B^2(S_R) = \frac{2(N - 1)}{R^2} \sigma^4 + \sigma^4\left(\frac{N - 1}{R} - 1\right)^2$$

$$= \frac{\sigma^4}{R^2} [2(N - 1) + (N - 1 - R)^2] \qquad (8.1.15)$$

The value of R minimizing $MSE(S_R)$ is readily found to be $R^* = N + 1$. Hence it follows directly that

$$MSE(S_{N+1}) \le MSE(S_R)$$

for all values of R and all m and σ^2. S_{N+1} is an example of a biased estimator, which, however, has smaller MSE than S_{N-1}, which is unbiased. It should be noted, however, that for large N, the difference between the biases of S_{N-1} and S_{N+1} is negligible.

c. *Estimation of* m^2. Two estimators of m^2 are of natural interest, namely,

$$S_1 = \overline{X}^2$$
$$S_2 = \overline{X}^2 - \frac{s^2}{N}$$

For S_1 we have

$$E(S_1) = E(\overline{X}^2) = V(\overline{X}) + [E(\overline{X})]^2 = m^2 + \frac{\sigma^2}{N}$$

whereas for S_2,

$$E(S_2) = E\left(\overline{X}^2 - \frac{s^2}{N}\right) = m^2 + \frac{\sigma^2}{N} - \frac{\sigma^2}{N} = m^2$$

Thus $\overline{X}^2$, which would seem most natural as an estimator of m^2, is biased. The respective values of the MSE are

$$MSE(S_1) = V(\overline{X}^2) + \frac{\sigma^4}{N^2} \quad \text{and} \quad MSE(S_2) = V(\overline{X}^2) + \frac{2}{N-1}\frac{\sigma^4}{N^2}$$

Again, in terms of MSE, S_2 is preferable to S_1 whenever $N > 3$. When $N = 2$, however, S_1 is preferred to S_2.

Example 8.2 The Poisson distribution, which arises frequently in engineering and industrial problems, provides many exercises in estimation, which will now be considered. The mean of the Poisson distribution under consideration will be denoted by λ.

a. *Estimate of* λ. Given that there is a Poisson process for which an event under consideration has a mean rate of occurrence per unit time which is denoted by λ. We can set up an experiment which yields these events, and we can observe and count them. In order to estimate λ, we specify some interval of time $[0, T]$ and count the number of occurrences during one such time interval of duration equal to T units of time. The number of occurrences in this time interval is a random variable which can be denoted by X. This random variable has a Poisson distribution with mean λT and can be expressed as follows:

$$\text{Prob } (X = j) = \frac{e^{-\lambda T}(\lambda T)^j}{j!} \qquad j = 0, 1, 2, \ldots$$

An unbiased estimator $S(X)$ of λ must satisfy the following relation:

$$E(S) = \sum_{j=0}^{\infty} S(j) \text{ Prob } (X = j) = \sum_{j=0}^{\infty} S(j) \frac{e^{-\lambda T}(\lambda T)^j}{j!} = \lambda \qquad \text{for all } \lambda > 0$$

$$(8.1.16)$$

Equation (8.1.16) can be simplified by multiplying both sides by $Te^{+\lambda T}$, yielding

$$\sum_{j=0}^{\infty} \frac{TS(j)(\lambda T)^j}{j!} = \lambda Te^{\lambda T} = \lambda T\left[1 + \lambda T + \frac{(\lambda T)^2}{2!} + \cdots\right]$$

$$= (\lambda T) + \frac{2(\lambda T)^2}{2!} + \frac{3(\lambda T)^3}{3!} + \cdots$$

Since both sides of this equation are expressed as a series of terms of the form $(\lambda T)^j/j!$, one can obtain conditions on $S(j)$ by equating coefficients of common terms as follows:

$$TS(j) = j \qquad j = 0, 1, 2, \ldots$$

Since the expansion of $e^{\lambda T}$ used above is unique, the infinite set of equations $S(j) = j/T$ *uniquely* determines the desired estimator. Again, since (8.1.16) was so set up that $E[S] = \lambda$, S is an unbiased estimator. On replacing j by X, we have

$$S(X) = \frac{X}{T}$$

as a unique unbiased estimator of λ for the experiment proposed, where the chance variable X is the number of occurrences of the event under consideration during a time interval $[0,T]$. One can obtain an unbiased estimate of λ, the mean rate of the Poisson process from observation by setting the process into operation and counting the number of occurrences during a time interval of T units of duration and dividing this number by T.

    b. Estimate of λ^2. As in part *a*, any unbiased estimator $S(X)$ of λ^2 must satisfy the relation

$$\sum_{j=0}^{\infty} T^2 S(j) \frac{(\lambda T)^j}{j!} = (\lambda T)^2\left[1 + (\lambda T) + \frac{(\lambda T)^2}{2!} + \cdots\right]$$

Again, on equating coefficients of like powers, we obtain

$$S(X) = \frac{X(X-1)}{T^2}$$

as a *unique* unbiased estimator. The experiment for estimating λ is the same as that for estimating λ^2, and the chance variable X is the number of occurrences of the event under consideration during a time interval of duration T time units.

c. Estimate of $1/\lambda$. Again, following the method used in parts *a* and *b*, we find that an unbiased estimator $S(X)$ of $1/\lambda$ must satisfy the relation

$$\sum_{j=0}^{\infty} \frac{S(j)}{T} \frac{(\lambda T)^j}{j!} = \frac{1}{\lambda T}\left[1 + (\lambda T) + \frac{(\lambda T)^2}{2!} + \cdots\right] \qquad \text{for all } \lambda > 0$$

A simplification of this relation can readily be found by multiplying through by λT and then multiplying numerator and denominator of each team of the left side of the above equality by $(j + 1)$, yielding

$$\sum_{j=0}^{\infty} \frac{(j+1)S(j)}{T} \frac{(\lambda T)^{j+1}}{(j+1)!} = 1 + \lambda T + \frac{(\lambda T)^2}{2!} + \cdots \qquad \text{for all } \lambda > 0$$

Expanding the left side, we obtain

$$\frac{S(0)}{T}(\lambda T) + \frac{2S(1)}{T}\frac{(\lambda T)^2}{2!} + \frac{3S(2)}{T}\frac{(\lambda T)^3}{3!} + \cdots$$

$$= 1 + (\lambda T) + \frac{(\lambda T)^2}{2!} + \frac{(\lambda T)^3}{3!} + \cdots \qquad \text{for all } \lambda > 0$$

To recapitulate, the estimator $S(X)$ of $1/\lambda$ must satisfy the sequence of three relations given above. The last relation, in particular, is interesting especially for small values of λ. Note that, for small λ, the right side is near 1. (This should be obvious since the series represents $e^{\lambda T}$, which approaches 1 as λ approaches 0.) But note that each term on the left side approaches zero as $\lambda \to 0$. This can better be seen by simplifying each term and writing the left side as follows:

$$\lambda T\left[\frac{S(0)}{T} + \frac{S(1)}{T}(\lambda T) + \frac{S(2)}{T}\frac{(\lambda T)^2}{2!} + \cdots\right]$$

The series in brackets is dominated by $e^{\lambda T}$ multiplied by a finite term which is the upper bound of $S(j)/T$ ($j = 0, 1, 2, \ldots, \infty$). Hence the expression in brackets is bounded, and its product by λT goes to zero with λ. Hence the relationship is not valid for small λ; whence an unbiased estimator does not exist, since the required condition cannot be satisfied by the estimator for all values of $\lambda > 0$.

This experiment does not provide an unbiased estimator, and here is a clear example of the fact that unbiased estimators of certain functions (functions of parameters of the distributions of random variables) do not always exist.

Does this imply that one cannot estimate $1/\lambda$? The absence of an unbiased estimator should not preclude the possibility of the existence of any "reasonable" estimator. It seems apparent, however, that since $1/\lambda$

goes to infinity as λ goes to zero, unbiasedness spoils the game. An unbiased estimator of $1/\lambda$ must blow up as $\lambda \to 0$. Hence we must look for other kinds of estimators. If a consistent estimator existed, but with some bias, not too much, such an estimator could be useful. It can be shown that $S(X) = T/X$, found from this experiment, is consistent. For small λ, however, it is quite possible that X will be found to be zero; whence often $S(X) = \infty$. Even though the likelihood of finding $X = 0$ may be small, its occurrence must not be discounted.

We may avoid this dilemma by formulating a different experiment. Begin observation of the process at any time $t = T_0$ and continue observing until R occurrences have taken place, noting the time T when the Rth occurrence has taken place. Denote the elapsed time $T - T_0$ by T_R. Then T_R/R is an unbiased estimator. It was indicated in Exercise 5.9 that $2\lambda T_R$ has a χ^2 distribution with $2R$ degrees of freedom. Hence

$$E(2\lambda T_R) = E(\chi_{2R}^2) = 2R$$

yielding

$$E\left(\frac{T_R}{R}\right) = E\left(\frac{2\lambda T_R}{2\lambda R}\right) = \frac{2R}{2\lambda R} = \frac{1}{\lambda}$$

Thus T_R/R is an unbiased estimator of $1/\lambda$.

Efficiency There are many estimators $S(X_1,X_2, \ldots ,X_N)$, as will be shown below, which have the property that the transformed chance variable $\sqrt{N}\,[S(X_1,X_2, \ldots ,X_N) - \theta]$ is normally distributed with zero mean and some variance denoted by V_S, as N approaches infinity. This fact is not astonishing in the light of the central limit theorem (Sec. 5.3). For this class of estimators, it is obviously desirable to minimize V_S, and in particular, for the limiting estimator, as N gets large, it is desirable that the limiting variance be smaller than the limiting variance for any other estimator. If such an estimator exists, it is called an *efficient* estimator.

Under particular circumstances, there may be several efficient estimators for a given parameter. It is not surprising, from the fact that efficient estimators satisfy the relation

$$\lim_{N\to 0} \text{in Prob } \sqrt{N}\,[S(X_1,X_2, \ldots ,X_N) - \theta] = 0$$

that efficient estimators are asymptotically unbiased, that is, unbiased in the limit. Efficient estimators are, as is to be expected, also consistent.

Sufficiency The concept of sufficiency of an estimator entails essentially just what the name of the concept colloquially implies. A *sufficient* estimator is one which is sufficient, under the attendant circumstances, for estimating the parameters under consideration. To be precise, however, we should express formally what the word sufficient implies, and not rely on each individual's intuition. In order to formalize the notion of sufficiency, the notion of information needs be considered—at least in some of its intuitive implications.

Let us take a rather simple problem which arises in the course of military or business planning: what is the mean height of males in a certain region and of a certain age range? If the aggregate of males to be studied is of the order of one million or more, a total count may be precluded and a sampling experiment may be in order. We need not discuss the experiment in detail, but it is necessary to bear in mind that the experiment is performed in order to get information about the parameter to be estimated. A natural question is, how much information is needed, or perhaps, what is the most information about the parameter in question that can be gotten from a process of observations? If we should measure the height of one man, is the result "informative" about the mean height? Only one observation tells nothing about the mean m (almost nothing, perhaps) unless, of course, the way in which the individual observed was selected has been specified. For it must be borne in mind that the mean m represents a characteristic of the whole aggregate and that the method of choosing the individual whose height is measured is the only link between the single observation and the value m. If the experiment calls for two or more observations, there seems to be a very natural estimator of m, and the "informativeness" of the estimator about the parameter has genuine bearing on the choice of estimators. The concept of sufficiency will be made precise by considering in a little detail the notion of the informativeness of a particular estimator in a simple situation.

Suppose that, in order to estimate the mean of the distribution of a given random variable whose distribution is normal with mean m and unit variance, just two independent observations are made. The first observation (of the sample of two) is a representative value of a random variable, which may be denoted by X_1. Similarly, the second observation is a measurement on random variable X_2. Both X_1 and X_2 have normal distributions with mean values equal to m and variances equal to unity. And of course X_1 and X_2 are independent. When one considers (X_1, X_2), one considers all the information that the experiment yields. The set (X_1, X_2), which is the sample of two random independent observations on the original chance variable whose mean one seeks to estimate, expresses, represents, or summarizes all the information that the experiment yields from a sample. What more can be said?

Suppose, however, we transform X_1 and X_2 into

$$Y_1 = \frac{X_1 + X_2}{2} = \bar{X} \qquad (8.1.17)$$

$$Y_2 = \frac{X_1 - X_2}{2}$$

The set (Y_1, Y_2) contains the same information, as does (X_1, X_2), since, given either set, the other is determined. Focusing attention on Y_1 and Y_2, we note that Y_1 is normally distributed with mean m and variance $\frac{1}{2}$, while Y_2 is independent of Y_1, also normally distributed with variance $\frac{1}{2}$, but with mean *zero*. It should be emphasized that the distribution of Y_2 does not involve m, and it is therefore plausible that the distribution of Y_2 cannot yield any information about m. We may then assert as a plausible principle (which has bearing on the notion of sufficiency): *any random variable whose distribution does not involve m cannot yield any information about m.*

Again, recognizing that (Y_1, Y_2) contains all the information in the original sample and that Y_2 can give no information about m, Y_1 contains all the information about m that the original sample contains. The random variable $Y_1 = \bar{X}$ is, then, an estimator S of m, which is as *informative* with respect to m as (X_1, X_2), which contains all the information that the experiment can provide. In other words, with respect to possible inference about m, the estimator $Y_1 = \bar{X}$ uses all the information contained in the sample (X_1, X_2) resulting from the experiment. The estimator $S = \bar{X}$ is said to be sufficient for m.

It is possible to view the foregoing in another manner. Suppose two experimenters attempt to estimate m (under the foregoing conditions); the first experimenter asks for (X_1, X_2), while the second experimenter asks only for $Y_1 = (X_1 + X_2)/2 = \bar{X}$. The second experimenter does not choose to know X_1 and X_2—only $\bar{X}$. Which of them has the "better" opportunity to estimate m? Which experimenter has more information relative to m? The answer proposed is that each experimenter has the same degree of information relative to m. In fact, the second experimenter can construct observations on random variable Y_2 from a table of random numbers. It is not necessary to know m in order to be able to construct observations from a normal distribution with zero mean and variance $\frac{1}{2}$. Then, with Y_1 and Y_2 established, observations on (X_1, X_2) can be reconstructed, by solving (8.1.17).

We may pursue the foregoing notions by considering estimating a parameter θ by means of N independent observations represented by $X_1, X_2, \ldots, X_N$. All the information yielded from this experiment is the N outcomes represented by $(X_1, X_2, \ldots, X_N)$. Under what conditions does an estimator $S(X_1, X_2, \ldots, X_N)$ contain all the information? We wish to learn more about an estimator under conditions of sufficiency. Let us consider the joint distribution of $(X_1, X_2, \ldots, X_N)$ as it is related to the joint distribution conditional on $S(X_1, X_2, \ldots, X_N)$ and the distribution of S itself. Let us use the notation $g(x_1, x_2, \ldots, x_N; \theta)$ for the unconditional *PDF* of $X_1, X_2, \ldots, X_N$; $G_2(x_1, x_2, \ldots, x_N; \theta \mid S)$ for the conditional *PDF*; and $G_1(S; \theta)$ for the distribution of S.

We may generally write

$$g(x_1, x_2, \ldots, x_N; \theta) = G_2(x_1, x_2, \ldots, x_N; \theta \mid S)G_1(S; \theta) \quad (8.1.18)$$

Suppose now there are two experimenters, to one of whom is given X_1, $X_2, \ldots, X_N$, representing the sample of N observations, and the other only $S(X_1, X_2, \ldots, X_N)$. When are they equally well off? The second experimenter could merely take $S(X_1, X_2, \ldots, X_N)$ and quit, but instead chooses to get all he can out of his observations. The second experimenter is as well off as the first experimenter if he can construct N random variables having the same distributions as $(X_1, X_2, \ldots, X_N)$. To carry this out, consider expression (8.1.18). G_2 is the joint distribution of $X_1, X_2, \ldots, X_N$ conditional on S, and G_1 is the distribution of S. Experimenter 2 now proceeds by first taking observations on S, which he has available. He then tries to construct, by means of a table of random numbers, observations from the conditional distribution G_2. This he can carry out only *if G_2 does not involve θ.*

Thus another way to view the sufficiency of an estimator $S(X_1, X_2, \ldots, X_N)$ is to consider the joint distribution of X_1, $X_2, \ldots, X_N$ *conditional* on $S(X_1, X_2, \ldots, X_N)$. We can define $S(X_1, X_2, \ldots, X_N)$ to be sufficient, for parameter θ, when the *conditional joint distribution* (discrete or continuous) *does not involve θ.*

In order to conclude this discussion on sufficiency on a firm basis, we shall put the remainder in formal and general terms, without, however, giving proofs, which are beyond the scope of this text. We begin with the following general definition.

Definition: sufficiency of a set $S_1(X_1, X_2, \ldots, X_N)$, $S_2(X_1, X_2,$ $\ldots, X_N), \ldots, S_r(X_1, X_2, \ldots, X_N)$ ***of estimators for*** $\theta_1, \theta_2, \ldots, \theta_k$ Given the random variable X whose PDF is expressed in terms of the k-parameter set $(\theta_1, \theta_2, \ldots, \theta_k)$; $(X_1, X_2, \ldots, X_N)$, a set of N random variables identically distributed with the same distribution as X, obtained by random independent sampling from the X universe; and an r set of estimators $(S_1, S_2, \ldots, S_r)$. The set $S_1(X_1, X_2, \ldots, X_N)$, $S_2(X_1, X_2, \ldots, X_N), \ldots, S_r(X_1, X_2, \ldots, X_N)$ of estimators is said to be *sufficient* for $(\theta_1, \theta_2, \ldots, \theta_k)$ if, and only if, the joint (discrete or continuous) distribution of $(X_1, X_2, \ldots, X_N)$ conditional upon $(S_1, S_2, \ldots, S_r)$ does not involve $(\theta_1, \theta_2, \ldots, \theta_k)$.

This definition is quite general, but does not suggest, or perhaps barely suggests, how to find sufficient estimators. In the example where only two observations were taken, it was shown [Eqs. (8.1.17) *et seq.*] how $g(x; \theta)$ could be factorized. This desired factorization can be performed under quite general conditions. In fact, as the reader may have conjectured from the foregoing definition of a sufficient estimator, the desired factorization is, under very general conditions, both necessary and sufficient for an estimator to be sufficient. This necessary and sufficient condition, which has been called the *Neyman factorization criterion*, can be formally expressed in the following theorem.

Theorem $(S_1, S_2, \ldots, S_r)$ constitutes a *sufficient* set of estimators for $(\theta_1, \theta_2, \ldots, \theta_k)$ if and only if the joint distribution function of the N random independent variables derived from the original universe by sampling in order to estimate the parameter set can be factorized as follows:

$$g(x_1, \ldots, x_N \mid \theta_1, \ldots, \theta_k) = G(S_1, \ldots, S_r \mid \theta_1, \ldots, \theta_k)$$
$$h(x_1, \ldots, x_N) \qquad (8.1.19)$$

where h *does not depend* on $(\theta_1, \theta_2, \ldots, \theta_k)$ and G is a function of $(x_1, x_2, \ldots, x_N)$ only in terms of $S_1, S_2, \ldots, S_r$, the sufficient estimators.

The importance of sufficient estimators lies in the fact that if a sufficient estimator exists, any possible nonsufficient estimators need not be considered; the sufficient estimator guarantees that all the information which a sample can yield with respect to influence on the parameters being estimated is being used.

Example 8.3 It is interesting to consider the estimation of (θ_1, θ_2), where θ_1 represents the mean m and θ_2 represents the variance σ^2 of a normal distribution. This can be done by setting up the joint distribution of the N identically and independently distributed normal chance variables arising from random independent observations on the original populations. The joint distribution of the set $(X_1, X_2, \ldots, X_N)$ is then

$$g(x_1, x_2, \ldots, x_N \mid m, \sigma^2) = \left(\frac{1}{\sigma\sqrt{2\pi}}\right)^N \exp\left[-\frac{1}{2\sigma^2}\sum_{i=1}^{N}(x_i - m)^2\right]$$
$$(8.1.20)$$

Starting with this distribution, we carry our examination further, as follows.

a. Estimators of (m, σ^2). Neither m nor σ^2 is known. From the sample of N random independent observations, we obtain (8.1.20), which on expansion of the exponent becomes

$$g = \left(\frac{1}{\sigma\sqrt{2\pi}}\right)^N \exp\left[-\frac{1}{2\sigma^2}\left(\sum_{i=1}^{N} x_i^2 - 2mN\bar{x} + Nm^2\right)\right]$$

$$= \left(\frac{1}{\sigma\sqrt{2\pi}}\right)^N \exp\left\{-\frac{N}{2\sigma^2}\left[(\bar{x} - m)^2 + \frac{\sum_{i=1}^{N}(x_i - \bar{x})^2}{N}\right]\right\} \qquad (8.1.21)$$

In accordance with the factorization theorem, we can look upon the right side of (8.1.21) as of the form

$$G(S_1, S_2 \mid \theta_1, \theta_2)$$

since G depends on the x_i only in terms of (S_1, S_2), where $S_1 = \bar{x}$ and $S_2 = \sum\limits_{i=1}^{N} (x_i - \bar{x})^2/N$. Hence, if we take $h = 1$ (independent of the parameters), we have an appropriate factorization so that (S_1, S_2) is a sufficient set for estimation of (m, σ^2).

b. *Estimation of σ^2, $m = 0$.* Here we are seeking a single estimator under the conditions given above. It is reasonable to set $m = 0$ in (8.1.20), obtaining

$$g = \left(\frac{1}{\sigma \sqrt{2\pi}} \right)^N \exp \left(- \frac{1}{2\sigma^2} \sum_{i=1}^{N} x_i^2 \right)$$

Again, letting $h = 1$, we then have $G = g$, and G is a function of the observations only in terms of $\sum\limits_{i=1}^{N} x_i^2$, which is, in accordance with the factorization theorem, a sufficient estimator for σ^2.

c. *Estimating m when $\sigma^2 = 1$.* In routine fashion, setting $\sigma^2 = 1$ in (8.1.21), we obtain $g = Gh$, where

$$h = \exp \left[-\frac{1}{2} \sum_{i=1}^{N} (x_i - \bar{x})^2 \right]$$
$$G = \left(\frac{1}{\sqrt{2\pi}} \right)^N \exp \left[- \frac{N}{2} (\bar{x} - m)^2 \right]$$

Since h is independent of the parameters and G is a function of the observations only in terms of $\bar{x}$, $S = \bar{x}$ is a sufficient estimator for m, when $\sigma^2 = 1$.

It is worth emphasizing the fact that sufficient estimators have been readily found, in the case of the normal distribution, for both parameters or for either one, given particular values of the other, following the principle expressed in the factorization theorem.

Example 8.4   The mean of the Poisson variate   Again, for a Poisson chance variable with mean λ, the joint distribution of N identically distributed chance variables representative of a sample of N random independent observations from the original Poisson population is

$$\frac{e^{-N\lambda} \lambda^{(x_1 + x_2 + \cdots + x_N)}}{x_1! x_2! \cdots x_N!} = \frac{e^{-N\lambda} \lambda^{N\bar{x}}}{x_1! x_2! \cdots x_N!}$$

Thus h may be taken as the reciprocal of the denominator, and G as the numerator of the above distribution; $\bar{x}$ is a sufficient estimator for the mean λ.

Invariance   We are all familiar with the notion that geometry— say, of the plane—deals with those properties of plane geometric entities which are invariant under certain transformations of the entities within the plane. This concept of invariance is expressed by the postulate: a geometric figure may be moved from place to place within the plane without changing its size or shape. (This postulate must be broadened in order to carry out some of the early congruence proofs.) The principle of invariance is even more important for the geometry of the sphere. Invariance underlies much of mathematical exercise. More importantly, perhaps, the use of the principle of invariance is intrinsic to the establishment of valid principles of the relationships of variables, which are used to represent experience, the physical world, or the social or physiological phenomena which we deign to examine (or any other observable phenomena). However one observes a certain phenomenon, by whatever scales of measure and in terms of whatever variables one formally (mathematically) represents that phenomenon, and however one transforms the variables of representation into another set of variables, thereby representing the phenomenon in other scales of measure, when one attempts to act upon the phenomenon as a result of the transformed measures, the outcome will be consistent with prediction; the relationships among the variables in terms of which the observed phenomenon is expressed will remain unchanged no matter how the scales of measure are transformed. This is essentially a postulate of science—albeit a rather universal one—which has been so consistently substantiated that, when the principle of invariance is violated, we seriously question the relationships—some people call them laws of nature (any scientific discipline)—which do not remain invariant. Many of the greatest scientific discoveries have resulted from the implications of invariance requirements in the formulation of laws of natural phenomena. It is then reasonable to expect that one property of "good" statistical estimators should be that of invariance. In fact, since all scientific relationships are in a sense statistical, the principle of invariance is indigenous to statistical inference in general.

The principle of sufficiency is one means by which finding suitable estimators can be reduced to searching a smaller class. In fact, the choice can be limited to estimators which are functions of the observed data via the sufficient estimators.

In this section, we further reduce the estimators for possible consideration by means of the invariance principle. This principle is commonly used in science, and states essentially that the essence of a scientific law should not depend on the particular coordinates (or units) in which they are expressed. For example, a law in thermodynamics should not depend, in any essential way, on whether temperature is expressed in centigrade or Fahrenheit. A law in mechanics should not depend on whether length is expressed in inches, feet, or centimeters. This same principle can often be fruitfully applied to problems of statistical inference. In this context, the principle asserts that if a problem is basically unchanged with a change of coordinates, the solution should also be essentially unchanged under this change of coordinates.

The significance of invariance in statistical estimation can best be introduced by means of a simple example. Consider a situation in which there is supposed to prevail some mean temperature m. Experience affords us the conviction that the temperature varies randomly and that repeated observations would be distributed in accordance with a normal distribution with mean m and variance σ^2. Let, then, the set $(X_1, X_2, \ldots, X_N)$ of N independent random variables be identically distributed, normal variates, with common mean m and common variance σ^2, which represent N independent observations on the temperature of the situation under consideration. Suppose, further, that the original observations are made on the centigrade scale, but that it is desired to estimate the mean on the Fahrenheit scale, where the Fahrenheit numbers are related to the centigrade numbers as follows:

$$X_F = \tfrac{9}{5}X_C + 32$$

In order to approach this problem, assume some estimator in the centigrade scale, $S(X_1, X_2, \ldots, X_N)$, and apply the above transformation to each random variable, obtaining

$$S(\tfrac{9}{5}X_1 + 32, \ \tfrac{9}{5}X_2 + 32, \ \ldots, \ \tfrac{9}{5}X_N + 32) \qquad (8.1.22)$$

as the estimator of m in Fahrenheit units. On the other hand, one can first find the estimate in centigrade units from $S(X_1, X_2, \ldots, X_N)$ and then transform this estimate as follows:

$$\tfrac{9}{5}S(X_1, X_2, \ldots, X_N) + 32 \qquad (8.1.23)$$

to the Fahrenheit scale. It is entirely natural to expect that the two estimates resulting from (8.1.22) and (8.1.23), respectively, should be identical. That is to say, it is indifferent whether the original observations are made on one or the other scale—the final results when expressed in the same units should be the same. More sophisticatedly, one can assert the principle of invariance, which requires in the present case that

$$S(\tfrac{9}{5}X_1 + 32, \ \tfrac{9}{5}X_2 + 32, \ \ldots, \ \tfrac{9}{5}X_N + 32)$$
$$= \tfrac{9}{5}S(X_1, X_2, \ldots, X_N) + 32 \qquad (8.1.24)$$

And one may rightfully require all possible estimators of m in this situation to satisfy (8.1.24). Again, in estimating a mean length, one may require that

$$S(12X_1, 12X_2, \ldots, X_N) = 12S(X_1, X_2, \ldots, X_N) \qquad (8.1.25)$$

where the observations are made in feet and the estimation is given in inches. More generally, then, if observations $(X_1, X_2, \ldots, X_N)$ are transformed linearly by the relation

$$Y_i = aX_i + b$$

then the principle of invariance requires that, for any numbers (a,b),

$$S(Y_1, Y_2, \ldots, Y_N) = S(aX_1 + b, aX_2 + b, \ldots, aX_N + b)$$
$$= aS(X_1, X_2, \ldots, X_N) + b \quad (8.1.26)$$

One may add a statistical reason to the natural feeling that the principle of invariance is reasonable, namely, that, given the random variable X, $E(aX + b) = aE(X) + b$. Hence we like our estimators to behave that way, to be invariant under linear transformations. Since this property may not be enjoyed by all estimators, the principle of invariance restricts the class of "good" estimators which need be examined in order to select the "best" (if there be such) estimator for realistic use.

In applying the invariance principle to estimation of σ^2, one must take cognizance of the fact that $V(aX + b) = a^2 V(X)$. Thus, for σ^2, the invariance principle requires that estimator T satisfy

$$T(aX_1 + b, aX_2 + b, \ldots, aX_N + b) = a^2 T(X_1, X_2, \ldots, X_N) \quad (8.1.27)$$

The two estimators $\bar{X}$ and $\sum_{i=1}^{N} (X_i - \bar{X})^2/(N - 1)$ are invariant estimators of m and σ^2, respectively.

In the estimation of the difference $m_1 - m_2$ of the means of two populations, denoting observations on the first population by (X_i) and on the second population by (Y_i), the invariance principle, together with the symmetries inherent in the order of taking differences, requires that a "good" estimator S satisfy the relation

$$S(aX_1 + b, aX_2 + b, \ldots, aX_N + b; aY_1 + b, aY_2 + b, \ldots, aY_N + b)$$
$$= aS(X_1, X_2, \ldots, X_N; Y_1, Y_2, \ldots, Y_N)$$
$$= -aS(Y_1, Y_2, \ldots, Y_N; X_1, X_2, \ldots, X_N) \quad (8.1.28)$$

For an estimator $T(X_1, X_2, \ldots, X_N; Y_1, Y_2, \ldots, Y_N)$ of σ_1^2/σ_2^2, the invariance principle requires that

$$T(aX_1 + b, aX_2 + b, \ldots, X_N + b; cY_1 + d, cY_2 + d, \ldots, cY_N + d)$$
$$= \frac{a^2}{c^2} T(X_1, X_2, \ldots, X_N; Y_1, Y_2, \ldots, Y_N)$$

It is well to note again that the principles of sufficiency and of invariance limit the class of estimators that need be considered; sufficient estimators do not always exist. These principles have important implications and, as may be expected, are not only important in estimation, but have a significant influence in the testing of hypotheses. This topic is considered next.

Application of Principles of Sufficiency and Invariance in Statistical Hypothesis Testing   The effectiveness of a test of statistical hypothesis is influenced to a high degree by the test statistic employed, which may or may not be a sufficient statistic. In order to observe the influence of a sufficient statistic, consider testing the simple hypothesis

$$H_0: \quad \theta = \theta_0 \qquad \text{against} \qquad H_1: \quad \theta = \theta_1$$

In accordance with the Neyman-Pearson lemma (Sec. 7.4), the optimal rejection region is determined by the likelihood-function ratio in the relation

$$\frac{L(x_1, x_2, \ldots, x_N \mid \theta_0)}{L(x_1, x_2, \ldots, x_N \mid \theta_1)} = \frac{g(x_1 \mid \theta_0) g(x_2 \mid \theta_0) \cdots g(x_N \mid \theta_0)}{g(x_1 \mid \theta_1) g(x_2 \mid \theta_1) \cdots g(x_N \mid \theta_1)} \leq k \quad (8.1.29)$$

where k is constant, which depends on the significance level (and x_i are the numerical values taken on by the chance variables X_i).

The practical application of (8.1.29) can be rather cumbersome. If, however, the factorization theorem is applicable to the particular likelihood function under consideration, then a considerable simplification is effected since (8.1.29) becomes

$$\frac{L(x_1, x_2, \ldots, x_N \mid \theta_0)}{L(x_1, x_2, \ldots, x_N \mid \theta_1)} = \frac{h(x_1, \ldots, x_N) G(S \mid \theta_0)}{h(x_1, \ldots, x_N) G(S \mid \theta_1)} = \frac{G(S \mid \theta_0)}{G(S \mid \theta_0)} \quad (8.1.30)$$

The h_2 in the numerator and the h_2 in the denominator are, of course, identical, since they do not involve the parameters. The factorization theorem is applicable where a sufficient statistic exists; whence the right side of (8.1.30) yields a simple form for the likelihood-function ratio when a sufficient statistic is available. The likelihood function is a function of the observations, but it is expressible in simple form in terms of a sufficient estimator when one exists.

As may be expected, the foregoing considerations can be generalized to composite hypotheses, but such material is beyond the scope of this text. The treatment of testing statistical hypotheses given in Chap. 7 does reveal, however, that the testing procedures have been developed in terms of sufficient estimators.

It would seem even more directly apparent that the principle of invariance must apply to statistical hypothesis testing. For again, if one were to test

$$H_0: \quad m_1 = m_2 \qquad \text{against} \qquad H_1: \quad m_1 \neq m_2$$

it seems reasonable to expect the result of such a test to be independent of the scale of measurement. Again, supposing a linear transformation of scale, $X' = aX + b$, $Y' = aY + b$, $E(X') = aE(X) + b$, and $E(Y') = aE(Y) + b$. Thus, if $m_1 = m_2$, it follows that $am_1 + b = am_2 + b$, so that the statistical test of hypothesis must lead to the same conclusion after a transformation of the chance variables as just given. One may put this in other words: if a transformation of variable leaves the hypothesis under test in the same form as originally formulated, the conclusion must remain invariant. To be more specific, if there are, say, three normal populations with means m_1, m_2, m_3 and known variances σ_1^2, σ_2^2, σ_3^2, the hypothesis H_0: $m_1 = m_2 = m_3$ can be tested against the alternative H_1; the three means are not identical by taking from each population a sample of N random independent observations. These observations can be represented by three sets of identically distributed random variables, $(X_1, X_2, \ldots, X_N)$, $(Y_1, Y_2, \ldots, Y_N)$, and $(Z_1, Z_2, \ldots, Z_N)$. If a general transformation $U' = aU + b$ is introduced, yielding, respectively, transformed means $m_1' = am_1 + b$, $m_2' = am_2 + b$, and $m_3' = am_3 + b$, H_0 becomes H_0': $m_1' = m_2' = m_3'$ and H_1 becomes H_1': the means are not identical. The formulation of the statistical test of hypothesis remains unchanged. The invariance criterion requires that the test criterion $(X_1, X_2, \ldots, X_N;\ Y_1, Y_2, \ldots, Y_N;\ Z_1, Z_2, \ldots, Z_N)$ being contained within rejection region R imply (where $X_i' = aX_i + b$, $Y_i' = aY_i + b$, $Z_i' = aZ_i + b$) that $(X_1', X_2', \ldots, X_N';\ Y_1', Y_2', \ldots, Y_N';\ Z_1', Z_2', \ldots, Z_N')$ be contained within rejection region R. The statistical test of hypothesis remains invariant to a linear transformation of the sample space, as required by the invariance principle.

The combined application of the principles of sufficiency and invariance sometimes reduces the number of rejection regions that need be considered in determining an appropriate test statistic. In testing, for example, for a normal variate the hypothesis

$$H_0:\ \sigma^2 \leq \sigma_0^2 \qquad \text{against} \qquad H_1:\ \sigma^2 > \sigma_0^2$$

the sufficiency principle asserts that one can express the observations in terms of the set of sufficient statistics $\left[\bar{X},\ \sum_{i=1}^{N} (X_i - \bar{X})^2 \right]$ without loss of generality. Then, for a shift in origin, $X_i' = X_i + b$, it is obvious, since $V(X') = V(X + b) = V(X)$, that H_0 and H_1 remain unaltered. And since

$$\sum_{i=1}^{N} \frac{X_i + b}{N} = \bar{X} + b$$

$$\sum_{i=1}^{N} [(X_i + b) - (\bar{X} + b)]^2 = \sum_{i=1}^{N} (X_i - \bar{X})^2$$

the rejection region R, which contains $\left[\bar{X},\ \sum_{i=1}^{N} (X_i - \bar{X})^2 \right]$, should also contain $\left[\bar{X} + b, \sum_{i=1}^{N} (X_i - \bar{X})^2 \right]$. This means that R should depend

only on $\sum_{i=1}^{N} (X_i - \bar{X})^2$, the sufficient statistic for σ^2. Hence one need merely consider rejection regions dependent on the sufficient statistic $\Sigma(X_i - \bar{X})^2$ in order to find directly the appropriate test statistic for testing hypotheses about σ^2.

Interpretation of Estimation in Terms of Loss Functions
Estimators have been considered on the basis of the probability of error of given magnitudes. Such criteria as mean-square error (MSE) and closeness, for example, may be set equivalent to the loss suffered by the

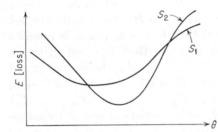

Figure 8.2

experimenter as a result of the error encountered in estimation. If S denotes an estimator of θ, then the loss due to estimation is dependent on the values that S takes on as the result of experiment and the value of θ. This loss may be denoted as $L(\theta,S)$. The form of the function L is usually such that $L(\theta,S)$ is small for S "close" to θ and grows larger as $\theta - S$ diverges. The merit of S as an estimator is usually assessed in terms of $E[L(\theta,S)]$, the smaller this expected loss, the better S.

If there are two estimators of θ, S_1 and S_2, S_1 is said to be at least as good as S_2 if

$$E[L(\theta,S_1)] \leq E[L(\theta,S_2)]$$

for all values of θ of interest to the experimenter. And of course, if the strict inequality holds, S_1 is preferred to S_2. On the other hand, it is possible that S_1 is preferred over one range of values of θ, and S_2 over another range, as shown in Fig. 8.2.

In practice, there are a number of simple loss functions of special interest. One such class is the quadratic loss functions of the form

$$L(\theta,S) = C(\theta)(\theta - S)^2 \qquad (8.1.31)$$

In particular, for $C(\theta) = 1$, we have

$$E[L(\theta,S)] = E[(\theta - S)^2]$$

which is the familiar mean-square error.   Sometimes $C(\theta)$ is taken as $1/\theta^2$, so that

$$E[L(\theta,S)] = \frac{E[(\theta - S)^2]}{\theta^2}$$

A somewhat different class of loss functions is of the form

$$L(\theta,S) = \begin{cases} 0 & |\theta - S| \leq t \\ 1 & \text{otherwise} \end{cases}$$

This leads to

$$E[L(\theta,S)] = \text{Prob } (|\theta - S| > t) = 1 - C(S \mid \theta,t)$$

Loss functions occupy a prominent place in statistical decision theory.   Further development of properties of loss functions is beyond the scope of this text.

8.1.2   Maximum-likelihood estimators

The discussion in the preceding section was of a general nature, dealing with requirements placed upon estimators and their properties.   In particular situations one is confronted with the problem of constructing estimators which are most suitable in these individual cases.   A variety of methods are available for such particular cases.   It is highly desirable, however, to have a method which is generally applicable to the construction of statistical estimators which have "good" properties.   An extremely important general method based on the principle of maximum likelihood has been developed chiefly by R. A. Fisher and will be discussed in some detail here.   This method makes use of the likelihood function, which has been discussed at length in the development of statistical hypothesis testing.

The Principle of Maximum Likelihood   In statistical hypothesis testing we made use of the likelihood ratio, comparing the likelihood of the observations obtained under H_0 with the likelihood of those obtained under H_1.   According to the Neyman-Pearson lemma, the choice between H_0 and H_1 is made optimally in terms of the ratio

$$\begin{aligned} \frac{L_0}{L_1} &= \frac{L(x_1,x_2, \ldots ,x_N \mid \theta_0)}{L(x_1,x_2, \ldots ,x_N \mid \theta_1)} \\ &= \frac{g(x_1 \mid \theta_0) \cdots g(x_N \mid \theta_0)}{g(x_1 \mid \theta_1) \cdots g(x_N \mid \theta_0)} \end{aligned} \qquad (8.1.32)$$

In more complicated tests such as

$$H_0: \quad \theta \text{ in } W \qquad \text{against} \qquad H_1: \quad \theta \text{ not in } W$$

the likelihood ratio is

$$\lambda(x_1, x_2, \ldots, x_N) = \frac{\max_W L(x_1, x_2, \ldots, x_N \mid \theta)}{\max_\Omega L(x_1, x_2, \ldots, x_N \mid \theta)} \qquad (8.1.33)$$

where W is contained in Ω, the space of all parameter values.

This use of the likelihood ratio implies that the numerator is, in a sense that must be specified, the "best" explanation of the data under hypothesis H_0. The rejection region is so determined that, for H_1 with "maximum likelihood," the test statistic falls in the rejection region. A concept quite analogous is used to find estimators.

In the case of estimating θ by $\hat\theta$, where it can be assumed that θ lies in Ω, it seems reasonable to choose $\hat\theta$ so that it maximizes $L(x_1, x_2, \ldots, x_N \mid \theta)$ for the sample $(x_1, x_2, \ldots, x_N)$. The values for $(x_1, x_2, \ldots, x_N)$ are obtained, of course, by experiment, and hence $\hat\theta$ is a function $\hat\theta(x_1, x_2, \ldots, x_N)$, where $(x_1, x_2, \ldots, x_N)$ represents the actual observations obtained by experiment. What is required now is a technique for obtaining a maximum of the likelihood function with respect to θ.

Often a maximum of L can be found in the conventional manner, so that $\hat\theta$ is a solution of

$$\frac{dL(x_1, x_2, \ldots, x_N \mid \theta)}{d\theta} = 0 \qquad (8.1.34)$$

And in particular, further conditions must be satisfied to assure that a solution of (8.1.34) is actually a maximum and not a minimum or a point of inflection. If a maximum does not exist, the supremum can be used. It may also happen that a maximum occurs at a boundary point and thus need not be a solution of 8.1.34. It is well to work out a simple example.

Example 8.5 N independent observations are taken from a normal distribution with mean m and variance σ^2 in order to estimate m and σ^2 by means of the maximum-likelihood procedure, yielding

$$L(x_1, x_2, \ldots, x_N \mid m, \sigma^2) = \left(\frac{1}{\sigma\sqrt{2\pi}}\right)^N \exp\left[-\frac{1}{2\sigma^2} \sum_{i=1}^{N} (x_i - m)^2\right] \qquad (8.1.35)$$

The derivatives of L with respect to m and σ^2 can be readily taken, but the procedure can often be much simplified by taking the derivatives of $\ln L$. Since the solutions of equations resulting from $\partial \ln L / \partial m = 0$ and $\partial \ln L / \partial \sigma^2 = 0$ are identical with those resulting from $\partial L / \partial m = 0$ and

$\partial L/\partial \sigma^2 = 0$, the use of $\ln L$ is to be preferred in many cases. Here

$$\frac{\partial \ln L}{\partial m} = \frac{2}{2\sigma^2} \sum_{i=1}^{N} (x_i - m) = 0$$

$$\frac{\partial \ln L}{\partial \sigma^2} = -\frac{N}{2\sigma^2} + \frac{1}{2\sigma^4} \sum_{i=1}^{N} (x_i - m)^2 = 0$$

(8.1.36)

The solutions are

$$\hat{m} = \bar{X}$$

$$\hat{\sigma}^2 = \frac{1}{N} \sum_{i=1}^{N} (x_i - \hat{m})^2$$

(8.1.37)

These estimates are quite familiar and intuitively reasonable. The variance estimate $\hat{\sigma}^2$ is, as has been shown earlier, slightly biased. What is more important, however, is that $\hat{m}$ and $\hat{\sigma}^2$ are functions of the sufficient statistics $\left[\bar{X}, \sum_{i=1}^{N} (x_i - \bar{X})^2\right]$. It can be shown that maximum-likelihood estimators are generally functions of sufficient statistics.

Example 8.6 Now consider a Poisson distribution with mean λT,

$$\frac{e^{-\lambda T}(\lambda T)^x}{x!} \qquad x = 0, 1, 2, \ldots$$

where T is some constant, and x is the number of events observed during time T. The likelihood function is

$$L(x \mid \lambda) = \frac{e^{-\lambda T}(\lambda T)^x}{x!} \qquad x = 0, 1, 2, \ldots$$

Again we have

$$\frac{\partial \ln L}{\partial \lambda} = -T + \frac{x}{\lambda T} T = 0$$

whence

$$\hat{\lambda} = \frac{x}{T}$$

This estimator is intuitively obvious since x is an estimate of λT and a sufficient statistic. Hence $\hat{\lambda} = x/T$ is a function of a sufficient statistic.

Example 8.7 **The parameter p of the binomial distribution** The likelihood function is

$$L(x \mid p) = \frac{N!}{x!(N-x)!} p^x (1-p)^{N-x}$$

and

$$\ln L = \ln N! - \ln x! - \ln (N-x)! + x \ln p + (N-x) \ln (1-p)$$

when p is the probability of a success, and x the number of successes in N independent trials.   Hence

$$\frac{\partial \ln L}{\partial p} = \frac{x}{p} + \frac{N - x}{1 - p}(-1) = 0$$

yielding

$$\hat{p} = \frac{x}{N}$$

This is quite analogous to the estimator of λ previously, where T replaces N.   Again, x contains all the information in the observation of N trials, and thus the estimator x/N is a function of a sufficient statistic.

Example 8.8   It has become practice recently to characterize the CDF of the service life of certain items by the exponential distribution $1 - e^{-t/m}$, where m is the mean life of the item.   A typical method of estimating m is to put N replicates of the item under life test, terminating the test after some predetermined time period T.   The number of failures which have occurred during the period $[0,T]$, denoted by X, seems to be a natural observation to make.   Can X be used to estimate m?   Can a likelihood estimator of m be obtained in terms of X?

The distribution of X can readily be expressed as the binomial, where p, the probability of failure during $[0,T]$, is given by $1 - e^{-T/m}$. Then the likelihood function of X is

$$L(x \mid m) = \frac{N!}{x!(N - x)!}(1 - e^{-T/m})^x(e^{-T/m})^{N-x}$$

A little trick may be used to find the maximum of L with respect to m. Since $1 - e^{-T/m}$ is a single-valued function of m, the maximum of L with respect to $1 - e^{-T/m}$ will yield the desired value $\hat{m}$.   If we let $p = 1 - e^{-T/m}$, the present likelihood function is identical with the likelihood in Example 8.7, where $\hat{p} = x/N$.   But the solution for m in this case is the same value as obtained for p in the previous case, where

$$\hat{p} = 1 - e^{-T/\hat{m}} = \frac{x}{N}$$

yielding

$$\hat{m} = \frac{-T}{\ln(1 - x/N)}$$

In this example the following principle was used: the maximum-likelihood estimator of $v(m)$, namely, $\hat{v}$, is equal to $v(\hat{m})$ when $v(m)$ is a single-valued function of m with a single-valued inverse.   This property of maximum-likelihood estimators, called the transformation property, is very useful in the search for estimators and will be used from time to time and commented on further.

Properties of Maximum-likelihood Estimators (MLE)   A very important property of *MLE* is the following: *when sufficient estimators* *exist, the MLE are functions of the observations* $X_1, X_2, \ldots, X_N$ *only in terms of the sufficient estimators.* In order to demonstrate this property, granting that a sufficient estimator exists, L is expressed in factored form:

$$L(x_1, x_2, \ldots, x_N \mid \theta) = G(S \mid \theta) h(x_1, x_2, \ldots, x_N)$$

where S is a sufficient estimator, and maximized with respect to θ (θ in some domain Ω). Since, however, h is independent of θ (and not equal to zero), the maximum of L with respect to θ will occur at the same value θ as is obtained from the maximum of $G[S(x_1, x_2, \ldots, x_N) \mid \theta]$ with respect to θ. Hence the resulting *MLE*, $\hat{\theta}$, can be expressed as a function of $X_1, X_2, \ldots, X_N$ only in terms of $S(X_1, X_2, \ldots, X_N)$, the sufficient estimator. This intuitive approach suggests the essential notions required to establish the *sufficiency property* of *MLE*, in the multiparameter case as well as in the single-parameter case.

The *transform property*, used in Example 8.8, states that *the MLE of a function* $v(\theta)$ *is that function of the MLE* $\hat{\theta}$, *namely,* $v(\hat{\theta})$, *when* $v(\theta)$ *is a single-valued function of* θ *with a single-valued inverse* (such a function is said to be one-one). This property can be demonstrated by looking at the inverse function $\theta = U(v)$, which itself is a single-valued function of v. One can then express the likelihood function as

$$L[x_1, x_2, \ldots, x_N \mid U(v)]$$

The *MLE* of v, $\hat{v}$ is obtained by finding the maximum of L with respect to v. Since L is a maximum for this expression for $\hat{\theta}$, it is the *MLE* of θ. Hence $\hat{\theta} = U(\hat{v})$ and $\hat{v} = v(\hat{\theta})$, since v is a single-valued function.

It is quite apparent that the transformation property is very useful since, once $\hat{\theta}$ is determined, the *MLE* for various single-valued functions $v(\theta)$ can be found directly without going through the laborious maximum-likelihood procedure each time.

Example 8.9 We shall now make further use of the transformation property. If in Example 8.5 we seek the *MLE* of m^3 and of σ, we obtain directly $\bar{X}^3$ and $\sqrt{\sum_{i=1}^{N}(X_i - \bar{X})^2/N}$, respectively, since $v(m) = m^3$ and $v(\sigma^2) = \sqrt{\sigma^2}$. Note that the *MLE* are not necessarily unbiased. In fact, $E(\bar{X}^3) = m^3 + 3m\sigma^2/N \neq m^3$ for $\sigma > 0$. Fortunately, the bias approaches zero as $N \to \infty$ for this case as well as for other maximum-likelihood estimators.

In Example 8.6 the *MLE* of λ was found to be x/T. The functions of λ, λ^2, $1/\lambda$, and $e^{-\lambda t}$ (probability that no events occur during time interval $[0,t]$) have the *MLE* $\hat{\lambda}^2 = (x/T)^2$, $1/\hat{\lambda} = T/x$, and $e^{-\hat{\lambda}t} = e^{-xt/T}$, respectively, obtained directly by application of the transformation property. Referring to Example 8.7, the *MLE* of the variance of the binomial distribution, $\sigma^2 = p(1 - p)N$, is readily found to be

$$N\hat{p}(1 - \hat{p}) = X(1 - X/N)$$

Asymptotic normalcy is another important property of *MLE*, stated here without proof: *the distribution of $\hat{\theta}$, an MLE of θ, approaches that of a normal distribution with mean θ and variance*

$$\sigma_{\hat{\theta}}^2 = \frac{1}{E\left[\left(\dfrac{\partial \ln L}{\partial \theta}\right)^2\right]} \qquad \text{as } N \to \infty \tag{8.1.38}$$

The denominator of (8.1.38) can be shown to equal $E[-(\partial^2 \ln L)/\partial\theta^2]$. This property is often referred to as the *asymptotic normality property*.

It can be shown, under very general conditions frequently encountered in practice, that *MLE* $\hat{\theta}$ is both *consistent* and *efficient*. The reader will find precise statements of these properties and of the conditions under which they hold, as well as generalizations to many parameters, in the literature.

The asymptotic variance of $v(\hat{\theta})$ can, under quite general conditions, be written in a form analogous to (8.1.38). This fact can be stated as follows:

Under rather general conditions, the asymptotic variance $\sigma_{\hat{v}}^2$ of the *MLE* $\hat{v}$ of $v(\theta)$ is given by [1]

$$\sigma_{\hat{v}}^2 = V(\hat{v}) = V[v(\hat{\theta})] = \left(\frac{dv}{d\theta}\right)^2 V(\hat{\theta}) = \frac{(dv/d\theta)^2}{E\left[\left(\dfrac{\partial \ln L}{\partial \theta}\right)^2\right]} = \frac{(dv/d\theta)^2}{E\left(-\dfrac{\partial^2 \ln L}{\partial \theta^2}\right)}$$
$$\tag{8.1.39}$$

Example 8.10   The usefulness of (8.1.38) and (8.1.39) can be shown by trying to obtain the asymptotic variances of a number of the *MLE* found in previous examples, such as $\hat{\lambda}$, $1/\hat{\lambda}$, and $e^{-\hat{\lambda}t}$ in Example 8.9. For $\hat{\lambda}$ one obtains, by straightforward steps,

$$-\frac{\partial^2 \ln L}{\partial \lambda^2} = \frac{X}{\lambda^2}$$

whence
$$E\left(-\frac{\partial^2 \ln L}{\partial \lambda^2}\right) = \frac{\lambda T}{\lambda^2} = \frac{T}{\lambda}$$

Therefore, applying (8.1.39) and noting that $dv/d\lambda = d\lambda/d\lambda = 1$, it follows that

$$\text{var}\ (\hat{\lambda}) = \frac{1}{T/\lambda} = \frac{\lambda}{T}$$

---

[1] This relation holds only for the case of one parameter. Where more than one parameter is involved another argument, leading to a more complicated expression, is necessary.

Again, for $v(\lambda) = 1/\lambda$, $dv/d\lambda = -1/\lambda^2$, and asymptotically,

$$\text{var}\left(\frac{1}{\bar{\lambda}}\right) = \frac{(-1/\lambda^2)^2}{T/\lambda} = \frac{1}{\lambda^3 T}$$

When $v(\lambda) = e^{-\lambda t}$, $dv/d\lambda = -te^{-\lambda t}$, and asymptotically

$$\text{var}(e^{-\hat{\lambda}t}) = \frac{(-te^{-\lambda t})^2}{T/\lambda} = \frac{\lambda t^2 e^{-2\lambda t}}{T}$$

The asymptotic variance relation can sometimes be used, so to speak, inversely, and simplify a laborious calculation. In Example 8.8 we considered the *MLE* of m, the mean of the exponential distribution $1 - e^{-t/m}$. The asymptotic variance of $\hat{m}$ cannot be obtained in simple direct fashion. If, however, we consider $v(m) = 1 - e^{-T/m}$, we can employ (8.1.39) directly, since

$$\text{var}[v(\hat{m})] = \left(\frac{dv}{dm}\right)^2 \text{var}(\hat{m})$$

while it is known that $1 - e^{-T/m}$ is equal to p, the probability of failure of an item during the time interval $[0, T]$. Hence, since $V[v(\hat{m})] = V(\hat{p}) = p(1 - p)/N$ in the binomial case,

$$\text{var}[v(\hat{m})] = \text{var}(1 - e^{-T/\hat{m}}) = \frac{(e^{-T/m})(1 - e^{-T/m})}{N}$$

where N is the number of trials, or in this case the number of items under operating test during $[0, T]$. Hence we can equate the above two expressions, obtaining

$$\left(\frac{dv}{dt}\right)^2 \text{var}(\hat{m}) = \frac{e^{-T/m}(1 - e^{-T/m})}{N}$$

and solve for var $(\hat{m})$. Since $(dv/dm) = -(T/m^2)e^{-T/m}$,

$$\text{var}(\hat{m}) = \frac{e^{-T/m}(1 - e^{-T/m})}{N(T^2/m^4)e^{-2T/m}}$$

This expression is exact only in the limit as N goes to ∞. Approximately, however, we have, for large N,

$$\text{var}(\hat{m}) \cong \frac{m^2}{N}\left[\frac{1 - e^{-T/m}}{e^{-T/m}(T/m)^2}\right]$$

8.2 Interval estimation

In the previous sections we were concerned with point estimators for parameters, and various criteria for assessing their merit were developed.

To make such estimators more meaningful, some measure of error should accompany them. In fact, often what is desired is a range of values wherein the parameter may be said to lie, with some specified assurance. In this section we shall study, without going into extensive details, how such intervals can be constructed. These intervals, called *confidence intervals*, are based on the observations and contain the parameter value with specified odds.

In a wide range of problems the focus of interest is only indirectly on parameter values. Of more vital interest may be knowledge of where a substantial fraction of the underlying population may be expected to lie. For example, a manufacturer wishing to assess a production process for items having characteristics within certain tolerances is more directly concerned with making inferences about the range of values in which most of his production will lie than with estimating the mean of their distribution. An artilleryman is concerned with inference about the area in which most of his shots will fall. An ecologist, studying the wanderings of a species, wants to know something about the range of distance from their original habitat where his wandering species may be expected to be found after a certain elapsed time. We shall study methods of constructing intervals suited for answering such questions. Such intervals are called *tolerance intervals*. While confidence intervals bracket parameter values with specified odds, tolerance intervals bracket a region, containing a given fraction of the underlying population, with specified odds. These notions will be made precise.

8.2.1 Confidence intervals

In order to introduce the basic notions, we begin with an example concerning the mean m of a normal distribution having known variance σ^2. Suppose that we can perform N independent observations on the universe, represented by random variables $X_1, X_2, \ldots, X_N$. On the basis of these observations, we wish, with specified odds, to bracket m with an interval. A reasonable estimate for m is the arithmetic average $\bar{x}$. But of course $\bar{x}$ has some region of variation from m, so that we should try to estimate some quantity which can be added to, and some quantity which can be subtracted from, $\bar{x}$ such that we can bet with some odds that m falls within $\bar{x} - a$ and $\bar{x} + b$. As a first step, it seems reasonable to standardize the random variable $\bar{x}$ by the transformation $Z = \sqrt{N} \, (\bar{x} - m)/\sigma$. Thus Z has the standard normal distribution. We note here two important characteristics of Z, namely, Z *has a distribution which does not depend on knowledge about* m, *but* Z *nevertheless involves the unknown* m. It follows that

$$\text{Prob}\left(-Z_{1-\alpha/2} \leq \frac{\bar{x} - m}{\sigma/\sqrt{N}} \leq Z_{1-\alpha/2} \right) = 1 - \alpha \qquad (8.2.1)$$

Now, the inequality in (8.2.1) can be represented as an inequality about m, as follows:

$$\text{Prob}\left(\bar{x} - \frac{Z_{1-\alpha/2}\sigma}{\sqrt{N}} \leq m \leq \bar{x} + \frac{Z_{1-\alpha/2}\sigma}{\sqrt{N}} \right) = 1 - \alpha \qquad (8.2.2)$$

An alternative expression for (8.2.2) is

$$\text{Prob}\left(m \text{ lies within the interval } \bar{x} \pm \frac{Z_{1-\alpha/2}\sigma}{\sqrt{N}} \right) = 1 - \alpha \qquad (8.2.3)$$

The random element involved in (8.2.3) is $\bar{x}$. The interval $\bar{x} \pm Z_{1-\alpha/2}\sigma/\sqrt{N}$ is a random interval with mid-point $\bar{x}$ and length $2Z_{1-\alpha/2}\sigma/\sqrt{N}$. Thus, if one wishes to bracket m within an interval of length L with *confidence coefficient* $1 - \alpha$, one can find a suitable sample size N by solving $L = 2Z_{1-\alpha/2}\sigma/\sqrt{N}$. Consequently,

$$N = \frac{4Z_{1-\alpha/2}^2 \sigma^2}{L^2} \qquad (8.2.4)$$

The random interval $\bar{x} \pm Z_{1-\alpha/2}\sigma/\sqrt{N}$ may or may not, in any particular case, contain the value m. The frequency interpretation of the probability statement (8.2.3) is: when the procedure of taking N random, independent observations and constructing the associated random interval is repeated many times, approximately $(1 - \alpha)$ per cent of the intervals will contain m. It should again be noted that this statement can be made without knowledge about m. The determination of the interval depends, however, on the fact that x has the normal distribution, which can always be normalized by a transformation such as $Z = \sqrt{N}\,(\bar{x} - m)/\sigma$. Equations (8.2.1) and (8.2.2) then follow naturally. We may note that the type of interval in which m has been imbedded is symmetrical about the observed $\bar{x}$. Symmetry about some observed statistic is not, however, to be expected of confidence intervals in general. In the present case of the interval L, for a given $(1 - \alpha)$, the probability that m will lie within L (from which odds are determined) is of fixed length since $Z_{1-\alpha/2}$, σ, and N are constants. This need not always be the case.

In most practical cases, σ^2 will not be known in advance of experiment. Hence, in searching for a confidence interval for m, it will be necessary to estimate σ^2, the quantity on which the length of the confidence interval basically depends, from experiment by some estimator such as s^2. If we now proceed analogously with the case for σ^2 known, we obtain a new random variable $t = \sqrt{N}\,(\bar{x} - m)/s$, which has the two desirable properties, namely, t involves m and the distribution of t is known. For it is precisely the Student t distribution with $(N - 1)$ degrees of freedom. Proceeding again as in the case where σ^2 was known, we can assert that

$$\text{Prob}\left(-t_{1-\alpha/2,N-1} \leq \frac{\bar{x} - m}{s/\sqrt{N}} \leq t_{1-\alpha/2,N-1}\right) = 1 - \alpha \qquad (8.2.5)$$

This is equivalent, however, to

$$\text{Prob}\left(\bar{x} - \frac{t_{1-\alpha/2}s}{\sqrt{N}} \leq m \leq \bar{x} + \frac{t_{1-\alpha/2}s}{\sqrt{N}}\right) = 1 - \alpha$$

which asserts that m will lie in the interval determined by $\bar{x} \pm t_{1-\alpha/2,N-1}s/\sqrt{N}$ with odd $1 - \alpha$ to 1, or

$$\text{Prob}\left(m \text{ lies within the interval } \bar{x} \pm \frac{t_{1-\alpha/2}s}{\sqrt{N}}\right) = 1 - \alpha \qquad (8.2.6)$$

Thus $\bar{x} \pm t_{1-\alpha/2,N-1}s/\sqrt{N}$ is a confidence interval with confidence coefficient $1 - \alpha$. In this case, as distinct from the case when σ^2 is known, the length of the random interval, $2t_{1-\alpha/2,N-1}s/\sqrt{N}$, is not constant. We illustrate the basic ideas further with some examples.

Example 8.11   Confidence interval for the variance of a normal distribution   As in all problems of estimation, were we to search for a confidence interval for the variance σ^2 of a normal distribution, we should take N independent observations, which are represented by random variables $X_1, X_2, \ldots, X_N$. It seems to be established, that is, effective, practice to find a random variable involving σ^2 with known distribution. An estimate of σ^2 which comes to mind is the sample variance s^2. What do we know about the distribution of s^2? We recall that $(N - 1)s^2/\sigma^2$ has a χ^2 distribution with $N - 1$ degrees of freedom and, in fact, meets our requirements since it involves σ^2 and has a known distribution. These facts can be expressed as

$$\text{Prob}\left[\chi^2_{\alpha/2,N-1} \leq \frac{(N - 1)s^2}{\sigma^2} \leq \chi^2_{1-\alpha/2,N-1}\right] = 1 - \alpha \qquad (8.2.7)$$

and reformulated so as to provide an interval for σ^2 as follows:

$$\text{Prob}\left[\frac{(N - 1)s^2}{\chi^2_{1-\alpha/2,N-1}} \leq \sigma^2 \leq \frac{(N - 1)s^2}{\chi^2_{\alpha/2,N-1}}\right] = 1 - \alpha$$

The random interval

$$\left[\frac{(N - 1)s^2}{\chi^2_{1-\alpha/2,N-1}} ; \frac{(N - 1)s^2}{\chi^2_{\alpha/2,N-1}}\right] \qquad (8.2.8)$$

forms, therefore, a confidence interval for σ^2 with confidence coefficient $1 - \alpha$. [The odds are $1 - \alpha$ to α that, under the given conditions, σ^2 will lie within the interval (8.2.8).]

For a confidence interval for σ^2 that is bounded from below but unbounded from above, the expression in (8.2.7) can, by analogy, be replaced by

$$\text{Prob}\left[\frac{(N-1)s^2}{\sigma^2} \leq \chi^2_{1-\alpha,N-1}\right] = 1 - \alpha$$

which may be written in the following form:

$$\text{Prob}\left[\frac{(N-1)s^2}{\chi^2_{1-\alpha,N-1}} \leq \sigma^2\right] = 1 - \alpha$$

yielding the random interval

$$\left[\frac{(N-1)s^2}{\chi^2_{1-\alpha,N-1}}; +\infty\right]$$

This is a lower one-sided confidence interval for σ^2, with confidence coefficient $1 - \alpha$.

Example 8.12   Confidence interval for the difference of means $m_X - m_Y$ **of two normal distributions with common variance** σ^2 Often the confidence interval for the difference of two (normal) means is of interest, and therefore two sets of N random independent observations each, $X_1, X_2, \ldots, X_N$ and $Y_1, Y_2, \ldots, Y_N$, are taken, respectively, from the two normal universes. The estimator for $m_X - m_Y$ is, most appropriately, $\bar{X} - \bar{Y}$, which can be transformed to the standard normal variate

$$Z = \frac{(\bar{X} - \bar{Y}) - (m_X - m_Y)}{\sigma\sqrt{2/N}} \tag{8.2.9}$$

which has, again, the desired properties of both involving $m_X - m_Y$ and having a definite distribution when σ^2 is known. Hence it follows that

$$\text{Prob}\left[-Z_{1-\alpha/2} \leq \frac{(\bar{X} - \bar{Y}) - (m_X - m_Y)}{\sigma\sqrt{2/N}} \leq Z_{1-\alpha/2}\right] = 1 - \alpha \tag{8.2.10}$$

which can also be written as

$$\text{Prob}\left[m_X - m_Y \text{ lies within } (\bar{X} - \bar{Y}) \pm Z_{1-\alpha/2}\sigma\sqrt{\frac{2}{N}}\right] = 1 - \alpha$$

Thus $\bar{X} - \bar{Y} \pm Z_{1-\alpha/2}\sigma\sqrt{2/N}$ is a suitable confidence interval for $m_X - m_Y$ with confidence $1 - \alpha$.

If σ^2 is unknown, instead of Z, as in (8.2.9), form the random variable

$$t = \frac{(\bar{X} - \bar{Y}) - (m_X - m_Y)}{s\sqrt{2/N}}$$

This is again a Student t distribution, but now with $2(N - 1)$ degrees of freedom, where s^2 is the pooled sample variance $(s_X{}^2 + s_Y{}^2)/2$. Proceeding as before, a confidence interval of the form

$$(\bar{X} - \bar{Y}) \pm t_{1-\alpha/2, 2(N-1)} s \sqrt{2/N}$$

is obtained. One can proceed as in the previous example (by similar methods) to obtain one-sided confidence intervals.

Example 8.13   Confidence interval for the ratio of the variances of two normal populations   The comparison of the respective variances of two normal populations is of frequent interest. Toward this end the interval within which the ratio of these variances lies is sought again by conventional random independent sampling. Suppose, then, that we have two sets of independent identical random variables $X_1, X_2, \ldots, X_N$ and $Y_1, Y_2, \ldots, Y_N$ representing the two random samples from their respective normal universes. By letting $s_X{}^2$ and $s_Y{}^2$, the sample variances, estimate $\sigma_X{}^2$ and $\sigma_Y{}^2$, respectively, we can form

$$F = \frac{s_X{}^2/\sigma_X{}^2}{s_Y{}^2/\sigma_Y{}^2}$$

which has the F distribution with $(N - 1, N - 1)$ degrees of freedom. Again, since F involves $\sigma_X{}^2/\sigma_Y{}^2$ and has a distribution independent of $\sigma_X{}^2$ and $\sigma_Y{}^2$, we can write

$$\text{Prob} \left(F_{\alpha/2, N-1, N-1} \leq \frac{s_X{}^2/\sigma_X{}^2}{s_Y{}^2/\sigma_Y{}^2} \leq F_{1-\alpha/2, N-1, N-1} \right) = 1 - \alpha$$

which can be rewritten as

$$\text{Prob} \left(\frac{s_X{}^2}{s_Y{}^2} F_{\alpha/2, N-1, N-1} \leq \frac{\sigma_X{}^2}{\sigma_Y{}^2} \leq \frac{s_X{}^2}{s_Y{}^2} F_{1-\alpha/2, N-1, N-1} \right) = 1 - \alpha$$

Consequently,

$$\left(\frac{s_X{}^2}{s_Y{}^2} F_{\alpha/2, N-1, N-1}; \frac{s_X{}^2}{s_Y{}^2} F_{1-\alpha/2, N-1, N-1} \right)$$

forms an appropriate confidence interval for $\sigma_X{}^2/\sigma_Y{}^2$. In a manner similar to that used in the previous examples, lower and upper one-sided confidence intervals can be derived.

Example 8.14   Confidence intervals for the mean rate of a Poisson process and for the ratio of the rates of two Poisson processes   Suppose we wish to derive a confidence interval for the mean rate λ based on observing the random time period T during which a specified number k of events occurs. As indicated in Sec. 7.6, the random variable $2\lambda T$ has a χ^2 distribution with $2k$ degrees of freedom and is a suitable starting point for constructing a confidence interval since it involves λ

and its distribution does not.   One can directly obtain a one-sided confidence interval by selecting a percentile point of the random variable χ^2 (with $2k$ degrees of freedom).   At the α percentile,

$$\text{Prob } (2\lambda T \geq \chi^2_{\alpha,2k}) = 1 - \alpha$$

or equivalently, we have

$$\text{Prob}\left(\lambda \geq \frac{\chi^2_{\alpha,2k}}{2T}\right) = 1 - \alpha$$

Consequently, $(\chi^2_{\alpha,2k}/2T; +\infty)$ forms a suitable lower bounded, one-sided confidence interval.   In a similar manner it can be shown that $(\chi^2_{\alpha/2,2k}/2T;$ $\chi^2_{1-\alpha/2,2k} / 2T)$ forms a two-sided confidence interval.

For the problem of the ratio λ_1/λ_2 of two Poisson processes, we suppose that we have the random times T_1 and T_2 during which k events occur in each of the two Poisson processes, respectively.   Using the fact that

$$\frac{2\lambda_1 T_1/2k}{2\lambda_2 T_2/2k}$$

has an F distribution with $(2k,2k)$ degrees of freedom, we can write

$$\text{Prob}\left(F_{\alpha/2,2k,2k} \leq \frac{\lambda_1 T_1}{\lambda_2 T_2} \leq F_{1-\alpha/2,2k,2k}\right) = 1 - \alpha$$

Thus

$$\text{Prob}\left(\frac{T_2}{T_1} F_{\alpha/2,2k,2k} \leq \frac{\lambda_1}{\lambda_2} \leq \frac{T_2}{T_1} F_{1-\alpha/2,2k,2k}\right) = 1 - \alpha$$

and therefore

$$\left(\frac{T_2}{T_1} F_{\alpha/2,2k,2k}; \frac{T_2}{T_1} F_{1-\alpha/2,2k,2k}\right)$$

is a two-sided confidence interval for λ_1/λ_2, with confidence coefficient $1 - \alpha$.

Relation of Confidence Intervals to Hypothesis Testing   In the previous section, the construction of confidence intervals for a parameter θ depended on finding a random variable involving θ but whose distribution was independent of θ.   Definite probability statements can be made involving such a random variable by which θ can be explicitly "penned in," or bracketed.   If at first writing θ appears in an involved expression, it is usually possible to rewrite these first probability statements as specific probability statements for random intervals bracketing θ.   This procedure cannot, of course, always be carried out.   There are, however, a variety of techniques of general applicability which can be drawn upon, one of which we shall describe here without going into extensive detail.

Consider a distribution $g(x \mid \theta)$ depending on a parameter θ which may have values in a set Ω. Suppose, further, that N independent observations described by random variables $X_1, X_2, \ldots, X_N$ can be made. A *confidence region* $R(X_1, X_2, \ldots, X_N)$ with *confidence coefficient* $1 - \alpha$ is a random set of values in Ω such that

$$\text{Prob } [\theta \text{ in } R(X_1, X_2, \ldots, X_N) \mid \theta] = 1 - \alpha \qquad \text{for all } \theta \text{ in } \Omega \quad (8.2.11)$$

If the region $R(X_1, \ldots, X_N)$ is always an interval for the domain of definition, (8.2.11) represents a confidence interval. How can one, in general, find regions $R(X_1, \ldots, X_N)$ satisfying (8.2.11)?

Suppose that we have the problem of testing the simple hypothesis

$$H_0: \quad \theta = \theta_0 \qquad \text{against} \qquad \theta \neq \theta_0$$

Let $A(\theta_0)$ be an acceptance region for testing H_0, having significance level α. The region $A(\theta_0)$ is a set of values of $(X_1, X_2, \ldots, X_N)$. We recall that the test procedure in this case is to accept $\theta = \theta_0$ when $(X_1, X_2, \ldots, X_N)$ lies in $A(\theta_0)$. Also, since the significance level is α,

$$\text{Prob } [(X_1, X_2, \ldots, X_N) \text{ in } A(\theta_0) \mid \theta_0] = 1 - \alpha$$

Suppose, now, that we have for each θ in Ω an *associated acceptance region*[1] $A(\theta)$, for which

$$\text{Prob } [(X_1, X_2, \ldots, X_N) \text{ in } A(\theta) \mid \theta] = 1 - \alpha \qquad \theta \text{ in } \Omega \quad (8.2.12)$$

Having such a family of acceptance regions, $A(\theta)$, we are in a position to find "suitable" confidence regions $R(X_1, X_2, \ldots, X_N)$. These regions are defined as follows:

θ *is in* $R(X_1, X_2, \ldots, X_N)$, *if and only if* $(X_1, X_2, \ldots, X_N)$ *is in* $A(\theta)$.

That is, $R(X_1, X_2, \ldots, X_N)$ contains all those values θ in for which $(X_1, X_2, \ldots, X_N)$ leads to acceptance of θ. From this definition of $R(X_1, X_2, \ldots, X_N)$ and (8.2.11), it follows that

$$\text{Prob } [\theta \text{ in } R(X_1, X_2, \ldots, X_N) \mid \theta]$$
$$= \text{Prob } [(X_1, X_2, \ldots, X_N) \text{ in } A(\theta) \mid \theta] = 1 - \alpha$$

Consequently, $R(X_1, X_2, \ldots, X_N)$ is a confidence region for θ with confidence coefficient $1 - \alpha$ (the region becomes a confidence interval when R is an interval).

The importance of this relationship lies, on the one hand, in the fact that all the results of hypothesis testing can be directly adopted for finding suitable confidence intervals. On the other hand, if confidence intervals are available, they may be used for hypothesis testing. In fact, if we wish to test $H_0: \theta = \theta_0$, we may utilize $R(X_1, X_2, \ldots, X_N)$ for a

[1] An acceptance region as defined here need not be an interval.

statistical-hypothesis-testing procedure by accepting H_0 when θ_0 lies within $R(X_1, X_2, \ldots, X_N)$ and rejecting otherwise. This procedure has the required significance level α. A further advantage of the relationship between hypothesis testing and confidence intervals is that optimum test procedures lead to confidence intervals having optimum properties. These questions will, however, not be further explored since they lead beyond the scope of this text.

To illustrate the previous ideas, let us reconsider the problem of finding a confidence interval for the mean m of a normal distribution with unknown variance σ^2. In Sec. 7.5.1, it was shown that a suitable acceptance region $A(m)$ for testing H_0: mean $= m$ at significance level α consists of $X_1, X_2, \ldots, X_N$ such that

$$\left| \frac{\bar{x} - m}{s/\sqrt{N}} \right| \leq t_{1-\alpha/2, N-1} \tag{8.2.13}$$

This relationship is equivalent to

$$-t_{1-\alpha/2, N-1} \frac{s}{\sqrt{N}} \leq \bar{x} - m \leq t_{1-\alpha/2, N-1} \frac{s}{\sqrt{N}} \tag{8.2.14}$$

The sets $R(X_1, X_2, \ldots, X_N)$ are found now to contain all those values of m which satisfy relation (8.2.14). It follows, further, that $R(X_1, \ldots, X_N)$ consists of values m such that

$$\bar{x} - t_{1-\alpha/2, N-1} \frac{s}{\sqrt{N}} \leq m \leq \bar{x} + t_{1-\alpha/2, N-1} \frac{s}{\sqrt{N}}$$

The bounds in this case form a confidence interval with confidence coefficient $1 - \alpha$.

Example 8.15   One-sided and two-sided confidence intervals for the parameter p of a binomial variate   Suppose that the probability of "success" of a binomial variate is p. The experiment consists of N random independent trials, and the result is described in terms of the random variable X, the number of successes.

A one-sided confidence interval is obtained by considering the simple hypothesis

$$H_0: \quad p = p_0 \quad \text{against} \quad H_1: \quad p = p_1 > p_0$$

The acceptance region $A(p_0)$ is given by

$$x \leq B_{1-\alpha}(N, p_0)$$

where $B_{1-\alpha}(N, p_0)$ equals a value k such that

$$\sum_{i=0}^{k} \frac{N!}{i!(N-i)!} p_0{}^i (1 - p_0)^{N-i} = 1 - \alpha$$

For each p there is an acceptance region $A(p)$ which contains all x such that

$$x \leq B_{1-\alpha}(N,p) \tag{8.2.15}$$

A confidence region $R(x)$ can now be obtained consisting of all those values p satisfying (8.2.15). Since $B_{1-\alpha}(N,p)$ for α and N fixed is an increasing function of p, $R(x)$ is an interval of the form $(p',1)$, where p' is the solution of

$$x = B_{1-\alpha}(N,p') \tag{8.2.16}$$

and depends on x, α, and N.

In order to solve Eq. (8.2.16) for p', we utilize an important relation (not proved here), namely,

$$\text{Prob } (X \leq x) = \sum_{i=0}^{x} \frac{N!}{i!(N-i)!} p^i (1-p)^{N-i}$$

$$= 1 - \text{Prob} \left[F < \frac{(N-x)p}{(x+1)(1-p)} \right] \tag{8.2.17}$$

where F is a random variable with the F distribution with $[2(x+1), 2(N-x)]$ degrees of freedom. Hence (8.2.16) is equivalent to

$$\text{Prob} \left[F < \frac{(N-x)p'}{(x+1)(1-p')} \right] = \alpha$$

Therefore

$$\frac{(N-x)p'}{(x+1)(1-p')} = F_{\alpha, 2(x+1), 2(N-x)} \tag{8.2.18}$$

Solving, we obtain p', where

$$p' = \frac{(x+1)F_{\alpha, 2(x+1), 2(N-x)}}{(N-x) + (x+1)F_{\alpha, 2(x+1), 2(N-x)}} \tag{8.2.19}$$

Another useful form of (8.2.19) is obtained by using the reciprocal relationship for the F distribution, namely,

$$F_{\alpha, 2(x+1), 2(N-x)} = \frac{1}{F_{1-\alpha, 2(N-x), 2(x+1)}}$$

Substituting in (8.2.19), we obtain

$$p' = \frac{x+1}{(x+1) + (N-x)F_{1-\alpha, 2(N-x), 2(x+1)}} \tag{8.2.20}$$

For example, when $N = 50$ and $x = 29$, the estimate of p is $29/50 = 0.58$. A 95 per cent confidence interval is therefore $(p',1)$, where

$$p' = \frac{(30)}{(30) + (21)(1.58)} = 0.47$$

Thus $(0.47,1)$ is a lower, one-sided 95 per cent confidence interval under the stated conditions.

In order to obtain a two-sided confidence interval, consider, for each p,

$$H_0: \quad \text{fraction of successes} = p$$

against

$$H_1: \quad \text{fraction of successes} \neq p$$

The resulting acceptance region $A(p)$ is (Sec. 7.6)

$$B_{\alpha/2}(N,p) < x \leq B_{1-\alpha/2}(N,p) \tag{8.2.21}$$

But (8.2.21) precisely provides a $(1 - \alpha)$ per cent confidence interval $R(x)$ consisting of those values of p which satisfy (8.2.21). Again, using relation (8.2.17), a suitable confidence interval is given by $(\underline{p},\bar{p})$, where

$$\bar{p} = \frac{(x + 1)F_{1-\alpha/2,2(x+1),2(N-x)}}{(N - x) + (x + 1)F_{1-\alpha/2,2(x+1),2(N-x)}}$$

and

$$\underline{p} = \frac{x}{x + (N - x + 1)F_{1-\alpha/2,2(N-x+1),2x}}$$

For example, when $x = 20$ and $N = 50$, the estimate of $p = {}^{20}\!/_{50} = 0.40$. A two-sided 99 per cent confidence interval for p is then $(\underline{p},\bar{p})$, where

$$\bar{p} = \frac{21F_{0.995,42,60}}{30 + 21F_{0.995,42,60}} = 0.59$$

$$\underline{p} = \frac{20}{20 + 31F_{0.995,62,40}} = 0.23$$

Example 8.16 Suppose that the lifetime of an item can be described by a random variable whose CDF is $1 - e^{-t/m}$ with mean lifetime m. Consider N items placed on life test for a period of time T, after which the items are examined and the number of failures, X, noted. Can we use this type of data to furnish a confidence interval for m? The probability p of a failure during $[0,T]$ is given by $p = 1 - e^{-T/m}$. Hence the distribution of X is binomial, with mean "fraction success" equal to p. By methods previously described, a confidence interval for p can be obtained. Since, for fixed T, p is a decreasing function of m, the confidence interval for p can be translated into one for m. Thus, if a two-sided confidence interval for p is $(\underline{p},\bar{p})$, the corresponding confidence interval for m is $(\underline{m},\bar{m})$, where $\underline{m}$ and $\underline{m}$ are determined from

$$\bar{p} = 1 - e^{-T/\underline{m}} \qquad \underline{p} = 1 - e^{-T/\bar{m}}$$

which yields

$$\underline{m} = \frac{-T}{\ln(1 - \bar{p})} \qquad \bar{m} = \frac{-T}{\ln(1 - \underline{p})} \tag{8.2.22}$$

The use of $(m,\bar{m})$ can be illustrated simply by taking $N = 50$, $X = 20$, and $T = 12$ months. Then the estimate of p is $p = {}^{20}\!/_{50} = 0.40$, and the corresponding estimate of the mean life m is obtained from $0.40 = 1 - e^{-12/m}$, yielding $m = 23.4$ months. In Example 8.15 a two-sided, 99 per cent confidence interval for p was found to be $(0.23, 0.59)$ when $X = 20$. The corresponding confidence interval for m is found from Eqs. (8.2.22), substituting 0.23 for p, 0.59 for $\bar{p}$, and 12 for T. This results in $(16.4, 46)$.

The procedure is analogous for one-sided confidence intervals.

Example 8.17 Referring again to Example 7.8, recall that the lifetime of an item could fall into one of three intervals $[0, T]$, $(T, 2T]$, $(2T, \infty]$, with respective probabilities

$$p_1 = 1 - e^{-T/m}$$
$$p_2 = e^{-T/m} - e^{-2T/m} = e^{-T/m}(1 - e^{-T/m})$$
$$p_3 = e^{-2T/m}$$

Denoting $e^{-T/m}$ by p, $p_1 = 1 - p$, $p_2 = p(1 - p)$, and $p_3 = p^2$. Can an effective confidence interval be constructed for m by observing the number of failures occurring during each of the three intervals?

Suppose that N items are placed on life test and examined at the end of T months and then, at the end of $2T$ months, yield X_1, X_2, and X_3 random variables, representing the number of failures occurring during each of the three time intervals, respectively. How shall one construct a confidence interval for m based on observation of X_1, X_2, and X_3? Again, a confidence interval will be obtained for $p = e^{-T/m}$ and then converted into one for m. For this purpose, let us utilize the correspondence between confidence intervals and tests of statistical hypotheses, beginning with a test of the multinomial assumption

$$H_0: \quad [1 - p, p(1 - p), p^2] = [1 - p_0, p_0(1 - p_0), p_0^2] \quad \text{against} \quad H_1:$$
$$H_0 \text{ not true}$$

An acceptance region $A(p_0)$ is given, for large N, by the goodness-of-fit test:

$$\frac{[X_1 - N(1 - p_0)]^2}{N(1 - p_0)} + \frac{[X_2 - Np_0(1 - p_0)]^2}{Np_0(1 - p_0)} + \frac{(X_3 - Np_0^2)^2}{Np_0^2}$$
$$\leq \chi^2_{1-\alpha, 2} \quad (8.2.23)$$

Thus, for each p, there is a corresponding acceptance region $A(p)$. A suitable confidence region for p may then be specified as all those values of p_0 for which (8.2.3) is satisfied. One may graphically find this region, for any values (X_1, X_2, X_3), by plotting the left-hand side of (8.2.23) as a function of p_0 and noting the values of p_0 (in this case they constitute an interval) which satisfy the required inequality. For a set of assumed values $X_1 = 50$, $X_2 = 30$, $X_3 = 20$, $N = 100$, and $\alpha = 0.05$, inequality (8.2.23) becomes

$$f(p) = \frac{[50 - 100(1 - p)]^2}{100(1 - p)} + \frac{[30 - 100p(1 - p)]^2}{100p(1 - p)} + \frac{(20 - 100p^2)^2}{100p^2}$$
$$\leq 5.99 \quad (8.2.24)$$

(with $\chi^2_{0.95,2} = 5.99$). The graph of the left side of (8.2.24) is given in Fig. 8.3. The resulting interval for p is approximately $(0.37, 0.57)$.

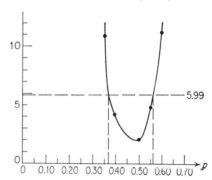

Figure 8.3

In order to find a 95 per cent, two-sided confidence interval for m, one solves the two equations (for $T = 3$)

$$0.37 = e^{-3/m} \qquad 0.57 = e^{-3/\bar{m}}$$

obtaining $m = 3.0$ and $\bar{m} = 5.4$. Thus $[3.0, 5.4]$ is the required 95 per cent confidence interval for m, based on observations $X_1 = 50$, $X_2 = 30$, and $X_3 = 20$. This is a narrower interval than would have been obtained by observing only one value X for time period $[0,6]$.

8.2.2   Tolerance intervals

In previous sections, intervals were determined within which an unknown parameter of a given distribution could be expected to lie with specified odds. The basis for determining this type of interval is, of course, a random independent sample of observations on the process whose output is governed by the given distribution. One can, however, determine another type of interval within which one can assert that a predetermined fraction of N future observations will lie, again with specified odds, and again as a result of a random independent sample of observations on the process. But in determining such intervals, the most important cases arise when the form of the distribution is not known.

Typical and important uses for such intervals arise in the economic control of manufactured products. A very successful manufacturer of small springs which are produced and delivered in very large lots is able to add this guarantee with each lot: characteristic A of the springs in this lot will be within L_1 and L_2, β per cent of the time; that is, β per cent of the springs in this lot will fall within L_1 and L_2 for characteristic A. This assertion is made with confidence $1 - \alpha$. This type of interval is inherently like the interval which, in industrial practice, specifies the "tolerances" of a dimension of a manufactured item. The term *tolerance interval* therefore seems quite appropriate. The concept of a tolerance interval is quite recent, having arisen from the work of W. A. Shewhart and S. S. Wilks, who developed the first tolerance interval in two short classical papers. These intervals were derived on a distribution-free and nonparametric basis. All that was required was that the process behave so that the outcomes appeared to come from a distribution. The criterion for this is some evidence that the process is in statistical control with respect to the dimension under consideration.

It is important to note that the tolerance interval was a novel contribution to statistical theory. With the work of Student, Fisher, Neyman, and Pearson, the confidence interval was established. The confidence interval is determined from experiment and statistical inference and applies to a parameter. In order to obtain a confidence interval one reasons from observed outcomes to a characteristic, a parameter, of a distribution. It is reasonable to expect, therefore, that one should be able to argue from the existence of a distribution to the location of outcomes of random "expressions" of the distribution. One should be able to calculate by probabilistic principles where random outcomes of a process will fall. An interval within which a given percentage of a random sample drawn from a universe will fall is then a *probability interval*. It was argued, however, that since such an interval required complete determination of the distribution, the interval could be only an abstraction, and not one determined by observation on a process. For in order to have the mean and, where necessary, the standard deviation of a distribution representing outcomes of a process, these parameters must necessarily be estimated by experiment. It was argued that an interval so determined could not be a probability interval.

Shewhart was interested in a statistical method for finding this type of interval, for he wanted to establish "tolerances" scientifically. In many years of inquiry among engineers, he discovered that engineers required from about 100 to 500 observations on a process, when it was running well, in order to be able to specify realistic tolerances for dimensions of manufactured items. Something more consistent than the intuitive approach of the operating engineer was sought, namely, a tolerance interval, a sort of experimental probability interval, which could be analytically determined from observations on the process outcomes. Many statisticians rejected this problem, but Wilks came up with the following procedure. Given a process operating in a state of statistical control and from it a sample of n observations on a particular characteristic; note L_1 the smallest and L_2 the greatest of the magnitudes of the characteristic under observation (Fig. 8.4). Then it can be argued that of the next N observations, β per cent will fall between L_1 and L_2, and this statement can be asserted with a confidence $1 - \alpha$. One of Wilks's results which squares with operating experience is the following. If from a process in statistic control a sample of 100 observations is taken on characteristic X, at least 95 per cent of all the future observations (assuming that the process remains indefinitely in statistical control) will lie between L_1 and L_2 95 per cent of the time. Hence, for practical purposes, if 95 per cent conformance is satisfactory and if one is satisfied if this happens only 95 per cent of the time, one may set process tolerances L_1 and L_2 from a sample of 100 observations. By taking 500 observations, one can establish tolerances L_1 and L_2 for 99 per cent of future product with a 99 per cent confidence.

The tolerance interval is a probability statement hedged by a statement of odds. Any statement about occurrences must be hedged by a specification of the percentage of the time that the statement will be

Figure 8.4

found to be true. A very valuable aspect of Wilks's tolerance interval is that it is both distribution-free and parameter-free. Tolerances set in this manner are realistic, since they do not depend on the form of distribution of outcomes of a process.

Following the work of Wilks, a number of investigators, notably Wald, Wolfowitz, and Bowker, developed tolerance limits based on knowledge of the distribution. Principally, a normal distribution was assumed, and symmetrical tolerance limits were set about the mean. Of course, these tolerance limits, that is to say, the tolerance interval established for an assumed distribution, are, on the average, less than their counterparts of the Wilks type—as might be expected when so much more knowledge is assumed. The realistic merits of such a tolerance interval may, however, be suspect. Certainly, the Wilks interval is much simpler to use in practice.

In discussing the Wilks interval, reference was made to the fraction of the future N observations which are expected to fall between L_1 and L_2. One may, however, avail oneself of L_1 and L_2 in another way. Suppose one has made a lot of 100,000 small springs under statistical control. Then it is reasonable to sample this lot without regard to order and to make predictions based on the measurements of the items in the sample. Suppose one applied a tension test on the springs, measuring the tension resulting from a specified stretch. Then the least tension L_1 and the greatest tension L_2, resulting from test of a random independent sample of 200 springs, can be expected to include 96 per cent (or more) of the values of tension that would be obtained were all the 100,000 springs put to this test, in 96 per cent of such large lots. The spring manufacturer can feel confident that his prediction of tolerance limits which are to include at least 96 per cent of magnitudes of spring tension will be true in 96 out of 100 such lots. This is a guarantee which has strong operational appeal.

A further word before establishing some tolerance intervals. There can be one-sided tolerance intervals as well as two-sided ones, obtained in the same manner. One can also set up intervals bounded by the second-largest and by the second-smallest values, and so on. Tolerance intervals are also referred to as prediction intervals, which indeed they are, where the prediction is "hedged" by a confidence statement.

We shall now develop the formal relations between n, the number of random independent observations made on the outcomes of process (or the number of random independent observations made on a given characteristic of items which constitute a very large aggregate); β, the fraction of the population which will lie between L_1 and L_2; and α, the probability that less than fraction β of the observed characteristic lies between L_1 and L_2. Let, then, $X_1, X_2, \ldots, X_n$ be a set of independent random variables identically distributed with $PDF = f(x)$ and $CDF = F(x)$, such that the set $(X_1, X_2, \ldots, X_n)$ represents the observations made. Let L_1 and L_2 be the minimum and the maximum of the n observations. The fraction which will lie within L_1 and L_2 is designated by

$$F = \int_{L_1}^{L_2} f(x) \, dx = F(L_2) - F(L_1) \qquad (8.2.25)$$

Although $f(x)$ is unspecified, it turns out that F *has a distribution which is independent of $f(x)$*. (F is, of course, a random variable, since it depends on L_1 and L_2, which are random variables.) Furthermore, it was indicated in Sec. 4.8 that if X has a CDF $F(x)$, then the $F(X)$, itself a random variable, has a uniform distribution in $[0,1]$. F therefore is independent of $f(x)$, and $F(X_1), F(X_2), \ldots, F(X_n)$ are n values drawn by random independent sampling from a universe which is uniformly distributed on $[0,1]$. This may be represented by the relation $(x_1 \leq x_2)$

$$\text{Prob } [F_1 \leq F(X) \leq F_2] = \text{Prob } (x_1 \leq X \leq x_2) = F(x_2) - F(x_1)$$
$$= F_2 - F_1$$

Returning to $F = F(L_2) - F(L_1)$, note that F is a random variable with the same distribution as the fraction of the interval $[0,1]$ covered by n independent observations taken at random from a uniform distribution. In order to find the joint distribution of $F(L_1)$ and $F(L_2)$, partition $[0,1]$ as in Fig. 8.5, where a and b are two numbers in the interval.

The probability of the observations lying as designated in Fig. 8.5 can be expressed by drawing upon the multinomial distribution, whence is obtained

$$\text{Prob } [a \le F(L_1) \le a + \Delta; b \le F(L_2) \le b + \delta]$$

$$= \frac{n!}{0!1!(n - 2)!1!0!} a^0 \Delta^1 (b - a - \Delta)^{n-2} \delta^1 (1 - b - \delta)^0$$
$$= n(n - 1)(b - a - \Delta)^{n-2} \Delta \delta \qquad (8.2.26)$$

The joint density distribution of $F(L_1)$ and $F(L_2)$ in terms of a and b,

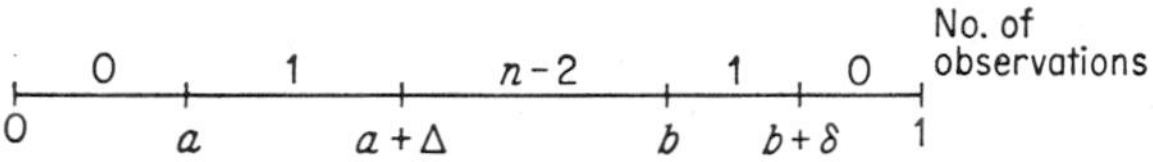

Figure 8.5

that is at (a,b), is obtained from (8.2.26) by letting $\Delta \to 0$ and $\delta \to 0$ independently.   Thereby we have

$$f(a,b) = \lim_{\substack{\Delta \to 0 \\ \delta \to 0}} \frac{\text{Prob } [a \le F(L_1) \le a + \Delta; b \le F(L_2) \le b + \delta]}{\Delta \delta}$$

$$= n(n - 1)(b - a)^{n-2} \qquad \text{where } 0 \le a \le b \le 1 \qquad (8.2.27)$$

The CDF of $F(L_2) - F(L_1)$ is then, letting $F(L_2) - F(L_1) = W$,

$$F(w) = \text{Prob } [F(L_2) - F(L_1) \le w] = \iint_{b - a \le w} n(n - 1)(b - a)^{n-2} \, da \, db$$

The above integral, using the notation simplification $Z = b - a$, $t = a$, evaluates to

$$F(w) = n(n - 1) \left(\frac{w^{n-1}}{n - 1} - \frac{w^n}{n} \right) = nw^{n-1} - (n - 1)w^n \qquad (8.2.28)$$

The density follows directly by differentiation of $F(w)$, yielding

$$f(w) = n(n - 1)w^{n-2}(1 - w) \qquad \text{where } 0 \le w \le 1 \qquad (8.2.29)$$

The tolerance interval can now be determined by setting the appropriate conditions on W.   The cumulative distribution of W is evaluated at β, which is the fraction of the future observations to lie between L_1 and L_2.   This, however, is the Prob $(W \le \beta)$, since $W = F(L_2) - F(L_1)$, where, recall, $F(x)$ is the cumulative density function of the original random variable which represents the random independent observations. We must set the probability that the fraction between L_1 and L_2 will be less than β, since this is the allowable error.   All this is contained in the equation

$$F(\beta) = \text{Prob } (W \le \beta) = \alpha \qquad (8.2.30)$$

where α is the allowable error. The meaning of (8.2.30) in terms of the original task of determining a tolerance interval is

Prob [intervals (L_1,L_2) cover at least fraction β of the universe] $= 1 - \alpha$

$$(8.2.31)$$

This, however, is precisely the statement that $[L_1,L_2]$ is a tolerance interval for a fraction β of the population and that we expect fraction β or more of all future observations to lie between L_1 and L_2 at least $100(1 - \alpha)$ per cent of the times that this experiment is performed.

It is desirable, of course, to determine the smallest n for which the desired tolerance interval can be found, and this value for n is a solution of (8.2.28), which reduces to

$$F(\beta) = n\beta^{n-1} - (n - 1)\beta^n = \alpha$$

As is customary, such transcendental equations are studied by trial and error. A rather good approximation, which simplifies calculation considerably, is

$$n \cong \tfrac{1}{4}\chi^2_{1-\alpha,4}\left(\frac{1 + \beta}{1 - \beta}\right) + \frac{1}{2}$$

For $\alpha = 0.05$, $\beta = 0.99$, we obtain

$$n \cong \tfrac{1}{4}(9.488)(1.99/0.01) + \tfrac{1}{2} = 473$$

This result was obtained on the basis of an infinite set of future observations and is interpreted as follows. When observations are made on 473 random independent outcomes of a statistically controlled process, then in 95 per cent of the times that this experiment is performed, at least 99 per cent of the observations made on all future outcomes of the process will lie between L_1 and L_2 as determined from the original sample of 473 observations. Another form of interpretation is, suppose that one has a very large aggregate of items (many thousand) and that a random independent sample of 473 items is taken from this lot. Suppose, further, that characteristic A is measured on each of the 473 items, yielding an L_1 and L_2 for these 473 observations. Then at least 99 per cent of the observations made on characteristic A of all the remaining items will lie between L_1 and L_2 in 95 per cent of the lots so studied. This latter interpretation is used by the spring manufacturer in guaranteeing dimensions of lots of springs.

The results that have been attained above have been based only on the assumption that observations have been made on a distribution, with no knowledge of the form of the distribution or its determining parameters. [It was assumed that $f(x)$ was continuous, but this is not very restrictive.] The interval $[L_1,L_2]$ is usually referred to a nonparametric tolerance interval (the term nonparametric seems to be used to mean distribution-free in most cases). It is reasonable to ask whether narrower tolerance intervals are obtained when the form of the distribution is supposed to be known. The case of the normal distribution has been studied where the mean and variance, however, remain unknown. Tolerance intervals in the form $(\bar{x} - ks, \bar{x} + ks)$ are obtained in this case, where $\bar{x}$ and s are estimated from the original sample and k is a function of n, α, and β and the number of future observations considered. This number, in most current tabulations of k, is assumed infinite. Comparison of the two types of interval cannot be readily made since L_1 and L_2 are observed quantities and k is not a function of the observations. Further considerations of tolerance intervals go beyond the scope of this text.

EXERCISES

8.1. Suppose X_1, X_2, and X_3 are three independent random variables such that $E(X_1) = E(X_2) = E(X_3) = \mu$ and $V(X_1) = 1$, $V(X_2) = 2$, and $V(X_3) = 3$. Given observations X_1, X_2, X_3, find an unbiased linear estimate of μ with minimum variance.

8.2. Suppose a random variable X is uniformly distributed between 0 and θ. A sample X_1, X_2, . . . , X_n of n independent observations is taken for estimating θ. Two possible estimators are being considered. One is given by $S_1 = C_1 \bar{X}$, where $\bar{X}$ is the arithmetic average. The other one is of the form $S_2 = C_2 \max (X_1, X_2, \ldots , X_n)$.

   a. What must C_1 be so that S_1 is unbiased?
   b. What is the density function of $\max (X_1, X_2, \ldots , X_n)$?
   c. What must C_2 be so that S_2 is unbiased?
   d. Compute variance of S_1 and S_2.
   e. Which estimator has the smaller variance?
   f. What must C_1 and C_2 be to minimize the mean-square error of S_1 and S_2?

8.3. Suppose X_1, X_2, and X_3 are independent random variables with mean μ and variance σ^2.

   a. Is $T = \frac{1}{2}X_1 + \frac{1}{4}X_2 + \frac{1}{4}X_3$ an unbiased estimate of μ?
   b. Is $T' = \frac{1}{3}X_1 + \frac{1}{3}X_2 + \frac{1}{6}X_3$ an unbiased estimate of μ?
   c. Find a linear unbiased estimator with minimum variance.
   d. What is the linear estimator with minimum mean-square error when the coefficient of variation σ/μ is known to be equal to 1?

8.4. Consider again Exercise 3.3. Let the failure distribution be given by the exponential distribution with mean a. For each of n cycles, it is noted whether failure with repair occurred or not. Let the results be denoted by X_1, X_2, . . . , X_n, where

$$X_j = \begin{cases} 1 & \text{if failure occurred in } j\text{th cycle} \\ 0 & \text{otherwise} \end{cases}$$

   a. Obtain an estimate of a on the basis of X_1, X_2, . . . , X_n when a maintenance interval of length m is used.
   b. How would you test the hypothesis H_0: $a = 2$ against H_1: $a > 2$ on the basis of X_1, . . . , X_n, using a maintenance interval m?
   c. Find a confidence interval for a on the basis of X_1, X_2, . . . , X_n.

d. Find the approximate variance of the estimator for a found in (a).

e. What is the best m to minimize the approximate variance found in (d)?

f. Is the estimator found in (a) a maximum-likelihood estimator?

8.5. The weights of four objects are to be determined on a balance scale. A reading consists of any arrangement of the four objects on the two pans of the scale and reading the marker in the center. Consider that the reading on any one weighing is a random variable with mean equal to the difference of the weights on each side of the scale and variance σ^2 (independent of the arrangement of the objects). Design four weighings so that it will be possible to estimate the weights of each object with an unbiased estimator having variance $\sigma^2/4$.

8.6. Consider a lake with N fish of a certain kind. Let n fish be chosen, tagged, and thrown back in the lake. Next, a random sample, with replacement, of k fish is taken from the lake. Let T be the number of tagged fish in the sample.

a. What is the distribution of T?

b. How can T be used for estimating N?

c. What is the approximate variance of the estimate obtained in (b)?

8.7. Observations 7, 8, 5, 4, and 10 are obtained on a random sample from an exponential distribution with unknown mean equal to m.

a. Find the maximum-likelihood estimate of m.

b. What is the variance of the estimate found in (a)?

8.8. Suppose that $X_1, X_2, \ldots, X_n$ are n independent observations from the uniform distribution over the interval $[0, U]$. Show that $T = \max (X_1, X_2, \ldots, X_n)$ is a sufficient estimator for U.

8.9. Suppose N items have an exponential lifetime distribution with mean m and are independent. The times $t_1, t_2, \ldots, t_r$ of the first r failure times are noted.

a. Show that $\hat{m} = [t_1 + t_2 + \cdots + t_r + (N - r)t_r]/r$ is a sufficient statistic for m. (HINT: Write $\hat{m}$ in terms of successive differences in failure times.)

b. Use the result of Exercise 5.9 to show that $2r\hat{m}/m$ has a χ^2 distribution with $2r$ degrees of freedom.

c. Use the result in (b) to obtain one-sided and two-sided confidence intervals for m.

8.10. The functioning of a piece of equipment depends on two major components (as in Exercise 2.23) A and B. A has one subcomponent, and B has two in parallel. Operation then depends on both A and B functioning. A operates if its subcomponent operates. B functions if either one of its subcomponents operate. Let p_A equal the probability of the subcomponent in A operating. Let p_B equal the probability of a subcomponent in B operating.

a. What is p_S, the probability of the equipment operating? To estimate p_A and p_B, each type of component was tested n times and the proportion of successful function noted. This gave estimates $\hat{p}_A$ and $\hat{p}_B$.

b. What is $V(\hat{p}_A)$ and $V(\hat{p}_B)$?

c. The values of $\hat{p}_A$ and $\hat{p}_B$ were substituted for p_A and p_B in the formula for p_S in (a) to obtain an estimate $\hat{p}_S$ for p_S. What is the approximate value of $V(\hat{p}_S)$? What is $E(\hat{p}_S)$? What is approximate $MSE(\hat{p}_S)$?

d. Suppose n_1 observations on functioning of the subcomponent of A are made and n_2 observations on those of B. No more than N experiments in all may be made $(n_1 + n_2 \leq N)$. What values of n_1 and n_2 will minimize $V(\hat{p}_S)$ approximately when a preliminary guess of $p_A = 0.8$ and $p_B = 0.5$ is assumed? Do the same for $MSE(\hat{p}_S)$.

8.11. The lifetime of an item has an exponential distribution with mean m. One hundred items were placed on life test for 200 hours. At the end of this period, the items were examined and 40 were defective.

    a. What is the maximum-likelihood estimate of m on the basis of these data?
    b. What is the approximate variance of estimate in (*a*)?
    c. Find a two-sided confidence interval for m with confidence coefficient $1 - \alpha$ = 0.90.
    d. Find a lower-sided confidence interval for m with confidence coefficient $1 - \alpha$ = 0.90.

8.12. Find a 95 per cent confidence interval for the difference in mean yield in Exercise 7.1.

8.13. How would you construct a confidence interval for b in Exercise 7.3 on the basis of X_1 and X_2?

8.14. Find a 90 per cent confidence interval for mean difference between dyes A and B in Exercise 7.6.

8.15. Find the 90 per cent confidence interval for difference in accidents in Exercise 7.8.

8.16. Find the 99 per cent confidence interval for difference in mean microammeter readings during prerecognition exposures and for difference of mean thresholds for neutral and critical words in Exercise 7.16.

8.17. Find a 90 per cent confidence interval for the ratio of variances of results with dyes A and B in Exercise 7.6.

8.18. Find a 90 per cent confidence interval for variance of threshold and microammeter response for the subjects for neutral words and for critical words. Also, find a 90 per cent confidence interval for the ratio of these variances (Exercise 7.16).

8.19. Prove that convergence in the mean of an estimator S to parameter θ implies convergence in probability. HINT: Use a variation of Tchebycheff's inequality.

8.20. In Example 8.2c find the approximate MSE of $S(X) = T/X$ (for $1/\lambda$) and compare with the MSE of estimator T_R/R.

8.21. Prove Eq. (8.1.39). HINT: Use Eq. (8.1.38).

8.22. Compare the approximate confidence interval in Example 8.17 with that obtained by observing only one value of X for a time period [0,6].

8.23. In Example 8.10, what is the best value of T to use for estimating m?

8.24. Suppose that N items are placed on life test. An item which fails is immediately replaced. Let t_r be the time of the rth failure. Assume that the distribution of lifetime is exponential with mean m.

    a. Show that $2Nt_r/m$ has a χ^2 distribution with $2r$ degrees of freedom.
    b. Twenty items are placed on test. The fifth failure is observed to occur 407 hours after the start of the life test. Give an unbiased estimate of m.
    c. Under the conditions in (*b*), find a two-sided 95 per cent confidence interval for m.

8.25. Consider a system which depends on the functioning in some way of k components. Let p_i be the probability that the ith component functions at any time (reliability of ith component). Furthermore, let $R(p_1, p_2, \ldots, p_k)$ be the reliability of the system as it depends on the reliabilities of the components. We shall assume, as is true of most physical systems, that when $p_i < p_i'$, then $R(p_1, p_2, \ldots, p_k) \leq R(p_1', p_2', \ldots, p_k')$. Let N_i observations on the ith component be made, resulting in a certain number of successes and failures. Let $[\underline{p_i}, \bar{p_i}]$ be a $1 - \alpha_i$ confidence interval for the probability of success obtained from the binomial distribution.

a. Show that $[R(\underline{p_1}, \underline{p_2}, \ldots, \underline{p_k}), R(\bar{p_1}, \bar{p_2}, \ldots, \bar{p_k})]$ is a $(1 - \alpha_1)(1 - \alpha_2) \cdots (1 - \alpha_k)$ confidence interval for $R(p_1, p_2, \ldots, p_k)$.

b. Consider a system where $R(p_1, p_2, p_3) = [1 - (1 - p_1)(1 - p_2)]p_3$, $N_1 = N_2 = N_3 = 100$, and the results give 90, 85, and 90 successes of components 1, 2, and 3, respectively. Letting $\alpha_1 = \alpha_2 = \alpha_3$, find a 94 per cent confidence interval for $R(p_1, p_2, p_3)$.

9

SAMPLING AND
ANALYSIS OF VARIANCE

In this chapter we further explore some inference problems relating to populations, and particularly to the experimental environment population (EEP), introduced in Sec. 7.5.2. We consider a measurable quantity X, associated with points in the EEP. In Sec. 9.1 we discuss the estimation of the mean $m = E(X)$ of X, where the expectation is taken over the EEP. Some sampling procedures for estimating m, such as random stratified and two-stage sampling, are described and compared.

In Sec. 9.2 the inference problem for means m_1, m_2, . . . , m_k of various measurable quantities $X_1, X_2, . . . , X_k$ over the EEP is studied. This leads to an analysis of the variations over the EEP as affected by the quantities being measured and the various strata of the EEP.

9.1 Some empirical and some formal aspects of sampling

A basic element in the process of statistical inference is that of sampling. We shall explore several different types of sampling procedures. Our interest is in estimating the mean $m = E(X)$ of some measurable quantity X, associated with points in the EEP. We may think of a bowl of chips where each chip has an X number associated with it. If there are N chips in the bowl with associated X values x_1, x_2, . . . , x_N, then $m = (x_1 + x_2 + \cdots + x_N)/N$.[1] To estimate m, we must take a sample, in some manner, and use the resulting x values as a basis for estimating m. It may be well to emphasize in this connection that *the basis of inferences for m lies in the process of sampling and the results obtained from the application of the sampling.* The results by themselves, without the specification of the sampling procedures, do not yield an adequate basis for inference. Several modes of sampling will now be examined.

---

[1] In this case all the values are assumed to be equally likely. In other cases, a weighted average must be taken.

9.1.1 Simple random sampling

The method of simple random sampling is widely used and consists of choosing a sample of, say, n chips (or points in the EEP) at random from the whole bowl. More specifically, we require that any set of n chips out of the total aggregate of N has an equal chance with any other such set of being chosen. Physically, this requirement may be satisfied when the chips are as "similar" as is possible and are "thoroughly mixed." Then one can choose one chip at a time, mixing the remaining chips thoroughly, after each choice, until n chips are chosen. The resulting X numbers, using this process, may be represented by random variables $X_1, X_2, \ldots, X_n$, where X_j is the X number on the chip resulting from the jth choice. In practice, it may be a difficult task to have conviction that a sampling procedure does in fact yield random samples. The problem of testing whether a process does result in random samples will not be discussed at present.

In order to estimate m from the sample, represented by random variables $X_1, X_2, \ldots, X_n$, we may take the arithmetic average $\bar{X}$ of the sample. That is, $\bar{X} = (X_1 + X_2 + \cdots + X_n)/n$, and it can be shown that

$$E(X) = \frac{1}{n} [E(X_1) + E(X_2) + \cdots + E(X_n)] = m \qquad (9.1.1)$$

Furthermore, the variance of $\bar{X}$ can be demonstrated to equal

$$V(\bar{X}) = \left(1 - \frac{n-1}{N-1}\right) \frac{\sigma^2}{n} \qquad (9.1.2)$$

where
$$\sigma^2 = \frac{1}{N} \sum_{i=1}^{N} (x_i - m)^2 \qquad (9.1.3)$$

is the variance of X over the whole EEP. When N is "sufficiently" large so that n/N is small, the quantity $\left(1 - \dfrac{n-1}{N-1}\right) \cong 1$ and

$$V(\bar{X}) \cong \frac{\sigma^2}{n}$$

the standard result for sampling from an infinite population. The factor $\left(1 - \dfrac{n-1}{N-1}\right)$ is usually called the *finite population correction factor*. When N is large, the factor of importance is the value of the sample size n, and not the proportion n/N, of the population sampled. For example, compare two situations where σ^2 is the same and $N_1 = 10,000,000$ and $n_1 = 1,000$, $N_2 = 1,000,000$ and $n_2 = 500$. In this case, $n_1/N_1 = 10^{-4}$ and $n_2/N_2 = 5 \times 10^{-4}$, and consequently, $n_2/N_2 > n_1/N_1$. However, the relative variance of the arithmetic averages $V(X_1)/V(X_2) \cong 0.50$, so that $V(\bar{X}_2) \cong 2V(\bar{X}_1)$, even though $n_2/N_2 = 5(n_1/N_1)$. Under a wide range of conditions, the variance of $\bar{X}$ depends essentially only on σ^2 and the sample size n. For the purpose of presenting the essential ideas, we shall assume that N is large and n/N small.

The precision of the sample estimate $\bar{X}$ of the population mean m depends on (1) the sample size and (2) the *variance per observation*, reflecting the variability or heterogeneity of the population with respect to characteristic X. Apart from increasing the sample size, the only way of increasing precision is to derive sampling procedures which, in effect, reduce the variance per observation. Recalling the discussion of paired comparisons in Sec. 7.5, it is worthwhile studying the effects of stratification of the population.

9.1.2 Stratified sampling

As pointed out in the previous section, the variance per observation is an important factor influencing the efficiency of sampling. Let us therefore analyze the variation σ^2 of X over the *EEP* more closely in order to see what it depends on. For this purpose, we divide the population into k disjoint and exhaustive strata $S_1, S_2, \ldots, S_k$. Let the proportion of the population in these various strata be $p_1, p_2, \ldots, p_k$. Furthermore, denote by m_j the mean of X over stratum j and write

$$m_j = E(X \mid S_j) \tag{9.1.4}$$

and let the variance of X over strata j be denoted by $\sigma_j{}^2$. That is,

$$\sigma_j{}^2 = V(X \mid S_j) \tag{9.1.5}$$

In order to compare various sampling procedures, we shall examine the variance σ^2 (over the *whole* population) as it is affected by $m_1, m_2, \ldots, m_k$ and $\sigma^2{}_1, \sigma^2{}_2, \ldots, \sigma^2{}_k$. The mean m of the whole population can be expressed in terms of $m_1, m_2, \ldots, m_k$ and $p_1, p_2, \ldots, p_k$ since

$$m = E(X) = E[E(X \mid S_j)] = E(m_j) = \sum_{j=1}^{k} p_j m_j \tag{9.1.6}$$

Again, using the fundamental definition, we have

$$\sigma^2 = E(X - m)^2 = E(X^2) - m^2 = E[E(X^2 \mid S_j)] - m^2$$

$$= \sum_{j=1}^{k} p_j E(X^2 \mid S_j) - m^2 \tag{9.1.7}$$

But $\qquad \sigma_j{}^2 = E[(X - m_j)^2 \mid S_j] = E(X^2 \mid S_j) - m_j{}^2 \tag{9.1.8}$

whence $\qquad\qquad E(X^2 \mid S_j) = \sigma_j{}^2 + m_j{}^2 \tag{9.1.9}$

Substituting $\sigma_j^2 + m_j^2$ for $E(X^2 \mid S_j)$ in (9.1.7), we have

$$\sigma^2 = \sum_j p_j(\sigma_j^2 + m_j^2) - m^2$$

$$= \sum_j p_j\sigma_j^2 + \sum_j p_j m_j^2 - m^2$$

$$= \sum_j p_j\sigma_j^2 + \sum_j p_j(m_j - m)^2 \tag{9.1.10}$$

σ^2 is composed of two terms, one due to variation *within* strata and another to variation *between* strata.

The variance V_R of $\bar{X}$, resulting from random sampling, can be expressed as

$$V_R = \frac{\sigma^2}{n} = \frac{1}{n}\sum_j p_j\sigma_j^2 + \frac{1}{n}\sum_j p_j(m_j - m)^2 \tag{9.1.11}$$

In order to take such advantage of the strata as is warranted, we introduce the *stratified sampling procedure*, which consists in drawing, at random, from each strata S_j a sample of size n_j. Various stratified sampling procedures result according to differing ways of choosing n_j.

Proportional Stratified Sampling Suppose the values p_1, p_2, . . . , p_k to be known and that n_j is chosen proportionally to p_j; that is,

$$n_j = np_j \tag{9.1.12}$$

The estimate of m is given by

$$\bar{X} = \sum_j p_j\bar{X}_j \tag{9.1.13}$$

where $\bar{X}_j$ is the sample average from the random sample in strata S_j. This estimate is unbiased since

$$E(\bar{X}) = \sum_j p_j E(\bar{X}_j) = \sum_j p_j m_j = m \tag{9.1.14}$$

The variance V_P of $\bar{X}$ is given by

$$V_P = V(\bar{X}) = \sum_j p_j^2 V(\bar{X}_j) = \sum_j p_j^2 \frac{\sigma_j^2}{n_j}$$

$$= \sum_j p_j^2 \frac{\sigma_j^2}{np_j} = \frac{1}{n}\sum_j p_j\sigma_j^2 \tag{9.1.15}$$

Hence V_P is exactly equal to the first term in the expression for V_R in (9.1.11), which results from variation within strata. The reduction in variance is

$$V_R - V_P = \frac{1}{n}\sum_j p_j(m_j - m)^2 \tag{9.1.16}$$

the component due to variation among strata. It is apparent that the advantage increases as the differences among strata increase. It is reasonable to ask whether the choice $n_j = np_j$ is the best one possible for minimizing variance. In answer to this question, we shall investigate a stratifying procedure called *optimal stratified sampling*.

Optimal Stratified Sampling The estimate of m resulting from the choice of samples of size n_j from strata S_j and the consequent strata averages $\bar{X}_j$ are given by

$$\bar{X} = \sum_j p_j \bar{X}_j$$

whose variance is

$$V(\bar{X}) = \sum_j p_j{}^2 \frac{\sigma_j{}^2}{n_j} \qquad (9.1.17)$$

The question is how to choose $n_1, n_2, \ldots, n_k$, subject to the restriction $n_1 + n_2 + \cdots + n_k = n$, in order to minimize $V(\bar{X})$ as given in (9.1.17).

A closer examination of the first term, the within-variation $(1/n)\Sigma p_j\sigma_j{}^2$ [Eq. (9.1.11)], is both revealing and clarifying. Consider

$$\bar{\sigma} = \sum_j p_j \sigma_j \qquad (9.1.18)$$

and

$$V_P = \frac{1}{n} \sum_j p_j \sigma_j{}^2 = \frac{1}{n} \sum_j p_j (\sigma_j + \bar{\sigma} - \bar{\sigma})^2$$

$$= \frac{1}{n} \left[\sum_j p_j \bar{\sigma}^2 + 2\bar{\sigma} \sum_j p_j (\sigma_j - \bar{\sigma}) + \sum_j p_j (\sigma_j - \bar{\sigma})^2 \right] \qquad (9.1.19)$$

(under proportional stratified sampling).

Since $\sum_j p_j (\sigma_j - \bar{\sigma}) = 0$ and $\sum_j p_j = 1$,

$$V_P = \frac{1}{n} \bar{\sigma}^2 + \frac{1}{n} \sum_j p_j (\sigma_j - \bar{\sigma})^2 \qquad (9.1.20)$$

For the purpose of finding optimal values $n_1, n_2, \ldots, n_k$ which minimize $V(\bar{X})$ in (9.1.17) (subject to the restriction $n_1 + n_2 + \cdots + n_k = n$), standard procedures of the calculus can be used. The resulting optimal values are given by

$$n_j = n \frac{p_j \sigma_j}{\displaystyle\sum_{i=1}^{k} p_i \sigma_i} \qquad (9.1.21)$$

The variance V_{OP} of $\bar{X}$ resulting from this optimal choice, obtained by substituting the value in (9.1.21) for n_j into (9.1.17), is

$$V_{OP} = \frac{1}{n} \left(\sum_j p_j \sigma_j \right)^2 = \frac{1}{n} \bar{\sigma}^2 \qquad (9.1.22)$$

This is the first term in the expression for V_P given in (9.1.20). The reduction in variance from that for proportional stratified sampling is

$$V_P - V_{OP} = \frac{1}{n} \sum_j p_j(\sigma_j - \bar{\sigma})^2 \tag{9.1.23}$$

It should be noted that different degrees of information are needed in order to apply the various stratified sampling procedures. The results are summarized in Table 9.1.

TABLE 9.1

Sampling procedure	*Variance*	*Required information about strata*
Random	$\dfrac{1}{n}\bar{\sigma}^2 + \dfrac{1}{n}\sum_j p_j(\sigma_j - \bar{\sigma})^2 + \dfrac{1}{n}\sum_j p_j(m_j - m)^2$	None
Proportional stratification	$\dfrac{1}{n}\bar{\sigma}^2 + \dfrac{1}{n}\sum_j p_j(\sigma_j - \bar{\sigma})^2$	$p_1, p_2, \ldots, p_k$
Optimum stratification	$\dfrac{1}{n}\bar{\sigma}^2$	$p_1, p_2, \ldots, p_k$ $\sigma_1{}^2, \sigma_2{}^2, \ldots, \sigma_k{}^2$

The results show that the gain in variance due to proportional stratified sampling, as compared with unrestricted random sampling, depends on the variation between strata means. The further gain resulting from the optimal choice of n_j is due to the variations among strata standard deviations. The reduction in variance with each procedure requires, however, successively more knowledge about the population strata.

The previous results may be modified by taking sampling costs into account. If, apart from a fixed overhead cost C_0, we assume a cost C_j per observation in strata S_j, the total cost C_T can be expressed as

$$C_T = C_0 + \sum_j C_j n_j \tag{9.1.24}$$

Using this expression for C_T and that for $V(\bar{X})$ given in (9.1.17), we may minimize $V(\bar{X})$ as a function of $n_1, n_2, \ldots, n_k$, subject to a cost restriction $C_T \leq C$, by standard procedures of the calculus. The resulting choice of n_j is given by

$$n_j = n \frac{p_j \sigma_j / \sqrt{C_j}}{\sum\limits_{i=1}^{k} p_i \sigma_i / \sqrt{C_i}} \tag{9.1.25}$$

The following example will help to illustrate some of these results.

Example 9.1 Consider two machines producing the same metal part whose important characteristic is its tensile strength. Suppose, further, that the respective mean tensile strengths of the two sets of parts resulting from the two machines are $m_1 = 60,000$ psi and $m_2 = 70,000$ psi and that the standard deviations σ_1 and σ_2 are both equal to $\sigma = 2,000$ psi. The parts are produced on each of the machines in equal number and go to some central location; there are, therefore, at any time, equal quantities of the parts from each machine.

Estimating the overall mean m of the parts may be approached by sampling from the yield of parts in one of two ways: (1) Pick n items at random from the central location, measure their respective tensile strengths, and let the arithmetic average $\bar{X}$ of these measurements be the estimate of m. This corresponds to simple random sampling. (2) Pick $n/2$ items at random from each machine's output and compute the respective arithmetic averages $\bar{X}_1$ and $\bar{X}_2$; estimate m by $\frac{1}{2}(\bar{X}_1 + \bar{X}_2)$. This corresponds to proportional stratified sampling.

The overall mean m can be expressed in terms of m_1 and m_2, namely, $m = \frac{1}{2}(m_1 + m_2) = 65,000$ psi. The variance for simple random sampling is

$$V_R(\bar{X}) = \frac{1}{n} \sum_i p_i \sigma_i{}^2 + \frac{1}{n} \sum_i p_i (m_i - m)^2$$

$$= \frac{1}{n} (\frac{1}{2} \times 2,000^2 + \frac{1}{2} \times 2,000^2) + \frac{1}{n} [\frac{1}{2}(m_1 - m)^2 + \frac{1}{2}(m_2 - m)^2]$$

$$= \frac{1}{n} (4 \times 10^6 + 25 \times 10^6) = \frac{1}{n} (29 \times 10^6)$$

For proportional stratified sampling the variance is $V_P(\bar{X}) = \frac{1}{n} (4 \times 10^6)$.

The percentage reduction in variance is $100(V_R - V_P)/V_R = 86$ per cent.

9.1.3 Two-stage sampling

In a variety of practical circumstances, a reasonable stratification may involve many strata. In such cases (and others as well) it seems natural to sample in two stages, the first consisting of selecting a random sample of s strata (sometimes called *primary units*) from the set of strata, and the second consisting of selecting a random sample of size n from each of the s strata in the first-stage sample. Some examples where two-stage sampling is natural and appropriate for estimation are:

1. The vitamin A content of butter produced in creameries where creameries compromise the primary units
2. The protein content of wheat produced in wheat fields
3. Insect infestation on leaves on a tree in an orchard

4. Red-blood-cell count in a population of men 30 to 40 years of age

5. The tensile strength of items produced on a large group of machines (the machines are the primary units in this case)

6. Some characteristic of industrial product packed in bales

Sampling Procedure and Optimum Allocation   The sn observations may be expressed as

$$y_{ij} = m_i + e_{ij} \qquad i = 1, \ldots, s; j = 1, 2, \ldots, n \quad (9.1.26)$$

where m_i is the mean of the ith primary unit, and e_{ij} is the error due to the jth choice within primary unit i. That is,

$$E(y_{ij} \mid S_i) = m_i \tag{9.1.27}$$

Also, if m is the mean value of the whole population,

$$m = E(m_i) \tag{9.1.28}$$

The values $m_1, m_2, \ldots, m_s$ are random variables in this context since the s strata are chosen at random from the population of strata. Equation (9.1.26) can be written as

$$y_{ij} = m + (m_i - m) + e_{ij} = m + t_i + e_{ij} \qquad E(t_i) = 0 \quad (9.1.29)$$

An estimate of m can be obtained from the overall arithmetic average of the y_{ij}. Averaging over j, one obtains[1]

$$y_{i\cdot} = m + t_i + \frac{1}{n}(e_{i1} + e_{i2} + \cdots e_{in}) = m + t_i + e_{i\cdot}. \quad (9.1.30)$$

The variance of $y_{i\cdot}$ is

$$V(y_{i\cdot}) = \frac{\sigma_e^2}{n} + \sigma_t^2 \tag{9.1.31}$$

where σ_e^2 is the variance of the e's (within strata variance), which is here assumed not to depend on strata. The variance σ_t^2 is the variance among strata. The overall average $y_{\cdot\cdot}$ is

$$y_{\cdot\cdot} = \frac{1}{sn} \sum_i \sum_j y_{ij} = m + t_{\cdot} + e_{\cdot\cdot} \tag{9.1.32}$$

where $t_{\cdot}$ denotes an average over i, $e_{\cdot\cdot}$ denotes an average over both i and j and

$$E(t_{\cdot}) = \frac{1}{s} \sum_i E(m_i - m) = 0 \qquad \text{and} \qquad E(e_{\cdot\cdot}) = 0$$

---

[1] The presence of dots in subscripts indicates an averaging over the relevant subscripts. Thus, $e_{i\cdot}$ indicates that the average was taken over subscript j:

$$e_{i\cdot} = (e_{i1} + e_{i2} + \cdots + e_{in})/n$$

Furthermore, the variance of $y..$ is given by

$$V(y..) = \frac{\sigma_e^2}{sn} + \frac{\sigma_t^2}{s} \qquad (9.1.33)$$

with σ_t^2 the variance *among* primary units and σ_e^2 the variance *within* primary units. In a later section we show how σ_t^2 and σ_e^2 can be estimated.

It is reasonable to seek a basis for determining the magnitudes of s and of n. One criterion is minimizing variance $V(y..)$. But since what can be done experimentally depends so much on what resources are available, the cost of sampling, as well as the cost of testing, must be considered, under the restriction of a finite upper bound of cost, denoted by C. The cost C, then, is to be expressed in terms of s and n and the individual costs involved. There is a unit cost of sampling strata; let such a cost be denoted by C_1 per stratum selected, and the cost of sampling for s strata be $C_1 s$. There is a cost for testing each unit in the overall sample, of which there are ns units, and also a cost for selecting ns units. Since each of the units is both selected and tested, the two costs can be combined and denoted by C_2, yielding $C_2 sn$ as the cost for processing the secondary units. The total cost is then

$$C = C_1 s + C_2 sn = s(C_1 + C_2 n) \qquad (9.1.34)$$

This relationship can be used to eliminate s from (9.1.33), yielding

$$V(y..) = \left(\frac{C_1 + C_2 n}{C}\right)\left(\sigma_t^2 + \frac{\sigma_e^2}{n}\right) \qquad (9.1.35)$$

an expression for $V(y..)$, in which n is the only variable with respect to the experiment. In a straightforward manner the value of n which minimizes $V(y..)$, under the cost constraints, is

$$n_0 = \frac{\sigma_e}{\sigma_t}\sqrt{\frac{C_1}{C_2}} \qquad (9.1.36)$$

It is interesting that the desired, variance-minimizing, number of observations per stratum does not depend upon C at all, but only upon the ratios σ_e/σ_t and C_1/C_2. The result has, of course, some intuitive appeal, since n_0 increases as the ratio of the intrinsic variance to the among-strata variance increases. And as the among-strata variance increases relatively to the intrinsic variance, fewer observations seem necessary to estimate (with the same cost) the overall mean. Furthermore, if the sampling of strata is costly relative to the cost of observations within strata, more observations are to be taken since more "cost" is to be put into "spreading" observations around rather than spreading strata around.

The desired number of strata primary units, which minimize $V(y..)$ with respect to the choice of strata, can be gotten, again, in straightforward fashion from (9.1.35) after substituting for s from (9.1.34). One uses the fact that (9.1.34) must hold at the optimum for both s and n and therefore yields

$$s_0 = \frac{C}{C_1 + C_2 n_0} \tag{9.1.37}$$

Estimation   This section is mainly concerned with estimating σ_t^2 and σ_e^2. In order to estimate σ_e^2, let us look at the sum of squares of the observations *within* the primary units. For each primary unit, we have n observations, and we may estimate σ_e^2 from that primary unit by taking the usual unbiased estimator of variance, which for the ith primary unit is denoted by s_i^2. Procceding formally again,

$$y_{ij} = m + t_i + e_{ij}$$
$$y_{i\cdot} = m + t_i + e_{i\cdot}$$

whence
$$y_{ij} - y_{i\cdot} = e_{ij} - e_{i\cdot} \tag{9.1.38}$$

Note that m and t_i drop out since i is fixed. Furthermore, since

$$s_i^2 = \frac{\sum\limits_j (y_{ij} - y_{i\cdot})^2}{n-1} = \frac{\sum\limits_j (e_{ij} - e_{i\cdot})^2}{n-1} \tag{9.1.39}$$

$E(s_i^2) = \sigma_e^2$. Also,

$$SSW = \sum_i \sum_j (y_{ij} - y_{i\cdot})^2 = \sum_i (n-1)s_i^2 \tag{9.1.40}$$

where SSW is called the within sum of squares (within strata). Then the expected value of SSW is

$$E(SSW) = \sum_i (n-1)E(s_i^2) = \sum_i (n-1)\sigma_e^2$$
$$= s(n-1)\sigma_e^2 \tag{9.1.41}$$

Since s and n are fixed,

$$E\left[\frac{SSW}{s(n-1)}\right] = \sigma_e^2 \tag{9.1.42}$$

and $\dfrac{SSW}{s(n-1)}$ is an unbiased estimate of σ_e^2.

It is natural to try estimating σ_t^2 from the sample averages of the primary units $y_{1\cdot}, y_{2\cdot}, \ldots, y_{s\cdot}$. From (9.1.30) and (9.1.32), we obtain $(y_{i\cdot} - y..) = (t_i - t.) + (e_{i\cdot} - e..)$; whence

$$Q = \sum_i (y_{i\cdot} - y..)^2 = \sum_i (t_i - t.)^2 + \sum_i (e_{i\cdot} - e..)^2 + 2\sum_i (t_i - t.)(e_{i\cdot} - e..)$$

The expected value of Q yields, however,

$$E(Q) = (s - 1)\sigma_t^2 + (s - 1)\frac{\sigma_e^2}{n} \tag{9.1.43}$$

since the expected value of $\sum_i (t_i - t.)(e_{i.} - e..)$ is zero. (The demonstration of this result is left as an exercise for the reader.)

The intrinsic variance σ_e^2 can be isolated by taking

$$E\left(\frac{nQ}{s - 1}\right) = \sigma_e^2 + n\sigma_t^2 \tag{9.1.44}$$

whence σ_t^2 can be obtained from (9.1.44) and (9.1.42). The form of the unbiased estimate of σ_t^2 will now be determined.

The quantity nQ is sometimes denoted by SSB, the between sum of squares (among strata), and is given by

$$SSB = n \sum_i (y_{i.} - y..)^2 \tag{9.1.45}$$

It is apparent that SSB by itself cannot serve as an estimate of σ_t^2, since it also involves σ_e^2. However, by combining SSB with SSW, we can remove the component due to σ_e^2 and obtain an estimate for σ_t^2. The unbiased estimates for σ_e^2 and σ_t^2, denoted by $\hat{\sigma}_e^2$ and $\hat{\sigma}_t^2$, are

$$\hat{\sigma}_e^2 = \frac{SSW}{s(n - 1)}$$
$$\hat{\sigma}_t^2 = \frac{1}{n}\left[\frac{SSB}{s - 1} - \frac{SSW}{s(n - 1)}\right] \tag{9.1.46}$$

which follow quite directly from (9.1.42) and (9.1.44). If $\hat{\sigma}_t^2$ turns out to be negative, we take zero as the estimate. These results may be conveniently summarized as in Table 9.2, usually referred to as an ANOVA (analysis of variance) table.

TABLE 9.2

Source of variation	Sum of squares	Degrees of freedom	Mean square	Expected mean square
Between primary units	SSB	$s - 1$	$\dfrac{SSB}{s - 1} = MSB$	$\sigma_e^2 + n\sigma_t^2$
Within primary units	SSW	$s(n - 1)$	$\dfrac{SSW}{s(n - 1)} = MSW$	σ_e^2
Total	$\sum_i \sum_j (y_{ij} - y..)^2$	$sn - 1$		

The last sum of squares in Table 9.2, $\sum_i \sum_j (y_{ij} - y_{..})^2$, can be expressed in terms of SSW and SSB as follows:

$$y_{ij} - y_{..} = (y_{ij} - y_{i\cdot}) + (y_{i\cdot} - y_{..})$$

whence, squaring and summing over j, one obtains

$$\sum_j (y_{ij} - y_{..})^2 = \sum_j (y_{ij} - y_{i\cdot})^2 + \sum_j (y_{i\cdot} - y_{..})^2 + 2 \sum_j (y_{ij} - y_{i\cdot})(y_{i\cdot} - y_{..})$$

The cross-product term, however, vanishes since $\sum_j (y_{ij} - y_{i\cdot}) = 0$ for all i. Hence, summing on i yields

$$SST = SSB + SSW \tag{9.1.47}$$

It is important to note here that the total variation SST is broken up into a *between-strata* variation and a *within-strata* (primary-unit) variation.

Calculations The following technique simplifies calculation of the entries in the ANOVA table. Let T_i be the total of the observations in primary unit i, and T the total of all the observations. Then

$$y_{..} = \frac{T}{sn} = \frac{T_1 + T_2 + \cdots + T_s}{sn}$$

and

$$y_{i\cdot} = \frac{T_i}{n}$$

It can be shown by algebraic manipulation that

$$SST = \sum_i \sum_j (y_{ij} - y_{..})^2 = \sum_i \sum_j y_{ij}^2 - \frac{T^2}{sn}$$

$$SSB = \frac{T_1^2 + T_2^2 + \cdots + T_s^2}{n} - \frac{T^2}{sn}$$

a considerable simplification of direct calculation. Furthermore, since $SST = SSB + SSW$ [Eq. (9.1.47)], $SSW = SST - SSB$. Hence all the relevant quantities can easily be calculated from $T_1, T_2, \ldots, T_s$ and $\sum_i \sum_j y_{ij}^2$.

Tests of Hypothesis and Confidence Intervals In the preceding development in this chapter, no use was made of the distributions of the t's and the e's. In order to test hypotheses and construct confidence intervals, the associated distribution functions must be known (or assumed to be known). Suppose that we consider first that:

1. The t's are normally distributed with zero mean and variance σ_t^2
2. The e's are normally distributed with zero mean and variance σ_e^2
3. The t's and e's are statistically independent.

We consider testing the hypothesis

$$H_0: \quad \sigma_t^2 = 0 \qquad \text{against} \qquad H_1: \quad \sigma_t^2 > 0$$

In the ANOVA table it is shown that $E[SSB/(s-1)] = E(MSB) = \sigma_e^2 + n\sigma_t^2$ and that $E[SSW/s(n-1)] = E(MSW) = \sigma_e^2$. Consequently, it seems natural to consider the ratio MSB over MSW in order to test $\sigma_t^2 = 0$. For if this ratio is large, that is to say, if

$$U = \frac{SSB/(s-1)}{SSW/s(n-1)} = \frac{MSB}{MSW} > k \qquad (9.1.48)$$

where k must be chosen so as to obtain a particular significance level, it is reasonable that the hypothesis $\sigma_t^2 = 0$ be rejected. Hence the distribution of U is required when the hypothesis $\sigma_t^2 = 0$ is true. It will be shown that U, when $\sigma_t^2 = 0$, has an F distribution with $s-1$ and $s(n-1)$ degrees of freedom.

In order to demonstrate this fact, it is necessary to make use of statistical independence of MSB and MSW (which will be demonstrated). Then we must prove that, in general, SSW is related to the χ^2 distribution with $s(n-1)$ degrees of freedom and that, when $\sigma_t^2 = 0$, SSB is related to the χ^2 distribution with $s-1$ degrees of freedom.

The mean within sum of squares, MSW, is a function only of s_1^2, $s_2^2 \ldots , s_s^2$, while the mean between sum of squares, MSB, is a function only of $y_1., y_2., \ldots , y_s.$. Since, for a normal distribution, the estimates of the mean and variance are independently distributed, MSW and MSB are also independently distributed. Furthermore, since the original observations are normally distributed and the $y_i.$ representable as

$$y_i. = m + t_i + e_i.$$

the $y_i.$ are normally distributed with mean m and variance $\sigma_t^2 + \sigma_e^2/n$. Therefore the ratios

$$\frac{\sum_i (y_i. - y..)^2}{\sigma_t^2 + \sigma_e^2/n} = \frac{n \sum_i (y_i. - y..)^2}{\sigma_e^2 + n\sigma_t^2} = \frac{SSB}{\sigma_e^2 + n\sigma_t^2} \qquad (9.1.49)$$

have the χ^2 distribution with $s-1$ degrees of freedom. Furthermore, for each i, $(n-1)s_i^2/\sigma_e^2$ has a χ^2 distribution with $n-1$ degrees of freedom. Hence

$$\frac{SSW}{\sigma_e^2} = \sum_{i=1}^{s} \frac{(n-1)s_i^2}{\sigma_e^2}$$

has a χ^2 distribution with $s(n-1)$ degrees of freedom. It follows from the definition of the F distribution, therefore, that

$$\frac{\dfrac{SSB/(\sigma_e^2 + n\sigma_t^2)}{s-1}}{\dfrac{SSW/\sigma_e^2}{s(n-1)}} = \frac{\dfrac{MSB}{\sigma_e^2 + n\sigma_t^2}}{\dfrac{MSW}{\sigma_e^2}} = \frac{MSB}{MSW} \left(\frac{\sigma_e^2}{\sigma_e^2 + n\sigma_t^2} \right) \qquad (9.1.50)$$

are ratios of χ^2 distributions with $s - 1$ and $s(n - 1)$ degrees of freedom. Therefore these ratios have an F distribution with $s - 1$ and $s(n - 1)$ degrees of freedom.

This result does not depend on the value of σ_t^2. When, however, the null hypothesis $\sigma_t^2 = 0$ is true, it follows from (9.1.50) that MSB/MSW has an $F_{s-1,s(n-1)}$ distribution. Consequently, we may choose the constant k in (9.1.48) as $F_{1-\alpha;\,s-1,s(n-1)}$ for any significance level α. The critical region for testing $\sigma_t^2 = 0$ is then

$$\frac{MSB}{MSW} > F_{1-\alpha;\,s-1;\,s(n-1)} \tag{9.1.51}$$

The power $\pi(V)$ of the test procedure for any alternative σ_t^2 is given by

$$\pi(V) = \mathrm{Prob}\left(\frac{MSB}{MSW} > F_{1-\alpha;\,s-1;\,s(n-1)} \,\Big|\, \sigma_t^2\right) \tag{9.1.52}$$

following (9.1.51). The power function obtained by multiplying both sides of the inequality in (9.1.52) by $\sigma_e^2/(\sigma_e^2 + n\sigma_t^2)$ satisfies the relations

$$\pi(V) = \mathrm{Prob}\left[\frac{MSB}{MSW}\left(\frac{\sigma_e^2}{\sigma_e^2 + n\sigma_2^t}\right) > \frac{\sigma_e^2}{\sigma_e^2 + n\sigma_t^2} F_{1-\alpha;\,s-1;\,s(n-1)}\right]$$

$$= \mathrm{Prob}\left[F > \left(\frac{\sigma_e^2}{\sigma_e^2 + n\sigma_t^2}\right) F_{1-\alpha;\,s-1;\,s(n-1)}\right]$$

$$= \mathrm{Prob}\left[F > \frac{F_{1-\alpha;\,s-1;\,s(n-1)}}{1 + nV}\right] \tag{9.1.53}$$

where $V = \sigma_t^2/\sigma_e^2$. The power F is revealed as a function of the degree of deviation of the true state of affairs from the null hypothesis only in terms of V. The power function as represented in (9.1.53) can be evaluated by means of the standard tables of the F distribution.

In order to derive a confidence interval for $V = \sigma_t^2/\sigma_e^2$, one can refer to the relationships given (in general form) in (9.1.50), which yield the fact that $(MSB/MSW)/(1 + nV)$ has an F distribution with $s - 1$ and $s(n - 1)$ degrees of freedom. Utilizing this fact for a significance level α, one obtains

$$\mathrm{Prob}\left(F_{\alpha/2;\,s-1;\,s(n-1)} \le \frac{MSB/MSW}{1 + nV} \le F_{1-\alpha/2;\,s-1;\,s(n-1)}\right) = 1 - \alpha$$

whence it follows that

$$\mathrm{Prob}\left[\frac{1}{n}\left(\frac{MSB/MSW}{F_{1-\alpha/2;\,s-1;\,s(n-1)}} - 1\right) \le V \le \frac{1}{n}\left(\frac{MSB/MSW}{F_{\alpha/2;\,s-1;\,s(n-1)}} - 1\right)\right]$$

$$= 1 - \alpha \tag{9.1.54}$$

Thus the expression in the brackets is a $(1 - \alpha)$ confidence interval for $V = \sigma_t^2/\sigma_e^2$. A word of caution is in place: it is not unlikely that the left boundary of the confidence interval is, in actuality, calculated to be negative; since V must be positive, the lower bound is taken to be zero.

9.2   Analysis of variance

In the discussion concerning two-stage sampling, the sn observations y_{ij} [(9.1.26) and (9.1.29)] are expressed as

$$y_{ij} = m_i + e_{ij} = m + t_i + e_{ij}$$

where m_i is the mean of the ith primary unit and e_{ij} is the deviation (error) due to the jth choice *within* primary unit i.   The quantities t_i are equal to $m_i - m$ and measure the differential effect of primary unit i, as compared with the overall mean m.   As an example, we may consider the mean tensile strength of items produced on a group of machines. If the group of machines is relatively large, we may choose a random sample of s machines out of the total and measure the tensile strengths y_{ij} of n items from each chosen machine.   In this case $m_i = m + t_i$, and t_i and e_{ij} are random variables with variances σ_t^2 and σ_e^2, respectively. The variance σ_t^2 is a measure of the effect of variability *among* the machines in a group of machines on the tensile strength of items produced on the machine, and σ_e^2 measures the variability within machines, that is to say, the effect on the tensile strength of items from an individual machine resulting from individual-machine variation.

The total variance of the observations y_{ij} equals $V(y_{ij}) = \sigma_t^2 + \sigma_e^2$. Consequently, we have in fact analyzed the variance into two components.   The quantities affecting y_{ij} are the overall mean m, t_i, and e_{ij}. Here m is a constant, while t_i and e_{ij}, because of the method of sampling, are random variables.   Constants such as m are called *systematic components*, while the random variables in the model, t_i and e_{ij}, are called *random components*.   In the two-stage sampling situation, the quantities of interest are m and the variances σ_t^2 and σ_e^2 of the random components.

Consider now a situation where there are a limited number s of machines which are of interest.   We may measure the tensile strengths of n items produced on each machine of interest.   Again, the measurement of the jth item on machine i is denoted by y_{ij} and, as before, can be expressed as

$$y_{ij} = m_i + e_{ij} = m + t_i + e_{ij}$$

In this case, however, in contrast with the previous situation, our interest lies in making inferences about these machines in particular.   (In the previous situation, interest was centered on the characteristics of the population of machines, as reflected by the sample of s machines.)   The quantities of interest in the present case are $m_1, m_2, \ldots, m_s$ (or m and $t_1, t_2, \ldots, t_s$) and σ_e^2.   In this case, $t_1, t_2, \ldots, t_s$ are *not* random variables, but systematic components, each peculiar to a given machine. The e_{ij} are, however, random variables. This situation is usually called the systematic-component model, or sometimes an example of *model* I, since aside from e_{ij}, systematic components are involved. The previous two-stage sampling situation is usually called a random-component model, or an example of *model* II, since aside from m, random components are involved.

Suppose that in the previous experiment we also focus on the workers manning the machines. Let y_{ijk} equal the tensile strength of the jth item produced on machine i by worker k. Then we can write

$$y_{ijk} = m_i + w_k + \alpha_{ik} + e'_{ijk} = m + t_i + w_k + \alpha_{ik} + e'_{ijk}$$

where m_i are the effects due to machines, w_k the effects due to workers, and α_{ik} the *interaction*, or the joint effect of machine i with worker k. The values e'_{ijk} are again random variables. This type of situation is called a two-way classification model since the series of measurements are made for several machine-worker combinations. The basic strata are classified by the two factors, machine and worker.

There are several models possible in this context according to whether the t_i and w_k are random variables or not (systematic or random components). If we are interested in the s particular machines, but the whole population of workers, then "machines" is a systematic component, while "workers" are random components. It should be emphasized that the relevant interest must be reflected in the method of sampling. That is to say, if machines are random components, this implies that the machines were actually obtained from a random sample of the whole population of machines of interest. The form of interest and the type of inference intended should indicate the method of sampling, which, in turn, implies the appropriate mathematical formulation.

When one of the two factors consists of random components while the other one is a systematic component, we have what is called a *mixed* model. This is the situation referred to just above. In this case it is interesting to note that, in effect, the variance σ_e^2 from the one-way classification includes variations due to workers and an interaction. In fact, if w, α, and e' are assumed independent, $\sigma_e^2 = \sigma_w^2 + \sigma_\alpha^2 + \sigma_{e'}^2$. The two-way classification can generally be viewed as a closer analysis of the sources of variation in the population of measurements (in this case the tensile strengths).

For the classification in terms of several factors, model I, model II, or the mixed model may be pertinent, depending on the focus of interest and the method of sampling. For example, if the interest in the two-way classification is in particular machines and particular workers, then several items should be measured from each machine-worker combination. In this case, t_i, w_k, and α_{ik} are systematic components and model I is appropriate. The parameters of interest are m, $(m_1, m_2, \ldots, m_s)$, (w_k), and (α_{ik}). For example, the values of α_{ik} may be of help in assigning machines to workers. If both, machines and workers, are random components, the sampling procedure consists of choosing at random a set of machines from the population of machines, a set of workers from the population of workers under consideration. Measurements are made of several items at random from the production of each chosen machine-worker combination. This is a model II type of situation.

In the subsequent sections, we shall study the analysis and interpretations suitable for the various models. *In all cases it is important to distinguish between systematic and random components* since they determine the appropriate sampling procedure and affect the interpretation of the results.

9.2.1 One-way classification—model I

The situations discussed in this section are concerned with comparing s quantities associated with points in the *EEP*. An example of such a situation, discussed previously, is studying and comparing s machines with respect to the tensile strengths of the items produced. Our concern here will be the particular s machines. Other examples might involve comparing several treatments of an illness, several types of raw material, several types of fertilizer, several types of storage method, etc. It should be noted that the comparison of several means is a generalization of the comparisons of two means, studied in Chap. 7.

1 The Model In the present experimental situation, we choose at random sn points in the *EEP* and randomly subdivide these experimental environment conditions into s sets of n.[1] Then, to each such set a strategy is assigned, resulting in a set of outcomes. Each outcome is quantitatively identified by a prescribed measurement (or observational) procedure, thereby yielding sn observations composed of s sets of n observations each. Each set corresponds to a specific strategy (or treatment). Denoting the sn observations by y_{ij} and the s means of the strategies by m_i, we have

$$y_{ij} = m_i + e_{ij} \qquad i = 1, \ldots, s; j = 1, \ldots, n \qquad (9.2.1)$$

where e_{ij} is the error. Equation (9.2.1) may also be written in terms of deviations from an overall mean m,

$$y_{ij} = m + (m_i - m) + e_{ij} = m + t_i + e_{ij} \qquad (9.2.2)$$

where $t_1 + t_2 + \cdots + t_s = 0$. We assume that $V(e_{ij})$, the variance of e_{ij}, does not depend on i and is denoted by σ_e^2. Moreover, we assume

---

[1] The populations under consideration will be assumed large, and the distinction between sampling with and without replacement can be neglected.

that the e_{ij} are independent. For $s = 2$, this situation corresponds to unpaired comparison, with equal but unknown variance, studied in Chap. 7.

2   Analysis of Variance, Confidence Intervals, and Tests of Hypotheses The parameters in the present situation are m_1, m_2, . . . , m_s (or equivalently, m and t_1, t_2, . . . , t_s) and σ_e^2. An analysis of the variations among the observations y_{ij}, similar to that made in Sec. 9.1.3, may be carried out. For the estimate of σ_e^2, the estimates of variance s_i^2 of the various treatment effects are pooled (summed on i) and multiplied by $(n - 1)$, yielding

$$SSW = \sum_i (n - 1)s_i^2 \tag{9.2.3}$$

Similarly, the magnitude of variation among the means, m_1, m_2, . . . , m_s, can be estimated from the s sample averages, $y_{1\cdot}$, $y_{2\cdot}$, . . . , $y_{s\cdot}$, by setting up

$$SSB = n \sum_i (y_{i\cdot} - y_{\cdot\cdot})^2 \tag{9.2.4}$$

It can be demonstrated, as was done in Sec. 9.1.3, that

$$E\left[\frac{SSW}{s(n - 1)}\right] = E(MSW) = \sigma_e^2$$

and

$$E\left(\frac{SSB}{s - 1}\right) = E(MSB) = \sigma_e^2 + \frac{n}{s - 1} \sum_{i=1}^s (m_i - m)^2$$

$$= \sigma_e^2 + \frac{n}{s - 1} \sum_i t_i^2 \tag{9.2.5}$$

(The reader may undertake this demonstration as an exercise.) The result is conveniently represented in the ANOVA table 9.3.

TABLE 9.3

Source of variation	Sum of squares	Degrees of freedom	Mean square	Expected mean square
Between	SSB	$s - 1$	MSB	$\sigma_e^2 + \dfrac{n}{s - 1} \sum_i t_i^2$
Within	SSW	$s(n - 1)$	MSW	σ_e^2
Total	$\sum_i \sum_j (y_{ij} - y_{\cdot\cdot})^2$			

Note that the analysis-of-variance scheme represented in Table 9.3 is like that of the two-stage sampling (one-way classification—model II) situation, except that the columns for $E(MS)$, the expected mean square, differ, as does the significance of the entries in the tables.

An important fact about the results in Table 9.3 is that they do not depend on distribution assumptions. To test hypotheses and obtain confidence intervals, however, distribution assumptions must be made. The assumption made in the further analysis of the present model is that the e_{ij} are independently and normally distributed with common variance σ_e^2.

A natural approach to determining what effects, if any, the s different treatments have upon the mean of a characteristic under consideration is to challenge these treatments, that is to say, to question whether the various means, $m_1, m_2, \ldots, m_s$, resulting under the action of the s different treatments, do in fact differ from one another. This question can best be expressed in the form of a test of the hypothesis

$$H_0: \quad m_1 = m_2 = \cdots = m_s$$

against

$$H_1: \quad m_1, m_2, \ldots, m_s \text{ not all equal}$$

with σ_e^2 not known. The null hypothesis H_0 can be expressed equivalently in terms of the t_i as $t_1 = t_2 = \cdots = t_s = 0$.

In order to test the null hypothesis H_0, one needs a function of the observations which, when H_0 is true, has a known distribution from which a critical region corresponding to any level of significance α can be determined. As in the two-stage sampling situation, the ratio MSB/MSW has an F distribution with $s - 1$ and $n(s - 1)$ degrees of freedom for H_0 true. (This fact will be demonstrated later.) Furthermore, when the t_i are not all zero, this ratio is usually greater than 1, since the ratio of the expected mean squares will be greater than 1 and increase with $\sum_i t_i^2$. This is as it should be, since this sum measures the deviation of the circumstances under observation from the truth of H_0. These are readily attested to by reference to the entries in Table 9.3. So far the procedure for testing the hypothesis H_0 against H_1 is quite analogous to that for determining the consequences of two-stage sampling, but differences will become apparent in the power functions which are studied later. The critical region for any α is

$$\frac{MSB}{MSW} > F_{1-\alpha;s-1;s(n-1)}$$

It is often desired to obtain confidence intervals for various combinations of the means $m_1, m_2, \ldots, m_s$, as well as for σ_e^2. In the first instance, consider an individual mean m_i which is the expected value of $y_{i\cdot}$, the arithmetic average of the observations in stratum i. Since the variance of $y_{i\cdot}$ is σ_e^2/n, by direct appeal to the definition, it follows that

$$\frac{y_{i\cdot} - m_i}{\sqrt{MSW}/\sqrt{n}} \qquad (9.2.6)$$

has the t distribution with $s(n-1)$ degrees of freedom [note also that MSW, the estimate of σ_e^2, has $s(n-1)$ degrees of freedom]. The desired confidence interval for a given α can be obtained, then, by direct application of the t distribution, which yields

$$\text{Prob}\left(-t_{1-\alpha/2;\,s(n-1)} \leq \frac{y_{i\cdot} - m_i}{\sqrt{MSW}/\sqrt{n}} \leq t_{1-\alpha/2;\,s(n-1)}\right) = 1 - \alpha \quad (9.2.7)$$

and in consequence, a $(1-\alpha)$-level confidence interval

$$y_{i\cdot} \pm t_{1-\alpha/2;\,s(n-1)} \sqrt{\frac{MSW}{n}} \qquad \text{for } m_i$$

In order to obtain a confidence interval for the difference $m_i - m_j$ between two specified means i and j, one can use the fact that

$$\frac{(y_{i\cdot} - y_{j\cdot}) - (m_i - m_j)}{\sqrt{MSW(1/n + 1/n)}} \qquad (9.2.8)$$

also is distributed as t, with $s(n-1)$ degrees of freedom. Therefore a $(1-\alpha)$-level confidence interval for $m_i - m_j$ is

$$(y_{i\cdot} - y_{j\cdot}) \pm t_{1-\alpha/2;\,s(n-1)} \sqrt{\frac{2MSW}{n}}$$

The quantity

$$t_{1-\alpha/2;\,s(n-1)} \sqrt{\frac{2MSW}{n}}$$

is sometimes called LSD, the least significant difference.

In general, a confidence interval for any linear combination $M = c_1 m_1 + c_2 m_2 + \cdots + c_s m_s$ of $m_1, m_2, \ldots, m_s$ can be obtained by adaptation of the techniques just used above. An unbiased estimate of M is L, the same linear combination as M with $y_{i\cdot}$ substituted for m_i. That is,

$$L = c_1 y_{1\cdot} + c_2 y_{2\cdot} + \cdots + c_s y_{s\cdot}. \qquad (9.2.9)$$

We use the fact that

$$\frac{L - M}{\sqrt{MSW}\,\sqrt{\Sigma c_i^2/n}} \qquad (9.2.10)$$

has a t distribution with $s(n-1)$ degrees of freedom. As a result, a $(1-\alpha)$ per cent confidence interval for M is

$$L \pm t_{1-\alpha/2;\, s(n-1)} \sqrt{\frac{MSW}{n}} \sqrt{\Sigma\, c_i^2} \qquad (9.2.11)$$

The parameter functions m_i and $m_i - m_j$, previously considered, are both linear functions of the m's. A special class of linear functions of $m_1, m_2, \ldots, m_s$ will now be studied, for reasons that will become apparent as we proceed.

Definition: linear contrast A *linear contrast* among m_1, m_2, $\ldots$, m_s is a linear combination $c_1 m_1 + c_2 m_2 + \cdots + c_s m_s$ such that $c_1 + c_2 + \cdots + c_s = 0$.

A *normalized contrast* is a contrast with the added property (also a restriction) that $c_1^2 + c_2^2 + \cdots + c_s^2 = 1$. Some examples of contrasts which are of practical interest are as follows:

1. The difference between two means, $m_i - m_j$; here $c_i = 1, c_j = -1$, and all other coefficients are zero.

2. Suppose we wish to compare two types of raw material, R_1 and R_2, used in making two types of equipment, E_1 and E_2. In this case, there can be four treatments (or strategies) for varying factors E and R, according to the combinations of raw material and equipment, $R_1 E_1$, $R_1 E_2$, $R_2 E_1$, and $R_2 E_2$. The mean effect of using these four combinations, of two factors each at two levels, may be represented by m_1, m_2, m_3, m_4. What comparisons may we wish to make? First, the two types of raw material can be compared by considering

$$M_1 = \tfrac{1}{2}(m_1 + m_2) - \tfrac{1}{2}(m_3 + m_4) = \tfrac{1}{2}m_1 + \tfrac{1}{2}m_2 - \tfrac{1}{2}m_3 - \tfrac{1}{2}m_4$$
$$(9.2.12)$$

This contrast compares the effects of material, since the raw-material influences remain the same in (m_1, m_2) and in (m_3, m_4). Differences in the effects of equipment are compared in

$$M_2 = \tfrac{1}{2}(m_1 + m_3) - \tfrac{1}{2}(m_2 + m_4) = \tfrac{1}{2}m_1 - \tfrac{1}{2}m_2 + \tfrac{1}{2}m_3 - \tfrac{1}{2}m_4$$
$$(9.2.13)$$

since the equipments are the same in (m_1, m_3) and (m_2, m_4). We may, of course, be interested in the interaction between raw material and equipment, that is, the difference between the mean effect with R_1 compared with the difference between the mean effect with R_2, expressed by

$$M_3 = \tfrac{1}{2}(m_1 - m_2) - \tfrac{1}{2}(m_3 - m_4) = \tfrac{1}{2}m_1 - \tfrac{1}{2}m_2 - \tfrac{1}{2}m_3 + \tfrac{1}{2}m_4$$
$$(9.2.14)$$

The reader may verify for himself that the interaction contrast obtained by comparing the difference of mean effect for E_1 with that for E_2 is also M_3.

The linear combinations M_1, M_2, and M_3 are contrasts. M_1 compares the two types of raw material; M_2, the two types of equipment; and M_3, their interaction. The coefficients of the parameter components, aside from a factor $\frac{1}{2}$, can be represented as in Table 9.4. It

TABLE 9.4

	m_1 (R_1, E_1)	m_2 (R_1, E_2)	m_3 (R_2, E_1)	m_4 (R_2, E_2)
M_1	$+1$	$+1$	-1	-1
M_2	$+1$	-1	$+1$	-1
M_3	$+1$	-1	-1	$+1$

should be noted, for future reference, that in any of these three contrasts, if the corresponding coefficients of pairs of contrasts are multiplied and then added, the result is zero. For example, for M_1 and M_2,

$$(+1)(+1) + (+1)(-1) + (-1)(+1) + (-1)(-1) = 0 \quad (9.2.15)$$

That is, if $M_1 = \sum_i c_{i1}m_i$ and $M_2 = \sum_i c_{i2}m_i$, then $\sum_i c_{i1}c_{i2} = 0$. Any pair of contrasts having this property is said to be *orthogonal*.

3. Another type of situation which involves contrasts is where a process 1 is presently used and two new processes 2 and 3 are being contemplated for adoption. For example, process 1 may be operated on the basis of one technical principle, while the two contemplated processes are to be based on two variations of another technical principle. One contrast of interest in this situation involves comparison of the new with the currently used standard principle as each affects the process. The contrast may then be represented by

$$M_1 = m_1 - \frac{1}{2}(m_2 + m_3) = m_1 - \frac{m_2}{2} - \frac{m_3}{2} \quad (9.2.16)$$

Another contrast of interest is the comparison of the two adaptations of the new principle, and this, of course, is expressed by

$$M_2 = m_2 - m_3 \quad \text{or} \quad m_3 - m_2 \quad (9.2.17)$$

Schematically, these contrasts can be represented as in Table 9.5. Again, we note that M_1 and M_2 are orthogonal contrasts.

TABLE 9.5

	Old principle	New principle	
	m_1	m_2	m_3
M_1	$+1$	$-\frac{1}{2}$	$-\frac{1}{2}$
M_2	0	$+1$	-1

In some cases one may wish to test hypotheses about these contrasts in sequence. For instance, first one may wish to decide whether or not the new principle is superior to the one presently in use ($M_1 = 0$ or $M_1 < 0$). If one "feels" that $M_1 < 0$, one may then try to decide which adaptation of the new principle to use ($M_2 \leq 0$ or $M_2 > 0$). Procedures for carrying out such a sequence of tests must be investigated carefully since the tests in the sequence may be dependent and the resulting significance level, at the end of the sequence of tests, may be difficult to establish. We shall comment further about this later.

4. A variety of experimental situations can be thought of in terms of the response $Y(x)$ of a variable as a function of a dependent controllable variable x. For example, $Y(x)$ may be an output of some kind in a chemical process, which is a function of the temperature level x. Often $Y(x)$ is a random variable whose mean changes with the level of x. This mean value $M(x) = E[Y(x)]$ as a function of x is sometimes called the regression of Y on variable x. In many cases one wishes to study the regression function $M(x)$. For example, the level x, where the maximum of $M(x)$ occurs, if it exists, is of interest in some cases, since this level x will maximize the expected yield of $Y(x)$. In other cases, one wishes to find out if $M(x)$ is linear, quadratic, or some other function of x. The procedure often used in these situations is to choose several levels of x (usually equally spaced) and to make a series of observations of $Y(x)$ at the various levels. If the levels are denoted by $x_0, x_0 + \Delta, \ldots, x_0 + (s - 1)\Delta$, we compare the corresponding s means $M(x_0)$, $M(x_0 + \Delta)$, $M(x_0 + 2\Delta), \ldots, M[x_0 + (s - 1)\Delta]$. Let us consider the special case with $s = 3$ levels at x_0, $x_0 + \Delta$, and $x_0 + 2\Delta$, assuming that $M(x)$ is a polynomial of quadratic form, at most:

$$M(x) = a + bx + cx^2 \tag{9.2.18}$$

We may wish to estimate, or test hypotheses about, the coefficients a, b, and c. In particular, we may want to know whether or not $c = 0$ and, if $c = 0$, whether or not b is also zero. We shall now show how some of these questions can be treated in terms of contrasts.

The means of Y at the three levels x_0, $x_0 + \Delta$, and $x_0 + 2\Delta$ are m_1, m_2, and m_3, where

$$m_1 = a + bx_0 + cx_0^2$$
$$m_2 = a + b(x_0 + \Delta) + c(x_0 + \Delta)^2 \qquad (9.2.19)$$
$$m_3 = a + b(x_0 + 2\Delta) + c(x_0 + 2\Delta)^2$$

Suppose we wish to test $c = 0$, that is, to test $M(x)$ for linearity in x. If $M(x)$ is linear, then $m_3 - m_2$ should equal $m_2 - m_1$. Thus, comparing these two differences would tell us something about linearity. We form, then, the difference

$$M_1 = (m_3 - m_2) - (m_2 - m_1) = m_1 - 2m_2 + m_3 \qquad (9.2.20)$$

which is a contrast among m_1, m_2, and m_3. One may write M_1 in terms of a, b, and c by obvious substitutions for m_1, m_2, and m_3, resulting in

$$M_1 = 2c\Delta^2 \qquad (9.2.21)$$

Hence $M_1 = 0$ only when $c = 0$ (assuming that $\Delta \neq 0$). To test $M(x)$ for linearity ($c = 0$) is equivalent to testing the contrast $M_1 = 0$.

A further contrast of interest is obtained from the difference between m_3 and m_1, namely,

$$M_2 = m_3 - m_1 = 2b\Delta + c(4x_0\Delta + 4\Delta^2) \qquad (9.2.22)$$

If $c = 0$, then $M_2 = 2b\Delta$ and can be used to test whether or not $b = 0$ [that is, $M(x) = a$]. In fact, the procedure used in some circumstances is to perform a sequence of tests, first for $M_1 = 0$ ($c = 0$); then, if one feels that $c = 0$, one may test for $M_2 = 0$. It should be noted that $M_2 = 0$ is equivalent to $b = 0$ only when $M_1 = 0$. Fortunately, it should be observed that M_1 and M_2 are orthogonal, making the analysis less involved.

Obviously, these procedures can be carried out for more than three levels of x, resulting in more complicated contrasts.

Returning to a consideration of the F test in connection with testing

$$H_0: \quad m_1 = m_2 = \cdots = m_s$$

against

$$H_1: \quad m_1, m_2, \ldots, m_s \text{ not all equal}$$

observe that the procedure is to use a critical region, at some significance level α, of the form $MSB/MSW > F_{1-\alpha; s-1, s(n-1)}$. As in the discussion concerning two-stage sampling, the validity of the test depends on the facts:

1. SSB and SSW are independent.
2. SSB/σ_e^2 has a χ^2 distribution with $s - 1$ degrees of freedom when $H_0: m_1 = \cdots = m_s$ is true.
3. SSW/σ_e^2 is χ^2 distributed with $s(n - 1)$ degrees of freedom.

Result 1 follows from the observation that SSB is a function of the sample averages $y_{1\cdot}$, $y_{2\cdot}$, . . . , $y_{s\cdot}$ and that SSW is a function only of the sample variances s_1^2, s_2^2, . . . , s_s^2. The independence of SSB and SSW follows from the fact that the sample average and sample variance are independent random variables for the normal distribution.

Result 2 is a consequence of the fact that, when $m_1 = m_2 = \cdots = m_s$, the sample averages $y_{1\cdot}$, $y_{2\cdot}$, . . . , $y_{s\cdot}$ can be considered as s observations from the same normal distribution whose variance is σ_e^2/n. Hence

$$\frac{\sum_i (y_{i\cdot} - y_{\cdot\cdot})^2}{\sigma_e^2/n} = \frac{n \sum_i (y_{i\cdot} - y_{\cdot\cdot})^2}{\sigma_e^2} = \frac{SSB}{\sigma_e^2} \tag{9.2.23}$$

has a χ^2 distribution with $s - 1$ degrees of freedom.

Result 3 follows from the fact that, for each i, $(n - 1)s_i^2/\sigma_e^2$ has a χ^2 distribution with $n - 1$ degrees of freedom. Consequently, from the additivity property of the χ^2 variate,

$$\frac{\Sigma(n - 1)s_i^2}{\sigma_e^2} = \frac{SSW}{\sigma_e^2} \tag{9.2.24}$$

is χ^2 distributed with $s(n - 1)$ degrees of freedom. The truth of result 2 is a consequence of H_0 being true, but result 3 is independent of the validity of this hypothesis.

In applications of the F test for testing whether $m_1 = m_2 = \cdots = m_s$, a problem which often arises is what action to take when H_0 is rejected. If the means are not equal, in what way can their inequality be usefully characterized? This question is not serious when comparing two means ($s = 2$), but is important when $s > 2$. To shed light on this matter, one must examine in greater depth the SSB. We shall break up SSB, the variation between the averages, into sources of variation which have empirical significance. This can be done in terms of the contrasts introduced previously.

Let us then examine more carefully

$$SSB = n\Sigma(y_{i\cdot} - y_{\cdot\cdot})^2 = n(\Sigma y_{i\cdot}^2 - sy_{\cdot\cdot}^2) \tag{9.2.25}$$

The basic idea of the next step is to make a linear transformation (basically a change in variables). In order to express the actual sum of squares which define SSB in terms of components that have empirical significance, it is necessary to make changes of variable, in fact, simple linear transformations of $y_{1\cdot}$, $y_{2\cdot}$, . . . , $y_{s\cdot}$ into L_1, L_2, . . . , L_s, where the L's are related to contrasts of interest. In general terms, the transformations are

$$L_1 = \frac{1}{\sqrt{s}} (y_{1\cdot} + y_{2\cdot} + \cdots + y_{s\cdot}) = \sqrt{s}\, y_{\cdot\cdot}$$

$$L_j = \sum_{r=1}^{s} c_{jr} y_{r\cdot}. \qquad j = 2, 3, \ldots, s \tag{9.2.26}$$

where:

(a)
$$\sum_{r=1}^{s} c_{jr} = 0 \qquad \text{for } j \geq 2$$

L_j is a contrast of the sample averages $y_{1\cdot}, y_{2\cdot}, \ldots, y_{s\cdot}$ and is an unbiased estimate of M_j, which is a contrast among $m_1, \ldots, m_s$, formally expressed as

$$E(L_j) = \sum_r c_{jr} E(y_{r\cdot}) = \sum_r c_{ji} m_r = M_j$$

(b) The coefficients satisfy

$$\sum_r c_{jr}^2 = 1 \qquad j \geq 2$$

That is, they are normalized contrasts among $y_{1\cdot}, y_{2\cdot}, \ldots, y_{s\cdot}$. Any contrast may be normalized by multiplying by a suitable constant.

(c) The coefficients satisfy

$$\sum_r c_{jr} c_{kr} = 0 \qquad j \neq k$$

this expression defines orthogonality of the contrasts L_j and L_k. It can be shown that there always exist contrasts $L_2, \ldots, L_s$ satisfying these three properties. Moreover, with s averages, there are no more than $s - 1$ mutually orthogonal contrasts. Finally, there usually are many ways of choosing $s - 1$ mutually orthogonal contrasts.

When properties a to c are satisfied, it can be shown that

$$L_1^2 + L_2^2 + \cdots + L_s^2 = y_{1\cdot}^2 + y_{2\cdot}^2 + \cdots + y_{s\cdot}^2 \tag{9.2.27}$$

(The actual demonstration is beyond the scope of this work.) The invariance of the sum of squares expressed by (9.2.27) is equivalent geometrically to the invariance of cartesian distance under a change by rotation. Consequently, on subtracting L_1^2 from both sides, one obtains

$$L_2^2 + L_3^2 + \cdots + L_s^2 = y_{1\cdot}^2 + y_{2\cdot}^2 + \cdots + y_{s\cdot}^2 - sy_{\cdot\cdot}^2$$

$$= \frac{1}{n}(SSB) \tag{9.2.28}$$

or
$$SSB = n(L_2^2 + L_3^2 + \cdots + L_s^2) \tag{9.2.29}$$

The importance of this relationship lies in the fact that SSB has been broken up into sum of squares of $(s - 1)$ terms, $nL_2^2 + nL_3^2 + \cdots +$

$nL_s{}^2$, each of which may be so chosen as to shed light on sources of variation among the means which have practical significance.

On examining the results further, we find that since L_j is a linear combination of normal random variables $y_1., y_2., \ldots, y_s.$, it is normally distributed with mean

$$M_j = E(L_j) = \sum_r c_{jr} m_r \qquad j \geq 2 \qquad (9.2.30)$$

and variance

$$V(L_j) = \sum_r c_{jr}{}^2 V(y_r.) = \sum_r c_{jr}{}^2 \frac{\sigma_e{}^2}{n} = \frac{\sigma_e{}^2}{n} \sum_r c_{jr}{}^2 = \frac{\sigma_e{}^2}{n} \qquad (9.2.31)$$

When the null hypothesis $H_0: m_1 = m_2 = \cdots = m_s = m$ *is true*, M_j *equals zero for* $j \geq 2$, since

$$M_j = \sum_r c_{jr} m_r = m \sum_r c_{jr} = 0 \qquad (9.2.32)$$

Thus, when H_0 is true, for each $j \geq 2$,

$$\frac{L_j{}^2}{\sigma_e{}^2/n} = \frac{nL_j{}^2}{\sigma_e{}^2} \qquad (9.2.33)$$

has a χ^2 distribution with 1 degree of freedom. And besides, it can be shown by means of the orthogonality condition that L_j and L_k ($j \neq k$) are independently distributed. It follows, therefore, that

$$\frac{SSB}{\sigma_e{}^2} = \frac{nL_2{}^2}{\sigma_e{}^2} + \frac{nL_3{}^2}{\sigma_e{}^2} + \cdots + \frac{nL_s{}^2}{\sigma_e{}^2} \qquad (9.2.34)$$

has a χ^2 distribution with $s - 1$ degrees of freedom. This is, in effect, a different proof of result 2, which was proved above.

In general, when H_0 is not necessarily true, we can find the expected MS_j due to contrast j from the relations

$$E(MS_j) = E\left(\frac{SS_j}{1}\right) = E\left(\frac{nL_j{}^2}{1}\right) = nE(L_j{}^2)$$

$$= n\left[V(L_j) + E(L_j)^2\right] = \frac{n\sigma_e{}^2}{n} + nM_j{}^2 = \sigma_e{}^2 + nM_j{}^2 \qquad (9.2.35)$$

Each L_j involves only the sample averages. Hence, again, each L_j is independent of SSW. Thus we may test the hypothesis that $M_j = 0$ by forming the critical region

$$\frac{nL_j{}^2/1}{MSW} > F_{1-\alpha;\, 1, s(n-1)} \qquad (9.2.36)$$

since $nL_j{}^2/MSW$ has an F distribution with 1 and $s(n-1)$ degrees of freedom. The results of this analysis may be presented as in the analysis-of-variance table 9.6.

TABLE 9.6

Source of variation	Sum of squares	Degrees of freedom	Mean square	Expected mean square
Contrast 2	$nL_2{}^2$	1	$nL_2{}^2$	$\sigma_e{}^2 + nM_2{}^2$
Contrast 3	$nL_3{}^2$	1	$nL_3{}^2$	$\sigma_e{}^2 + nM_3{}^2$
. . . .	. . . .	. . . .	. . . .	. . . .
Contrast s	$nL_s{}^2$	1	$nL_s{}^2$	$\sigma_e{}^2 + nM_s{}^2$
	SSB	$s-1$	MSB	$\sigma_e{}^2 + \dfrac{n}{s-1}\sum_i (m_i - m)^2$
Within	SSW	$s(n-1)$	MSW	$\sigma_e{}^2$
Total	$\sum_i \sum_j (y_{ij} - y_{..})^2$			

Table 9.6 shows how the variation among the observations may be analyzed as consequences of effects from different sources of variation. This process is much clarified by means of the concept of contrasts. The contrasts may formally be chosen in many ways. From a practical view-point, however, they should be chosen in the light of empirical significance in respect to the problem under consideration. Examples of meaningful contrasts were given previously. For instance, take Example 2, where two types of raw material used with two types of equipment were under consideration. Here there are four treatment means, m_1, m_2, m_3, and m_4. If $H_0\colon m_1 = m_2 = m_3 = m_4$ were tested by the F test and rejected, we should be concerned with whether the differences were due to the two types of raw material, the two types of equipment, their interaction, or some combination of these three. An analysis such as represented in Table 9.6 allows one to focus on these different sources of variation.

We have considered various tests of hypothesis in this section. It is well to examine the power of these tests. Examples of tests which were considered are

$$H_0\colon\ m_1 = m_2 = \cdots = m_s \quad\text{against}\quad H_1\colon\ m\text{'s not all equal} \tag{9.2.37}$$

and

$$H_0'\colon\ M_j = 0 \quad\text{against}\quad H_1'\colon\ M_j \neq 0 \tag{9.2.38}$$

These test situations may be put in the following general form:

$$H_0\colon\ l = 0 \quad\text{against}\quad H_1\colon\ l \neq 0 \tag{9.2.39}$$

where l is any sum of squares involving population means rather than sample averages. This is demonstrated for the sum of squares used in testing H_0 versus H_1, namely,

$$SSB = n \sum_i (y_{i\cdot} - y_{\cdot\cdot})^2$$

On replacing $y_{i\cdot}$ by m_i and $y_{\cdot\cdot}$ by m, one obtains

$$l = n \sum_i (m_i - m)^2$$

and condition $l = 0$ is equivalent to the hypothesis

$$H_0: \quad m_1 = m_2 = \cdots = m_s$$

Again, the sum of squares used for testing H_0' against H_1' is

$$nL_j^2 = n \left(\sum_r c_{jr} y_{r\cdot} \right)^2$$

Substituting the means for $y_{1\cdot}, y_{2\cdot}, \ldots, y_{s\cdot}$, one obtains

$$l = n \left(\sum_r c_{jr} m_r \right)^2 = nM_j^2$$

Therefore testing $H_0: M_j = 0$ is equivalent to testing $l = 0$ against some alternative.

It can be shown that the F test, just discussed, for comparing $l = 0$ against $l \neq 0$ has optimum properties, the demonstration of which, however, is beyond the scope of this text. Furthermore, the power function of these F tests can be shown to depend on three quantities, ϕ^2, f_1, and f_2, where:

$f_1 =$ number of degrees of freedom associated with SS used for test
$f_2 =$ number of degrees of freedom for within sum of squares, SSW, often called sum of squares due to error

$$\phi^2 = \frac{l}{\sigma_e^2(1 + f_1)}, \text{ a measure of deviation from the hypothesis } l = 0$$

In the case of testing $H_0: m_1 = m_2 = \cdots = m_s$, $f_1 = s - 1$, $f_2 = s(n - 1)$, and $\phi^2 = n \sum_i (m_i - m)^2 / s\sigma_e^2$. For testing an individual contrast, $H_0: M_j = 0$, $f_1 = 1$, $f_2 = s(n - 1)$, and $\phi^2 = nM_j^2/2\sigma_e^2$.

In Figs. 9.1 and 9.2 are given the 10 and 50 per cent points of the operating characteristic curves (curves, 1 minus the power function) for significance levels $\alpha = 0.01$ and $\alpha = 0.05$. These curves will give three points on the OC curve, namely, the $1 - \alpha$, 50, and 10 percentile, with sufficient accuracy so as to suggest what the results of the test procedures may be. More extensive tables of the OC curves (than those given here) as a function of f_1, f_2, and ϕ^2 are available.

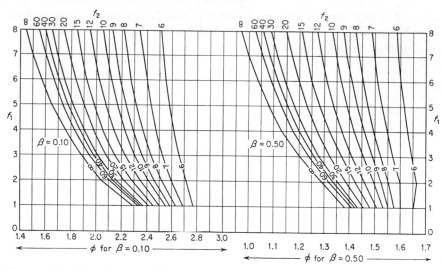

Figure 9.1 *From Acheson J. Duncan, Charts of the 10 Percent and 50 Percent Points of the Operating Characteristic Curves for Fixed Effects Analysis of Variance F Tests, $\alpha = 0.005$, J. Am. Statist. Assoc., chart I, pp. 345, 346.*

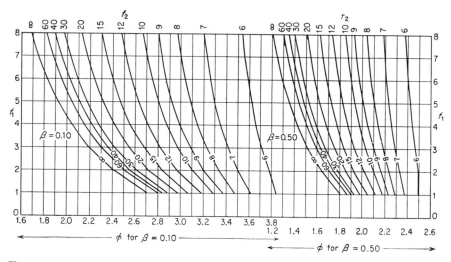

Figure 9.2 *From Acheson J. Duncan, Charts of the 10 Percent and 50 Percent Points of the Operating Characteristic Curves for Fixed Effects Analysis of Variance F Tests, $\alpha = 0.01$, J. Am. Statist. Assoc., chart II, pp. 345, 346.*

Figures 9.1 and 9.2 may be used in at least two ways: (1) to find the power as a function of l/σ_e^2 for s and n fixed, and (2) to find n to achieve a given power at a fixed value of l/σ^2 (with s given). As an example, consider testing the difference between the two types of raw material in (2). The contrast of interest here is M_1, as shown in Table 9.4.

$$M_1 = m_1 + m_2 - m_3 - m_4 \qquad (9.2.40)$$

This contrast can be normalized by dividing by 2, since $\sum_i c_i^2 = 4$. Thus the normalized contrast here is $M_1/2$. The estimate of $M_1/2$ is $L_1/2$, where

$$L_1 = y_1. + y_2. - y_3. - y_4. \tag{9.2.41}$$

The sum of squares associated with testing $M_1 = 0$ is $n(L_1/2)^2 = nL_1^2/4$ (after normalization). Thus $l = nM_1^2/4$. Consequently, $f_1 = 1$, $f_2 = s(n-1) = 4(n-1)$, and

$$\phi^2 = \frac{nM_1^2/4}{2\sigma_e^2} = \frac{nM_1^2}{8\sigma_e^2}$$

To illustrate the method of finding the OC curve, let there be four observations for each of the four treatment combinations ($n = 4$). Thus $f_1 = 1$, $f_2 = 12$, and $\phi^2 = M_1^2/2\sigma_e^2$. Furthermore, using a significance level $\alpha = 0.05$, we see from Fig. 9.1 that under these conditions

$$\phi_{0.50} \cong 1.5$$
$$\phi_{0.10} \cong 2.5 \tag{9.2.42}$$

Since $\phi^2 = M_1^2/2\sigma_e^2$, the corresponding values of the OC curve on the scale M_1/σ_e is found by equating

$$\phi_{0.50} = \frac{M_{1(0.50)}}{\sqrt{2}\,\sigma_e} \cong 1.5$$
$$\phi_{0.10} = \frac{M_{1(0.10)}}{\sqrt{2}\,\sigma_e} = 2.5 \tag{9.2.43}$$

resulting in values

$$\frac{M_{1(0.50)}}{\sigma_e} \cong 1.5\,\sqrt{2} \cong 2.12 \qquad \frac{M_{1(0.10)}}{\sigma_e} \cong 2.5\,\sqrt{2} \cong 3.54 \tag{9.2.44}$$

They are, therefore, three points on the OC curve, namely, (0,0.95), (2.12,0.50), and (3.54,0.10), shown in Fig. 9.3. We see from Fig. 9.3 that for $M_1/\sigma_e = 1$, the OC curve gives an error of the first kind larger than 50 per cent (hence power less than 50 per cent). Suppose we do not want the error, when $M_1/\sigma_e = 1$, to be more than 10 per cent. What value of n will satisfy this requirement? Trying different values of n, we compute $f_1 = 1$, $f_2 = 4(n-1)$ and find the corresponding $\phi_{0.10}$ from Fig. 9.1. In general, for this problem, $\phi^2 = \frac{n}{8}\left(\frac{M_1}{\sigma_e}\right)^2$. Thus $\phi_{0.10}$ may be compared, for successive values of n, with $\sqrt{n/8}$. For example, when $n = 16$, $f_2 = 60$ and $\phi_{0.10} \cong 2.3$, $\sqrt{n/8} = \sqrt{2} \cong 1.4$. When $n = 32$, $f_2 = 124$, and $\phi_{0.10} \cong 2.3$, $\sqrt{n/8} = \sqrt{4} \cong 2$, which is close enough for present purposes. Hence a sample size $n = 32$, per treatment combination, will give the required odds.

It should be noted that the power function for the present fixed-effect model involves the noncentral F distribution when H_0 is not true.

In the two-stage sampling situation, which is a random-component model, the power function generally involves only the central F distribution. Thus, for the one-way classification situation, the fixed-effect model and the random-component model differ in respect to the parameters of interest, the interpretation of results, and the power function. More differences will arise in the two-way classification situation.

3 *Individual, Group, and Multiple Comparisons* In the previous section, we studied ways of subdividing the between-variation sum of squares SSB in order to focus on individual sources of variation. The analysis rested on breaking up the sum of squares in terms of linear contrasts having specific empirical interpretations.

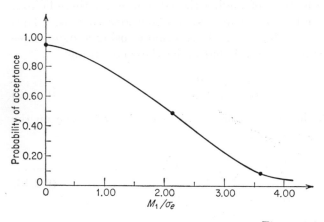

Figure 9.3

Sometimes, however, there are a priori reasons for classifying the s populations into two groups, denoted by A and C, respectively, and for testing the hypothesis that the population means within groups are the same but, perhaps, the two group means are different. Suppose that groups A and C are composed of K_A and K_C populations, respectively, where $K_A + K_C = s$. Then the $s - 1$ degrees of freedom obtaining between the s populations can be divided into three components, as follows:

1. Between populations within A: $K_A - 1$
2. Between populations within C: $K_C - 1$
3. Between groups A and C: $(s - 1) - (K_A - 1) - (K_C - 1) = 1$

If, within each population, the same number n of observations is made, then the number of observations made within groups A and C are, respectively, nK_A and nK_C. The sum of squares within group A is

$$SSA = n \sum_A (y_{i\cdot} - y_{\cdot A})^2 \qquad (9.2.45)$$

where the summation is taken over populations in group A, and $y_{\cdot A}$ is the average of observations in group A. The sum of squares within group C is, similarly,

$$SSC = n \sum_C (y_{i \cdot} - y_{\cdot C})^2 \qquad (9.2.46)$$

There are $K_A - 1$ and $K_C - 1$ degrees of freedom corresponding, respectively, to SSA and SSC. (This is so since there are $K_A - 1$ and $K_C - 1$ orthogonal contrasts within A and within C.) Since

$$(s - 1) - (K_A - 1) - (K_C - 1) = 1$$

there is 1 degree of freedom left corresponding to the sum of squares between groups A and C. This sum of squares must, however, equal SSB (the sum of squares between with $s - 1$ degrees of freedom) minus $SSA + SSC$. Thus the sum of squares between groups, $SSBG$, is

$$SSBG = SSB - SSA - SSC = \frac{nK_A K_C}{s} (y_{\cdot A} - y_{\cdot C})^2 \qquad (9.2.47)$$

from which the respective expected mean squares can be estimated. The results are summarized in the analysis-of-variance scheme in Table 9.7.

TABLE 9.7

Source of variation	Sum of squares	Degrees of freedom	Mean square	Expected mean square
Between groups A and C	$SSBG$	1	$MSBG$ $= \dfrac{SSBG}{1}$	$\sigma_e^2 + \dfrac{nK_A K_C}{s}(m_A - m_C)^2$
Within group A	$SSA = n \sum_A (y_{i \cdot} - y_{\cdot A})^2$	$K_A - 1$	MSA	$\sigma_e^2 + \dfrac{n}{K_A - 1} \sum_A (m_i - m_A)^2$
Within group C	$SSC = n \sum_C (y_{i \cdot} - y_{\cdot C})^2$	$K_C - 1$	MSC	$\sigma_e^2 + \dfrac{n}{K_C - 1} \sum_C (m_i - m_C)^2$
Between means	SSB	$s - 1$	MSB	$\sigma_e^2 + \dfrac{n}{s - 1} \sum_i (m_i - m)^2$
Within	SSW	$s(n - 1)$	MSW	σ_e^2
Total	$\sum_i \sum_j (y_{ij} - y_{\cdot \cdot})^2$			

The appropriate critical regions for the various tests of hypothesis can be obtained by looking at the column for $E(MS)$. For example, in order to test whether the means within group A are equal, we compare MSA with MSW to obtain a critical region.

$$\frac{MSA}{MSW} > F_{1-\alpha;\, K_A-1,\, s(n-1)} \tag{9.2.48}$$

To test whether groups A and C are different, we may compare $MSBG$ with MSW to obtain critical region

$$\frac{MSBG}{MSW} > F_{1-\alpha;\, 1,\, s(n-1)} \tag{9.2.49}$$

The power functions of the various tests can be obtained from the relevant sums of squares and by substituting means for sample averages and formulating the results in terms of l, as explained in section 2. The quantities ϕ^2 required for the tests are:

Between groups A and C: $\quad \phi^2 = \dfrac{n K_A K_C}{2 s \sigma_e^2} (m_A - m_C)^2 \tag{9.2.50}$

Within group A: $\quad \phi^2 = \dfrac{n}{K_A \sigma_e^2} \sum_A (m_i - m_A)^2 \tag{9.2.51}$

Within group C: $\quad \phi^2 = \dfrac{n}{K_C \sigma_e^2} \sum_C (m_i - m_C)^2 \tag{9.2.52}$

A common problem in using the analysis of variance, as previously discussed, is how to proceed when the null hypothesis $m_1 = m_2 = \cdots = m_s$ is rejected. It is natural to ask in what way these means differ. The rejection of the hypothesis merely indicates the untenability of $m_1 = m_2 = \cdots = m_s$, but does not imply any more. In fact, it is possible that all but m_1 are equal. This may be the case when the first treatment is a control or standard. The problem is usually that of dividing the treatments into homogeneous groups so that within a group the treatments are equally effective but treatments in different groups have unequal effects. It has been shown above that the desired discrimination among treatments and resulting means can be accomplished with the aid of the expedient of expressing the between sum of squares in terms of component sources of variation. It is apparent from the previous examples that a sequence of tests may be required in order to isolate the important factors in an experiment. How to carry out such a sequence of tests and maintain a prescribed overall significance level is a question to be answered.

Another problem, highlighting the need for sequenced testing, arises in the use of t tests for paired comparisons; comparison of individual treatments is undertaken by means of a series of t tests. A comparison criterion, called the least significant difference, is set up such that

$$LSD = t_{1-\alpha/2} \sqrt{MSW} \sqrt{\frac{2}{n}}$$

and the differences among pairs of sample averages $y_{1\cdot}$, $y_{2\cdot}$, . . . , $y_{s\cdot}$, corresponding to the s individual treatments, are compared with the LSD. A pair of sample averages which differ by more than the LSD are said to be significantly different. There are some logical difficulties associated with this intuitively appealing procedure, but in addition, the overall type I error is much greater than the nominal originally selected as a "tolerable" significance level. The actual overall error depends on the number of treatments. In fact, for six treatments and an LSD based on $\alpha = 0.05$, the overall error becomes 0.40, instead of the hoped-for 0.05 error of the first kind. There is good reason for this discrepancy since often some comparisons are made after the experimenter has looked at the data and has made other comparisons. The choice of the LSD, as of the 0.05 level, does not take into consideration these empirical (*de facto*) aspects of usual practice. One can illustrate this discrepancy by comparing the averages of the least and greatest treatment effects as in

$$P(s) = \text{Prob} \ (y_{M\cdot} - y_{L\cdot} \geq LSD \text{ in a } 5\% \text{ test} \mid m_1 = m_2 = \cdots = m_s)$$
$$(9.2.53)$$

where $y_{M\cdot}$ and $y_{L\cdot}$ are the maximum and minimum, respectively, of $y_{1\cdot}$, $y_{2\cdot}$, . . . , $y_{s\cdot}$. Some approximate values of $P(s)$ are given in Table 9.8.

TABLE 9.8

s	$P(s)$, %
2	5
3	13
6	40
10	60
20	90

A simple way to make an approximate computation is to consider that, for $s = 3$, $y_{M\cdot} - y_{L\cdot} \geq LSD$ is equivalent to any of three possible comparisons $y_{1\cdot} - y_{2\cdot} \geq LSD$, $y_{1\cdot} - y_{3\cdot} \geq LSD$, and $y_{2\cdot} - y_{3\cdot} \geq LSD$. Making the simplification that all three comparisons are independent (in fact, they are not, since the same MSW is used for all three), it follows that the chance that at least one of the inequalities holds $1 - (1 - \alpha)^3 = 1 - (0.95)^3 = 14$ per cent of the time. This value approximates 13 per cent.

What we are seeking is a method that will allow statements, with a known probability of error, for a *class of comparisons*. If we can do this, we may make comparisons in sequence and/or after looking at the data as long as the comparisons are within the specified class. Various procedures for this purpose have been developed. We shall discuss one of these, called the *Scheffé procedure*.

The class of comparisons considered here is that of *all contrasts*. We have given a number of examples of sets of contrasts which are of interest. If a contrast among the means $m_1, m_2, \ldots, m_s$ is denoted generically by

$$M = \sum_i c_i m_i \qquad (9.2.54)$$

with $c_1 + c_2 + \cdots + c_s = 0$, the estimate of M is the contrast L among the sample averages $y_1., y_2., \ldots, y_s.$, namely,

$$L = \sum_i c_i y_i. \qquad (9.2.55)$$

where the coefficients of the $y_i.$ are the same. The statement basic to the Scheffé procedure is

$$\mathrm{Prob}\left(|M - L| \leq S\,\frac{\sqrt{MSW}}{\sqrt{n}}\,\sqrt{\sum_i c_i^2}\ \text{for } all \text{ contrasts}\right) = 1 - \alpha$$

$$(9.2.56)$$

where
$$S^2 = (s - 1)F_{1-\alpha;\,s-1,\,s(n-1)} \qquad (9.2.57)$$

With this relationship we may single out any *one* or any *set* of contrasts (in sequence or not), even after looking at the data, and obtain a confidence interval which holds *simultaneously for all contrasts*. In particular, therefore, this relationship also holds for *any* contrast which may be suggested by the data.

In view of the relationship of confidence intervals to hypothesis testing, explored in Chap. 8, one can validly make any set of tests involving contrasts with prescribed *overall* significance level α. For example, in order to test whether $M_1 = 0$ and $M_2 = 0$, determine whether or not

$$L_1 \pm S\,\sqrt{\frac{MSW}{n}}\,\sqrt{\sum_i c_{i1}^2}$$

and
$$L_2 \pm S\,\sqrt{\frac{MSW}{n}}\,\sqrt{\sum_i c_{i2}^2}$$

cover zero.

The analysis of the one-way classification case has been carried out assuming that the number of observations from each population equals n. The case when there is possibly an unequal number from each population, $n_1, n_2, \ldots, n_s$, can be treated in an analogous manner with some modifications.

9.2.2   Two-way classification—model I

It is common experience that the magnitude of most "variables" is influenced by the magnitudes of more than one other variable. In the very simple situation of a simple electrical circuit where the relation $E = IR$ holds under conditions of "exact certainty" (Chap. 6), the electromotive force E is influenced, in an exactly determinable way, by the current I flowing and the resistance R over which E (also called potential drop) is measured. If the relation $E = IR$ were not established, a classical approach to determining the dependence of E upon I and R has been to hold R constant and vary I, measuring the resulting E. In practice, it is more practical to study $I = E/R$, since E and R can more readily be manipulated. Hence given, say, $E = 10$ volts, one might let $R = 1, 2, 5, 10,$ and 50 ohms, successively. The results $I = 10, 5, 2, 1, 0.2$ amperes might readily convince one that $I = E/R$. A cautious investigator would, however, try a number of values of E, say, $E = 1, 5, 20,$ and 50 volts, as well as 10 volts. This classical approach explores a range of pairs of (I,R) values, but does so by holding one of the manipulable variables constant while the other is varied, and then varying the first variable for a similar round of variation of the second variable. In this case, where each variable takes on 5 values, 25 repetitions of the experiment are required, without replications of the same value. Were the same procedure to be followed for 3 manipulable variables, 125 repetitions of the experiment would have been required. The number of experiments following this procedure becomes forbidding, even in the case of "exact certainty."

When, however, the circumstances of experiment entail inherent variation in the manipulable variables themselves, either because of non-reproducibility of repeated measurements on the same entity or because of change in the entity itself, it is necessary to discriminate between changes in the outcome variable resulting from the effects of "genuinely" different values of the manipulable variable and the variation of the outcomes due to random variation of the manipulable variables. Thus, in a lathe operation, the diameter of a metal rod may vary because of the setting of the cutting tool and also because of random variations in the hardness of the bar stock, the trueness of the cutting edge, the concentricity of the chuck, the trueness of the lead screw, and other conditions. If, then, one were to study the effects of cutting tools on the variation of the diameter of rods fashioned on a certain type of lathe, one would need to consider a number of different cutting tools and a number of different lathes (of the same type), for the lathes might exercise more than a random effect on the outcoming cylindrical rods. It would be quite uneconomical to use the policy "vary each factor over a specified range of factors, while holding all other variable factors constant" under the circumstances discussed above. Even for the two-"treatment" case of cutting tools and machines—since both treatments on replication yield variation in the outcomes—a method for using combinations of both treatments which permit testing the effects of each treatment, as well as the effects of treatment combinations, is desirable. We must bear in mind that we must be able to test hypotheses or make estimations so as to be able to assure ourselves in some degree that we are not mistaking random variations for real effects. What we seek, if possible, is a mixing of the random variation in such a way that "effective" variation in the outcomes resulting from the random variation of treatment effects is as small as is possible—hopefully, zero.

For purposes of developing the model I two-way classification, let us consider a set of circumstances where two factors affect a characteristic of a simple cylindrical metal part. Suppose we are interested in the cylinder diameter, and suppose further that there are four sources of rod stock from which the cylindrical parts can be fashioned and six machines on which the fabrication can be done. The individual effects of these two factors, namely, the four sources of raw material and the six machines and their joint effect, concern us. For the purpose of formal analysis, denote the raw-materials factor by A and the machine factor by C, while the cylinder diameter will be designated by

$$Y_{ijk} = m_{ij} + e_{ijk} \qquad \begin{cases} i = 1, 2, \ldots, a \\ j = 1, 2, \ldots, c \\ k = 1, 2, \ldots, n \end{cases} \qquad (9.2.58)$$

Equation (9.2.58) is often called the model since the random variables and the parameters which constitute Y_{ijk}, in essence, determine the "nature" of interpretation that will be given to the outcomes of the experiment. Again, the subscript i refers to the fact that the ith level of factor A is involved. Since A represents raw materials, an observation at level i refers to the ith raw material. In this example, i runs from 1 to 4. And a word about this in connection with model I: we are concerned with the four particular sources of raw materials. They are fixed factors. These four different sources are not a sample of a universe of sources about which we are trying to infer mean effect from a random sample—all the variants of the sources of raw materials are accounted for in the model. Similarly with the six machines.

The observations may then be considered to be made up of a component m_{ij} and a random variable e_{ijk}. For the ith A level and the jth C level, there are n observations y_{ijk} which constitute a random sample of the universe of observations possible by repetitive experiment under conditions that the ith A level and jth C level simultaneously prevail. Then it is natural that m_{ij} is the mean of the i-jth universe of observations. The deviation (error) of the kth observation on the i-jth level is then what is denoted by e_{ijk} and $E(e_{ijk}) = 0$. It is convenient (as was shown in Sec. 9.2.1) to express the m_{ij} in terms of "submeans." This can be done as follows:

$$m_{ij} = m.. + (m_{i\cdot} - m..) + (m_{\cdot j} - m..) + (m_{ij} - m_{i\cdot} - m_{\cdot j} + m..)$$
$$= m.. + a_i + c_j + d_{ij} \tag{9.2.59}$$

where
$$\sum_i a_i = \sum_j c_j = \sum_i d_{ij} = \sum_j d_{ij} = 0 \tag{9.2.60}$$

The component a_i consists of deviations of $m_{i\cdot}$ from the overall mean $m...$ But since $m_{i\cdot}$ is a mean itself, over all levels of the C factor, for a particular ith level of the A factor, one can define a_i as the measure of the deviation of the effect of the ith level of factor A from the overall mean, *averaged over all levels of* C. Similarly for c_j (with respect to the effects of the jth level of factor C). In order to interpret d_{ij}, observe that, for $d_{ij} = 0$,

$$m_{ij} = m.. + a_i + c_j \tag{9.2.61}$$

and therefore that

$$m_{ij'} - m_{ij} = c_{j'} - c_j$$

is independent of i, while

$$m_{i'j} - m_{ij} = a_{i'} - a_i$$

is independent of j.

In sum, then, in the case of model I, a_i, c_j, d_{ij}, and $m..$ are assumed to be unknown constants about which we wish to make inferences. We assume, further, that $V(Y_{ijk}) = \sigma_e^2$ and Y_{ijk} are uncorrelated.

The observations Y_{ijk} may be conveniently represented as in Table 9.9.

It is possible to consider the model now being studied as consisting of ac populations on each of which n observations have been taken and with means denoted by m_{ij}. Thereby one may pattern the development of relations among the observations and components after those of the one-way classification. The estimate of variance σ_e^2 may be estimated from the Y_{ijk} of any given i-jth population; whence the estimate may be expressed as

$$s_{ij}^2 = \sum_k \frac{(Y_{ijk} - Y_{ij\cdot})^2}{n - 1} \tag{9.2.62}$$

Since, therefore, the sum of squares within the i-jth population is $(n - 1)s_{ij}^2$, the pooled sum of squares within is

$$SSW = \sum_i \sum_j \sum_k (Y_{ijk} - Y_{ij\cdot})^2 = \sum_i \sum_j (n - 1)s_{ij}^2 \tag{9.2.63}$$

TABLE 9.9

C / A	1	2	. . .	j	. . .	c	Sample average	Mean
1	Y_{111} . . . Y_{11n}	Y_{121} . . . Y_{12n}	. . .	Y_{1j1} . . . Y_{1jn}	. . .	Y_{1c1} . . . Y_{1cn}	$Y_{1..}$	$m_{1.}$
2	Y_{211} . . . Y_{21n}	Y_{221} . . . Y_{22n}	. . .	Y_{2j1} . . . Y_{2jn}	. . .	Y_{2c1} . . . Y_{2cn}	$Y_{2..}$	$m_{2.}$
. . .	. . .	. . .	. . .	. . .	. . .	. . .	. . .	. . .
i	Y_{i11} . . . Y_{i1n}	Y_{i21} . . . Y_{i2n}	. . .	Y_{ij1} . . . Y_{ijn}	. . .	Y_{ic1} . . . Y_{icn}	$Y_{i..}$	$m_{i.}$
. . .	. . .	. . .	. . .	. . .	. . .	. . .	. . .	. . .
a	Y_{a11} . . . Y_{a1n}	Y_{a21} . . . Y_{a2n}	. . .	Y_{aj1} . . . Y_{ajn}	. . .	Y_{ac1} . . . Y_{acn}	$Y_{a..}$	$m_{a.}$
Sample average	$Y_{.1.}$	$Y_{.2.}$	. . .	$Y_{.j.}$	. . .	$Y_{.c.}$	$Y_{...}$	
Mean	$m_{.1}$	$m_{.2}$	. . .	$m_{.j}$	. . .	$m_{.c}$		$m_{..}$

The number of degrees of freedom associated with SSW is $(n-1)$ times the number of populations, that is, $ac(n-1)$. Hence the mean sum of squares within is

$$MSW = \frac{SSW}{ac(n-1)}$$

The expected value of the mean sum of squares within is

$$E(MSW) = \sigma_e^2$$

Study of the sum of squares between populations can take as a starting point the ac means m_{ij} of the ac populations where, for the i-jth population, $Y_{ij.}$ is an estimate of m_{ij}. Proceeding as in the one-way classification, one can express the sum of squares between as

$$SSB = n \sum_i \sum_j (Y_{ij\cdot} - Y...)^2 \qquad (9.2.64)$$

Associated with SSB are $ac - 1$ degrees of freedom. It is desirable to dissect this variation into the contributions to it of the A and C factors, respectively, and of their interaction, so as to shed light on the effects of these factors.

One may proceed by considering how to represent the differences among the effects due to the c levels of factor C. For each level i of factor A, there are n values of Y_{ijk} corresponding to some level j of factor C. One can compare the differences among the c levels of factor C by considering, say, the jth level to be held fast and averaging the Y_{ijk} over the $k = 1, 2, \ldots, n$ replications for each i level of factor A, and then averaging over the $i = 1, 2, \ldots, a$ levels of factor A, obtaining c averages $Y_{\cdot j\cdot}$. Then, in order to study the between variations due to the c levels of the C factor, we can consider the $c - 1$ orthogonal contrasts among these averages, namely,

$$\sum_{j=1}^{c} v_j Y_{\cdot j\cdot} \qquad (9.2.65)$$

each of which is an unbiased estimate of the corresponding contrast

$$\sum_{j}^{c} v_j m_{\cdot j} \qquad (9.2.66)$$

among the components $m_{\cdot 1}, m_{\cdot 2}, \ldots, m_{\cdot c}$. One can, furthermore, express contrasts (9.2.65) as contrasts among the ac averages $Y_{11\cdot}, Y_{12\cdot}, \ldots, Y_{1c\cdot}, Y_{21\cdot}, Y_{22\cdot}, \ldots, Y_{2c\cdot}, \ldots, Y_{a1\cdot}, Y_{a2\cdot}, \ldots, Y_{ac\cdot}$ as follows:

$$\sum_{j=1}^{c} v_j Y_{\cdot j\cdot} = \sum_{j=1}^{c} v_j \left(\frac{1}{a} \sum_{i=1}^{a} Y_{ij\cdot} \right) = \sum_{i=1}^{a} \sum_{j=1}^{c} \frac{v_j}{a} Y_{ij\cdot} \qquad (9.2.67)$$

Furthermore, there are $c - 1$ such orthogonal contrasts $V_1, V_2, \ldots, V_{c-1}$ and, similarly to the discussion in Sec. 9.2.1,

$$na(V_1^2 + V_2^2 + \cdots + V_{c-1}^2) = na \sum_{j=1}^{c} (Y_{\cdot j\cdot} - Y...)^2 = SSC \quad (9.2.68)$$

The coefficient na appears since $Y_{\cdot j\cdot}$ is an average over na observations. As a result of these considerations, SSC, called the sum of squares associated with factor C, has $c - 1$ degrees of freedom.

The sum of squares associated with factor A, SSA, is derived in the same manner as was SSC. In terms, then, of $(a - 1)$ orthogonal contrasts U_1, U_2, . . . , U_{a-1} among the averages $Y_1..$, $Y_2..$, . . . , $Y_{a\cdot\cdot}$,

$$SSA = nc \sum_i (Y_i.. - Y...)^2 = nc(U_1^2 + U_2^2 + \cdots + U_{a-1}^2) \quad (9.2.69)$$

An interesting relationship between any of the U contrasts and any V contrast is quite apparent.   For both can be written in terms of the $Y_{ij\cdot}$ as

$$U = \sum_i u_i Y_i.. = \sum_i \sum_j \frac{u_i}{c} Y_{ij\cdot}$$

$$V = \sum_j v_i Y_{\cdot j\cdot} = \sum_i \sum_j \frac{v_i}{a} Y_{\cdot j\cdot} \quad (9.2.70)$$

so that summing the products of corresponding coefficients yields

$$\frac{1}{ac} \sum_i \sum_j u_i v_j = \frac{1}{ac} \left(\sum_i u_i \right) \left(\sum_j v_j \right) = 0 \quad (9.2.71)$$

since each of the factors in parentheses is zero by definition of a contrast. Any of the U contrasts is orthogonal to any V contrast.

The significance of this last result is that SSA and SSC are independent components of the total between sum of squares SSB, with $a - 1$ and $c - 1$ degrees of freedom, respectively.   Since there are $ac - 1$ degrees of freedom associated with SSB, there remain $ac - 1 - (a - 1) - (c - 1) = ac - a - c + 1 = (a - 1)(c - 1)$ degrees of freedom to be accounted for.   These degrees of freedom are precisely the number to be accounted for by the interactions.   If, then, the difference $SSB - SSA - SSC$ can be interpreted as the sum of squares due to interactions and if $(a - 1)(c - 1)$ degrees of freedom are properly associated with this sum of squares, then variations between populations are fully accounted for.   By direct manipulation, it can be shown that

$$SSI = SSB - SSA - SSC = n \sum_i \sum_j (Y_{ij\cdot} - Y_i.. - Y_{\cdot j\cdot} + Y...)^2$$

$$(9.2.72)$$

and the expression on the right of (9.2.72) is what is intuitively meant by the variation due to interactions.   For $(Y_{ij\cdot} - Y_i..)$ accounts, at each level of factor A and each level of C, for the variation of the average within a population, averaged over the effects at every level of factor C. And $(Y_{\cdot j\cdot} - Y...)$ accounts for the variation of the average within a population and at each level of factor C, averaged over every level of factor A. Therefore $(Y_{ij\cdot} - Y_i..) - (Y_{\cdot j\cdot} - Y...)$ accounts for the difference between the two variations just mentioned, which is interpreted as the differences due to C levels averaged over A levels, or vice versa.   In either case all the variations due to the combined effects of C and A (or A and C)

are expressed by (9.2.72), which is properly representative of the sum of squares between. Since the differences for all A levels account for $(a - 1)$ degrees of freedom, while those for all C levels account for $(c - 1)$ degrees of freedom, the differences for the combined effects account for $(a - 1)(c - 1)$ degrees of freedom, whereby all degrees of freedom for between variation are accounted for.

It is apparent that $V = \sum_j v_j Y_{\cdot j}$ could be an estimate of $\sum_j v_j m_{\cdot j}$.

Furthermore, since

$$m_{\cdot j} = \frac{1}{a} \sum_i m_{ij}$$

by (9.2.59)

$$m_{\cdot j} = m_{\cdot\cdot} + c_j \tag{9.2.73}$$

Therefore

$$\sum_i v_j m_{\cdot j} = m_{\cdot\cdot} \sum_j v_j + \sum_j v_i c_j = \sum_j v_i c_j \tag{9.2.74}$$

and V is an unbiased estimate of a contrast among the c_j values. Similarly, any contrast U is an estimate of a contrast among $a_1, a_2, \ldots, a_a$.

The results of the foregoing analysis are summarized in Table 9.10. The fourth-row entry for the sum-of-squares column is the sum of the entries in the first three rows in that column. Similarly for the degrees-of-freedom column. These results determine the form of the mean sum of squares between entry in the fourth row of the MS column. Further subdivision of sums of squares is possible, and such subdivision can reveal insight into the variation of the mean response to particular levels of one of the factors (averaged over all levels of the other factors). Suppose, for example, that there are three levels for factor A and therefore 2 degrees of freedom associated with SSA. Then one can subdivide SSA into two components, one associated with 1 degree of freedom, which can be used for testing whether the function is quadratic, and another component to serve for testing the function for linearity.

The expected values, entries in the last column of Table 9.10, can be obtained by straightforward application of definitions. For example,

$$E(MSA) = E\left(\frac{SSA}{a - 1}\right) = E\left[\frac{nc}{a - 1} \sum_i (Y_{i\cdot\cdot} - Y_{\cdots})^2\right] \tag{9.2.75}$$

From (9.2.59)

$$Y_{i\cdot\cdot} = m_{\cdot\cdot} + a_i + e_{i\cdot\cdot} \qquad Y_{\cdots} = m_{\cdot\cdot} + e_{\cdots} \tag{9.2.76}$$

and therefore

$$\sum_i (Y_{i\cdot\cdot} - Y_{\cdots})^2 = \sum_i a_i^2 + \sum_i (e_{i\cdot\cdot} - e_{\cdots})^2 + 2 \sum_i a_i(e_{i\cdot\cdot} - e_{\cdots})$$

$$\tag{9.2.77}$$

TABLE 9.10

Source of variation	Sum of squares	Degrees of freedom	Mean square	Expected mean square
Factor A	$SSA = nc \sum_i (Y_{i..} - Y...)^2$	$a - 1$	$MSA = \dfrac{SSA}{a-1}$	$\sigma_e^2 + \dfrac{nc}{a-1} \sum_i a_i^2$
Factor C	$SSC = na \sum_j (Y_{.j.} - Y...)^2$	$c - 1$	$MSC = \dfrac{SSC}{c-1}$	$\sigma_e^2 + \dfrac{na}{c-1} \sum_j c_j^2$
Interaction of A and C	$SSI = n \sum_i \sum_j (Y_{ij.} - Y_{i..} - Y_{.j.} + Y...)^2$	$(a-1)(c-1)$	$MSI = \dfrac{SSI}{(a-1)(c-1)}$	$\sigma_e^2 + \dfrac{n}{(a-1)(c-1)} \sum_i \sum_j d_{ij}^2$
Between all effects	$SSB = n \sum_i \sum_j (Y_{ij.} - Y...)^2$	$ac - 1$	$MSB = \dfrac{SSB}{ac-1}$	$\sigma_e^2 + \dfrac{n}{ac-1} \sum_i \sum_j (m_{ij} - m..)^2$
Within	$SSW = \sum_i \sum_j \sum_k (Y_{ijk} - Y_{ij.})^2$	$ac(n-1)$	$MSW = \dfrac{SSW}{ac(n-1)}$	σ_e^2
Total	$\sum_i \sum_j \sum_k (Y_{ijk} - Y...)^2$			

The expectations yield

$$E\left(\sum_i a_i{}^2\right) = \sum_i a_i{}^2 \qquad E(e_i.. - e...) = 0 \qquad (9.2.78)$$

For $\sum_i (e_i.. - e...)^2$ the expectation is obtained by use of the fact that each $e_i..$ is normally distributed with zero mean and variance $\sigma_e{}^2/nc$. Since $e...$ is a sample average,

$$E\left[\sum_i (e_i.. - e...)^2\right] = \frac{a-1}{nc}\,\sigma_e{}^2 \qquad (9.2.79)$$

Therefore

$$E\left(\frac{SSA}{a-1}\right) = \frac{nc}{a-1}\,E\left(\sum_i a_i{}^2\right) + \left(\frac{nc}{a-1}\right)\left(\frac{a-1}{nc}\right)\sigma_e{}^2$$

$$= \sigma_e{}^2 + \frac{nc}{a-1}\sum_i a_i{}^2 \qquad (9.2.80)$$

There are three basic hypotheses to be tested under the present model, namely,

$$\begin{aligned}
H_0: &\quad a_i = 0 \text{ for all } i \\
H_0': &\quad c_j = 0 \text{ for all } j \\
H_0'': &\quad d_{ij} = 0 \text{ for all } i, j
\end{aligned}$$

In the customary manner the ratio of the corresponding sum of squares to the "error" sum of squares, MSW, is compared with the lower boundary of critical region for some significance level α, in order to reject the null hypothesis under consideration. As has been stated before, the lower boundary of the region relates to an F distribution with degrees of freedom equal to (df of numerator, df of denominator), evaluated at $100(1-\alpha)$ percentile. Thus

Reject

$$\begin{aligned}
&H_0 \text{ when } MSA/MSW > F_{1-\alpha;\,a-1,\,ac(n-1)} \\
&H_0' \text{ when } MSC/MSW > F_{1-\alpha;\,c-1,\,ac(n-1)} \\
&H_0'' \text{ when } MSI/MSW > F_{1-\alpha;\,(a-1)(c-1),\,ac(n-1)}
\end{aligned}$$

From the $E(MS)$ column of Table 9.10 it can be seen that when these null hypotheses are true, the ratios of the expected values of each of the respective numerators to denominators are equal to 1, as they should be. The following special conditions should be noted, however:

1. When there is no replication, that is, when $n = 1$,
   a. There is no test for H_0, H_0', and H_0'', since the error degrees of freedom $ac(n-1) = 0$.

b. If, besides, the interactions are assumed to be zero, that is, $d_{ij} = 0$, then by using MSI for the error term $E(MSI) = \sigma_e{}^2$, tests for H_0 and H_0' can be made.

2. When $n > 1$ and the d_{ij} are assumed equal to zero, it is appropriate that MSI, properly weighted, be included in the error term since $E(MSI)$ as well as $E(MSW)$ equals $\sigma_e{}^2$. This term is then

$$MSW' = \frac{SSI + SSW}{(a-1)(c-1) + ac(n-1)} \qquad (9.2.81)$$

We now turn to the determination of confidence intervals. Those for m_{ij}, $m_{i\cdot}$, and $m_{\cdot j}$ can be obtained in the conventional manner, since a random variable such as $Y_{i\cdot\cdot}$, for example, has a normal distribution with mean $m_{i\cdot}$ and variance $\sigma_e{}^2/cn$. Therefore

$$\frac{Y_{i\cdot\cdot} - m_{i\cdot}}{\sqrt{MSW}/\sqrt{cn}} \qquad (9.2.82)$$

has a Student t distribution with $ac(n-1)$ degrees of freedom and

$$Y_{i\cdot\cdot} \pm t_{1-a/2}\sqrt{\frac{MSW}{cn}}$$

is the conventional $(1-\alpha)$-level confidence interval for $m_{i\cdot}$. Similarly, confidence intervals for multiple comparisons for contrasts between A and C effects can be set up by means of the Scheffé procedure. As an example, one can express directly

$$\text{Prob}\left(\left|\sum_i q_i m_{i\cdot} - \sum_i q_i Y_{i\cdot\cdot}\right| \leq S'\sqrt{\frac{MSW}{cn}}\sqrt{\sum_i q_i{}^2}\right.$$

$$\left. \text{for } all \text{ contrasts}\right) = 1 - \alpha \qquad (9.2.83)$$

where $(S')^2 = (a-1)F_{1-\alpha;\,(a-1),ac(n-1)}$.

A look at the power function for the tests of the various hypotheses is in order. Following conventional procedures, the power functions can be obtained by specifying appropriately the values for ϕ^2, f_1, and f_2. Thus we have:

For H_0: $a_i = 0$

$$\phi^2 = \frac{cn}{a\sigma_e{}^2}\sum_i a_i{}^2 \qquad f_1 = a - 1, f_2 = ac(n-1)$$

For H_0': $c_j = 0$

$$\phi^2 = \frac{an}{c\sigma_e{}^2}\sum_j c_j{}^2 \qquad f_1 = c - 1, f_2 = ac(n-1)$$

For H_0'': $\quad d_{ij} = 0$

$$\phi^2 = \frac{n}{(a-1)(c-1)+1} \sum_i \sum_j \frac{d_{ij}^2}{\sigma_e^2} \qquad f_1 = (a-1)(c-1), f_2 = ac(n-1)$$

As a final consideration in connection with this model, the following sequence of steps is offered as a means of carrying out the computations for Table 9.10 in a systematic fashion, requiring the least effort.

1. Compute row totals $R_1, R_2, \ldots, R_a$.
2. Compute column totals $C_1, C_2, \ldots, C_c$.
3. Compute within totals $W_{11}, W_{12}, \ldots, W_{ac}$.
4. Compute overall total $T = R_1 + \cdots + R_a = C_1 + \cdots + C_c$.
5. Calculate

$$\sum_i \sum_j \sum_k Y_{ijk}^2$$

6. Calculate

$$\sum_j \frac{C_j^2}{an}$$

7. Calculate

$$\sum_i \frac{R_i^2}{cn}$$

8. Calculate

$$\sum_i \sum_j \frac{W_{ij}^2}{n}$$

9. Calculate the correction due to mean

$$\frac{T^2}{acn}$$

10. Calculate

$$SSA = \sum_i \frac{R_i^2}{cn} - \frac{T^2}{acn}$$

11. Calculate

$$SSC = \sum_j \frac{C_j^2}{an} - \frac{T^2}{acn}$$

12. Calculate

$$SSW = \sum_i \sum_j \sum_k Y_{ijk}^2 - \sum_i \sum_j \frac{W_{ij}^2}{n}$$

13. Calculate

$$SST = \sum_i \sum_j \sum_k Y_{ijk}^2 - \frac{T^2}{acn}$$

14. The interaction sum of squares is then obtained by subtraction, where $SSI = SST - SSW - SSA - SSC$.

9.2.3   Two-way classification—model II and mixed model

In the previous section we analyzed the two-way model with fixed effects. The model there was

$$Y_{ijk} = m.. + a_i + c_j + d_{ij} + e_{ijk} \qquad \left\{ \begin{array}{l} i = 1, \ldots, a \\ j = 1, \ldots, c \\ k = 1, \ldots, n \end{array} \right. \qquad (9.2.84)$$

In the fixed-effect model, a_i, c_j, and d_{ij} are constants about which inference is to be made. As an example, we considered an experiment with a machines and c different sources of raw material; we are interested specifically in these a machines and the particular c sources of raw materials. A fixed-effect-model formulation was required in that situation. There are, however, other situations where a machines are chosen randomly from a population of machines and c sources of raw materials are chosen randomly from a population of raw-material sources, and the prime interest lies in these populations. A random-component (model II) formulation is relevant in this situation, and a_i, c_j, and d_{ij} are random variables. There is also a mixed-model formulation, in which some of the quantities are fixed while others are random.

Now we shall discuss the random-component model given by

$$Y_{ijk} = m.. + a_i + c_j + d_{ij} + e_{ijk} \qquad (9.2.85)$$

where a_i, c_j, d_{ij}, and e_{ijk} are assumed to be normal random variables with zero means and variances σ_a^2, σ_c^2, σ_d^2, and σ_e^2, respectively. Furthermore, a_i, c_j, d_{ij}, and e_{ijk} are independent and

$$\begin{aligned} E(Y_{ijk}) &= m.. \\ V(Y_{ijk}) &= \sigma_a^2 + \sigma_c^2 + \sigma_d^2 + \sigma_e^2 \end{aligned} \qquad (9.2.86)$$

Thus the variation in Y_{ijk} has various components of variance about which inference is to be made. An analysis-of-variance scheme for breaking up the total sum of squares SST into meaningful components is carried out identically as in the fixed-effect model, and is indicated in Table 9.11.

TABLE 9.11

Source of variation	Sum of squares	Degrees of freedom	Expected mean square
Factor A	SSA	$a - 1$	$\sigma_e^2 + n\sigma_d^2 + cn\sigma_a^2$
Factor C	SSC	$c - 1$	$\sigma_e^2 + n\sigma_d^2 + an\sigma_c^2$
Interaction	SSI	$(a - 1)(c - 1)$	$\sigma_e^2 + n\sigma_d^2$
Within	SSW	$ac(n - 1)$	σ_e^2

The expected mean squares $E(MS)$ are obtained in a straightforward way. For example, in order to derive $E(MSA)$, note that

$$Y_{ijk} = m.. + a_i + c_j + d_{ij} + e_{ijk}$$
$$Y_{i..} = m.. + a_i + c. + d_{i.} + e_{i..} \qquad (9.2.87)$$
$$Y... = m.. + a. + c. + d.. + e...$$

and form:

$$\sum_i (Y_{i..} - Y...)^2 = \sum_i (a_i - a.)^2 + \sum_i (d_{i.} - d..)^2 + \sum_i (e_{i..} - e...)^2$$
$$+ 2\sum_i (a_i - a.)(d_{i.} - d.) + 2\sum_i (a_i - a.)(e_{i..} - e...)$$
$$+ 2\sum_i (d_{i.} - d..)(e_{i..} - e...)$$

In view of the independence assumption, the expectation of the mean sum of squares within A becomes

$$E(MSA) = E\left[\frac{cn\sum_i (Y_{i..} - Y...)^2}{a - 1}\right] = \sigma_e^2 + n\sigma_d^2 + cn\sigma_a^2 \qquad (9.2.88)$$

We shall briefly consider a mixed-model situation and then specify tests of hypotheses for both model II and the mixed model. We may let the c_j be the fixed effect, so that in the example of the machine and sources of raw materials, we are interested in the population of machines but only in c specific sources of raw materials.

For this mixed-effect model we use the same sets of sums of squares as in model II, namely, SSA, SSC, SSI, and SSW. The $E(MS)$ (expected mean sums of squares), however, differ in important respects among the fixed, random, and mixed-effect models. These differences can be seen clearly in Table 9.12, where the analysis-of-variance tables for each of the three models have been put together for A, C, interaction, and within contributions to the variance. We are now in a position to note some important differences between the models in terms of hypothesis testing. In the fixed-effect model we compare MSA with MSW to test $H_0: a_i = 0$, while in the random and mixed models, we test $H_0: \sigma_a^2 = 0$ by comparing MSA with MSI (and not MSW). That is, we test for fixed-effect factors by comparing the mean square of the factor with MSW and for random effects with MSI, except for testing for interaction $d_{ij} = 0$ and $\sigma_d^2 = 0$, where MSI/MSW is the relevant ratio. An important consequence of this fact occurs in the case when $n = 1$. For the fixed-effect model no test for $a_i = 0$ can be made without assuming that $d_{ij} = 0$. However, for the random-component model, this problem does not arise since MSA, for example, is tested against MSI and not MSW. The only test which cannot be made in the random-component model, when $n = 1$, is testing the hypothesis $\sigma_d^2 = 0$.

TABLE 9.12

Source of variation	Sum of squares	Degrees of freedom	Mean square	E(MS) (fixed), model I	E(MS) (random), model II	E(MS) (mixed)
Factor A	SSA	$a - 1$	MSA	$\sigma_e^2 + \dfrac{nc}{a-1}\sum a_i^2$	$\sigma_e^2 + n\sigma_d^2 + cn\sigma_a^2$	$\sigma_e^2 + n\sigma_d^2 + cn\sigma_a^2$
Factor C	SSC	$c - 1$	MSC	$\sigma_e^2 + \dfrac{na}{c-1}\sum c_j^2$	$\sigma_e^2 + n\sigma_d^2 + an\sigma_c^2$	$\sigma_e^2 + \dfrac{na}{c-1}\sum_j c_j^2$
Interaction	SSI	$(a-1)(c-1)$	MSI	$\sigma_e^2 + \dfrac{n}{(a-1)(c-1)}\sum_i\sum d_{ij}^2$	$\sigma_e^2 + n\sigma_d^2$	$\sigma_e^2 + n\sigma_d^2$
Within	SSW	$ac(n-1)$	MSW	σ_e^2	σ_s^2	σ_e^2

EXERCISES

9.1. The *Charpy notch impact test* gives rather variable results. The data which follow were taken primarily to determine whether the five testing machines of one large steel company give consistent results. The machines were calibrated before the data were taken. The values reported are the number of foot-pounds absorbed in breaking the notched specimens by the fall of a ballistic pendulum. Each value in the body of the table is the average of 18 breaks. The error variance computed from the individual breaks was 6.00 (foot-pounds).

Temperature, °F	Machine					Means
	a	b	c	d	e	
−20	28.3	28.1	28.6	36.8	33.2	31.0
32	38.0	37.2	37.6	47.6	46.0	41.3
70	45.7	42.8	46.9	53.1	59.1	48.9
120	55.2	49.1	61.7	59.7	64.5	58.0
Means	41.8	39.3	43.7	49.3	50.0	44.8

a. Do the data give evidence of differences among the machines?
b. Is there evidence of machine-temperature interaction?
c. Give a complete analysis-of-variance table.
d. Justify the model you decided to use (model I or II).

9.2. Samples of three fuses were taken every hour for one day from a process making 10-ampere fuses. The fuses were blown and the current measured, with the following results:

Hour							
1	2	3	4	5	6	7	8
10.2	9.7	10.6	10.1	9.8	10.2	9.5	9.9
10.1	9.9	10.1	9.8	10.0	10.1	10.1	9.9
10.3	10.4	9.9	10.3	10.2	10.0	9.7	9.7

Assume that the current measurements are normally distributed within each group, with a common variance for all groups. Test the hypothesis at the 5 per cent level of significance that the process remained the same during the day.

9.3. In a study concerning storage conditions, all combinations of the following two factors were tested:

Relative humidity: 20 per cent and 35 per cent
Length of storage: 4 weeks and 8 weeks

A life test was made, and the length of life was recorded for two replications per combination.

Length of storage, weeks	Relative humidity	
	20%	35%
4	10	16
	7	18
	8	15
8	11	10
	12	7
	10	9

a. Estimate all relevant parameters.
b. Carry out the analysis of variance and make appropriate tests (use $\alpha = 0.05$ level).
c. Suggest practical applications of the results.
d. Draw the power curve for the relative-humidity effect, estimating σ_e^2 from the data.

9.4. The yield of a process $Y(t)$ depends on the temperature t, which is a variable that may be controlled. The expected yield at temperatures was assumed to be at most a second-degree polynomial; that is,

$$E[Y(t)] = a + bt + ct^2$$

Three observations on yield were made for each of the following three temperature levels: $t = 70°F$, $80°F$, and $90°F$. The results are:

Temperature level		
70°F	80°F	90°F
15.62	15.76	15.46
16.00	15.73	15.68
15.93	15.74	15.21

a. Using appropriate contrasts, estimate parameters a, b, and c.
b. Set up an analysis-of-variance table and test whether $c = 0$ ($\alpha = 0.05$).
c. Test whether temperature has an effect ($b = c = 0$).
d. Use the multiple-comparison method of Scheffé to decide on the appropriate degree of polynomial.
e. How many observations do you estimate would be needed to conclude that $c > 0$ if $c = 0.002$ (with odds 9 to 1)?

9.5. In a process two chemical compositions E_1 and E_2 are being considered. Furthermore, two process times T_1 and T_2 are under study. For each of the four treatment combinations, five observations of a characteristic were made, giving the following results:

E_1		E_2	
T_1	T_2	T_1	T_2
160	170	190	250
190	240	210	260
200	210	190	270
140	150	230	210
160	220	180	200

a. Set up the analysis-of-variance table.
b. Obtain the components of the treatment sum of squares due to each of the contrasts of interest.
c. Compute confidence intervals for the contrasts (compare the t-test procedure with the Scheffé procedure).
d. Estimate and draw the power curve ($\alpha = 0.05$). If the replications are increased to 10, draw the modified power curve (estimate σ_e^2 from the data).

9.6. A number of machines were chosen from a population of machines and operated by five workers chosen from a population. The rates of output were measured, giving the following results:

Worker	Machine			
	1	2	3	4
1	20	22	16	20
2	17	24	13	19
3	30	26	34	30
4	12	18	15	16
5	24	28	23	21

a. Estimate the variability of worker and machine populations.
b. Test whether there is any variability between the machines ($\alpha = 0.05$).

9.7. Some characteristic of items packed in bales was under study. For this purpose, five bales were chosen at random and a sample of four items in each bale were examined, with the following results:

Bale				
1	2	3	4	5
12	9	22	4	16
14	16	18	10	20
8	5	26	7	15
12	11	22	8	13

a. Estimate the variability between bales and within bales.

b. Estimate the optimum number of items per bale to choose, for estimating overall mean, if costs are $C_1 = 100$ and $C_2 = 2$.

9.8. Five localities are to be compared on the basis of a certain characteristic. A random sample of 15 people was chosen in each locality. Suppose that past experience indicates that $\sigma_e^2 = 90$.

a. Suppose a 5 per cent level of significance test is to be made for equality between the localities with respect to the mean of the characteristic under consideration. Would the analysis of variance have a 90 per cent chance of detecting the circumstance where four of the localities had equal mean but the other one had a mean five units higher?

b. How many people per locality must be sampled to satisfy the requirement in (a)?

9.9. Prove Eq. (9.1.1).

9.10. Prove Eq. (9.1.2).

9.11. In the two-stage sampling procedure, how would you test $H_0: \sigma_t^2/\sigma_e^2 = \lambda$ against $H_1: \sigma_t^2/\sigma_e^2 > \lambda$?

9.12. Demonstrate Eq. (9.2.5).

9.13. Demonstrate the relation in Eq. (9.2.47).

9.14. Show that $\chi_{\beta,n}^2 = nF_{\beta,n,\infty}$.

9.15. Show that an appropriate rejection region for testing the equality of s normal population means in a one-way classification model I when σ_e^2 is known is $SSB/\sigma_e^2 > \chi_{1-\alpha,s-1}^2$.

9.16. Using the arcsine transformation, show how the equality between s binomial populations can be tested.

9.17. Using the square-root transformation, show how the equality of s Poisson populations can be tested.

10

LINEAR REGRESSION

Phenomena considered in the text up to this point were expressed in terms of random variables under circumstances where the expected value of a given random variable remained constant, even though the conditions under which the random variable was observed changed. For example, in sampling from a population, the random variables obtained, $X_1, X_2, \ldots, X_n$, have a common mean μ. Repeated experiment yielded (or were expected to yield) the same phenomenon. Even in the analysis of variance, where detection of changes in the mean of observed outcomes of observations was sought in response to changes in the experimental environment, a common hypothesis under test was the constancy of the mean. In general, the mean—the expected value of a random variable—did not vary in a way which was functionally related to an independent nonrandom variable. In nature, of course, many variables are functionally dependent upon some other variable which has a seeming priority of choice, for which reason it is called the independent variable. For example, the monetary value of a loan may be $V = p + pit = a + bt$, where i represents an interest rate, t is the time during which the loan is held, and p equals the original value of the loan. It would be difficult to give a sensible meaning to V as a random variable. There are, however, innumerable cases of a random variable so related to a (supposed) nonrandom variable that the random variable's "true" value varies with the magnitude of the independent variable.

Suppose we consider the distance traversed by a steel sphere rolling down an inclined track. The distance L can be expressed as a simple function of $T = t - t_0$ (t_0 is the time at which the sphere is released), and the elapsed time T can be expressed as a function of the distance traversed. Assume that the distances can be marked off exactly from the starting point and that an observer with a stop watch notes the times at which the sphere passes the marker points. However painstakingly he works, the observer cannot read the stop watch without error. He is confronted with the task of determining the elapsed time as a function of the distance traversed on the basis of his observations.

We shall briefly consider such problems as part of the general problem of representation of data and inferring functional relationships.

10.1 Representation of data

It is common practice to represent data graphically, for graphical representation offers considerable insight.   Often, appropriate functional relationship is suggested by one of a few alternative forms of graphical representation.   We shall look at some instances.

10.1.1 Graphical representation

Suppose that the observer of the rolling sphere came up with these observations:

TABLE 10.1

$L \equiv distance$	$T \equiv time$
10	0.00
40	0.98
90	2.03
160	3.07
250	3.94
360	5.02
490	6.06
640	6.96
810	8.03
1,000	9.01

Suppose that we plot these data on a cartesian coordinate system as in Fig. 10.1*a*.   One's first impression on viewing the plotted points is that they could lie on a "smooth" curve of a rather familiar form.   But there do seem to be some slight irregularities, some deviations from an "ideal smooth" curve.   Nevertheless, one might conclude with some conviction that T is a simple function of L.   The question is, however, what function?

This question may or may not be a simple one to answer, but a practical man (an engineer or a scientist) required to take action uses a humble method ready at hand and "passes a smooth curve through the plotted points."   By what criterion?   On the basis of what assumptions?   With what degree of validity?   These are questions that the individual who has need of using a table such as Table 10.1 must consider with only partial success.   Since, however, most questions about natural phenomena can be answered only incompletely, this should be no cause for despair.   One can use a simple intuitive argument: T is increasing with L; a sequence of chords joining successive points has such a regularity of

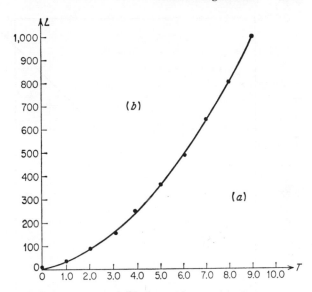

Figure 10.1   (a) The number pairs from Table 10.1; (b) smooth curve determined by (a).

growth that the points "should" lie on a smooth curve; but since T was measured by an observer trying to read a stop watch when the sphere lined up with the distance markers, there was opportunity for error, even for mistake; the apparent deviations from a hypothetical smooth curve are random deviations due to measurement error.   For practical purposes then, one may (even without conscious argument about validity of action) draw a smooth curve as in Fig. 10.1b and use it for interpolating values of T for values of L within the range of observation.   We have yet to consider the mathematical form of the curve to be, and shall do so in the next section.   First, however, we shall look at some other data.

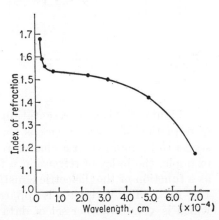

Figure 10.2

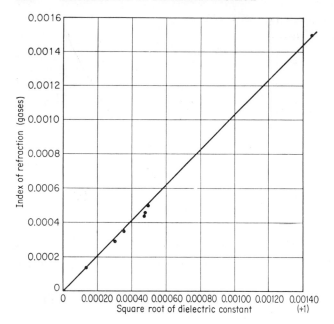

Figure 10.3

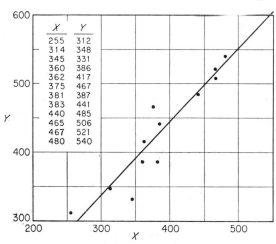

Figure 10.4

Figure 10.2 is a representation on cartesian coordinates of the index of refraction of quartz n versus the wavelength of light w. Again there seems to be more than a chance relationship, but what is it? Another example, the index of refraction n for yellow light through various gases as a function of the dielectric constant ϵ at room temperature, is given in Fig. 10.3. The variable n is apparently a linear function of the abscissa, which is $\sqrt{\epsilon}$. Another set of data is given in Fig. 10.4. The variables are not identified, for the only interest of these data is that they appear to be represented by a straight line.

Relations between two variables may be fruitfully established by graphical representation. The important task is, however, to find a more precise representation, a mathematical relationship if possible, which suggests possible structural relationship between the variables and offers a means of interpolation. Structural relationship is not necessarily found by these means. When, however, the experimenter suspects a structural relationship, he may be guided toward a possible mathematical form by attempting various forms of graphical representation.

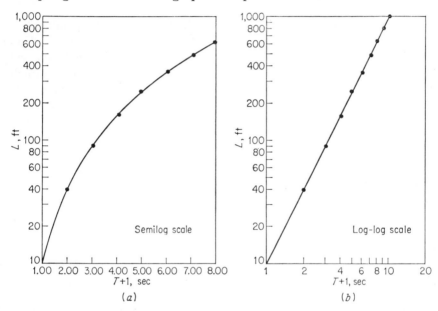

Figure 10.5

In undertaking to express the relationship between two variables, there are two stages, the first being that of selecting the appropriate function, the second of determining the parameters so that the resulting function is satisfied by the observed values in accordance with some chosen criterion. We shall make one attempt at this with data in Table 10.1, by graphical means. Suppose we try semilog coordinate (Fig. 10.5a) and log-log coordinate (Fig. 10.5b) graph paper. Since zero is way off to the left, we try to add a constant to the given abscissa values; the first convenient number that comes to mind is 1. Hence L is plotted against $T + 1$, first on semilog paper in Fig. 10.5a. The result is not very encouraging, so a try is made on log-log paper (Fig. 10.5b). The result is very encouraging, for it appears quite reasonable to draw a straight line, as illustrated, which seems to fit the data.

By conventional elementary techniques we can readily find a unique formal relation between T and L. If we accept the fact that the points in Fig. 10.5b do lie on a straight line, by using the coordinates of the first and last points we can get a reasonably accurate estimate of the slope of the graphically fitted line. By a little pragmatic juggling we shall assume that the value of T for the last point is 9.00, and not 9.01, ascribing the quantity 0.01 to measurement error. Then, remembering that graph paper was designed for logarithms to the base 10, we have

$$\log 10 - \log 1 = A \; (\log 1{,}000 - \log 10)$$

which is $1 = A(2)$, or $A = 0.5$. Similarly, for any point (T,L), $\log(T + 1) - \log 1 = 0.5 \; (\log L - \log 10)$, or $T + 1 = (L/10)^{1/2}$. Upon a little reflection it can be seen that this is precisely the distance traversed–time-elapsed relation for a body under constant acceleration, namely, $L = (\frac{1}{2})at^2$. For if $T + 1$ represents t, the time elapsed from rest for the sphere to traverse distance L, then the equation becomes $t = (L/10)^{1/2}$, or $L = 10t^2 = (\frac{20}{2})t^2$, a form that is derived analytically for bodies moving under a constant force. The acceleration is 20 feet per second per second, and the well-known distance-time-acceleration relation results. In the present case, a sequence of observations of high accuracy suffices to yield a relationship which innumerable replications of experiment confirm and which, therefore, gives credence to the analytically derived relation, based on intuitive presuppositions. (That observation must serve as the basis for physical "law" is eminently shown by the success of Kepler's inferences from Tycho Brahe's data and the subsequent formal solution of the two-body problem by Newton.) Graphical analysis is often the starting point, even where subsequent formal analysis yields rather simple mathematical relations.

Analysis of the other sets of data given here is left to the reader as an exercise in "graphical" representation.

10.1.2   Mathematical representation of data

By mathematical representation of data we mean merely the expression of a dependent variable in terms of an independent variable. (We limit discussion to two variables in order to simplify the rhetoric involved.) In the previous section we illustrated simple graphical representation and the fact that mathematical representation could follow from graphical representation. On the other hand, one can proceed directly analytically from the data. Suppose we translate graphical characterization to formal elements for some simple functions, bearing in mind that a straight line is the simplest function; namely, for any two points (x_1,y_1) and (x_2,y_2) on a straight line, $(y_2 - y_1)/(x_2 - x_1)$ is a constant. This property suggests that we study the difference between coordinate values, one way being to take differences of the coordinates for successive values of the

independent variable.   First and second differences for Table 10.1 are
given in Table 10.2.

TABLE 10.2

L	T	ΔL	ΔT	$\Delta^2 L$	$\Delta^2 T$
10	0				
40	0.98	30	0.98		
90	2.03	50	1.05	20	0.07
160	3.07	70	1.04	20	−0.01
250	3.94	90	0.97	20	−0.07
360	5.02	110	1.08	20	0.11
490	6.06	130	1.04	20	−0.04
640	6.96	150	1.00	20	−0.04
810	8.03	170	1.07	20	0.07
1,000	9.01	190	0.98	20	−0.09

The first differences of T are approximately constant.   The first
differences of L are increasing, but by constant increments; whence the
second differences are constant.   If the first differences ΔT are constant,
L is a quadratic function of T, and therefore (under appropriate restrictions), T can be expressed in terms of $\sqrt{L}$.   It does not serve the purpose of the present discussion to go into the mathematical and statistical
niceties here.   It suffices to observe that by formal techniques, and in
this case quite simple ones, we arrived at the same conclusion as by
graphical techniques.   Some definite criteria are, of course, necessary in
order to conclude that a given function satisfactorily represents the given
data.   We might, as a result of testing the successive differences in Table
10.2, try to show that $L = a + bT + cT^2$ is satisfied by the observed
values given in Table 10.1, or we might try $T - t_0 = A\sqrt{L}$.   The
present step has been merely to find a form of function which, we believe
with conviction, is satisfied by the original data in accordance with some
specified criterion.   If the values of T were integers $(0, 1, \ldots, 9)$, then
unique values of a, b, and c could be found such that the 10 pairs of $\{L, T\}$
values satisfied $L = a + bT + cT$.   This result might give an investigator strong conviction that a quadratic function does express the structural relationship between L and T, and equivalently, a square-root
relationship expresses T in terms of L.

We must consider the fact, however, that the actual data do not
exactly satisfy the mathematical relations we have suggested.   In the
present case a principle is needed to strengthen our conviction.   This
principle must arise from the nature of the experiment and the numerical
values of observed outcomes.   From the experiment we come up with
an argument something like this: L is known without error; T is observed
under circumstances where error undoubtedly occurs.   The quadratic
and square-root relationships seem quite plausible, but the constants

remain to be determined.   The question becomes how to find the parameters, now that the suggested functions for relating L and T are accepted.

The task of answering this question will be taken up in the remainder of this chapter.   The answers will be far from complete and perhaps not fully satisfactory to the reader.   Nevertheless, a useful body of techniques will be developed for determining (under specified conditions) the appropriate values of the parameters of the functions chosen to represent data.

One question, however, remains inadequately answered in the present state of knowledge, namely, is there one function whose mathematical form is "best" suited to express "the" relationship among the data?   A little reflection will show that the question of a "best" and unique function to be associated with observations does not have a simple answer. Consider, for example, the data in Fig. 10.4.   A straight line has been so drawn that it seems reasonable that other values of y corresponding to selected values of x (within the range of observation) can be estimated with considerable confidence as to the accuracy of the estimation.   On the other hand, it is possible to determine a polynomial of the eleventh degree in x which passes through each of the observed points.   One can postulate many other functions, $y = f(x)$, which can serve satisfactorily for estimation of y values.   Which function to choose depends on many factors.   Criteria of choice of function have not yet been made precise enough to provide a procedure of unique choice.   There are a few techniques which are suggestive, although the originator of data does have to use his insight into the likely structural relation between variables in order to make a selection.

Study of successive differences is often quite helpful.   Suppose we examine the data in Fig. 10.4.   The first differences are:

Δx	Δy
59	36
31	-17
15	55
2	31
75	50
6	-80
2	54
57	44
15	21
2	15
13	19

While these first differences are not constant, they exhibit some regularity.   Only two differences are negative.   Although the differences do exhibit irregularity, the ratios of five of the differences, $\Delta y / \Delta x$, lie between 0.715 and 1.64. Seven out of twelve points lie close to the line fitted by inspection, and the same number lie above as do below. These properties indicate possible linearity, distorted by random variation. It does not seem to make sense to consider a polynomial of the second degree or higher. This formal approach to discovering a functional relation is thwarted by the variation in y, yet it seems "practical" to try to fit a straight line to these data.

Polynomials can be identified by the behavior of successive differences which vary quite like the derivatives. The nth derivative of an nth-degree polynomial is a constant, and the $(n + 1)$st derivative is zero. The same property can be shown to be true for the corresponding y differences obtained for constant x differences. Hence, if data are obtained for constant increments of the independent variable and if y is "close" to a polynomial in form, the degree of the polynomial is equal to the order of the approximately constant y difference. Since y will usually be subject to variation, its differences will rarely be constant. On the other hand (if the variation is random), some order of difference will exhibit changes in sign as in the example above. This change in sign for some order of y differences for successive observed values of y is a signal that y may be a polynomial in x of degree equal to the order of y differences at which the changes in sign occur. Here is a technique which may help fix on the degree of a polynomial, where the experimenter has knowledge which leads him to believe that the y may be a polynomial in x.

Again, there are possible exponential relations, logarithmic relations, and simple combinations of exponentials, powers, and constant terms which frequently arise. Table 10.3 gives procedures for testing the data in terms of differences, which suggest functions which the data may satisfy. Having selected a function, and under the specification that the independent variable is known without error, there are procedures for estimating the parameters of the selected function. In the remainder of this chapter, some of these techniques will be presented.

10.2 General linear regression

10.2.1 Introduction and general model

In a variety of circumstances one is concerned with a random variable $Y(x)$, depending on a variable x. This random variable $Y(x)$ is sometimes called the yield associated with level x. Some examples are: $Y(x)$ is the output of a process with temperature at level x; $Y(x)$ is the volume of sales of a commodity at time x; $Y(x)$ is the extinction time of an animal associated with dosage concentration x of an insecticide.

In this presentation we shall assume that x is an independent varia-

TABLE 10.3

Procedures and Criteria for Testing the Suitability of Various Assumed Forms of Equations to Represent Given Data*

Case	Assumed form of equation	Procedures based on a constant value for Δx		Criterion of suitability
		Plot, then make table of:	Obtain these successive differences:	
1	$y = a + bx + cx^2 + \cdots + qx^n$	$y = f(x)$	$\Delta y; \Delta^2 y; \Delta^3 y; \cdots; \Delta^n y$	$\Delta^n y$ is constant
2	$y = a + \dfrac{b}{x} + \dfrac{c}{x^2} + \cdots + \dfrac{q}{x^n}$	$y = f\left(\dfrac{1}{x}\right)$	$\Delta y; \Delta^2 y; \Delta^3 y; \cdots ; \Delta^n y$	$\Delta^n y$ is constant
3	$y^2 = a + bx + cx^2 + \cdots + qx^n$	$y^2 = f(x)$	$\Delta y^2; \Delta^2 y^2; \Delta^3 y^2; \cdots ; \Delta^n y^2$	$\Delta^n y^2$ is constant
4	$\log y = a + bx + cx^2 + \cdots + qx^n$	$\log y = f(x)$	$\Delta(\log y); \Delta^2(\log y); \cdots; \Delta^n(\log y)$	$\Delta^n(\log y)$ is constant
5	$y = a + b(\log x) + c(\log x)^2$	$y = f(\log x)$	$\Delta y; \Delta^2 y$	$\Delta^2 y$ is constant
6	$y = ab^x + ae^{b'x}$	$\log y = f(x)$	$\Delta(\log y)$	$\Delta(\log y)$ is constant
7	$y = a + bc^x = a + be^{c'x}$	$y = f(x)$	$\Delta y; \log \Delta y; \Delta(\log \Delta y)$	$\Delta(\log \Delta y)$ is constant
8	$y = a + bx + cd^x = a + bx + ce^{d'x}$	$y = f(x)$	$\Delta y; \Delta^2 y; \log \Delta^2 y; \Delta(\log \Delta^2 y)$	$\Delta(\log \Delta^2 y)$ is constant
9	$y = ax^b$	$\log y = f(\log x)$	$\Delta(\log y)$	$\Delta(\log y)$ is constant
10	$y = a + bx^c$	$y = f(x)$	$\Delta y; \log \Delta y; \Delta(\log \Delta y)$	$\Delta(\log \Delta y)$ is constant
11	$y = axe^{bx}$	$\ln y = f(x)$	$\Delta \ln y; \Delta \ln x$	$(\Delta \ln y - \Delta \ln x)$ is constant

* From Archie G. Worthing and Joseph Geffner, "Treatment of Experimental Data," John Wiley & Sons, Inc., New York, 1942. Used with permission of the author and publisher.

ble and that N such values have been selected, denoted by $x_1, x_2, \ldots,$ x_N. It is further assumed that the x_i are *known exactly;* the x_i are not random variables. This should be borne in mind throughout the chapter.[1] To each x is associated a random variable $Y(x)$. In the general linear-regression model to be discussed, it is assumed that

$$E[Y(x)] = \beta_0 g_0(x) + \beta_1 g_1(x) + \cdots + \beta_m g_m(x) \qquad (10.2.1)$$

where $\beta_0, \beta_1, \ldots, \beta_m$ are unknown constants, and the $m + 1$ functions $g_i(x)$ $(i = 0, \ldots, m)$ are known functions of x. Furthermore, the random variables $Y_j = Y(x_j)$ $(j = 1, 2, \ldots, N)$ are assumed independent with the same variance σ^2. Another way to represent this model is to write

$$\begin{aligned} Y_j = Y(x_j) &= \beta_0 g_0(x_j) + \beta_1 g_1(x_j) + \cdots + \beta_m g_m(x_j) + \epsilon_j \\ &= m(x_j) + \epsilon_j \end{aligned} \qquad (10.2.2)$$

with $\epsilon_1, \epsilon_2, \ldots, \epsilon_N$ independent, $E(\epsilon_j) = 0$, and $V(\epsilon_j) = \sigma^2$. This model is called the general linear-regression model, since $m(x)$ is linear in the unknown parameters $\beta_0, \beta_1, \ldots, \beta_m$.

The assumption of constant variance σ^2 is not as serious a restriction as it may at first seem. In fact, all that is required is that $V[Y(x)] = \sigma^2 F^2(x)$, where $F(x)$ is a known function of x. In this case, we can, by the transformation $Y^*(x) = Y(x)/F(x)$, formulate it as in Eq. (10.2.2), where we have

$$Y^*(x_j) = \frac{Y(x_j)}{F(x_j)} = \beta_0 \frac{g_0(x_j)}{F(x_j)} + \beta_1 \frac{g_1(x_j)}{F(x_j)} + \cdots + \beta_m \frac{g_m(x_j)}{F(x_j)} + \frac{\epsilon_j}{F(x_j)}$$
$$(10.2.3)$$

By setting

$$g_i^*(x) = \frac{g_i(x)}{F(x)} \qquad \text{and} \qquad \epsilon_j^* = \frac{\epsilon_j}{F(x)}$$

we obtain

$$Y_j^* = \beta_0 g_0^*(x_j) + \beta_1 g_1^*(x_j) + \cdots + \beta_m g_m^*(x_j) + \epsilon_j^* \qquad (10.2.4)$$

where $g_i^*(x)$ are known functions, and

$$V(\epsilon_j^*) = \frac{1}{F^2(x_j)} V(\epsilon_j) = \frac{\sigma^2 F^2(x_j)}{F^2(x_j)} = \sigma^2$$

The model in Eq. (10.2.4) is of the same form as in Eq. (10.2.2).

The model in Eq. (10.2.2) is more general than may be apparent at first glance. Some special cases will illustrate the variety of situations which can be formulated in terms of the present model.

---

[1] When both the X_i and the Y_i are random variables, quite another problem develops.

1. Regression function $m(x)$ is linear in x, namely,

$$m(x) = \beta_0 + \beta_1 x \qquad \text{and} \qquad Y_j = \beta_0 + \beta_1 x + \epsilon_j \qquad (10.2.5)$$

Here $m = 1$, $g_0(x) = 1$, and $g_1(x) = x$. This is straight-line regression and is of wide use in engineering and the physical sciences, where many empirical relationships between two variables seem to be representable by straight lines.

2. Regression function $m(x)$ is a polynomial in x, namely,

$$m(x) = \beta_0 + \beta_1 x + \beta_2 x^2 + \cdots + \beta_m x^m$$

and
$$Y_j = \beta_0 + \beta_1 x_j + \beta_2 x_j^2 + \cdots + \beta_m x_j^m + \epsilon_j \qquad (10.2.6)$$

Here $g_i(x) = x^i$ $(i = 0, \ldots, m)$.

3. Regression function $m(x)$ is a trigonometric function of x, namely,

$$m(x) = \beta_0 + \sum_{i=1}^{n} \beta_i \sin \frac{2\pi x}{T_i} + \sum_{i=1}^{n} \beta_{n+i} \cos \frac{2\pi x}{T_i} \qquad (10.2.7)$$

where $T_1, T_2, \ldots, T_n$ are *known periods*. The value of $m = 2n$, and

$$g_i(x) = \begin{cases} 1 & i = 0 \\[2mm] \sin \dfrac{2\pi x}{T_i} & i = 1, 2, \ldots, n \\[2mm] \cos \dfrac{2\pi x}{T_{i-n}} & i = n+1, n+2, \ldots, 2n \end{cases} \qquad (10.2.8)$$

This type of model is often useful in representing cyclical phenomena. When the periods $T_1, T_2, \ldots, T_n$ are not known, the problem is beyond linear regression and will not be treated here.

4. Sometimes a combination of cases 1 and 3 may be useful; that is,

$$m(x) = \beta_0 + \beta_1 x + \beta_2 \sin \frac{2\pi x}{12} + \beta_3 \cos \frac{2\pi x}{12} \qquad (10.2.9)$$

Here $m = 3$, $g_0(x) = 1$, $g_1(x) = x$, $g_2(x) = \sin(2\pi x/12)$, and $g_3(x) = \cos(2\pi x/12)$. This model is often used in connection with time series where x denotes time. The first two terms, $\beta_0 + \beta_1 x$, may represent a *linear trend*, while the last two terms $\beta_2 \sin(2\pi x/12) + \beta_3 \cos(2\pi x/12)$ may represent a yearly *seasonal variation*.

Some examples of nonlinear regression problems are the following cases 5 and 6.

5. The regression function $m(x)$ is exponential in x, namely,

$$Y_j = \beta_0 e^{+\beta_1 x} + \epsilon_j \qquad (10.2.10)$$

Here β_0 and β_1 do not enter linearly in $m(x)$. It should be noted that the error ϵ_j is here assumed to be additive to $m(x)$. If, on the other hand, the error ϵ_j enters into the model in a multiplicative way, as in

$$Y_j = \epsilon_j \beta_0 e^{+\beta_1 x} \tag{10.2.11}$$

logarithmic transformation reduces Eq. (10.2.11) to

$$\begin{aligned} Y_j^* = \ln Y_j &= \ln \beta_0 + \beta_1 x + \ln \epsilon_j \\ &= \beta_0^* + \beta_1 x + \epsilon_j^* \end{aligned} \tag{10.2.12}$$

where $Y_j^* = \ln Y_j$, $\beta_0^* = \ln \beta_0$, and $\epsilon_j^* = \ln \epsilon_j$, which is in the general linear-regression form.

6. A regression function $m(x)$ of wide use in representing growth phenomena is the *logistic* function

$$m(x) = \frac{\beta_0}{1 + \beta_1 e^{-\beta_2 x}} \tag{10.2.13}$$

which does not fall into the linear-regression framework. Special methods are required for determining the coefficients in Eq. (10.2.13). An

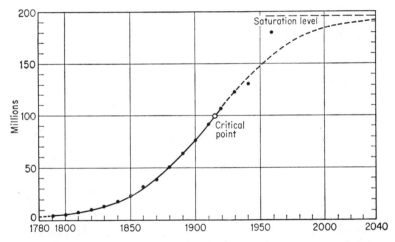

Figure 10.6 The logistic curve for the population of the United States. (*From Harold T. Davis, "Theory of Econometrics," Principia Press*, Bloomington, Ind., 1941.)

example of the logistic function fitted to natural phenomena is shown in Fig. 10.6, where the population of the United States at 10-year intervals from 1790 to 1950 has been represented as a function of time in years. The "fit" until 1950 is very good. Nevertheless, the population for 1960 as estimated from the curve in Fig. 10.6 deviates considerably from the actual 1960 population. This example illustrates the fact that, however well a regression function may represent (fit) the given data, prediction of future occurrence may be far afield. This, however, is another and quite deep problem.

We shall now introduce some of the problems which are to be treated here, in connection with the general linear-regression model.

1. Given observations $Y_1, Y_2, \ldots, Y_N$ at $x_1, x_2, \ldots, x_N$, respectively, to estimate $\beta_0, \beta_1, \ldots, \beta_m$ and σ^2.

2. Given $Y_1, Y_2, \ldots, Y_N$ at levels $x_1, x_2, \ldots, x_N$ to *predict* Y_{N+1} at a given level x_{N+1}.

3. Given N observations $Y_1, Y_2, \ldots, Y_N$ at levels $x_1, x_2, \ldots, x_N$ and M observations $Y_1', Y_2', \ldots, Y_M'$ at an unknown level x_0. The problem here is to make inferences about x_0. This is called the problem of *discrimination*. The first set of N observations is usually needed to estimate something about the regression function $m(x)$. This information is then utilized for making inference about x_0. This type of situation often arises in connection with bioassay problems.

4. Given observations $Y_1, Y_2, \ldots, Y_N$ at levels $x_1, x_2, \ldots, x_N$ to find confidence intervals and test hypotheses about $\beta_0, \beta_1, \ldots, \beta_m$.

5. Test of adequacy of the model.

10.2.2 Criteria for estimating parameters

There are a variety of methods for estimating the parameters $\beta_0, \beta_1, \ldots, \beta_m$. We shall look at several reasonable methods, which all lead to the same estimates.

Least Squares With this method we form the quadratic error function

$$Q(\beta_0, \beta_1, \ldots, \beta_m) = \sum_{i=1}^{N} \left[Y_i - \sum_{j=0}^{m} \beta_j g_j(x_i) \right]^2$$

$$= \sum_{i=1}^{N} [Y_i - m(x_i)]^2 = \epsilon_1^2 + \epsilon_2^2 + \cdots + \epsilon_N^2$$

$$(10.2.14)$$

Q is obviously a function of $Y_1, Y_2, \ldots, Y_N$ and is therefore a random variable. Treating Q for the present as a function of $\beta_0, \beta_1, \ldots, \beta_m$, the *principle of least squares* estimates $\beta_0, \beta_1, \ldots, \beta_m$ as those values of the parameters which minimize $Q(\beta_0, \beta_1, \ldots, \beta_m)$.

The usual way of finding these minimizing values is to set the $(m + 1)$ first partial derivatives of Q, with respect to each β_j, equal to zero. Hence we obtain

$$\frac{\partial Q}{\partial \beta_k} = -2 \sum_{i=1}^{N} \left[Y_i - \sum_{j=0}^{m} \beta_j g_j(x_i) \right] g_k(x_i) \qquad k = 0, 1, \ldots, m \quad (10.2.15)$$

In order to avoid confusion, since in (10.2.15) we sum on β_j, we have distinguished the different equations by giving the particular β with

respect to which we are differentiating the subscript k.   Simplification
of (10.2.15) yields

$$\frac{\partial Q}{\partial \beta_k} = -2 \left\{ \sum_{i=1}^{N} g_k(x_i) Y_i - \sum_{j=0}^{m} \beta_j \left[\sum_{i=1}^{N} g_k(x_i) g_j(x_i) \right] \right\} \quad (10.2.16)$$

Setting each of these $(m + 1)$ derivatives equal to zero, we obtain a set of
$(m + 1)$ equations referred to as the *normal equations:*

$$\sum_{j=0}^{m} \hat{\beta}_j \left[\sum_{i=1}^{N} g_k(x_i) g_j(x_i) \right] = \sum_{i=1}^{N} g_k(x_i) Y_i \quad (10.2.17)$$

where $k = 0, 1, \ldots, m$, and the β's are designated as $\hat{\beta}_j$, which are
those values which satisfy the normal equations and are the estimates
of the true values of the β's.

In order to simplify notation, we denote

$$\sum_{i=1}^{N} g_k(x_i) g_j(x_i) \qquad \text{by } a_{kj}$$

and
$$\sum_{i=1}^{N} g_k(x_i) Y_i \qquad \text{by } M_k$$

Thus we may write (10.2.17) as

$$\sum_{j=0}^{m} a_{kj} \hat{\beta}_j = M_k \qquad k = 0, 1, \ldots, m \quad (10.2.18)$$

This is a set of $(m + 1)$ simultaneous equations with $(m + 1)$ unknowns
$\hat{\beta}_0, \hat{\beta}_1, \ldots, \hat{\beta}_m$.   For example, for the special case $m = 1$, we have

$$\begin{aligned} a_{00}\hat{\beta}_0 + a_{01}\hat{\beta}_1 &= M_0 \\ a_{10}\hat{\beta}_0 + a_{11}\hat{\beta}_1 &= M_1 \end{aligned} \quad (10.2.19)$$

Any of the standard methods for solving systems of simultaneous equations may be employed to solve (10.2.18) for the least-squares estimators.
In this text, we shall not discuss special problems which may arise when
more than one solution exists and where there is redundancy in system
(10.2.18).

Linear   Unbiased   Minimum   Variance   (LUMV)   Another
approach for estimating $\beta_0, \beta_1, \ldots, \beta_m$ is to set some special requirements.   With the *LUMV* method we require that the estimates be:

1. Linear functions of $Y_1, Y_2, \ldots, Y_N$
2. Unbiased

The criterion adopted here is: among all estimators satisfying conditions
1 and 2, the one which *minimizes the variance* of the estimates is chosen.

The resulting estimates are said to be *LUMV* estimates. It can be shown that the *LUMV* estimates are the same as the least-squares estimates. This important result is known as *Markoff's theorem*. The proof of this result will not be presented here. The reader may try to verify this result when $m = 1$.

Maximum-likelihood Estimates   Another approach for estimating $\beta_0, \beta_1, \ldots, \beta_m$ is to apply the maximum-likelihood principle. At this state an important point is to be noted; namely, the method of least squares and *LUMV do not* depend on the distributions of $Y_1, Y_2, \ldots, Y_N$. Study of the statistical properties of the estimators will, however, require assumptions about these distributions, as does the principle of maximum-likelihood estimation.

For the moment we assume that $Y_1, Y_2, \ldots, Y_N$ have a common normal distribution. Since $Y_1, Y_2, \ldots, Y_N$ are independent, the joint *PDF* is

$$
\begin{aligned}
g(y_1, y_2, \ldots, y_N) &= \left(\frac{1}{\sigma\sqrt{2\pi}}\right)^N \exp\left\{-\frac{1}{2\sigma^2}\sum_{i=1}^{N}\left[y_i - \sum_{j=0}^{m}\beta_j g_j(x_i)\right]^2\right\} \\
&= \left(\frac{1}{\sigma\sqrt{2\pi}}\right)^N \exp\left[-\frac{1}{2\sigma^2}Q(\beta_0, \beta_1, \ldots, \beta_m)\right]
\end{aligned}
$$

(10.2.20)

It is readily apparent that maximizing $g(y_1, y_2, \ldots, y_N)$ with respect to $\beta_0, \beta_1, \ldots, \beta_m$ is equivalent to minimizing $Q(\beta_0, \beta_1, \ldots, \beta_m)$. Hence the maximum-likelihood estimates are the same as the least-squares estimates. The principle of maximum likelihood also yields an estimate $\hat{\sigma}^2$ for σ^2. In fact,

$$\frac{\partial \ln g}{\partial \sigma} = -\frac{N}{\sigma} + \frac{Q}{\sigma^3} = 0 \tag{10.2.21}$$

whence
$$\hat{\sigma}^2 = \frac{Q(\hat{\beta}_0, \hat{\beta}_1, \ldots, \hat{\beta}_m)}{N} \tag{10.2.22}$$

This, however, is not an unbiased estimate, which is given by

$$s^2 = \frac{Q(\hat{\beta}_0, \hat{\beta}_1, \ldots, \hat{\beta}_m)}{N - (m+1)} = \frac{\sum_{i=1}^{N}\left[Y_i - \sum_{j=0}^{m}\hat{\beta}_j g_j(x_i)\right]^2}{N - (m+1)} \tag{10.2.23}$$

where $N - (m+1)$ represents the number of degrees of freedom.

The properties of the least-squares estimates $\hat{\beta}_0, \hat{\beta}_1, \ldots, \hat{\beta}_m$ may now be summarized as follows:

1. Unbiased.
2. Linear in $Y_1, Y_2, \ldots, Y_N$. [It is apparent from Eq. (10.2.18) that the estimates $\hat{\beta}_0, \hat{\beta}_1, \ldots, \hat{\beta}_m$ are also linear functions of $M_0, M_1, \ldots, M_m$.]
3. Of minimum variance.

4. Of maximum likelihood when $Y_1, Y_2, \ldots, Y_N$ are normally distributed.

5. Satisfying the transformation property. In particular, the least-squares estimate of any linear function $\alpha = c_0\beta_0 + c_1\beta_1 + \cdots + c_m\beta_m$ of $\beta_0, \beta_1, \ldots, \beta_m$ is the same linear function $c_0\hat{\beta}_0 + c_1, \hat{\beta}_1 + \cdots + c_m\hat{\beta}_m$ of $\hat{\beta}_0, \hat{\beta}_1, \ldots, \hat{\beta}_m$. This result follows essentially from the transformation

$$\alpha_0 = c_0\beta_0 + c_1\beta_1 + \cdots + c_m\beta_m$$
$$\alpha_1 = \beta_1$$
$$\cdot \ \cdot \ \cdot \ \cdot \ \cdot$$
$$\alpha_m = \beta_m$$

Thus, when $c_0 \neq 0$, to each set $\beta_0, \beta_1, \ldots, \beta_m$ there is a corresponding unique set $\alpha_0, \alpha_1, \ldots, \alpha_m$. Although Q may be written in terms of β's or α's, the resulting two minima are equal. Thus

$$\hat{a}_0 = c_0\hat{\beta}_0 + c_1\hat{\beta}_1 + \cdots + c_m\hat{\beta}_m$$

When $Y_1, Y_2, \ldots, Y_m$ are normally distributed, this follows from the transformation property of the maximum-likelihood estimators.

10.3 Straight-line regression

In this section we discuss in detail the important special case where the mean regression line $m(x)$ is also linear in x; that is,

$$Y(x_j) = \beta_0 + \beta_1 x_j + \epsilon_j \qquad j = 1, \ldots, N \qquad (10.3.1)$$

(It should be emphasized again that the values which the x_j take on are assumed to be known without error.) In this case $m = 1$, $g_0(x) = 1$, and $g_1(x) = x$. For convenience of presentation we shall assume that

$$\sum_{i=1}^{N} x_j = N\bar{x} = 0$$

This does not reduce the generality of the problem since, if $\bar{x} \neq 0$, then $\beta_0 + \beta_1 x$ may be replaced by $\beta_0^* + \beta_1^* x^*$, where $x^* = x - \bar{x}$. As is apparent, $\Sigma x_j^* = \Sigma(x_j - \bar{x}) = 0$, which means merely that the origin of x has been shifted to $\bar{x}$. The parameters β_0, β_1 and β_0^*, β_1^* have the relations $\beta_0^* = \beta_0 + \beta_1\bar{x}$ and $\beta_1^* = \beta_1$.

10.3.1 The estimates

The normal equations for estimates $\hat{\beta}_0$ and $\hat{\beta}_1$ are

$$\hat{\beta}_0 \sum_{i=1}^{N} (1)(1) + \hat{\beta}_1 \sum_{i=1}^{N} (1)(x_i) = \sum_{i=1}^{N} (1)Y_i = M_0$$

$$\tag{10.3.2}$$

$$\hat{\beta}_0 \sum_{i=1}^{N} (x_i)(1) + \hat{\beta}_1 \sum_{i=1}^{N} (x_i)(x_i) = \sum_{i=1}^{N} x_i Y_i = M_1$$

Since $\sum\limits_{i=1}^{N} x_i = 0$, the solutions are readily found to be

$$\hat{\beta}_0 = \frac{\sum\limits_{i=1}^{N} Y_i}{N} = \frac{1}{N} M_0 = \bar{Y}$$

$$\hat{\beta}_1 = \frac{\sum\limits_{i=1}^{N} x_i Y_i}{\sum\limits_{i=1}^{N} x_i^2} = \frac{1}{\frac{1}{N}\sum\limits_{i=1}^{N} x_i^2} M_1$$

(10.3.3)

Thus $\hat{\beta}_0$ and $\hat{\beta}_1$ are linear functions in M_0, M_1 and also in Y_1, Y_2, . . . , Y_N. In fact,

$$\hat{\beta}_0 = \frac{1}{N} Y_1 + \frac{1}{N} Y_2 + \cdots + \frac{1}{N} Y_N$$

$$\hat{\beta}_1 = d_1 Y_1 + d_2 Y_2 + \cdots d_N Y_N$$

(10.3.4)

where $\qquad d_j = \dfrac{x_j}{\sum\limits_{i=1}^{N} x_i^2}$ (10.3.5)

As a special case it may be noted that if we have $2p + 1$ equally spaced observations h units apart, then we may denote the x_i by

$$-ph, \; -(p-1)h, \; \ldots, \; -h, \, 0, \, +h, \, 2h, \; \ldots, \; +ph$$

whereupon the estimates become

$$\hat{\beta}_0 = \bar{Y}$$

$$\hat{\beta}_1 = \frac{3}{hp(p+1)(2p+1)} \sum_{i=-p}^{+p} i Y_i$$

(10.3.6)

since $2(1 + 2^2 + 3^2 + \cdots + p^2) = p(p+1)(2p+1)/3$.

10.3.2   Distribution theory

We have not made any distribution assumptions about Y_1, Y_2, . . . , Y_N. In order to study the statistical properties of $\hat{\beta}_0$ and $\hat{\beta}_1$, however, it is necessary to specify the distributions of Y_1, Y_2, . . . , Y_N, which we assume to be normal, with finite means and variance.

Since $\hat{\beta}_0$ and $\hat{\beta}_1$ are linear functions of Y_1, Y_2, . . . , Y_N, $\hat{\beta}_0$ and $\hat{\beta}_1$ are also normally distributed, with mean and variances specified as follows:

$$E(\hat\beta_0) = \frac{1}{N} \sum_{i=1}^{N} E(Y_i) = \frac{1}{N} \sum_{i=1}^{N} (\beta_0 + \beta_1 x_i) = \beta_0 + \beta_1 \bar{x} = \beta_0$$

$$E(\hat\beta_1) = E\left(\frac{\sum_{i=1}^{N} x_i Y_i}{\sum_{i=1}^{N} x_i^2}\right) = \frac{1}{\sum_{i=1}^{N} x_i^2} \sum_{i=1}^{N} x_i E(Y_i) \qquad (10.3.7)$$

$$= \frac{1}{\sum_{i=1}^{N} x_i^2} \sum_{i=1}^{N} x_i (\beta_0 + \beta_1 x_i) = \beta_1$$

$$V(\hat\beta_0) = V(\bar{Y}) = \frac{\sigma^2}{N}$$

$$V(\hat\beta_1) = V\left(\frac{\sum_{i=1}^{N} x_i Y_i}{\sum_{i=1}^{N} x_i^2}\right) = \frac{1}{(\sum_{i=1}^{N} x_i^2)^2} \sum_{i=1}^{N} x_i^2 V(Y_i) \qquad (10.3.8)$$

$$= \frac{1}{(\sum_{i=1}^{N} x_i^2)^2} \sum_{i=1}^{N} x_i^2 \sigma^2 = \frac{\sigma^2}{\sum_{i=1}^{N} x_i^2}$$

It may also be shown that $\hat\beta_0$ and $\hat\beta_1$ are independent. This follows essentially from the orthogonality of the two linear forms in $Y_1, \ldots,$ Y_N, which express $\hat\beta_0$ and $\hat\beta_1$, namely,

$$\hat\beta_0 = \frac{1}{N} Y_1 + \frac{1}{N} Y_2 + \cdots \frac{1}{N} Y_N \qquad (10.3.9)$$

and $$\beta_1 = d_1 Y_1 + d_2 Y_2 + \cdots + d_N Y_N$$

Hence the sum of the products of corresponding coefficients equals

$$\frac{1}{N} d_1 + \frac{1}{N} d_2 + \cdots + \frac{1}{N} d_N = \frac{1}{N} \sum_{i=1}^{N} d_i = \frac{1}{N \sum_{i=1}^{N} x_i^2} \sum_{i=1}^{N} x_i = 0$$

satisfying the orthogonality condition.

Another quantity of interest is $m(x) = \beta_0 + \beta_1 x$ for any particular x. To estimate $m(x)$ we note that it is linear in β_0 and β_1, and thus the least-squares estimate $\hat{m}(x)$ is $\hat\beta_0 + \hat\beta_1 x$. Since $\hat{m}(x)$ is linear in $Y_1, Y_2, \ldots,$ Y_N, it is also normally distributed with mean and variance:

$$E[\hat{m}(x)] = E(\hat\beta_0 + \hat\beta_1 x) = \beta_0 + \beta_1 x = m(x)$$
$$V[\hat{m}(x)] = V(\hat\beta_0 + \hat\beta_1 x) = V(\hat\beta_0) + x^2 V(\hat\beta_1)$$
$$= \frac{\sigma^2}{N} + \frac{x^2 \sigma^2}{\Sigma x_i^2} = \sigma^2 \left(\frac{1}{N} + \frac{x^2}{\sum_{i=1}^{N} x_i^2}\right) \qquad (10.3.10)$$

A further fact to be noted is that the estimated regression line $\hat{m}(x)$ passes through $(0, \bar{Y})$. This follows directly from

$$\hat{m}(0) = \hat{\beta}_0 + \hat{\beta}_1 0 = \bar{Y} \qquad (10.3.11)$$

10.3.3 Confidence intervals for the parameters of the least-squares regression line

The method of least squares provides estimates of the parameters β_0 and β_1 given by Eq. (10.3.3). It is desirable, however, to have some estimate of the degree of deviation of the estimates $\hat{\beta}_0$ and $\hat{\beta}_1$ from β_0 and β_1, respectively, and also of s^2 from σ^2, since an estimate of σ^2 is necessary in order to formulate the β_0 and β_1 confidence intervals. The σ^2 estimate is given by

$$s^2 = \frac{\sum_{i=1}^{N} [Y_i - \hat{m}(x_i)]^2}{N - 2} \qquad (10.3.12)$$

Under circumstances where β_0 and β_1 are given, an estimate of σ^2 is

$$\frac{\sum_{i=1}^{N} [Y_i - m(x_i)]^2}{N} = \frac{\sum_{i=1}^{N} \epsilon_i^2}{N}$$

The denominator in Eq. (10.3.12) equals the number of degrees of freedom in the estimation of σ^2 by s^2. Since in determination of s^2, $\hat{m}(x_i)$ is used in place of $m(x)$, not all the differences $Y_i - \hat{m}(x_i)$ are independent. The $\hat{m}(x_i)$ are dependent upon $\hat{\beta}_0$ and $\hat{\beta}_1$, each of which is determined from the x_i, whence, even though there are N independently chosen x_i, only $N - 2$ of the differences are independent. The reason behind this will be discussed in a later section where the relationship between regression and the analysis of variance is explored.

Furthermore, it can be shown that $(N - 2)s^2/\sigma^2$ has a χ^2 distribution with $N - 2$ degrees of freedom and is independent of $\hat{\beta}_0$ and $\hat{\beta}_1$.

Confidence Interval for σ^2 Since $(N - 2)s^2/\sigma^2$ is χ^2 distributed with $N - 2$ degrees of freedom, we may write, without requiring knowledge about σ^2,

$$\text{Prob}\left[\chi^2_{\alpha/2, N-2} \leq \frac{(N - 2)s^2}{\sigma^2} \leq \chi^2_{1-\alpha/2, N-2} \right] = 1 - \alpha \qquad (10.3.13)$$

Inverting and multiplying Eq. (10.3.13) by $(N - 2)s^2$, we have

$$\text{Prob}\left[\frac{(N - 2)s^2}{\chi^2_{1-\alpha/2, N-2}} \leq \sigma^2 \leq \frac{(N - 2)s^2}{\chi^2_{\alpha/2, N-2}} \right] = 1 - \alpha \qquad (10.3.14)$$

Consequently,

$$\left[\frac{(N - 2)s^2}{\chi^2_{1-\alpha/2, N-2}} ; \frac{(N - 2)s^2}{\chi^2_{\alpha/2, N-2}} \right] \qquad (10.3.15)$$

is a $(1 - \alpha)$ per cent confidence interval for σ^2. One-sided confidence intervals (upper or lower) may be obtained in a similar manner.

   Confidence Intervals for $\hat{\beta}_0$ and β_1   Since β_0 is a linear function of normal random variables Y_1, Y_2, . . . , Y_N, it is also normally distributed. Hence

$$Z = \frac{\hat{\beta}_0 - \beta_0}{\sigma_{\hat{\beta}_0}} = \frac{\hat{\beta}_0 - \beta_0}{\sigma/\sqrt{N}} \tag{10.3.16}$$

has the standard normal distribution with zero mean and unit variance.

   Because $\hat{\beta}_0$ and s^2 are independent and $(N - 2)s^2/\sigma^2$ is distributed as χ^2, $Z\sqrt{N-2}/\sqrt{\chi^2}$ has a t distribution with $N - 2$ degrees of freedom. Consequently, we may write

$$\text{Prob}\left(-t_{1-\alpha/2,N-2} \leq \frac{\hat{\beta}_0 - \beta_0}{s/\sqrt{N}} \leq +t_{1-\alpha/2,N-2}\right) = 1 - \alpha \tag{10.3.17}$$

Rewriting in terms of an interval for β_0, we arrive at the following $(1 - \alpha)$ per cent confidence interval:

$$\left(\hat{\beta}_0 - t_{1-\alpha/2,N-2}\frac{s}{\sqrt{N}}; \hat{\beta}_0 + t_{1-\alpha/2,N-2}\frac{s}{\sqrt{N}}\right) \tag{10.3.18}$$

By a similar argument the following $(1 - \alpha)$ per cent confidence interval for β_1 may be obtained:

$$\left(\hat{\beta}_1 - t_{1-\alpha/2,N-2}\frac{s}{\sqrt{\Sigma x_i^2}}; \hat{\beta}_1 + t_{1-\alpha/2,N-2}\frac{s}{\sqrt{\Sigma x_i^2}}\right) \tag{10.3.19}$$

   Confidence Interval for $m(x)$ at Any Particular Chosen x   The least-squares estimate of $m(x)$ is $\hat{m}(x) = \hat{\beta}_0 + \hat{\beta}_1 x$, a linear combination of $\hat{\beta}_0$ and $\hat{\beta}_1$, normally distributed and with variance

$$V[\hat{m}(x)] = \sigma^2\left(\frac{1}{N} + \frac{x^2}{\Sigma x_i^2}\right) \tag{10.3.20}$$

Since s^2 is independent of $\hat{\beta}_0$ and $\hat{\beta}_1$, it is also independent of $\hat{m}(x)$ and forms an independent estimate of σ^2. Thus

$$\frac{\hat{m}(x) - m(x)}{s\sqrt{1/N + x^2/\Sigma x_i^2}} \tag{10.3.21}$$

has a t distribution with $N - 2$ degrees of freedom. Applying the usual procedure, we obtain the following $(1 - \alpha)$ per cent confidence interval for $m(x)$, for any specified x:

$$\left[\hat{m}(x) - t_{1-\alpha/2,N-2}\, s\sqrt{\frac{1}{N} + \frac{x^2}{\Sigma x_i^2}}; \hat{m}(x) + t_{1-\alpha/2,N-2}\, s\sqrt{\frac{1}{N} + \frac{x^2}{\Sigma x_i^2}}\right] \tag{10.3.22}$$

The bounding curves of this interval are a pair of hyperbolas.

It should be emphasized that this is *not* a confidence interval for the *whole* line $m(x) = \beta_0 + \beta_1 x$ (for a whole range of values of x). For example, for any two values of x, say, x^* and x^{**}, we can find confidence intervals for $m(x^*)$ and $m(x^{**})$, respectively. The chance of $m(x^*)$ and $m(x^{**})$ *both* falling in their respective interval is *not* $1 - \alpha$. If the two intervals were independent (which they are not, since they both depend on s^2), the chance would actually be $(1 - \alpha)^2$. In the next section we shall find a multiple confidence interval for the whole line $m(x)$.

Multiple Confidence Interval for Mean Regression Line $m(x)$

The procedure for finding a confidence interval for the *whole* line is somewhat complicated. The basic approach is to note first that the regression line $m(x) = \beta_0 + \beta_1 x$ is completely determined by the pair of values (β_0, β_1). That is, to each line there is a corresponding unique pair (β_0, β_1), and to each pair a unique line. The next step is to obtain a confidence region for the parameter pair (β_0, β_1). To each point within this region there is a corresponding regression line. Thus one can find the family of lines compatible with parameter pairs within the confidence region. This will then result in the desired confidence set for the whole line. That is, one may say with $(1 - \alpha)$ per cent chance of being correct that the true regression line $m(x) = \beta_0 + \beta_1 x$ lies within the confidence set in the (m, x) plane.

To carry out this procedure we note that $\hat{\beta}_0$ and $\hat{\beta}_1$ are independently and normally distributed. Hence

$$\left(\frac{\hat{\beta}_0 - \beta_0}{\sigma/\sqrt{N}}\right)^2 + \left(\frac{\hat{\beta}_1 - \beta_1}{\sigma/\sqrt{\Sigma x_i^2}}\right)^2 \tag{10.3.23}$$

has a χ^2 distribution with 2 degrees of freedom and is distributed independently of $(N - 2)s^2/\sigma^2$, which is χ^2 distributed with $N - 2$ degrees of freedom. By forming a "suitable" ratio of the two χ^2 variables, we obtain the random variable

$$\frac{\dfrac{N(\hat{\beta}_0 - \beta_0)^2}{\sigma^2} + \dfrac{(\Sigma x_i^2)(\hat{\beta}_1 - \beta_1)^2}{\sigma^2}}{\dfrac{(N-2)s^2}{\dfrac{\sigma^2}{N-2}}} = \frac{N}{2}\left(\frac{\hat{\beta}_0 - \beta_0}{s}\right)^2 + \frac{\Sigma x_i^2}{2}\left(\frac{\hat{\beta}_1 - \beta_1}{s}\right)^2$$

$$\tag{10.3.24}$$

which has the F distribution with $(2, N - 2)$ degrees of freedom. It follows therefore that

$$\text{Prob}\left[\frac{N}{2}\left(\frac{\hat{\beta}_0 - \beta_0}{s}\right)^2 + \frac{\Sigma x_i^2}{2}\left(\frac{\hat{\beta}_1 - \beta_1}{s}\right)^2 \leq F_{1-\alpha, 2, N-2}\right] = 1 - \alpha \tag{10.3.25}$$

This leads precisely to the $(1 - \alpha)$ per cent confidence region for (β_0, β_1):

$$\frac{N}{2}\left(\frac{\hat{\beta}_0 - \beta_0}{s}\right)^2 + \frac{\Sigma x_i^2}{2}\left(\frac{\hat{\beta}_1 - \beta_1}{s}\right)^2 \leq F_{1-\alpha, 2, N-2} \qquad (10.3.26)$$

which is a region bounded by an ellipse.

In order to obtain a confidence region for $m(x) = \beta_0 + \beta_1 x$ in the (m,x) plane, holding for *all* x, we must find the family of lines consistent with values (β_0, β_1) within the confidence ellipse specified in Eq. (10.3.26).

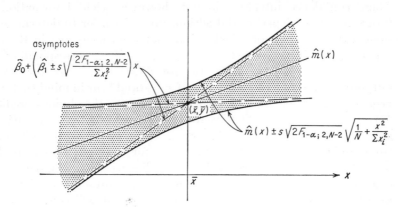

Figure 10.7

We state the result here without demonstration since it leads to mathematical considerations beyond the scope of this text. The resulting set of values in the (m,x) plane is the region bounded by the two hyperbolas

$$\hat{\beta}_0 + \hat{\beta}_1 x \pm s \sqrt{2F_{1-\alpha, 2, N-2}} \sqrt{\frac{1}{N} + \frac{x^2}{\Sigma x_i^2}} \qquad (10.3.27)$$

The center line is $\hat{m}(x) = \hat{\beta}_0 + \hat{\beta}_1 x$, and the asymptotes are

$$\hat{\beta}_0 + \left(\hat{\beta}_1 \pm s \sqrt{\frac{2F_{1-\alpha, 2, N-2}}{\Sigma x_i^2}}\right) x \qquad (10.3.28)$$

The final statement which may be made is

$$\text{Prob}\left[\hat{m}(x) - s\sqrt{2F_{1-\alpha, 2, N-2}}\sqrt{\frac{1}{N} + \frac{x^2}{\Sigma x_i^2}} \leq m(x) \leq \hat{m}(x)\right.$$
$$\left. + s\sqrt{2F_{1-\alpha, 2, N-2}}\sqrt{\frac{1}{N} + \frac{x^2}{\Sigma x_i^2}} \text{ for all } x\right] = 1 - \alpha \qquad (10.3.29)$$

The case for σ^2 known was first presented by Working and Hotelling.[1] The multiple confidence region for $m(x)$ is depicted in Fig. 10.7. It should be noted that this gives a wider range of values for $m(x)$

[1] Working and Hotelling, Application of the Theory of Error to the interpretation of Trends, *Journal of the American Statistical Association*, supplement, vol. 24, pp. 73–85, 1929.

than the confidence interval obtained in Eq. (10.3.22) for $m(x)$ at any specified x.

10.3.4 Prediction interval

We have considered the precision of the estimates of the parameters of a regression line $m(x) = \beta_0 + \beta_1 x$, in terms of confidence intervals for the "true" coefficients β_0 and β_1. Confidence intervals have also been found for a particular $m(x)$ (for a given value of x) and for the whole line. These confidence intervals do not, however, yield information about future results of experimental action, taken in order to determine Y_0 for some value $x = x_0$, for which Y has not been measured in the original experiment which yielded Y_1, Y_2, . . . , Y_N, corresponding to x_1, x_2, . . . , x_N. We do want to use $\hat{m}(x) = \hat{\beta}_0 + \hat{\beta}_1 x$ for predictive purposes. If we select some value of x_{N+1} (and bear in mind that x_{N+1} has been assumed to be determinable without error), the obvious prediction is $Y_{N+1} = \hat{\beta}_0 + \hat{\beta}_1 x_{N+1}$. That is to say, we believe that measuring $Y(x)$ at $x = x_{N+1}$ should yield $\hat{\beta}_0 + \hat{\beta}_1 x_{N+1}$. This prediction is quite different from saying that the true value $m(x_0)$ for some x_0 is estimated to be $\hat{\beta}_0 + \hat{\beta}_1 x_0$ and that the true value $m(x_0)$ lies within a confidence-interval estimate with a specified confidence. The present prediction is an assertion as to how the $(N + 1)$st measurement will come out. It is a hazardous assertion, of a probability nature. Since, however, we do not know the true parameters of the distribution of $Y(x)$ but must make the prediction from $\hat{m}(x) = \hat{\beta}_0 + \hat{\beta}_1 x$, we can assert this probability statement about a real phenomenon only if we hedge it with a confidence statement of this nature: there is an interval (to be specified below) within which we expect the measurement Y_{N+1} to fall, and our confidence in this assertion is $(1 - \alpha)$ (where α is the usual symbol for the magnitude of the error with which confidence statements are made). This type of interval is called a prediction interval and is a probability interval hedged by a declaration of confidence. We shall now proceed to derive a prediction interval for the observation made at x_{N+1}.

In searching for the aforementioned prediction interval, we must bear in mind that our prediction of the observed value for Y_{N+1} is subject to sources of error. In the first place, the estimate $\hat{m}(x_{N+1})$ is a linear function of $\hat{\beta}_0$ and $\hat{\beta}_1$ and therefore subject to errors arising in these two estimates. Again, the actual value y_{N+1} which is observed will deviate from the "true" value $m(x_{N+1})$ because of experimental error. Therefore an expression must be formed for an interval which entails these two sources of error, and in order to do this, one must specify a random variable which is subject to these two sources of error and at the same time lends itself to the formation of the desired prediction interval.

Toward this end we consider the random variables Y_{N+1} and the estimate $\hat{m}(x_{N+1})$ and form their difference

$$Z = Y_{N+1} - \hat{m}(x_{N+1}) \tag{10.3.30}$$

The random variable Z expresses the error made in predicting Y_{N+1} to be $\hat{m}(x_{N+1})$. Now it is up to us to find the distribution of Z, which is, of course, a normal variate, since it is a linear function of Y_{N+1} (assumed to have a normal distribution with variance σ^2), $\hat{\beta}_0$, and $\hat{\beta}_1$. The variance of Z is

$$V(Z) = V(Y_{N+1}) + V[\hat{m}(x_{N+1})]$$

since Y_{N+1} and $\hat{m}(x_{N+1})$ are independent. Hence

$$V(Z) = \sigma^2 + \sigma^2 \left(\frac{1}{N} + \frac{x_{N+1}^2}{\Sigma x_i^2} \right) = \sigma^2 \left(1 + \frac{1}{N} + \frac{x_{N+1}^2}{\Sigma x_i^2} \right) \quad (10.3.31)$$

and $\qquad E(Z) = 0$

Following the conventional technique, we form a t random variate with $Y_{N+1} - \hat{m}(x_{N+1})$ in the numerator and establish bounds on the t variate for a prescribed probability $1 - \alpha$. The t variate is obtained as the quotient

$$\frac{\dfrac{Y_{N+1} - \hat{m}(x_{N+1})}{\sqrt{V(Z)}}}{\left(\dfrac{\sum\limits_{i=1}^{N} [Y_i - \hat{m}(x_i)]^2}{\sigma^2(N-2)} \right)^{1/2}} \quad (10.3.32)$$

The sum of squares in (10.3.32) is, however, equal to $(N-2)s^2$, where s^2 *is the unbiased estimate* of σ^2 and $N-2$ is the number of degrees of freedom of the estimate. Expression (10.3.32) therefore reduces to

$$\frac{Y_{N+1} - \hat{m}(x_{N+1})}{s \sqrt{1 + 1/N + x_{N+1}^2/\Sigma x_i^2}} = t_{N-2} \quad (10.3.33)$$

where the degrees of freedom equal $N-2$.

On selecting a "risk" level α, one can then assert that

$$\text{Prob} \left[-t_{1-\alpha/2,N-2} \leq \frac{Y_{N+1} - \hat{m}(x_{N+1})}{s \sqrt{1 + \dfrac{1}{N} + \dfrac{x_{N+1}^2}{\Sigma x_i^2}}} \leq t_{1-\alpha/2,N-2} \right] = 1 - \alpha \quad (10.3.34)$$

This can be rewritten as follows:

$$\text{Prob} \left[\hat{m}(x_{N+1}) - t_{1-\alpha/2,N-2} \left(s \sqrt{1 + \frac{1}{N} + \frac{x_{N+1}^2}{\Sigma x_i^2}} \right) \leq Y_{N+1} \right.$$
$$\left. \leq \hat{m}(x_{N+1}) + t_{1-\alpha/2,N-2} \left(s \sqrt{1 + \frac{1}{N} + \frac{x_{N+1}^2}{\Sigma x_i^2}} \right) \right] = 1 - \alpha \quad (10.3.35)$$

The $(1 - \alpha)$ per cent prediction interval for Y_{N+1} is

$$\hat{m}(x_{N+1}) \pm t_{1-\alpha/2,N-2} \left(s \sqrt{1 + \frac{1}{N} + \frac{x_{N+1}^2}{\Sigma x_i^2}} \right) \quad (10.3.36)$$

The following properties of the prediction interval are worth noting:

1. The prediction interval for the "next" observation Y_{N+1} is greater than the confidence interval for the mean $m(x)$ of $Y(x)$.

2. The average spread of the prediction interval increases as x_{N+1} increases.

3. The probability attached to the prediction interval holds for only a single prediction: the magnitude of the prediction interval depends on estimates $\hat{\beta}_0$, $\hat{\beta}_1$, and s^2. Successive predictions are not independent, so that the error of successive predictions is not determined.

10.3.5   Problem of discrimination

In the field of bioassay, anthropology, and other sciences, it is often the case that the quantity $Y(x)$ is observed without observation on x. Nevertheless, one can get some information about the relation of Y_i to x_i by observing $Y_1, Y_2, \ldots, Y_N$ corresponding to $x_1, x_2, \ldots, x_N$, where, as in regression analysis, these values of x are known without error.   Suppose now that it is possible to make an observation $Y(x_0)$ for some x_0, where, however, x_0 cannot be measured.   This occurs where the effects of certain dosages of a drug are measurable and it is desired to determine the dosage administered when, on occasion, the effect of the drug is observed but the dosage is unknown.   Hence it is desired to infer the "cause" x_0 from observation of the effect $Y(x_0)$.   One may look upon this as "inverse" regression.

Suppose one had N observations $Y_1, Y_2, \ldots, Y_N$ at known levels $x_1, x_2, \ldots, x_N$ and M observations at a specific, but unknown, level x_0. We shall apply the maximum-likelihood principle to estimate β_0, β_1, and x_0.

Accordingly, the likelihood L is formed from $Y_1, Y_2, \ldots, Y_N$ and $Y_1', Y_2', \ldots, Y_M'$:

$$L = \left(\frac{1}{\sigma\sqrt{2\pi}}\right)^{N+M} \exp\left[-\frac{1}{2\sigma^2}\sum_{i=1}^{N}(Y_i - \beta_0 - \beta_1 x_i)^2\right.$$

$$\left. -\frac{1}{2\sigma^2}\sum_{j=1}^{M}(Y_j' - \beta_0 - \beta_1 x_0)^2\right] \quad (10.3.37)$$

By the conventional techniques we obtain

$$\hat{\beta}_0 = \bar{Y}$$
$$\hat{\beta}_1 = \frac{\Sigma Y_i x_i}{\Sigma x_i^2}$$
$$\hat{x}_0 = \frac{\bar{Y}' - \hat{\beta}_0}{\hat{\beta}_1} \quad (10.3.38)$$

where $\bar{Y}' = (Y_1' + Y_2' + \cdots + Y_M')/M$.   In this manner β_0 and β_1 are estimated from $Y_1, Y_2, \ldots, Y_N$, and x_0 is estimated from the resulting regression line, which is expressed in terms of $\hat{\beta}_0$ and $\hat{\beta}_1$.

In order to find a confidence interval for x_0, an estimate of σ^2 must be formed for which the observations $Y_1, Y_2, \ldots, Y_N$ and $Y'_1, Y'_2, \ldots, Y'_M$ are to be used, pooling the separate estimates. Thus

$$s_1{}^2 = \frac{\displaystyle\sum_{i=1}^{N} (Y_i - \hat{\beta}_0 - \hat{\beta}_1 x_i)^2}{N-2} \qquad N-2 \text{ degrees of freedom}$$

$$s_2{}^2 = \frac{\displaystyle\sum_{j=1}^{M} (Y'_j - \bar{Y}')^2}{M-1} \qquad M-1 \text{ degrees of freedom}$$

(10.3.39)

On pooling the estimates $s_1{}^2$ and $s_2{}^2$, we obtain

$$s^2 = \frac{(N-2)s_1{}^2 + (M-1)s_2{}^2}{N+M-3}$$

$$= \frac{\displaystyle\sum_{i=1}^{N} (Y_i - \hat{\beta}_0 - \hat{\beta}_1 x_i)^2 + \sum_{j=1}^{M} (Y'_j - \bar{Y}'_j)^2}{N+M-3}$$

(10.3.40)

as an unbiased estimate of σ^2.

Again, in order to find the confidence interval for x_0, the deviation

$$W = \bar{Y}' - \hat{\beta}_0 - \hat{\beta}_1 x_0$$

is formed. It is a normal variate with zero mean, which becomes the required numerator of the Student t variate on division by σ_W. The denominator for this variate can be formed from

$$\frac{(N-2)s_1{}^2}{\sigma^2} + \frac{(M-1)s_2{}^2}{\sigma^2}$$

which has a χ^2 distribution with $N+M-3$ degrees of freedom. Hence

$$\frac{W/\sigma_W}{\sqrt{\dfrac{(N-2)s_1{}^2 + (M-1)s_2{}^2}{\sigma^2(N+M-3)}}}$$

(10.3.41)

has the t distribution with $N+M-3$ degrees of freedom, bearing in mind that s and W are independent.

In order to reduce and simplify (10.3.41), we find

$$V(W) = V(\bar{Y}') + V(\hat{\beta}_0) + x_0{}^2 V(\hat{\beta}) = \sigma^2 \left(\frac{1}{M} + \frac{1}{N} + \frac{x_0{}^2}{\displaystyle\sum_{i=1}^{N} x_i{}^2} \right)$$

(10.3.42)

(since $\bar{Y}'$, $\hat{\beta}_0$, and $\hat{\beta}_1$ are mutually independent). The form of Eq. (10.3.41) then reduces to

$$\frac{\bar{Y}' - \hat{\beta}_0 - \hat{\beta}_1 x_0}{\sigma \sqrt{\dfrac{1}{M} + \dfrac{1}{N} + x_0^2 \sum_{i=1}^{N} x_i^2}} \div \sqrt{\frac{(N + M - 3)s^2}{\sigma^2(N + M - 3)}}$$

$$= t_{N+M-3} = \frac{\bar{Y}' - \hat{\beta}_0 - \hat{\beta}_1 x_0}{s \sqrt{\dfrac{1}{M} + \dfrac{1}{N} + x_0^2 \sum_{i=1}^{N} x_i^2}} \qquad (10.3.43)$$

the Student t variate with $N + M - 3$ degrees of freedom. For a specified risk level α we then have

$$\text{Prob}\left(-t_{1-\alpha/2, N+M-3} \leq \frac{\bar{Y}' - \hat{\beta}_0 - \hat{\beta}_1 x_0}{s \sqrt{\dfrac{1}{M} + \dfrac{1}{N} + x_0^2 \sum_{i=1}^{N} x_i^2}} \leq t_{1-\alpha/2, N+M-3}\right)$$

$$= 1 - \alpha \qquad (10.3.44)$$

As in previous derivations of confidence intervals, the inequality in (10.3.44) can be converted into an interval bounding x_0 with odds $(1 - \alpha)$ to α. The actual conversion is left as an exercise for the reader. This interval can also be used to test hypotheses about x_0.

10.3.6   Relationship with analysis of variance and test of linearity

In order to clarify some of the previous sections, let us consider the linear-regression model for the straight line $\beta_0 + \beta_1 x$ in terms of the analysis of variance. Each of the levels of x, x_i may be thought to correspond to a normal population with mean $\beta_0 + \beta_1 x_i$ and variance σ^2. This is a special case of the one-way analysis of variance (model I) with $n = 1$ observations per population, namely, Y_1, Y_2, . . . , Y_N (there are N normal populations). We know that there are $N - 1$ degrees of freedom associated with the sum of squares between, $SSB = \Sigma(Y_i - \bar{Y})^2 = \Sigma Y_i^2 - N\bar{Y}^2$, corresponding to $N - 1$ orthogonal contrasts among Y_1, Y_2, . . . , Y_N. One of these contrasts is due to β_1. This normalized contrast is

$$\frac{\Sigma x_i Y_i}{\sqrt{\Sigma x_i^2}} = \sqrt{\Sigma x_i^2} \frac{\Sigma x_i Y_i}{\Sigma x_i^2} = \hat{\beta}_1 \sqrt{\Sigma x_i^2} \qquad (10.3.45)$$

Since

$$\frac{1}{\sqrt{\Sigma x_i^2}} \Sigma x_j = 0 \qquad \text{and} \qquad \frac{1}{\Sigma x_i^2} \sum_j x_j^2 = 1 \qquad (10.3.46)$$

$$E\left(\frac{\Sigma x_i Y_i}{\sqrt{\Sigma x_i^2}}\right) = \frac{\beta_0 \Sigma x_i}{\sqrt{\Sigma x_i^2}} + \frac{\beta_1 \Sigma x_i^2}{\sqrt{\Sigma x_i^2}} = \beta_1 \sqrt{\Sigma x_i^2} \qquad (10.3.47)$$

and is zero only when $\beta_1 = 0$ (all x_i not zero). The sum of squares associated with this contrast is $\hat{\beta}_1^2 \Sigma x_i^2$. Any contrast, with coefficient $c_1, c_2, \ldots, c_N$, orthogonal to the previous one, has mean zero, since

$$E(\Sigma c_i Y_i) = \Sigma c_i(\beta_0 + \beta_1 x_i) = \beta_0 \Sigma c_i + \beta_1 \Sigma c_i x_i = 0 \qquad (10.3.48)$$

where $\Sigma c_i = 0$ and $\Sigma c_i x_i = 0$ (orthogonality). There are $N - 2$ such contrasts orthogonal to $(x_1, x_2, \ldots, x_N)$. The sum of squares associated with $(c_1, c_2, \ldots, c_N)$ is $(\Sigma c_i Y_i)^2$ with expected value $E(\Sigma c_i Y_i)^2 = \sigma^2$ (if c's are normalized). Hence SSB may be broken up into two parts:

$$\left(\frac{\Sigma x_i Y_i}{\sqrt{\Sigma x_i^2}} \right)^2 = \hat{\beta}_1^2 \Sigma x_i^2 \qquad \text{1 degree of freedom}$$

$$\Sigma(Y_i - \bar{Y})^2 - \hat{\beta}_1 \Sigma x_i^2$$
$$= \Sigma Y_i^2 - N\bar{Y}^2 - \hat{\beta}_1^2 \Sigma x_i^2 \qquad N - 2 \text{ degrees of freedom} \qquad (10.3.49)$$
$$= \Sigma Y_i^2 - N\hat{\beta}_0^2 - \hat{\beta}_1^2 \Sigma x_i^2 \qquad \text{since } \hat{\beta}_0 = \bar{Y}$$

The latter part may be shown algebraically to equal $(N - 2)s^2$ (incidently, this shows why s^2 is independent of $\hat{\beta}_0$ and $\hat{\beta}_1$). This may be presented in an analysis-of-variance table.

TABLE 10.4

Source of variation	Sum of squares	Degrees of freedom	Mean square	Expected mean square
β_1	$\hat{\beta}_1^2 \Sigma x_i^2$	1	$\hat{\beta}_1^2 \Sigma x_i^2$	$\sigma^2 + \beta_1^2 \Sigma x_i^2$
Error	$\Sigma Y_i^2 - N\hat{\beta}_0^2 - \hat{\beta}_1^2 \Sigma x_i^2$	$N - 2$	$s^2 = \dfrac{\Sigma Y_i^2 - N\hat{\beta}_0^2 - \hat{\beta}_1^2 \Sigma x_i^2}{N - 2}$	σ^2
Total	$\Sigma(Y_1 - \bar{Y})^2 = \Sigma Y_i^2 - N\hat{\beta}_0^2$			

It should be pointed out that $E(s^2) = \sigma^2$ only when the model $\beta_0 + \beta_1 x$ holds. For example, if the actual mean regression line were $\beta_0 + \beta_1 x + \beta_2 x^2$, then $E(s^2) \neq \sigma^2$.

From the analysis-of-variance table 10.4, one can readily obtain an F test for the null hypothesis $H_0: \beta_1 = 0$; namely, reject H_0 when

$$\frac{\hat{\beta}_1^2 \Sigma x_i^2}{s^2} > F_{1-\alpha, 1, N-2} \qquad (10.3.50)$$

Now let us consider a more general case where there are n observations for each level of x. The previous equations may be applied, since there was no essential restriction that all $x_1, x_2, \ldots, x_N$ be different. Suppose, then, that k of the $x_1, x_2, \ldots, x_N$ are different and $N = nk$. Let these k different levels of x be denoted by $x_1', x_2', \ldots, x_k'$.

Thus we have

$$\text{At } x_1': \quad Y_{11}, \, Y_{12}, \, \ldots \, , \, Y_{1n}$$
$$\text{At } x_2': \quad Y_{21}, \, Y_{22}, \, \ldots \, , \, Y_{2n}$$
$$\cdots \cdots \cdots \cdots \cdots \cdots$$
$$\text{At } x_k': \quad Y_{k1}, \, Y_{k2}, \, \ldots \, , \, Y_{kn}$$

(10.3.51)

The estimates for β_0 and β_1 are

$$\hat{\beta}_0 = \frac{1}{N} \sum_i Y_i = \frac{1}{nk} \sum_i \sum_j Y_{ij} = \frac{1}{k} \sum_i \left(\frac{\sum_j Y_{ij}}{n} \right) = \frac{1}{k} \sum_i Y_{i\cdot} = Y_{\cdot\cdot}$$

$$\hat{\beta}_1 = \frac{\Sigma x_i Y_i}{\Sigma x_i^2} = \frac{\Sigma x_i' Y_{i\cdot}}{\Sigma (x_i')^2}$$

(10.3.52)

In other words, they are the same linear forms as before except that $Y_{1\cdot}, \, Y_{2\cdot}, \, \ldots \, , \, Y_{k\cdot}$ are used instead of $Y_1, \, Y_2, \, \ldots \, , \, Y_N$.

The total sum of squares $SST = \sum_i \sum_j (Y_{ij} - Y)^2 = \sum_i \sum_j Y_{ij}^2 - nkY_{\cdot\cdot}^2$

is divided into two parts, SSB and SSW, where

$$SSB = n \sum_i (\bar{Y}_i - Y_{\cdot\cdot})^2 = n(\Sigma \bar{Y}_{i\cdot}^2 - kY_{\cdot\cdot}^2)$$
$$SSW = \sum_i \sum_j (Y_{ij} - Y_{i\cdot})^2$$

(10.3.53)

The $nk - 1$ degrees of freedom among $Y_{11}, \, \ldots \, , \, Y_{kn}$ are divided up into one due to β_1 (with 1 degree of freedom), leaving $nk - 2$ degrees of freedom, $k(n - 1)$ of which are associated with SSW. The remaining $(nk - 1) - (1) - k(n - 1) = k - 2$ degrees of freedom are due to the $k - 2$ orthogonal contrasts among $Y_{1\cdot}, \, Y_{2\cdot}, \, \ldots \, , \, Y_{k\cdot}$ other than that due to β_1. It is important to note at this point that $SSW/k(n - 1) = MSW$ is an unbiased estimate of σ^2 regardless of whether $m(x)$ is linear in x or not. However, the sum of squares due to the $k - 2$ degrees of freedom (other than β_1) among $Y_{1\cdot}, \, Y_{2\cdot}, \, \ldots \, , \, Y_{k\cdot}$ does depend on the linearity. This is represented in the analysis-of-variance table 10.5. An appropriate test for linearity can now be obtained by comparing MSL with MSW, which rejects when

$$\frac{MSL}{MSW} > F_{1-\alpha;\,k-2;\,k(n-1)}$$

(10.3.54)

It should be pointed out that this *forms a test for linearity for* $m(x)$ *only within the range of* x's $(x_1', x_2', \, \ldots \, , x_k')$ *for which observations are made.* In practice, care must be taken in this respect since one may have a linear-regression model $m(x) = \beta_0 + \beta_1 x$ for a range of values of x but not in some other range. This is especially important in time series where x is time and a test for linearity during one period of time is no evidence of linearity at some future period.

TABLE 10.5

Source of variation	Sum of squares	Degrees of freedom	Mean square	Expected mean square
β_1	$n\hat{\beta}_1^2\Sigma(x_i')^2$	1	$n\hat{\beta}_1^2\Sigma(x_i')^2$	$\sigma^2 + n\beta_1^2\Sigma x_i^2$
Due to regression	$n\Sigma(Y_i. - Y..)^2 - n\hat{\beta}_1^2\Sigma(x_i')^2 = SSL$	$k-2$	$MSL = \dfrac{n\Sigma\bar{x}_i.^2 - nkY..^2 - n\hat{\beta}_1^2\Sigma(x_i')^2}{k-2}$	$\sigma^2 +$ (terms due to non-linearity)^2
Between	SSB	$k-1$		
Within	SSW	$k(n-1)$	MSW	σ^2

EXERCISES

10.1. In relation to Exercise 9.4, assume that

$$E[Y(t)] = \beta_0 + \beta_1 t$$

Use the data in the example

    a. To find least-squares estimates of β_0 and β_1.
    b. To find the confidence interval for β_0 and β_1.
    c. To find the prediction interval for $Y(100°F)$.
    d. To test for linearity.
    e. To test the assumption of constant variance.

10.2. In the following data x denotes the curing time in days and Y the logarithm of the tensile strength of test pieces of cement.

Y	1.103	1.374	1.421	1.521	1.596
x	1	2	3	7	28

Assume that Y is normally distributed with mean $\beta_0 + \beta_1/x$ and variance σ^2. From the given data,

    a. Estimate β_0, β_1, and σ^2.
    b. Find the confidence intervals for β_0, β_1, and σ^2.
    c. Find the prediction interval for $Y(30)$.
    d. Test $H_0: \beta_1 = 0$ against $\beta_1 \neq 0$.
    e. Find the multiple confidence region for the whole regression line.
    f. Do (a) to (e) when $V[Y(x)] = \sigma^2 x^2$.

10.3. Assume $Y_1, Y_2, \ldots, Y_5$ are independent random variables with means $\beta_0 + \beta_1 x_i$ and common variance σ^2. The following data are observed:

Y	3	4	6	6	7
x	-2	-1	0	1	2

    a. Find the estimates of β_0, β_1, and σ^2.
    b. Find the variance of estimates $\hat{\beta}_0$ and $\hat{\beta}_1$.
    c. How do (a) and (b) change if $V[Y(x)] = \sigma^2 x^4$?

10.4. The yield Y from a plot of land resulting when x pounds of fertilizer are used on the plot is assumed normally distributed with constant unknown variance σ^2 and with

$$E[Y(x)] = \beta_0 x + \beta_1 x^2$$

where β_0 and β_1 are unknown.
    From the following record of yields resulting from various quantities of fertilizers

Y	1	3	4	4	2
x	1	2	3	4	5

a. Give least-squares estimates of β_0 and β_1.
b. Give an estimate of the optimum amount of fertilizer x^* to use on the plot.
c. Show that the hypothesis that $x^* = 1$ is equivalent to the hypothesis that $\beta_0 + 2\beta_1 = 0$.
d. Give a 95 per cent prediction interval of Y when $x = 6$.
e. Give a 95 per cent confidence interval for x^*. (HINT: Use a t statistic involving $\beta_0 + 2\beta_1 x^*$.)

10.5. Suppose $Y_1, Y_2, \ldots, Y_N$ are independent and normally distributed with $E(Y_i) = \beta_0 + \beta_1 x_i$ and $V(Y_i) = x_i^2 \sigma^2$. Assuming that $x_1, x_2, \ldots, x_N$ are known constants, find the maximum-likelihood estimators of the unknown parameters $(\beta_0, \beta_1, \sigma^2)$ in the special case where $\sum_{i=1}^{n} (1/x_i) = 0$.

10.6. Suppose the following data are given:

Y	1	2	1	3	2	1	1
t	0	$\pi/6$	$\pi/3$	$\pi/2$	$2\pi/3$	$5\pi/6$	π

Assume $Y_i = \beta_0 \sin t_i + \beta_1 \cos t_i + \epsilon_i$, where $E(\epsilon_i) = 0$ and $V(\epsilon_i) = \sigma^2$.

a. Derive the least-squares estimates of β_0 and β_1.
b. If the model is given by $Y_i = \beta_0 + \beta_1 t_i + \beta_2 \sin t_2$, find the least-squares estimates of β_0, β_1, and β_2.

10.7. Suppose

$$Y_i = \beta_0 + \beta_1 x_i + \epsilon_i \qquad i = 1, 2, 3$$

with ϵ_i independent, $E(\epsilon_i) = 0$, var $(\epsilon_i) = \sigma^2$ (*known*). Find x_1, x_2, x_3 such that $V(\hat{\beta}_0 + \hat{\beta}_1/2)$ is minimized, where $\hat{\beta}_0$ and $\hat{\beta}_1$ are least-squares estimates of β_0 and β_1.

10.8. A certain plastic gave the following deflections Y in a tension machine when loaded with the amounts shown, x. The loads are exactly determined, and the distributions of Y for fixed x may be assumed normal, with constant variance over their x range.

x	Y
2	7.5
3	18.6
4	19.0
5	23.9
6	32.5
7	30.0
8	40.5
9	50.0
10	40.0
11	56.3
12	60.5
13	62.5
14	70.0

a. Find the least-squares line to fit these data (estimate slope and intercept).
b. Find the prediction interval for $Y(16)$.
c. Find the multiple confidence interval for the regression line.
d. Test the hypothesis that the slope is zero.

10.9. Assume that N independent observations $Y_1, Y_2, \ldots, Y_N$ are made and that $E(Y_i) = m + \epsilon_i$ and $V(Y_i) = \sigma^2$. Furthermore, assume that $m/\sigma = \theta$ is known. We wish to find an estimator S for m of the form $S = a_0 + a_1 Y_1 + \cdots + a_N Y_N$ which minimizes the mean-square error MSE of S. Compare this estimator with the usual linear unbiased estimate $\bar{Y}$ for m.

10.10. Assume N independent observations $Y_1, Y_2, \ldots, Y_N$, where $E(Y_i) = \beta_1 x$ (that is, β_0 is known to be zero).

a. Find the least-squares estimate of β_1.
b. Find the confidence interval for β_1.
c. Find the prediction interval for $Y(x)$.
d. Find the confidence interval for $m(x) = \beta_1 x$.
e. Find the multiple confidence region for the *whole* regression line.

10.11. Consider the straight-line regression model with $Y(x) = \beta_0 + \beta_1 x + \epsilon$ with $V(\epsilon) = \sigma^2$.

a. If β_0, β_1, and σ^2 are known and Y is observed, find the confidence interval for associated x.
b. Do (a) when σ^2 is not known and $Y_1, Y_2, \ldots, Y_N$ at $x_1, x_2, \ldots, x_N$ are given.

10.12. Using the confidence ellipse in (10.3.26) for $\hat{\beta}_0$ and $\hat{\beta}_1$ to construct a test of hypothesis for $H_0: \beta_0 = \beta_0{}^0$ and $\beta_1 = \beta_1{}^0$. (HINT: Use the relationship between confidence regions and hypothesis testing.)

10.13. The straight-line regression model with $Y_i = \beta_0 + \beta_1 x_i + \epsilon_i$ with $E(\epsilon_i) = 0$ and $V(\epsilon_i) = \sigma^2$ was developed in this chapter assuming that $\bar{x} = 0$. Find the least-squares estimates for β_0 and β_1 when $\bar{x}$ is not assumed zero. Also, find an expression for $V(\hat{\beta}_0)$ and $V(\hat{\beta}_1)$ for this case.

10.14. Prove Markoff's theorem for $m = 1$ and for $m = 2$.

10.15. Show how to obtain results in the last column of Table 10.3 for cases 1, 9, 10, and 11.

11

DECISION MAKING UNDER UNSTABLE UNCERTAINTY; STATISTICAL STABILITY AND CONTROL

We began our discussion of the subject matter of this text with consideration of variability in the data used as a basis for decision making (any and all decision making) and the need for some manner of consistent and reliable guidance in making decisions—answering questions about the world around us. The task of decision making was formulated in terms of a choice among alternatives, and the system for such choice (if any) which we are seeking we called scientific inference. Probability and statistical inference were to be offered as intrinsic means for decision making, "scientific" decision making.

It was natural (Sec. 1.1) to present a problem for decision, a problem of the type which might regularly arise in engineering, science, or industry. For this the rolling of steel bars was considered. Many questions arose for decisions by the manufacturer of the steel bars. A serious question was: in order to maximize profits (or minimize losses) in the repetitive operation of cutting steel bars to a 10-foot length (± 0.30 foot), where shall the cutoff point be set? The answer seems so obvious: set the cutoff at 10 feet. Yet this was found not to be the correct answer because of the effects of variability in the cutting operation and the losses from oversize and undersize bars. From this and a number of other examples, the importance of variability in repetitive operations became manifest, as well as the need for study of formal probability.

Later it became apparent that answering questions about natural phenomena was a nonformal process, however formalized the procedures of statistical inference were made and however much of formal probability was employed. There was need to reconsider the "real" aspects of decision making and to make some attempt to bridge the seeming gap between the apparent inverse (inductive) procedure of inferring an action which would lead to desired future results, on the basis of past observations, and the deductive procedure of directly calculating outcomes, under given assumptions, on the basis of probabilistic relations. It is a simple matter to calculate what fraction of bars to expect of length greater than 9.7 feet on the assumption of a normal distribution (of bar lengths) with mean 10.0 feet and standard deviation of, say, 0.10. But determining the expected number of bars (out of a lot of 10,000 or 100,000 or so) greater than 9.7 feet on the basis of a sample of 10, 25, 100, or more bars was seen to be a much more subtle problem. Some puzzling aspects of decision making were considered in Chap. 6.

Subsequently, various inferential procedures which can be used in decision making were taken up, and in fact Chaps. 7 to 10 contain an exposition on statistical inference. Nevertheless, all the techniques presented are useful only if the situations to which they are applied are statistically stable. Either explicit or tacit, to every estimation procedure, to every test of hypothesis, to every variance analysis, and to every regression procedure demonstrated, there was the assumption that the data upon which inference was to be made came from a statistical universe. For if an inference is to be meaningful, and action should follow, the situation should not then change so that the action taken does not produce the desired result. That is to say, there should in *reality* be an experimental environment in which the experiment (action) yields outcomes which can be thought of as coming from a statistical distribution which may, further, be expected not to change cavalierly. In operational terms, we may say that we have conviction that the *causal system* governing the experimental situation, and therefore responsible for the outcomes, is a *"constant" chance-cause system*. Under these circumstances we may have confidence in the empirical validity of the statistical inferences made on the basis of the observed data. We shall develop these remarks further, using such examples, wherever possible, as will give realistic significance to these ideas.

11.1 Examples of unstable uncertainty

In Chap. 6 decision making is considered in terms of a fourfold classification of circumstances under which questions for decision arise. The weakest basis for decision is referred to as unstable uncertainty. Under these conditions the evidence is lacking that statistical inference can be made with conviction—or perhaps it might be better to state that the implications of the evidence at hand are that such evidence as is available is not adequate for decision. One must bear in mind that statistical inference can be made (with an appraisal of error) only when there is a statistical universe which is being observed. In many situations this is not the case, and attempts at statistical inference, however sharply formulated, do not lead to verifiable results. In particular, this is true of on-going processes. Hence one is confronted with the task of distinguishing between situations of stable and unstable uncertainty. We need criteria for determining from the outcomes of repeated experiment whether the experimental environment is statistically stable or not. Such criteria evolve from "judgments" of experience; in order to do this we shall examine the outcomes of a number of experimental situations.

Suppose we consider first the data in Fig. 11.1. Here are 24 numbers observed in time order where the central line represents the average of these observations. Can we make any inference about future outcomes

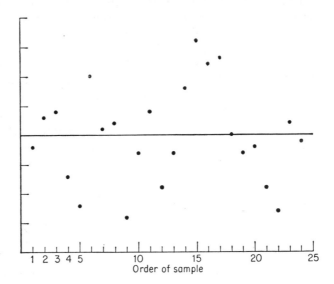

Figure 11.1 Stable or unstable process.

from the process which generated these numbers? If we knew that they were generated by random selection from a specified universe, we could estimate the standard deviation from this sample, and therefore use distribution theory in order to determine some numerical criteria with which to decide whether the results observed in Fig. 11.1 could have come from such a statistical universe. But this would involve us in a redundancy, for if we had all the necessary knowledge about the process being observed, we should not need a criterion or set of criteria to tell us what we already knew.

We must look a bit deeper and identify an on-going process in terms which are observable and yet concur with our intuitive notions. A process can, of course, be identified by its outcomes, but if this were the only identification available, we should not be able to reconstruct a process, and therefore could not take advantage of experience. We might then identify a process in terms of an experiment and its experimental environment. The experiment consists of all those factors which the process designer and the process operator can manipulate or at least choose as input variables which influence the process. The experimental environment consists of the remaining factors which can influence the process. The distinction between the experiment-manipulatable causes and the experimental environment–nonmanipulatable causes is not always clear-cut. For example, humidity was once a very important environmental variable affecting textile-manufacturing processes. With the advent of economically practical air conditioning, humidity becomes an experimental factor (or cause) in textile operations. For purposes of guiding our decision making, we may consider all the factors influencing the process (whether manipulatable or not) in abstract terms as constituting the "causal system" governing the process and yielding a set of observable outcomes. Then, on referring back to our fourfold classification of decision situations, we can view each decision situation (experiments, processes, daily tasks, etc.) in terms of the degree of determinacy of effect by cause. We shall examine Fig. 11.1 in this sense, and in order to do so, we postulate the existence of causal systems and of relations such as cause and effect, and we describe the experiment and experimental environment in such intuitively observable terms as seem to present themselves.

The data plotted in Fig. 11.1 (somewhat masked) come from a process for preparing an insulating material that is used to wrap cables which carry high-voltage current. A somewhat coarse cloth, which comes in 1,000-foot rolls of 50-inch width (the length of roll and cloth are, of course, conventional), is run through a liquid bath and picks up this liquid in successive stages of partial drying and redipping. After the first dipping the cloth is elevated some 60 feet through a heated tower and then sent back again through the bath and up again for drying. The thin cloth comes out finally as a somewhat thicker, yet pliable, non-porous sheet. The sheet is rolled again, but this time into two 500-foot rolls.

As one can readily surmise, there are many "causes" which influence the final product. The ultimate sheet (which is cut into narrow strips) must meet many specifications, some of them quite critical. The narrow strips which are wrapped around cables must protect the high-voltage-carrying cables against moisture and against possible electrical leakage. One important test consists of taking a 5-inch square of the cable cloth and subjecting it to high voltage between $\frac{1}{2}$-inch-diameter electrodes. The voltage is successively stepped up from 5,000 volts until the breakdown point at which the cloth is punctured. The breakdown occurs somewhere in the region of 15,000 volts. This breakdown voltage is divided by the thickness of the cloth (where the electrodes were in contact), giving the dielectric strength in volts per millimeter (vpm). One important specification is that the dielectric strength be greater than 1,000 vpm. In order to account to some extent for natural variation, test samples are taken from the first 5 feet of the roll, from a middle section, and from the last 5 feet. Thus there is a sampling of each 500-foot roll and also a sampling from a part which is common to two rolls—consecutive rolls which together make up a 1,000-foot roll. The samples are identified in time order of production. Hence the 24 samples in Fig. 11.2 represent 8 initial rolls, or 16 finished rolls. We can assume that all 16 rolls were completed in an essentially continuous process, even though the process may have extended over a considerable period of time. Again we ask, can we or can we not consider the coating process (in making this insulator cloth) to be statistically stable?

We ask, more specifically, will successive pieces of insulator cloth be uniform with respect to dielectric strength? By uniform we mean within certain bounds. If we plot test results on individual specimens, in time order of production, will they all fall between two parallel lines which represent bounds of variation? Essentially we should like, even in the face of variation, the output characteristics of an on-going process to fall within bounds. We should like to feel that the variation will not get out of bounds and that we can forecast an upper and a lower value of the characteristic under consideration, between which most of the values of this characteristic will fall. In the case of insulator cloth the characteristic of present interest is dielectric strength. We may consider output of this production process to be a sequence of dielectric strengths occurring in an identifiable time order. We observe certain of these dielectric strengths in groups of five under circumstances which make us believe that these outcomes should be all alike. If there is some variation among the outcomes in a sample, we attribute that variation to chance. Some such variation may occur in every sample. But one sample is taken at the beginning of a roll, and the next one 500 feet later, and the next another 500 feet thereafter. Then we get another roll of plain cloth which goes into the process. Hence, if something changes in the process, successive samples may differ by more than would be expected from chance variation alone. Note that we intuitively postulated a, so to speak, inherent variation, which we called "chance" variation, and suggested there could be a more doughty variation which must necessarily be labeled "nonchance" variation. Nonchance variation may produce nonuniform outcomes, outcomes outside the parallel bounds. Hence the question before us is how to distinguish chance from nonchance variation—how to set such parallel bounds so that we can be alerted to the presence of nonchance variation.

For the present we shall answer this question didactically. In Fig. 11.2 the two parallel lines specify a region within which all 24 sample averages of dielectric strength should fall if only chance variation were present. But there are six sample averages which are outside these bounds, and we must be warned that the process cannot be expected to perform in a uniform manner in the future.   We cannot expect that in the future the averages of the dielectric strengths of five specimens of insulating cloth (selected as specified above) will lie between 990 and 1,110 vpm.   Furthermore, it must be borne in mind that if the apparent spread of the averages of samples of five is ± 50 units about an estimated mean value, the individual values can spread by more than ± 100 units.   The individual values are not to be stressed now; we do stress, however, that on the basis of the evidence contained in Fig. 11.2, we cannot have confidence in the uniformity of the future product from this process.

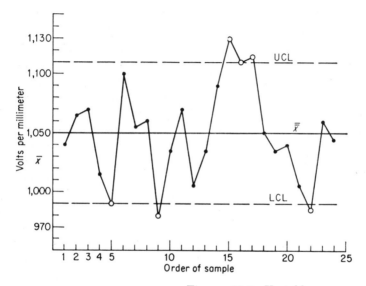

Figure. 11.2   Unstable process.

It is reasonable to ask on what grounds we feel that the parallel bounds displayed in Fig. 11.3 serve as a criterion for uniformity of the process outcomes.   We shall take up this question in greater detail in Sec. 11.2.   We can, however, suggest this notion, which may already have suggested itself to the reader: if the only variation to which the outcomes of a process are subject is chance, inherent, natural variation, that is, what we have called random variation, then from a large sampling of the outcomes we should be able to estimate the standard deviation of the universe of outcomes to a close approximation.   And then we can approximate the standard deviation of sample averages which should distribute themselves approximately normally around the estimated grand mean of the universe, and almost all of them within two bounds located at $\bar{x} \pm k\sigma_{\bar{x}}$, where k is greater than, say, 2.5 (the precise choice of k will be discussed in Sec. 11.2).   Sample averages outside these bounds would then be suspect, or perhaps the process might be suspect; that is, the prospect of anticipating future outcomes of the process might be subject to doubt. We shall move now to another example.

In Fig. 11.3 is a sequence of 175 outcomes of a process, taken in time order. Is this an example of a stable or an unstable process? Do these outcomes seem to form a uniform sequence? As a first effort, a histogram of the first 100 observations is plotted. All that one can say about this is that it is reasonable-looking. There is a suggestion that these observations may have come from a normal universe, and a normal distribution with the mean and standard deviation of the histogram is drawn. Intuitively, it appears that the histogram could readily be a sampling from the normal universe represented by the normal curve. Yet none of these intuitive comments have any bearing on whether or not the process which generated these 175 observations is stable or nonstable.

In accordance with the primitive notion of stability which has been suggested, we shall form the bounds $\bar{x} \pm 3\sigma_x$ and project them across the sequence chart. Thus we have outcome 60 just below the lower bound, but then no other extremes until the 154th outcome. It is difficult to pass judgment except to say that, following this outcome, there is suspicion that the earlier apparent uniformity (except for outcome 60) has been lost. Examination of the frequency diagrams and the individuals in sequence does not seem to be convincingly revealing.

It may be well to examine sample averages, averages of samples of five each. In such a small sample of outcomes taken in quick order, there may prevail only "inherent" variation. If some nonchance cause were to contaminate the process, it should make itself felt by changes taking place between samples. Hence we shall plot the sequence of 35 sample averages (of which the 175 individual items are constituted) and also the sequences of sample ranges. On the $\bar{x}$ chart are plotted the bounds $\bar{x} \pm 3(\bar{R}/\sqrt{5}\ d_2)$ and the grand average $\bar{x}$, where both $\bar{x}$ and $\bar{R}$ are calculated from the first 20 samples. ($\bar{R}/d_2$ is an unbiased estimate of the standard deviation of x, a normal variate, R is the range of a sample, and $\bar{R}$ is the average range of a number of samples of size n. The factor d_2 varies, of course, with n.) On the R chart are plotted the corresponding ranges, their average $\bar{R}$, and upper and lower bounds. The bounds for $\bar{R}$ are at $\bar{R} + 3\sigma_R$ and zero. Since $\bar{R} - 3\sigma_R$ is negative, for $n = 5$, the lower bound is placed at $R = 0$. These results are displayed in Fig. 11.4.

Note first off that the first 20 sample averages are well within the bounds. In fact, even though the sample averages shift quite a bit, none of these 20 values of $\bar{x}$ comes close to the control limits; these bounds are the conventional Shewhart 3-sigma control limits, designated as UCL and LCL. This state of affairs continues through the 25th sample, but

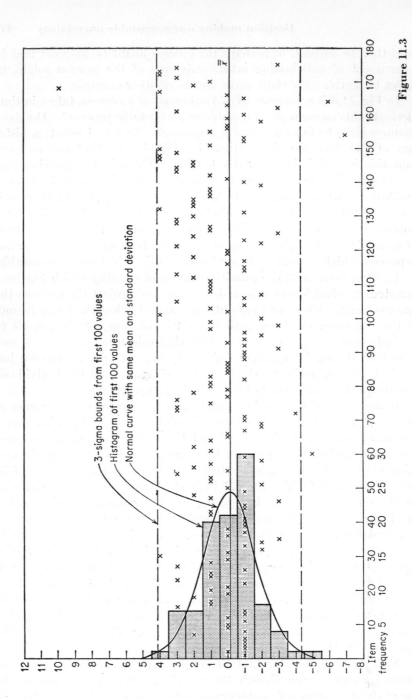

3-sigma bounds from first 100 values

Histogram of first 100 values

Normal curve with same mean and standard deviation

Item frequency 5

Figure 11.3

thereafter six sample averages fall outside the upper control limit.   This is clearly an example of unstable uncertainty, of an unstable process. Nevertheless, the first 20 sample averages do not seem like the remaining 15; these 20 do not seem like an example of an unstable process. Here we have a period in a process history which exhibits marked instability after a period which in contrast seems to have been quite stable.

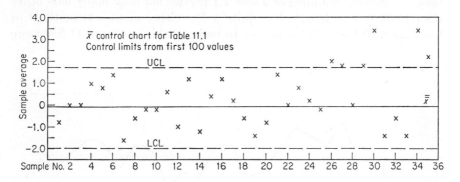

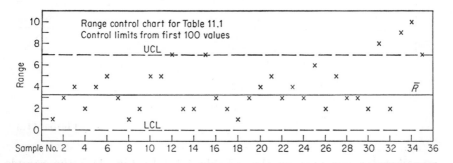

Figure 11.4

We point this out as an example of the fact that although our aim in practice is in general to exercise constraint on a process or experimental situation so as to transform states of instability into states of stability, often, in spite of our best efforts, situations degenerate into states of instability.

We may try to compare the corresponding R chart with the $\bar{x}$ chart just discussed.   We find no correlation between the two for the first 25 sample values.   The R chart does not exhibit instability until the 31st sample.   As was to be expected, the sample average and sample range are statistically independent chance variables, and indications of correlated behavior would be unusual.   Nevertheless, the samples from the 31st and beyond exemplify unstable uncertainty in both the sample averages and ranges.   This example will be discussed further in the next section.

11.2   Examples of stable uncertainty

For the first of these examples we refer back to Table 1.1 of the lengths of 100 steel bars, representing a sampling in time order from the early stages of the rolling of 10,000 steel bars to the specification 10.00 ± 0.30 feet.   This is a mechanized process which should produce 10-foot steel bars.   A cursory scanning of Table 1.1 reveals not only many bars other than 10.00 feet in length, but quite a few either greater than 10.30 or less than 9.70 feet.   What are we to make of this?   Figure 11.5 is more

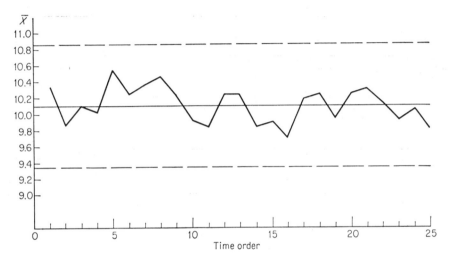

Figure 11.5

revealing for our purpose than Table 1.1.   In Fig. 11.5 the sample averages of groups of four are plotted in time order.   (Figure 11.5 is identical with Fig. 1.5, except for the outer lines UCL and LCL.)   The sample averages fall on either side of the grand average $\bar{x} = 10.12$, 13 above and 12 below.   A first impression of symmetry of the sample averages about the grand average of all the 100 lengths observed is supported by symmetry of the individual lengths about their grand average. One of our naïve intuitions about how the outcomes of a repeated experiment might distribute themselves is confirmed by these results (the experiment is the production process of rolling steel bars to a specified length).   The overall average is not exactly the aimed-at value, but close enough to it for comfort.   What causes the variation in lengths? That we may not know—perhaps at one moment the rolling has thinned out the bar, or the cutoff tool has wavered, or the roller speed has temporarily increased.   At any rate, we may not be able to identify specific causes which produce length variations.   We may say with impunity (but not with resignation) that it seems as though the variability observed in the lengths of rolled bar stock is due to chance. For the moment we shall not go any deeper, other than to say that the variability "looks well-behaved."

But we are not interested in variability for its own sake—we are interested in the bars that are still to be produced. Will the variability for the whole run be no greater than that exhibited in the present sample of 100 bars? Will the results of this experiment change markedly with time? Specifically, we are interested in estimating in advance the percentage of the total run which will be outside the allowable tolerances and in determining how to adjust the process so that the order for 10,000 bars can be filled at the least cost, with the production facilities at our disposal. Hence we need, at least, criteria which tell us that the outcomes of the process are consistent over time. In order to answer fully the two questions posed, we need more than just a criterion (or set of criteria) which indicates consistency of the outcomes over time, but we shall limit ourselves to this quest for the present.

As an example of stable uncertainty we offer Fig. 11.5, which represents in time order of occurrence the averages of 25 samples of bar lengths, each sample consisting of lengths of four bars produced consecutively. Successive samples, however, have not been manufactured in consecutive order, for time has been permitted to intervene between successive observed samples. The reasons for selecting specimens and samples in the manner described are quite simple—and essential to our purpose. We are trying to learn something about the variation in bar length; observations of individual bar lengths, whether in consecutive order of production or intermittent, cannot provide a formal basis for forecasting future individual bar lengths. For example, referring to Table 1.1, we find bars 8, 9, and 10 to be decreasing and under 10 feet whereas bar 11 is 11.23 feet long. Any number of similar examples can be found. This phenomenon may lead us to consider bar-length variation to be random, but from the evidence thus far adduced, this is too strong a conclusion. We need more evidence of nondeterminability of bar length and some evidence of the predictability of the location of percentiles of bar lengths from among the 100 bar lengths under consideration, as well as evidence of the predictability of averages of samples. We further need some evidence that time order of production does not affect bar length if we are to conclude that the bar lengths vary in a random manner. We need an operational criterion (or a set of such criteria) for random variation. Therefore it is necessary to introduce into our experimental environment a nonchance cause, a cause that we can identify, to which we can associate nonchance variation. (Note the apparent circularity of our procedure— it seems to be inherent in the phenomenon of discovery that we somehow divine what we are to discover.) Time order is a nonchance, an identifiable factor.   A sufficient time is permitted to elapse between the taking of successive samples so that (1) transient nonchance causes can enter the experimental environment of a process, and (2) evolving causes can grow and be detected.   Such effects can be experienced "in time"; that is to say, extensive experience has demonstrated that during a "sufficient" lapse of time between observations, observable changes do occur in the experimental environment (the system of causes governing a process). We need to be able to detect such changes.

How can we detect changes in the experimental environment, the process, the causal system under observation?   To discover change there must be change, and this change is expressed in the variations in the outcomes of the repeated experiment, the outcomes of the process.   We may therefore be able to fall back on our notions of statistical inference (and the underlying rules of probability) in order to provide criteria to distinguish between random variation and nonrandom variation.   The reader may recall that difficulty was experienced in the earlier chapters in defining the concept "randomness."   Yet we here use the expression "random variation" freely.   What we hope to do is attach empirical conditions to outcome variations such that when we take action in a certain way because we believe the process to be subject only to random variation (or to some nonrandom change), we shall be disappointed only infrequently.   Let us look into variation further.

Suppose we again look at Table 1.1 and note the ranges of the various samples.   One is greater than 2 feet, and three are less than $\frac{1}{2}$ foot.   Does this tell us anything; is the range of the seventh sample too great to represent chance variation?   (The term chance may be thought of as having more genuinely empirical or operational significance than the term random—but what's in a word?)   Going back to the sample averages, we seem to get more enlightening insight into the chance or nonchance nature of the bar lengths if we look at Fig. 11.5.   It seems that there is no intuitively apparent "system" to the variability of the sample averages.   The grand average does not seem to be changing. This is encouraging since we do want all the bar lengths to be the same; we permit them to vary a bit, but our intuition suggests symmetrical parallel bounds for a time series of bar lengths and of averages of small samples of bar lengths.   If we hold to the following notions: bar length should be "constant"; in order that bar lengths be "constant," the process which yields the bars must be "constant" in some sense; the only sense in which the process can be "constant" is in the sense that the governing causal system is "constant."   For the sake of simplicity we suppose that the setting of cutoff is unvarying and that a number of not identifiable causes combine to produce the variation which we observe.

The results plotted in Fig. 11.5 may be taken as a typical example of outcome from a process in a state of statistical stability.   All sample averages lie between the upper and lower control limits which have been obtained from $\bar{\bar{x}} \pm 3s_{\bar{x}}$, where the estimated standard deviation of the sample averages has been obtained from the ranges of the samples. We hope that this is an estimate of inherent variation due only to chance

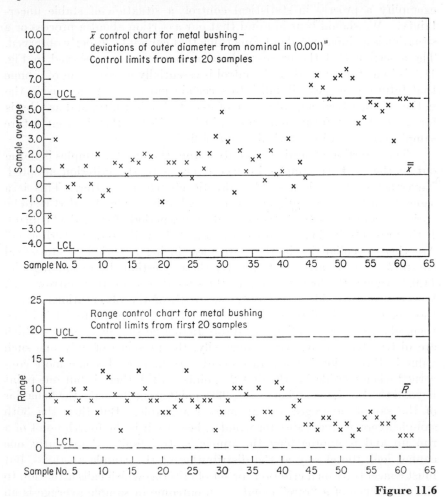

Figure 11.6

causes. We may ask, further, whether this criterion of statistical stability is enough to assure us that future outcomes of the process will fall within preassigned bounds—not the bounds for sample averages, but the bounds for the individual outcomes. No categorical answer can be given. Greater insight can be obtained by looking into other examples.

An example of the output of a machine process is given in Fig. 11.6. Again the control limits for $\bar{x}$ have been obtained from the estimated standard deviation, which has been determined from an average of the ranges of the first 20 samples. These limits have been projected over the total run of 62 samples. The first 20 sample averages are well within the specified bounds, and so are the next 24 samples. By the criterion we have already expressed, these outcomes—the first 44 samples— exemplify a process in statistical control, a situation of stable uncertainty. We should bear in mind that our assertion about a process or a situation is an inference about something that cannot be directly observed. The assertion that the process whose outcomes are represented in Fig. 11.6 is in a state of statistical control is essentially an assertion of a hope that future outcomes will fall into a certain pattern. We are using the notion of statistical control as one of essential uniformity, and as a basis for forecast that future outcomes will be uniform, that is, that future sample averages will fall within control limits.

The assertion of statistical control from the first 20 samples is borne out in the next 24 samples in accordance with the criterion adopted. Nevertheless, there is a sudden drastic change thereafter. This is a signal for action and caution in the future, but it should also alert us to be curious about behavior of outcomes during a period of statistical control. Is the present criterion the only one available? Is it a powerful criterion? Are there peculiarities in the outcomes during a period of statistical control? We can attempt to answer these questions by examining Fig. 11.6. Among the first 20 samples the spread seems rather narrow. If, however, one considers that only one-tenth of the observations among those of a normally distributed variate exceed the grand mean ± 1.5 sigma, then, allowing for sampling variations among 20 sample averages which are distributed approximately normally, the presence of only one such value in this region is not a rare event. In fact, we become more concerned when considering the first 28 points. Still, there is but one point beyond the 1.5-sigma region. The 29th point seems to make the behavior of the sample averages appear more reasonable. But then the 30th sample average gives cause for wonder, because it is the fourth point of a run up and is approaching the upper control limit. Apparently one cannot look too closely at the distribution of the sample averages, but must concentrate on a criterion (or set of criteria) which calls attention to the occurrence of a "rare" event. An outcome (a sample average is an outcome among the distribution of sample averages) outside the 3-sigma control limits is an event with odds of more than 300 to 1 against it and has been chosen for discrimination between what "ought not" occur and what may be expected to occur. Experience has shown that the 3-sigma control-limit criterion of Shewhart has been a successful discriminating signal. So long as all sample averages in a sequence of a certain length lie within these control limits, we may safely act as though the situation is one of stable uncertainty.

If, however, we choose to probe further, we may look for runs up or down and runs above or below the grand mean. Among the first 20 points there is no run up or down of more than three points. Such runs are not uncommon and no cause for alarm. On the other hand, points 12 to 18 are all above grand average, and this event (for a normal distribution) is sufficiently uncommon to call for attention. It would seem that the grand mean has shifted upward as the result of some nonchance cause. Nevertheless, from the 19th to the 28th point, no unusual event occurs. We have not called attention to the ranges, which, apart from providing an estimate of inherent variation, can give evidence of the presence of nonchance causes. Again, however, among the first 28 ranges there is no disturbing signal.

To recapitulate, if we examine the $\bar{x}$ chart of Fig. 11.6, we find that, by the criterion of 3-sigma control limits, the process which generated the first 20 sample averages is in a state of statistical control; or in other words, these 20 sample averages exemplify a situation of stable uncertainty. We can make predictions about the near future with some conviction. This conviction is based on the postulate that such variation as has been exhibited is like that which would be exhibited by outcomes of random sampling from a universe; or in other words, and in an operational sense, the causes of variation constitute a fixed set of "chance" causes, that is, causes which it is not within one's means to identify. This conviction cannot continue unsupported by further evidence, and we must take further observations on the process. This conviction continues (and may in fact be reinforced) so long as the 3-sigma criterion is satisfied. (The 3-sigma criterion has been designated by Shewhart as criterion 1. We shall use the symbol SSC 1 as an abreviation for statistical stability criterion 1.) At any time, however, SSC 1 may not be satisfied, and we must be alert to this possibility. Extensive experience suggests that the state of statistical stability is not a common occurrence in nature, and certainly not in man-designed processes. In processes and operations in engineering, science, industry, business, behavioral systems, and other situations, the initial stages must be studied for evidence of the state of stability—usually the initial stages are unstable and empirical effort is necessary to bring about stability and to maintain stability. While SSC 1 is a very useful criterion for alerting the observer to the presence of nonchance causes of variation, it alone is not a guarantee of stability. The presence of runs is evidence of possible changes in the causal system which SSC 1 is slower to detect. In Fig. 11.6 the first 44 sample averages satisfy SSC 1, yet samples 12 to 18 and 21 to 31 give cause for concern. It appears, during these sequences, that the grand mean has moved upward and that the sought-after uniformity will not be maintained. Perhaps we should look at the ranges for possible explanation. At first one finds complete satisfaction of SSC 1. On looking closer one finds the average of ranges 25 to 44 much smaller than that for ranges 1 to 24. Then again, ranges 45 to 62 are indeed much smaller than the rest. Apparently there have been changes in the causal system. But since ranges 1 to 20 have been relatively large, the spread of the control limits used has been large enough to contain all the sample averages up through the 44th. Furthermore, the decrease in the ranges after the 24th sample may account for the containment of the sample averages even though some nonchance cause may have tended to push the grand mean upward. For even though the grand mean increased, since the standard deviation of the sample averages decreased, as did the standard deviation of the individuals, the spread of the sample averages was narrowed and so did not exceed the original upper 3-sigma control limit.

A few more points of interest may be garnered from further examination of Fig. 11.6. Sample average 45 is considerably outside the upper control limit. The jump is so great that in actual practice one hardly needs a control chart or statistical analysis to lead one to believe that there has been a significant change in the cause system. When, however, one considers that the magnitudes being dealt with are of the order of thousandths of an inch, one may feel impelled to use a somewhat formalized decision-making procedure. Apart from the marked shift in the grand mean of this machining process while samples 45 to 52 have been produced, the feature of interest is the narrow spread of these sample averages. This, of course, should have resulted from a substantial decrease in the inherent variability of the individual outcomes, and indeed, as the range chart shows, the variation has decreased considerably. In fact, in contrast to an $\bar{R}$ of more than 8.85 for samples 1 to 20, $\bar{R}$ for samples 45 to 62 is 3.78. (Note in Fig. 11.4 that the grand mean shifted while the average range did not change, during one period, whereas in another period the grand mean returned to its original level while the range increased considerably. Here again we see apparently independent behavior of the grand mean and the average range.)

There is even another change in the causal system (Fig. 11.6), this time evidenced by a decrease in the grand mean of the sample averages. Since the outcomes are deviations from the specification value of the bushing that is being machined, this decrease is welcome. It is only proper, however, to interpret these changes empirically, in operational terms. We have been using probability calculations and statistical inference as a basis for decision making, assuming in some situations probabilistic certainty and in others stable uncertainty. At the moment we have been exploring procedures for assuring us that we have a situation or process which is statistically stable. The control charts presented as exemplifying states of statistical stability have also exemplified evidence of unstability, or rather, of a change from the previous stable state. The use of probability and statistical inference as a basis for decision is meaningful provided there is stability.   Hence the notion of statistically stable processes is vital to effective use of statistical inference.   And the understanding of statistically stable processes can be acquired only by making decisions in real situations and observing the effectiveness of these decisions.   Hence the evidence in Fig. 11.6 is valuable, not merely as an example of how certain outcomes from what is called a stable process behave, but as material for the analysis of process behavior under possible causal change.   We shall disclose how the data in Fig. 11.6 came to be as they are.

The first sample was obtained shortly after the machine setup had been made and the inspector was satisfied that parts near the nominal would be produced.   The specifications permitted deviations of as much as 0.010 inch.   The machine was not in the best shape, yet past experience had indicated that about 95 per cent of the outside diameters of the bushings would be within the tolerance limits.   The early results of this operation were consistent with this experience.   Nevertheless, the operator made occasional adjustments which prevented the deviations from becoming greater.   The deviations did seem to vary from one to the other side of the nominal so as to preclude too great a deviation, either positively or negatively.   Such adjustment is not always effective; in many cases attempts to "suppress" random variation only accentuate the variation, increasing it and leading to exaggerated oscillation.   The present variation resulted from a combination of a worn bearing on the main shaft and some inherent vibration of the machine and of the cutting tool.   The grand average was dependent on the degree of wear of some of the parts, the accuracy of tool setting, and the accuracy of calibration of setting indicators.   In the present case a production run was ended after the 44th sample, and a machine overhaul was made.   Various adjustments were made, including replacement of bearings and other worn parts and a general tightening up, which greatly reduced the variation. The tool setting was not, however, modified, nor was any calibration undertaken.   The overhaul was effective in reducing the variation among the outside diameters of successive bushings, but did not make for great accuracy in setting the cutting tool.   Hence, when a new setup was ready and a number of initial parts were found to be within the upper tolerance and successive parts quite uniform, the inspector let the process roll. Later an adjustment was requested (because the sample averages were outside the initial control limits which were projected so as to apply under the new setup), and the grand average was brought down so that sample 53 and beyond fell inside the upper control limit.

This case is not offered as an example of good statistical stability, but as an example of the fact that stability is not all-enduring, that processes have finite terminations, and that the "same" process may behave quite differently when reinstituted.   The price of statistical inference for real ends is not perfunctory analysis, and the effectiveness of statistical inference is closely associated not only with formal decision, but with action taken in order to make inference operationally valid. In the present case further work on the machine and the tools brought about genuine accuracy in tool setting (especially after genuine recalibration) and produced a statistically stable process, so that the variation of the outcomes was about half that of the allowable tolerance.

11.3 An example from physics

Many professional people distinguish in some esoteric way between engineering and science, crowning science with some sort of halo of superiority which is reflected even in the constancy of scientific measurements. To be sure, industrial operations exist in the realm of the mundane, where observations are subject to considerable variation. Hence it is felt that only where precision and accuracy are not great, do questions of statistical stability arise. In Table 11.1 are given 500 observations, which are replications of the measurement of the position of a spectral line to a least count of 0.001 millimeter. This set of measurements[1] was made under replication conditions as nearly "identical" as laboratory techniques permitted. They represent a very high standard of scientific measurement. Are they "better" than observations commonly obtained from production processes? Simple control-chart analysis by means of criterion I and a simple consideration from the theory of runs will be used to inquire into the statistical stability of the data. Since only a little space can be devoted to this excursion, further analysis will be suggested in the exercises.

In Fig. 11.7 the $\bar{x}$ and the range-control charts (samples of five observations) for Table 11.1 are given. The control limits are based on the total 100 samples. What can one say about the source of the observations? We shall look at some of the calculations. The grand average for all 500 observations $\bar{\bar{x}}$ is 78.92; the average range $\bar{R}$ is 8.23. Hence the 3-sigma control limits are $78.92 \pm (0.577)8.23 = 83.67$ and 74.17, respectively. One can use these figures to implement criterion I either by comparing each $\bar{x}$ in Table 11.1 with the calculated control limits or by scanning Fig. 11.7. In either case, criterion I for sample averages is satisfied for all 100 $\bar{x}$ values. The value closest to a control limit occurs for samples 56 and 75, namely, $\bar{x} = 82.6$, which is $3.68/1.583 = 2.325s$ from $\bar{\bar{x}}$. If the sample *averages* had a normal distribution (in the event

---

[1] This work was undertaken by Raymond T. Birge in a study of the method of least squares as means for interpreting errors of measurements. The study (without the data) was presented in an article, The Calculation of Errors by the Method of Least Squares, *The Physical Review*, vol. 40, 1932. The table of observations was given to Eugene L. Grant, who presented them in his work "Statistical Quality Control," 2d ed., McGraw-Hill Book Company, Inc., New York, 1952.

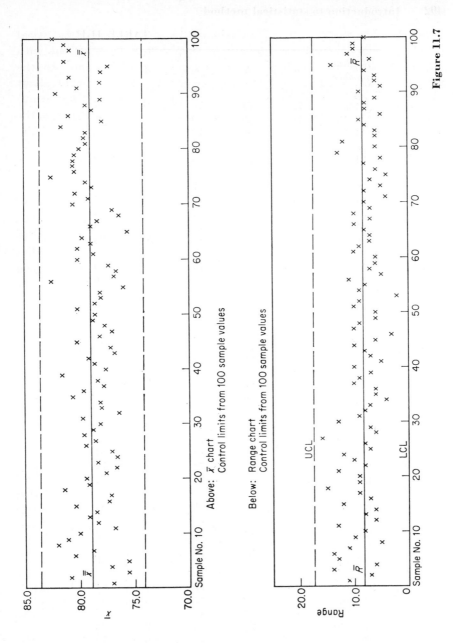

Above: $\bar{x}$ chart
    Control limits from 100 sample values

Below: Range chart
    Control limits from 100 sample values

Figure 11.7

TABLE 11.1*

Reading number	a	b	c	d	e
1–5	77	74	73	84	77
6–10	78	85	80	81	80
11–15	75	69	72	83	79
16–20	75	80	79	74	78
21–25	70	74	83	72	79
26–30	73	81	87	82	79
31–35	78	79	78	74	85
36–40	83	79	83	81	84
41–45	81	88	79	80	78
46–50	77	80	85	70	78
51–55	72	75	73	85	79
56–60	78	82	80	76	76
61–65	79	75	83	81	78
66–70	82	76	78	78	79
71–75	86	79	79	84	74
76–80	76	75	77	82	77
81–85	79	77	72	77	81
86–90	83	75	82	90	77
91–95	80	78	83	81	74
96–100	79	80	79	75	84
101–105	81	74	73	74	86
106–110	77	82	75	74	75
111–115	75	74	83	76	84
116–120	72	84	73	77	77
121–125	76	75	81	79	74
126–130	80	75	81	78	83
131–135	75	89	75	73	81
136–140	76	82	77	81	82
141–145	82	75	81	79	77
146–150	71	74	84	81	81
151–155	80	75	77	83	84
156–160	73	73	77	78	81
161–165	80	74	81	78	77
166–170	80	76	80	77	78
171–175	78	82	84	80	79
176–180	79	77	78	81	83
181–185	83	73	81	74	78
186–190	82	78	82	77	73
191–195	80	85	78	81	84
196–200	78	77	79	72	82

TABLE 11.1 (*Continued*)

Reading number	a	b	c	d	e
201–205	78	77	79	77	82
206–210	76	77	83	81	79
211–215	82	75	77	74	76
216–220	82	81	72	74	77
221–225	78	79	80	81	80
226–230	77	76	76	79	78
231–235	74	83	80	75	73
236–240	76	80	77	82	73
241–245	82	76	79	78	79
246–250	81	79	75	78	86
251–255	78	82	75	81	85
256–260	82	82	81	73	75
261–265	79	77	78	79	77
266–270	79	77	80	82	73
271–275	70	76	83	76	75
276–280	88	85	77	79	84
281–285	74	78	77	76	79
286–290	77	78	73	75	80
291–295	77	74	78	78	80
296–300	76	82	81	81	81
301–305	82	78	73	83	78
306–310	79	81	76	80	85
311–315	83	81	76	76	79
316–320	81	78	77	79	84
321–325	76	77	72	73	80
326–330	83	74	76	84	78
331–335	78	75	82	80	77
336–340	77	75	82	76	72
341–345	78	79	73	75	80
346–350	82	76	77	84	84
351–355	79	82	78	79	78
356–360	83	83	81	75	80
361–365	80	78	77	77	82
366–370	82	75	80	81	79
371–375	82	85	84	81	81
376–380	82	83	79	81	77
381–385	83	83	75	79	83
386–390	78	83	80	79	83
391–395	81	78	87	82	74
396–400	80	81	79	77	83

TABLE 11.1   (*Continued*)

Reading number	a	b	c	d	e
401–405	79	75	73	85	85
406–410	77	80	83	79	79
411–415	79	76	80	82	80
416–420	84	85	79	77	81
421–425	73	74	81	79	82
426–430	82	83	81	78	81
431–435	79	84	77	76	78
436–440	77	85	79	77	79
441–445	77	76	77	82	78
446–450	77	86	83	83	82
451–455	79	78	83	82	79
456–460	82	76	78	78	76
461–465	80	79	79	81	85
466–470	81	79	73	79	78
471–475	82	84	79	70	72
476–480	78	79	80	85	85
481–485	80	72	81	70	75
486–490	80	87	82	78	77
491–495	88	79	82	78	80
496–500	83	87	81	82	79

* These data are taken from E. H. Grant, "Statistical Quality Control," 2d ed., McGraw-Hill Book Company, Inc., New York, 1952, pp. 72–74. Used with permission.

that the process—the individual outcomes—was statistically stable, the distribution of the $\bar{x}$ would have been approximately normal), sample averages equal to or greater than 82.6 might have been expected "not more than 1 per cent of the time." A so-called rigorous interpretation of this statement does not apply unhedged to the present situation, nor is a rigorous interpretation necessarily helpful or essential. The essence of the present data is that if probability and statistical inference have any bearing on nature, we might expect a relative frequency of about 1/100 for sample averages equal to 82.6 or greater. Hence one occurrence here is in accordance with expectation. The reader may find it an interesting exercise to estimate the probability of the occurrence of $\bar{x} \geq 82.6$ once among a hundred such samples, provided that $\bar{x}$ has a normal distribution, $\Phi(\bar{x};78.92,1.583)$. It is left to the reader to frame this exercise meaningfully. At any rate, for our present purposes, it is well to note that even under circumstances of exceptionally precise repetitive scientific experiment, "rare" events do occur.

But let us look further. The number of values above $\bar{\bar{x}}$ are 48, with 52 below. Again one can show that this is not a rare occurrence. But if one considers the distribution of the number above the grand average between the first 50 samples and the second 50 samples, one finds it to be 18 versus 30. If the probability of an $\bar{x}$ value greater than the grand average 78.92 were "truly" $\frac{1}{2}$ and the distribution were symmetrical and if the successive outcomes were independent, then the probability of the 18-versus-30 occurrence (that is, 18 or less values of $\bar{x} > 78.92$ among 50 random independent sample selections and 30 or more values of $\bar{x} > 78.92$ among another 50 random independent selections) can be shown to be $\leq \frac{1}{32}$, a rather "unlikely" event.

Now let us look at samples 74 to 84. Here are 11 successive values of $\bar{x}$, all above the grand average. Given any $\bar{x}_n$, and assuming independence and symmetry about the "true" average, such a "run above," or longer, has a probability of occurrence not greater than

$$(\tfrac{1}{2})^{10} \sum_{i=0}^{\infty} (\tfrac{1}{2})^i = \tfrac{1}{512}$$

That is, if $\bar{\bar{x}} = 78.92$ were the true mean and our assumptions held, we might regard this run as a rather rare event. Or we might choose to question the stability of the chance-cause system underlying the occurrence of these observations. One may, of course, raise the question as to whether, in the light of the fact that $\bar{\bar{x}}$ is the result of a finite number of observations, one can reason as we did. If, however, we invoke any statistical guidance, we start with the assumption that our observations came by a process of random selection—a "constant" source—and then we challenge that assumption by comparing results with expectations. We are playing it safe when we question the statistical stability of the causal system generating the run of averages of samples 74 to 84.

There may be a hitch here if we attempt to justify concern about this run on the basis of formal probability calculations. In order to make formal statistical inference we must obey the rules of the game (rules set down in this work). We have not provided a way for optional stopping, as is being done when we consider only samples 74 to 84. Were we to choose, say, to look at all 100 samples, a "run above" of 11 may not be so unusual an event. In fact, since these observations are being looked at in the order of occurrence, and since we are questioning existence of a "constant chance-cause system," it hardly makes sense to ask in advance for a particular number of samples to look at. For example, the probability of one "run above" of 11 in a sample of 17 is not more than 0.01. Suppose we chose at random the number of the sample with which we were to begin the count of samples. How should we choose this number? Should we choose among 0, 1, 2, . . . , 9, or 0, 1, 2, . . . , 25, or 0, 1,

2, . . . , 100? Suppose, in any case, that we chose a number which we shall denote by ν, and that before we reached ν, any of the following events occurred: one sample value $\bar{x}_i (i < \nu)$ outside control limits, a "run below" of 9, a sequence of 14 $\bar{x}$ values alternating above and below the median. Since the decision resulting from applying criteria of statistical stability defines action on the process, questions arise as to the logical and operational connections between control chart procedures and statistical hypothesis testing. One way of looking at such a run is to consider all to be well up to sample 74, but that thereafter signs of meaningful change were being manifested. By the time seven successive $\bar{x}_i$ ($\bar{x}_{75}, \bar{x}_{76}, \ldots , \bar{x}_{81}$) occur, it is correct to estimate (under the assumptions expressed) that a group like $\bar{x}_{74}, \bar{x}_{75}, \ldots , \bar{x}_{81}$ represented an event whose probability was not greater than $\frac{1}{128}$. Under such circumstances it is wise to be cautious and to look upon such a run as an event rare enough to require investigation, or at least caution.[1]

Returning to samples 74 to 84, there is sufficient evidence to wonder whether the grand average has moved up. Certain probabilistic considerations have been used to reach this state of concern; but precise formal probabilities do not form the essential basis since the very basis on which probability calculations are made is being questioned. What is important here is the fact that in a sequence of scientific data of the highest order of both accuracy and precision, sequences of observations occur which lead one to question the statistical stability of the process generating the data. Further examination of the data of Table 11.1 is suggested in the exercises that follow. A warning, if not a conclusion, resulting from the present discussion is that statistical stability is not readily come by, and therefore valid application of statistical inference is not to be taken for granted.

11.4 Some statistical control techniques

Volumes of journals have been filled with various notions on statistical control in general and on quality control in particular. We cannot comprehensively embrace this body of knowledge here. We set out to give the role of statistical stability in decision making, and in order to provide some basis for application, we shall consider a number of techniques in common use.

Much of the terminology of quality-control practice comes from industrial usage. In Fig. 11.6 are control charts of variables—control charts for sample averages and for sample ranges. Since these charts

---

[1] A rigorous treatment of the theory of runs above and below the grand mean, in conjunction with k-sigma limits, has been given in a forthcoming paper, Double Limit and Run Control Charts: Exact Statistical Properties, by J. Tiago de Oliveira and S. B. Littauer.

are used largely in places of industrial manufacture, simple and quick methods of representation are required.   Hence, in establishing SSC 1, Shewhart decided, after a number of years of experience in trying out his novel idea, that detection of a change in the chance-causal system is readily reflected when a sample average $\bar{x}_i$ falls outside the bounds $\bar{\bar{x}} \pm 3\sigma_{\bar{x}}$.   This presupposes one can know $\sigma_{\bar{x}}$, whereas in practice one can at best get an unbiased estimate of σ_x.   Hence, in practice, the two bounds called upper and lower control limits, respectively (denoted by UCL and LCL), are set at $\bar{\bar{x}} \pm 3s_{\bar{x}}$, where $s_{\bar{x}}$ is the unbiased estimate of $\sigma_{\bar{x}}$.   Since we wish $\sigma_{\bar{x}}$ to reflect an intrinsic variation due only to a chance-cause system, $\sigma_{\bar{x}}$ is estimated from within the small samples.   And since the variation between the $\bar{x}_i$ is to reflect the detectable causes— changes in the cause system that are economically worth looking for—the elapsed time between successive samples is set as great as is practically feasible.   The elapsed time should not be too great, since, if undesirable causes enter the system, a defective product will be made, thereby raising the cost of production.   Hence, since making observations involves some cost: increasing n may increase the accuracy of estimating σ_x (from which parameter $\sigma_{\bar{x}}$ is determined), but also admit runs and extraneous causes; increasing the elapsed time between successive samples decreases direct cost, improves chances for detecting extraneous (nonchance) causes, but increases the losses due to defective product that could be made in the interim; increasing the separation between the control limits decreases the losses from wrong decisions that the cause system has changed, but also decreases the chances of discovering the presence of nonchance causes; since all these conflicting costs result from decisions about how to set the parameters of SSC 1, namely, n, ν (elapsed number of outcomes between successive observed samples), and k (the multiple of $\sigma_{\bar{x}}$), some "compromise" solution is needed.   Shewhart settled upon small samples of $n = 4$ or 5 and $k = 3$, leaving the spacing between successive samples to be determined by the quality-control engineer.   For years "± 3-sigma" control limits have worked effectively, as have $n = 4$ or 5 (although, of course, other values of n have been used).   The basis for establishing the sampling procedure and SSC 1 is, of course, in part economic.   And Shewhart, on the basis of his experience, established control limits at $\bar{\bar{x}} \pm 3s_{\bar{x}}$.   For purposes of simplicity, uniformity of practice was urged, and for the other types of control chart that are in common practice, Shewhart suggested again using 3-sigma control limits.[1]   While the

---

[1] There have been a few efforts at establishing n, sample spacing, and k formally. Acheson J. Duncan, in The Economic Design of $\bar{X}$ Charts Used to Maintain Current Control of Process, *Journal of the American Statistical Association*, vol. 51, has done some interesting work on this problem.   In the recent work of J. Tiago de Oliveira and S. B. Littauer, *ibid.*, and Techniques for Economic Control Chart Operation, other aspects of this problem have been taken up.

basis for analyzing control charts has made judgmental use of probability and statistical inference, the practice has stood the test of time, and time may yet bring formal improvements.   We shall now consider the $\bar{x}$ and R control chart, bearing in mind that on empirico-economic grounds 3-sigma control limits have been chosen as minimizing the losses from decision as to whether or not a process is in a state of statistical stability.

The $\bar{x}$ Control Chart   We shall give here merely the techniques for making calculations in the use of these control charts.   Comprehensive analysis of process behavior requires a text in itself.   Our aim in this chapter has been merely to alert the reader to the problem of the diagnosis of causes of nonanticipated behavior, or in other words, to a method of inquiry which can never quite be formalized.   While techniques of statistical inference are used, the validity of the assumptions made often has more bearing on the "truth" of these inferences than does the soundness of the statistical procedures themselves.

For the $\bar{x}$ chart we shall need the following quantities:

n	Number of items (measurements, observations, etc.) in a sample
i	Sample number (order in the sequence of samples), or the observation number (order in the sequence of observations)
x_i	ith observation
$\bar{x}_i$	Average of x values constituting the ith sample
$\bar{\bar{x}}$	Average of the $\bar{x}_i$ of any given number of samples
$\bar{R}$	Average of the R_i of any given number of samples
s_i	Estimate of the standard deviation of X as made from the ith sample
$\bar{s}_x$	Average of the s_i from any given number of samples
s_x	An unbiased estimate of σ_x
$s_{\bar{x}}$	An unbiased estimate of $\sigma_{\bar{x}}$
σ_x	"True" (usually unknown) standard deviation of X
$\sigma_{\bar{x}}$	"True" (usually unknown) standard deviation of $\bar{X}$; $\sigma_x = \sqrt{n}\,\sigma_{\bar{x}}$
UCL	Upper control limit
LCL	Lower control limit

The standard deviation of X should be estimated from within the samples.   Let the sample estimate be

$$\hat{s}_x = \frac{(x_1 - \bar{x})^2 + (x_2 - \bar{x})^2 + \cdots + (x_n - \bar{x})^2}{n}$$

(Note that $\hat{s}_x$ as defined here is biased.)   It can be shown that when X is a random variable with normal distribution,

$$E(\hat{s}_x) = c_2 \sigma_x$$

where $c_2 = \sqrt{2/n}\left(\frac{n-2}{2}\right)! \div \left(\frac{n-3}{2}\right)!$.   Hence if N samples of size n

are taken,

$$\frac{\bar{\bar{s}}_x}{c_2}$$

is an unbiased estimate of σ_x.

Again, by integration methods we have

$$\frac{\bar{R}}{d_2}$$

which is also an unbiased estimate of σ_x.   The factor d_2, dependent on n, cannot be expressed in closed form.   Both c_2 and d_2 are given in Table A.8 in the Appendix.

Since it is quite tedious to calculate s_x for each sample, it is common practice to consider R, and not s_x (except where the sample size may be very large and measurements very accurately made).   Hence, in setting up a control chart for $\bar{X}$, take, as prescribed above, $N \geq 20$ samples of size $n = 4$ or 5 and determine the $N \{\bar{x}_i, R_i\}$, $\bar{\bar{x}}$, and $\bar{R}$ and then find $s_{\bar{x}} = (\bar{R}/d_2)\sqrt{n}$.   Hence the control limits become

$$\bar{\bar{x}} \pm 3\,\frac{\bar{R}}{d_2\,\sqrt{n}} = \bar{\bar{x}} \pm A_2\bar{R}$$

where $A_2 = 3/d_2\sqrt{n}$ is given in Table A.8.   We shall check A_2 for $n = 4$: $d_2 = 2.059$; whence $3/4.118 = 0.728 \cong 0.73$ as tabulated.   We are not going any further into the analysis of an $\bar{x}$ chart since the earlier discussion should suffice for the purposes of this text.

The R Control Chart   It might be remarked at the outset that the sample range and sample average are independently distributed for the normal distribution.   Therefore the R chart can be interpreted independently of the $\bar{x}$ chart, although the study of their joint behavior is revealing. R is itself a chance variable, and therefore has a standard deviation which can be calculated, although the distribution cannot be given in closed form.   In conventional practice the control limits are given as follows:

$$UCL = D_4\bar{R}$$
$$LCL = D_3\bar{R}$$

where D_3 and D_4 are given in Table A.8.

We shall not give the factors for determining control limits for the s control chart, but leave that as an exercise for the reader.

The Control Chart for Fraction Defective p   In industrial practice items are often inspected by "go–no go" gauges and classified as defective or satisfactory.   Given any sample size n, if x is the number of defectives in the sample, $x/n = p$ is a random variable which characterizes the fraction defective.   The distribution of p, given n (and our usual assumptions), is binomial.   Eschewing much detail that can be con-

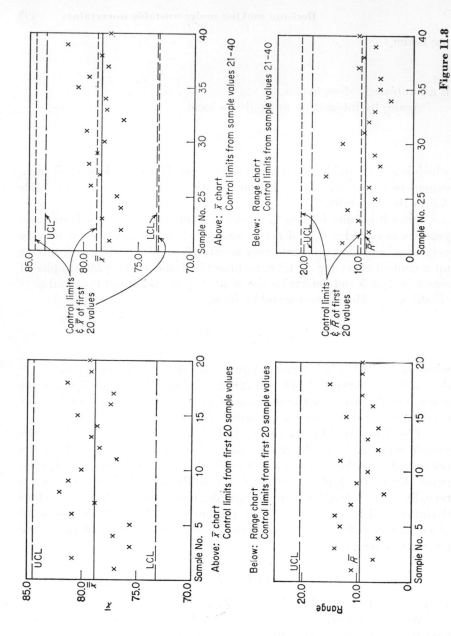

Above: $\bar{x}$ chart
Control limits from sample values 21–40

Below: Range chart
Control limits from sample values 21–40

Above: $\bar{x}$ chart
Control limits from first 20 sample values

Below: Range chart
Control limits from first 20 sample values

Figure 11.8

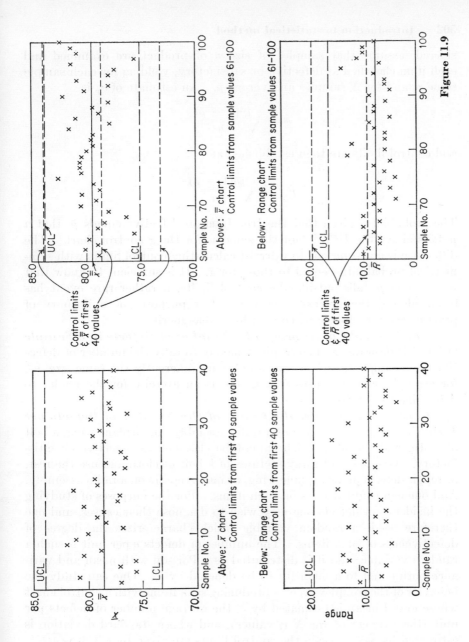

Above: $\bar{x}$ chart
Control limits from sample values 61-100

Below: Range chart
Control limits from sample values 61-100

Above: $\bar{x}$ chart
Control limits from first 40 sample values

Below: Range chart
Control limits from first 40 sample values

Figure 11.9

sidered, assume that samples of size n of product are examined and each item classified as defective or satisfactory, yielding for each sample some p_i and for N samples an average $\bar{p}$. An estimate of σ_p is

$$s = \sqrt{\frac{\bar{p}(1 - \bar{p})}{n}}$$

and control limits are then established at

$$\bar{p} \pm 3 \sqrt{\frac{\bar{p}(1 - \bar{p})}{n}}$$

The probability, given that the true fraction defective equals $\bar{p}$, that a p_i falls above the UCL is not the same as for the $\bar{x}$ control chart. The difference is not sufficient to warrant calculating control limits with symmetrical probabilities equal to those for $\bar{x}$. It is sufficient to know that when some p_i falls outside the control limits, a rather rare event has occurred and the process is suspect. For purposes of uniformity of practice the use of 3-sigma control limits has merit.

    The Control Chart for np, the Number of Defects in a Sample Often it is desirable and convenient merely to tally the number of defectives in a sample, as when the samples are inherently the same size, as, for example, crates of eggs. It is left as an exercise for the reader to determine the control limits.

    Control Chart for c, the Count of the Number of Defects per Unit There are items such as a radio assembly, an airplane wing, a bolt of cloth, and the like, which cannot be classified as defective or satisfactory. One may cut away sections of a bolt of cloth and use the rest, or repair defects in an airplane wing, or make repairs on a radio assembly. And one can count defects on such items. For the purposes of studying the incidence of defects one may wish to diagnose their causes, and one therefore needs a random variable which characterizes the degree of defectiveness of such items. The number of defects c per unit is such a random variable, and it is distributed as a Poisson with mean and variance both equal to a quantity to be denoted by c'. One can study the behavior of the complex process producing such items with a control chart whose grand mean is estimated by $\bar{c}$, the average number of defects per unit (the average of the N c_i values), and whose standard deviation is estimated by $\sqrt{\bar{c}}$. Again the control limits are given by $\bar{c} \pm 3 \sqrt{\bar{c}}$.

EXERCISES

    Exercises 1 to 5 refer to the data of Table 11.1 and Figs. 11.8 and 11.9.

    11.1. Consider samples 76 to 100 as a self-contained group of outcomes. Analyze them for statistical stability with respect to $\bar{x}$ and R.

11.2. As in Exercise 11.1, analyze samples 21 to 40.

11.3. Suppose that samples 21 to 40 were followed directly by samples 76 to 100. Suppose, further, that when sample 40 came on the scene you analyzed sequence 21 to 40 for statistical stability. Interpret the outcomes of samples 76 to 100 as direct successors.

11.4. Suppose that the data of Table 11.1 are normally distributed with mean $\mu = 78.92$ and standard deviation $\sigma = 8.23$ and that the observations constituting samples 74 to 84 are outcomes of random independent sampling from this universe. Do you consider this set of samples consistent with the original universe?   (Use the sample ranges for estimating the variance of samples 74 to 84.)

11.5. On the assumption that samples 74 to 84 represent 55 random independent observations from a normal universe, find the confidence interval for the mean, using four different estimates of σ:

    a. Estimate σ from the sample ranges.
    b. Estimate σ from the sample standard deviations.
    c. Estimate σ from all 55 observations.
    d. Estimate σ from the 11 $\bar{x}$ values.

11.6. Samples of five items are taken from a process at regular intervals. $\bar{x}$ and R are calculated for each sample for a certain quality characteristic x.   The sums of the $\bar{x}$ and R values for the first 25 samples are $\Sigma \bar{x}_i = 358.50$ and $\Sigma R_i = 9.80$.

    a. Compute control limits for the $\bar{x}$ and R charts.
    b. If the specification limits are 14.40 ± 0.45, what conclusions can you draw concerning the ability of the process to produce items within specifications?
    c. What percentage of the items will fall outside specifications if the process is in control (assume normality)?

11.7. The process average has been shown to be 0.03.   Your control chart for fraction defective calls for taking daily samples of 800 items.

    a. What is the chance that, if the process average should suddenly shift to 0.06, you would catch the shift on the first sample after the shift?
    b. What is the expected number of days until the shift will be detected?

11.8. Suppose that the control limits of an $\bar{X}$ chart have been set at 37.06 (*LCL*) and 41.48 (*UCL*) on a certain operation in a textile plant, for samples of 10 items taken at hourly intervals.

    a. If it has been decided to reduce the sample size to four per hour, what should the new control limits be?
    b. If specification limits for the item are 33.00 to 47.00, what per cent defective items will be produced?

11.9. The average fraction defective of a controlled process has been shown to be 0.03.   Your control chart calls for taking daily samples of 400 items.   What is the probability that, if the process average should suddenly shift to 0.06, you would catch the shift:

    a. On the first sample.
    b. On or before the second sample taken after the shift.

11.10. The average demand for a certain spare part, over a long period of time, has been 25 per month.   If 35 units are needed this month, would you conclude that there has been a significant increase in demand, calling for increased supplies?

11.11. Explain the reasoning behind the basic requirement that subgroups should be chosen as homogeneous as possible, and yet differ as much as possible among one another.

11.12. A manufacturer purchases small bolts in cartons that usually contain several thousand bolts. As part of the acceptance procedure for these bolts, 250 bolts are selected at random from each carton and are subjected to visual inspection for certain defects. In a shipment of 10 cartons, the respective percentages of defectives in the samples from each carton are 0, 0, 0.4, 0.8, 0, 2.0, 0.4, 0, 0, and 0.8. Does this shipment of bolts appear to exhibit statistical control with respect to the quality characteristics examined in this inspection?

11.13. Explain:

a. Why a chart of ranges, or a chart for standard deviation, should be used in conjunction with a chart for means.

b. The meanings of chance and assignable causes and the distinction between them.

c. The value of being in a state of statistical control.

11.14. The following are means and ranges of 20 samples of 5 each. The data pertain to the overall lengths of a base manufactured on several similar machines. The measurements are in inches.

Group no.	$\bar{X}$	Range	Group no.	$\bar{X}$	Range
1	0.8372	0.010	11	0.8380	0.006
2	0.8324	0.009	12	0.8322	0.002
3	0.8318	0.008	13	0.8356	0.013
4	0.8344	0.004	14	0.8322	0.005
5	0.8346	0.005	15	0.8306	0.008
6	0.8332	0.011	16	0.8372	0.011
7	0.8340	0.009	17	0.8382	0.006
8	0.8344	0.003	18	0.8346	0.005
9	0.8308	0.002	19	0.8360	0.004
10	0.8350	0.006	20	0.8374	0.006

$$\bar{\bar{X}} = 0.8345 \qquad \bar{R} = 0.0067$$

The above samples were taken every 30 minutes in order of production. The production rate is 400 per hour. Specifications call for a minimum dimension of 0.8200 and a maximum of 0.8400.

a. Does the process appear to be in control? Explain your answer.

b. Regardless of the answer to (a) and assuming control, how many defectives do you expect it to produce during the next 2 hours?

c. If the process average shifts upward to $\bar{X}' = 0.8370$, how long will it take on the average to get a point outside 3-sigma control limits?

d. What is the expected number of defectives produced, under conditions of (c), until a point is found outside control limits?

11.15. Assume that a 3-sigma $\bar{x}$ chart is in operation and that the mean level is m and standard deviation of the individual measurements is σ. Further, let n denote the subgroup size, Δ the interval of time between subgroups, and r the sampling rate equal to n/Δ. Suppose the process level changes from m to m', where $\delta = m' - m > 0$, and is in control at this new level (σ remains the same). Let $T(\delta)$ denote the length of time after the shift until a subgroup average will show a point out of limits, and $N(\delta)$ the number of subgroups until this event occurs (assume that the $\bar{x}$'s are approximately normally distributed).

    a. What is the distribution of $N(\delta)$?
    b. What is $E[N(\delta)]$?
    c. What is $E[T(\delta)]$?
    d. Let $n = 4$, $\sigma = 2$, $\delta = 2$, and $\Delta = 5$. What is $E[T(2)]$?
    e. Keeping n, σ, and δ from (*d*), what should Δ be so that $E[T(2)] = 10$?
    f. Keeping $\Delta = 5$, what should n be so that $E[T(2)] = 10$?
    g. Keeping sampling rate $r = \frac{4}{5}$ fixed, what is the best n and Δ so that $E[T(2)]$ is minimized?
    h. Under the same conditions as (*g*), what is the best n and Δ so that $E[T(4)]$ is minimized? Similarly, what is the best n and Δ so that $E[T(1)]$ is minimized? What conclusions can you draw?

APPENDIX

TABLE A.1
Cumulative Normal Distribution*

$$\Phi(x) = \int_{-\infty}^{x} \frac{1}{\sqrt{2\pi}} e^{-t^2/2} dt$$

x	.00	.01	.02	.03	.04	.05	.06	.07	.08	.09
.0	.5000	.5040	.5080	.5120	.5160	.5199	.5239	.5279	.5319	.5359
.1	.5398	.5438	.5478	.5517	.5557	.5596	.5636	.5675	.5714	.5753
.2	.5793	.5832	.5871	.5910	.5948	.5987	.6026	.6064	.6103	.6141
.3	.6179	.6217	.6255	.6293	.6331	.6368	.6406	.6443	.6480	.6517
.4	.6554	.6591	.6628	.6664	.6700	.6736	.6772	.6808	.6844	.6879
.5	.6915	.6950	.6985	.7019	.7054	.7088	.7123	.7157	.7190	.7224
.6	.7257	.7291	.7324	.7357	.7389	.7422	.7454	.7486	.7517	.7549
.7	.7580	.7611	.7642	.7673	.7704	.7734	.7764	.7794	.7823	.7852
.8	.7881	.7910	.7939	.7967	.7995	.8023	.8051	.8078	.8106	.8133
.9	.8159	.8186	.8212	.8238	.8264	.8289	.8315	.8340	.8365	.8389
1.0	.8413	.8438	.8461	.8485	.8508	.8531	.8554	.8577	.8599	.8621
1.1	.8643	.8665	.8686	.8708	.8729	.8749	.8770	.8790	.8810	.8830
1.2	.8849	.8869	.8888	.8907	.8925	.8944	.8962	.8980	.8997	.9015
1.3	.9032	.9049	.9066	.9082	.9099	.9115	.9131	.9147	.9162	.9177
1.4	.9192	.9207	.9222	.9236	.9251	.9265	.9279	.9292	.9306	.9319
1.5	.9332	.9345	.9357	.9370	.9382	.9394	.9406	.9418	.9429	.9441
1.6	.9452	.9463	.9474	.9484	.9495	.9505	.9515	.9525	.9535	.9545
1.7	.9554	.9564	.9573	.9582	.9591	.9599	.9608	.9616	.9625	.9633
1.8	.9641	.9649	.9656	.9664	.9671	.9678	.9686	.9693	.9699	.9706
1.9	.9713	.9719	.9726	.9732	.9738	.9744	.9750	.9756	.9761	.9767
2.0	.9772	.9778	.9783	.9788	.9793	.9798	.9803	.9808	.9812	.9817
2.1	.9821	.9826	.9830	.9834	.9838	.9842	.9846	.9850	.9854	.9857
2.2	.9861	.9864	.9868	.9871	.9875	.9878	.9881	.9884	.9887	.9890
2.3	.9893	.9896	.9898	.9901	.9904	.9906	.9909	.9911	.9913	.9916
2.4	.9918	.9920	.9922	.9925	.9927	.9929	.9931	.9932	.9934	.9936
2.5	.9938	.9940	.9941	.9943	.9945	.9946	.9948	.9949	.9951	.9952
2.6	.9953	.9955	.9956	.9957	.9959	.9960	.9961	.9962	.9963	.9964
2.7	.9965	.9966	.9967	.9968	.9969	.9970	.9971	.9972	.9973	.9974
2.8	.9974	.9975	.9976	.9977	.9977	.9978	.9979	.9979	.9980	.9981
2.9	.9981	.9982	.9982	.9983	.9984	.9984	.9985	.9985	.9986	.9986
3.0	.9987	.9987	.9987	.9988	.9988	.9989	.9989	.9989	.9990	.9990
3.1	.9990	.9991	.9991	.9991	.9992	.9992	.9992	.9992	.9993	.9993
3.2	.9993	.9993	.9994	.9994	.9994	.9994	.9994	.9995	.9995	.9995
3.3	.9995	.9995	.9995	.9996	.9996	.9996	.9996	.9996	.9996	.9997
3.4	.9997	.9997	.9997	.9997	.9997	.9997	.9997	.9997	.9997	.9998

x	1.282	1.645	1.960	2.326	2.576	3.090	3.291	3.891	4.417
$\Phi(x)$	.90	.95	.975	.99	.995	.999	.9995	.99995	.999995
$2[1 - \Phi(x)]$	.20	.10	.05	.02	.01	.002	.001	.0001	.00001

* From Alexander M. Mood, "Introduction to the Theory of Statistics," McGraw-Hill Book Company, Inc., New York, 1950. Used by permission.

TABLE A.2

Cumulative Poisson Distribution*

c' or np'	0	1	2	3	4	5	6	7	8	9
0.02	980	1,000								
0.04	961	999	1,000							
0.06	942	998	1,000							
0.08	923	997	1,000							
0.10	905	995	1,000							
0.15	861	990	999	1,000						
0.20	819	982	999	1,000						
0.25	779	974	998	1,000						
0.30	741	963	996	1,000						
0.35	705	951	994	1,000						
0.40	670	938	992	999	1,000					
0.45	638	925	989	999	1,000					
0.50	607	910	986	998	1,000					
0.55	577	894	982	998	1,000					
0.60	549	878	977	997	1,000					
0.65	522	861	972	996	999	1,000				
0.70	497	844	966	994	999	1,000				
0.75	472	827	959	993	999	1,000				
0.80	449	809	953	991	999	1,000				
0.85	427	791	945	989	998	1,000				
0.90	407	772	937	987	998	1,000				
0.95	387	754	929	984	997	1,000				
1.00	368	736	920	981	996	999	1,000			
1.1	333	699	900	974	995	999	1,000			
1.2	301	663	879	966	992	998	1,000			
1.3	273	627	857	957	989	998	1,000			
1.4	247	592	833	946	986	997	999	1,000		
1.5	223	558	809	934	981	996	999	1,000		
1.6	202	525	783	921	976	994	999	1,000		
1.7.	183	493	757	907	970	992	998	1,000		
1.8	165	463	731	891	964	990	997	999	1,000	
1.9	150	434	704	875	956	987	997	999	1,000	
2.0	135	406	677	857	947	983	995	999	1,000	

* From E. L. Grant, "Statistical Quality Control," 2d ed., McGraw-Hill Book Company, Inc., New York, 1952. Used by permission.

TABLE A.2

Cumulative Poisson Distribution (*Continued*)

c / c' or np'	0	1	2	3	4	5	6	7	8	9
2.2	111	355	623	819	928	975	993	998	1,000	
2.4	091	308	570	779	904	964	988	997	999	1,000
2.6	074	267	518	736	877	951	983	995	999	1,000
2.8	061	231	469	692	848	935	976	992	998	999
3.0	050	199	423	647	815	916	966	988	996	999
3.2	041	171	380	603	781	895	955	983	994	998
3.4	033	147	340	558	744	871	942	977	992	997
3.6	027	126	303	515	706	844	927	969	988	996
3.8	022	107	269	473	668	816	909	960	984	994
4.0	018	092	238	433	629	785	889	949	979	992
4.2	015	078	210	395	590	753	867	936	972	989
4.4	012	066	185	359	551	720	844	921	964	985
4.6	010	056	163	326	513	686	818	905	955	980
4.8	008	048	143	294	476	651	791	887	944	975
5.0	007	040	125	265	440	616	762	867	932	968
5.2	006	034	109	238	406	581	732	845	918	960
5.4	005	029	095	213	373	546	702	822	903	951
5.6	004	024	082	191	342	512	670	797	886	941
5.8	003	021	072	170	313	478	638	771	867	929
6.0	002	017	062	151	285	446	606	744	847	916

	10	11	12	13	14	15	16
2.8	1,000						
3.0	1,000						
3.2	1,000						
3.4	999	1,000					
3.6	999	1,000					
3.8	998	999	1,000				
4.0	997	999	1,000				
4.2	996	999	1,000				
4.4	994	998	999	1,000			
4.6	992	997	999	1,000			
4.8	990	996	999	1,000			
5.0	986	995	998	999	1,000		
5.2	982	993	997	999	1,000		
5.4	977	990	996	999	1,000		
5.6	972	988	995	998	999	1,000	
5.8	965	984	993	997	999	1,000	
6.0	957	980	991	996	999	999	1,000

Cumulative Poisson Distribution (*Continued*)

c / c' or np'	0	1	2	3	4	5	6	7	8	9
6.2	002	015	054	134	259	414	574	716	826	902
6.4	002	012	046	119	235	384	542	687	803	886
6.6	001	010	040	105	213	355	511	658	780	869
6.8	001	009	034	093	192	327	480	628	755	850
7.0	001	007	030	082	173	301	450	599	729	830
7.2	001	006	025	072	156	276	420	569	703	810
7.4	001	005	022	063	140	253	392	539	676	788
7.6	001	004	019	055	125	231	365	510	648	765
7.8	000	004	016	048	112	210	338	481	620	741
8.0	000	003	014	042	100	191	313	453	593	717
8.5	000	002	009	030	074	150	256	386	523	653
9.0	000	001	006	021	055	116	207	324	456	587
9.5	000	001	004	015	040	089	165	269	392	522
10.0	000	000	003	010	029	067	130	220	333	458

	10	11	12	13	14	15	16	17	18	19
6.2	949	975	989	995	998	999	1,000			
6.4	939	969	986	994	997	999	1,000			
6.6	927	963	982	992	997	999	999	1,000		
6.8	915	955	978	990	996	998	999	1,000		
7.0	901	947	973	987	994	998	999	1,000		
7.2	887	937	967	984	993	997	999	999	1,000	
7.4	871	926	961	980	991	996	998	999	1,000	
7.6	854	915	954	976	989	995	998	999	1,000	
7.8	835	902	945	971	986	993	997	999	1,000	
8.0	816	888	936	966	983	992	996	998	999	1,000
8.5	763	849	909	949	973	986	993	997	999	999
9.0	706	803	876	926	959	978	989	995	998	999
9.5	645	752	836	898	940	967	982	991	996	998
10.0	583	697	792	864	917	951	973	986	993	997

	20	21	22
8.5	1,000		
9.0	1,000		
9.5	999	1,000	
10.0	998	999	1,000

10	09	73	25	33	76	52	01	35	86	34	67	35	48	76	80	95	90	91	17	39	29	27	49	45
37	54	20	48	05	64	89	47	42	96	24	80	52	40	37	20	63	61	04	02	00	82	29	16	65
08	42	26	89	53	19	64	50	93	03	23	20	90	25	60	15	95	33	47	64	35	08	03	36	06
99	01	90	25	29	09	37	67	07	15	38	31	13	11	65	88	67	67	43	97	04	43	62	76	59
12	80	79	99	70	80	15	73	61	47	64	03	23	66	53	98	95	11	68	77	12	17	17	68	33
66	06	57	47	17	34	07	27	68	50	36	69	73	61	70	65	81	33	98	85	11	19	92	91	70
31	06	01	08	05	45	57	18	24	06	35	30	34	26	14	86	79	90	74	39	23	40	30	97	32
85	26	97	76	02	02	05	16	56	92	68	66	57	48	18	73	05	38	52	47	18	62	38	85	79
63	57	33	21	35	05	32	54	70	48	90	55	35	75	48	28	46	82	87	09	83	49	12	56	24
73	79	64	57	53	03	52	96	47	78	35	80	83	42	82	60	93	52	03	44	35	27	38	84	35
98	52	01	77	67	14	90	56	86	07	22	10	94	05	58	60	97	09	34	33	50	50	07	39	98
11	80	50	54	31	39	80	82	77	32	50	72	56	82	48	29	40	52	42	01	52	77	56	78	51
83	45	29	96	34	06	28	89	80	83	13	74	67	00	78	18	47	54	06	10	68	71	17	78	17
88	68	54	02	00	86	50	75	84	01	36	76	66	79	51	90	36	47	64	93	29	60	91	10	62
99	59	46	73	48	87	51	76	49	69	91	82	60	89	28	93	78	56	13	68	23	47	83	41	13
65	48	11	76	74	17	46	85	09	50	58	04	77	69	74	73	03	95	71	86	40	21	81	65	44
80	12	43	56	35	17	72	70	80	15	45	31	82	23	74	21	11	57	82	53	14	38	55	37	63
74	35	09	98	17	77	40	27	72	14	43	23	60	02	10	45	52	16	42	37	96	28	60	26	55
69	91	62	68	03	66	25	22	91	48	36	93	68	72	03	76	62	11	39	90	94	40	05	64	18
09	89	32	05	05	14	22	56	85	14	46	42	75	67	88	96	29	77	88	22	54	38	21	45	98
91	49	91	45	23	68	47	92	76	86	46	16	28	35	54	94	75	08	99	23	37	08	92	00	48
80	33	69	45	98	26	94	03	68	58	70	29	73	41	35	53	14	03	33	40	42	05	08	23	41
44	10	48	19	49	85	15	74	79	54	32	97	92	65	75	57	60	04	08	81	22	22	20	64	13
12	55	07	37	42	11	10	00	20	40	12	86	07	46	97	96	64	48	94	39	28	70	72	58	15
63	60	64	93	29	16	50	53	44	84	40	21	95	25	63	43	65	17	70	82	07	20	73	17	90
61	19	69	04	46	26	45	74	77	74	51	92	43	37	29	65	39	45	95	93	42	58	26	05	27
15	47	44	52	66	95	27	07	99	53	59	36	78	38	48	82	39	61	01	18	33	21	15	94	66
94	55	72	85	73	67	89	75	43	87	54	62	24	44	31	91	19	04	25	92	92	92	74	59	73
42	48	11	62	13	97	34	40	87	21	16	86	84	87	67	03	07	11	20	59	25	70	14	66	70
23	52	37	83	17	73	20	88	98	37	68	93	59	14	16	26	25	22	96	63	05	52	28	25	62
04	49	35	24	94	75	24	63	38	24	45	86	25	10	25	61	96	27	93	35	65	33	71	24	72
00	54	99	76	54	64	05	18	81	59	96	11	96	38	96	54	69	28	23	91	23	28	72	95	29
35	96	31	53	07	26	89	80	93	54	33	35	13	54	62	77	97	45	00	24	90	10	33	93	33
59	80	80	83	91	45	42	72	68	42	83	60	94	97	00	13	02	12	48	92	78	56	52	01	06
46	05	88	52	36	01	39	09	22	86	77	28	14	40	77	93	91	08	36	47	70	61	74	29	41
32	17	90	05	97	87	37	92	52	41	05	56	70	70	07	86	74	31	71	57	85	39	41	18	38
69	23	46	14	06	20	11	74	52	04	15	95	66	00	00	18	74	39	24	23	97	11	89	63	38
19	56	54	14	30	01	75	87	53	79	40	41	92	15	85	66	67	43	68	06	84	96	28	52	07
45	15	51	49	38	19	47	60	72	46	43	66	79	45	43	59	04	79	00	33	20	82	66	95	41
94	86	43	19	94	36	16	81	08	51	34	88	88	15	53	01	54	03	54	56	05	01	45	11	76
98	08	62	48	26	45	24	02	84	04	44	99	90	88	96	39	09	47	34	07	35	44	13	18	80
33	18	51	62	32	41	94	15	09	49	89	43	54	85	81	88	69	54	19	94	37	54	87	30	43
80	95	10	04	06	96	38	27	07	74	20	15	12	33	87	25	01	62	52	98	94	62	46	11	71
79	75	24	91	40	71	96	12	82	96	69	86	10	25	91	74	85	22	05	39	00	38	75	95	79
18	63	33	25	37	98	14	50	65	71	31	01	02	46	74	05	45	56	14	27	77	93	89	19	36
74	02	94	39	02	77	55	73	22	70	97	79	01	71	19	52	52	75	80	21	80	81	45	17	48
54	17	84	56	11	80	99	33	71	43	05	33	51	29	69	56	12	71	92	55	36	04	09	03	24
11	66	44	98	83	52	07	98	48	27	59	38	17	15	39	09	97	33	34	40	88	46	12	33	56
48	32	47	79	28	31	24	96	47	10	02	29	53	68	70	32	30	75	75	46	15	02	00	99	94
69	07	49	41	38	87	63	79	19	76	35	58	40	44	01	10	51	82	16	15	01	84	87	69	38

* From W. J. Dixon and F. J. Massey, Jr., "Introduction to Statistical Analysis," McGraw-Hill Book Company, Inc., New York, 1957. Reproduced with permission from tables of the RAND Corporation.

09	18	82	00	97	32	82	53	95	27	04	22	08	63	04	83	38	98	73	74	64	27	85	80	44
90	04	58	54	97	51	98	15	06	54	94	93	88	19	97	91	87	07	61	50	68	47	66	46	59
73	18	95	02	07	47	67	72	62	69	62	29	06	44	64	27	12	46	70	18	41	36	18	27	60
75	76	87	64	90	20	97	18	17	49	90	42	91	22	72	95	37	50	58	71	93	82	34	31	78
54	01	64	40	56	66	28	13	10	03	00	68	22	73	98	20	71	45	32	95	07	70	61	78	13
08	35	86	99	10	78	54	24	27	85	13	66	15	88	73	04	61	89	75	53	31	22	30	84	20
28	30	60	32	64	81	33	31	05	91	40	51	00	78	93	32	60	46	04	75	94	11	90	18	40
53	84	08	62	33	81	59	41	36	28	51	21	59	02	90	28	46	66	87	95	77	76	22	07	91
91	75	75	37	41	61	61	36	22	69	50	26	39	02	12	55	78	17	65	14	83	48	34	70	55
89	41	59	26	94	00	39	75	83	91	12	60	71	76	46	48	94	97	23	06	94	54	13	74	08
77	51	30	38	20	86	83	42	99	01	68	41	48	27	74	51	90	81	39	80	72	89	35	55	07
19	50	23	71	74	69	97	92	02	88	55	21	02	97	73	74	28	77	52	51	65	34	46	74	15
21	81	85	93	13	93	27	88	17	57	05	68	67	31	56	07	08	28	50	46	31	85	33	84	52
51	47	46	64	99	68	10	72	36	21	94	04	99	13	45	42	83	60	91	91	08	00	74	54	49
99	55	96	83	31	62	53	52	41	70	69	77	71	28	30	74	81	97	81	42	43	86	07	28	34
33	71	34	80	07	93	58	47	28	69	51	92	66	47	21	58	30	32	98	22	93	17	49	39	72
85	27	48	68	93	11	30	32	92	70	28	83	43	41	37	73	51	59	04	00	71	14	84	36	43
84	13	38	96	40	44	03	55	21	66	73	85	27	00	91	61	22	26	05	61	62	32	71	84	23
56	73	21	62	34	17	39	59	61	31	10	12	39	16	22	85	49	65	75	60	81	60	41	88	80
65	13	85	68	06	87	64	88	52	61	34	31	36	58	61	45	87	52	10	69	85	64	44	72	77
38	00	10	21	76	81	71	91	17	11	71	60	29	29	37	74	21	96	40	49	65	58	44	96	98
37	40	29	63	97	01	30	47	75	86	56	27	11	00	86	47	32	46	26	05	40	03	03	74	38
97	12	54	03	48	87	08	33	14	17	21	81	53	92	50	75	23	76	20	47	15	50	12	95	78
21	82	64	11	34	47	14	33	40	72	64	63	88	59	02	49	13	90	64	41	03	85	65	45	52
73	13	54	27	42	95	71	90	90	35	85	79	47	42	96	08	78	98	81	56	64	69	11	92	02
07	63	87	79	29	03	06	11	80	72	96	20	74	41	56	23	82	19	95	38	04	71	36	69	94
60	52	88	34	41	07	95	41	98	14	59	17	52	06	95	05	53	35	21	39	61	21	20	64	55
83	59	63	56	55	06	95	89	29	83	05	12	80	97	19	77	43	35	37	83	92	30	15	04	98
10	85	06	27	46	99	59	91	05	07	13	49	90	63	19	53	07	57	18	39	06	41	01	93	62
39	82	09	89	52	43	62	26	31	47	64	42	18	08	14	43	80	00	93	51	31	02	47	31	67
59	58	00	64	78	75	56	97	88	00	88	83	55	44	86	23	76	80	61	56	04	11	10	84	08
38	50	80	73	41	23	79	34	87	63	90	82	29	70	22	17	71	90	42	07	95	95	44	99	53
30	69	27	06	68	94	68	81	61	27	56	19	68	00	91	82	06	76	34	00	05	46	26	92	00
65	44	39	56	59	18	28	82	74	37	49	63	22	40	41	08	33	76	56	76	96	29	99	08	36
27	26	75	02	64	13	19	27	22	94	07	47	74	46	06	17	98	54	89	11	97	34	13	03	58
91	30	70	69	91	19	07	22	42	10	36	69	95	37	28	28	82	53	57	93	28	97	66	62	52
68	43	49	46	88	84	47	31	36	22	62	12	69	84	08	12	84	38	25	90	09	81	59	31	46
48	90	81	58	77	54	74	52	45	91	35	70	00	47	54	83	82	45	26	92	54	13	05	51	60
06	91	34	51	97	42	67	27	86	01	11	88	30	95	28	63	01	19	89	01	14	97	44	03	44
10	45	51	60	19	14	21	03	37	12	91	34	23	78	21	88	32	58	08	51	43	66	77	08	83
12	88	39	73	43	65	02	76	11	84	04	28	50	13	92	17	97	41	50	77	90	71	22	67	69
21	77	83	09	76	38	80	73	69	61	31	64	94	20	96	63	28	10	20	23	08	81	64	74	49
19	52	35	95	15	65	12	25	96	59	86	28	36	82	58	69	57	21	37	98	16	43	59	15	29
67	24	55	26	70	35	58	31	65	63	79	24	68	66	86	76	46	33	42	22	26	65	59	08	02
60	58	44	73	77	07	50	03	79	92	45	13	42	65	29	26	76	08	36	37	41	32	64	43	44
53	85	34	13	77	36	06	69	48	50	58	83	87	38	59	49	36	47	33	31	96	24	04	36	42
24	63	73	87	36	74	38	48	93	42	52	62	30	79	92	12	36	91	86	01	03	74	28	38	73
83	08	01	24	51	38	99	22	28	15	07	75	95	17	77	97	37	72	75	85	51	97	23	78	67
16	44	42	43	34	36	15	19	90	73	27	49	37	09	39	85	13	03	25	52	54	84	65	47	59
60	79	01	81	57	57	17	86	57	62	11	16	17	85	76	45	81	95	29	79	65	13	00	48	60

TABLE A.3
Random Numbers (*Continued*)

```
03 99 11 04 61   93 71 61 68 94   66 08 32 46 53   84 60 95 82 32   88 61 81 91 61
38 55 59 55 54   32 88 65 97 80   08 35 56 08 60   29 73 54 77 62   71 29 92 38 53
17 54 67 37 04   92 05 24 62 15   55 12 12 92 81   59 07 60 79 36   27 95 45 89 09
32 64 35 28 61   95 81 90 68 31   00 91 19 89 36   76 35 59 37 79   80 86 30 05 14
69 57 26 87 77   39 51 03 59 05   14 06 04 06 19   29 54 96 96 16   33 56 46 07 80

24 12 26 65 91   27 69 90 64 94   14 84 54 66 72   61 95 87 71 00   90 89 97 57 54
61 19 63 02 31   92 96 26 17 73   41 83 95 53 82   17 26 77 09 43   78 03 87 02 67
30 53 22 17 04   10 27 41 22 02   39 68 52 33 09   10 06 16 88 29   55 98 66 64 85
03 78 89 75 99   75 86 72 07 17   74 41 65 31 66   35 20 83 33 74   87 53 90 88 23
48 22 86 33 79   85 78 34 76 19   53 15 26 74 33   35 66 35 29 72   16 81 86 03 11

60 36 59 46 53   35 07 53 39 49   42 61 42 92 97   01 91 82 83 16   98 95 37 32 31
83 79 94 24 02   56 62 33 44 42   34 99 44 13 74   70 07 11 47 36   09 95 81 80 65
32 96 00 74 05   36 40 98 32 32   99 38 54 16 00   11 13 30 75 86   15 91 70 62 53
19 32 25 38 45   57 62 05 26 06   66 49 76 86 46   78 13 86 65 59   19 64 09 94 13
11 22 09 47 47   07 39 93 74 08   48 50 92 39 29   27 48 24 54 76   85 24 43 51 59

31 75 15 72 60   68 98 00 53 39   15 47 04 83 55   88 65 12 25 96   03 15 21 91 21
88 49 29 93 82   14 45 40 45 04   20 09 49 89 77   74 84 39 34 13   22 10 97 85 08
30 93 44 77 44   07 48 18 38 28   73 78 80 65 33   28 59 72 04 05   94 20 52 03 80
22 88 84 88 93   27 49 99 87 48   60 53 04 51 28   74 02 28 46 17   82 03 71 02 68
78 21 21 69 93   35 90 29 13 86   44 37 21 54 86   65 74 11 40 14   87 48 13 72 20

41 84 98 45 47   46 85 05 23 26   34 67 75 83 00   74 91 06 43 45   19 32 58 15 49
46 35 23 30 49   69 24 89 34 60   45 30 50 75 21   61 31 83 18 55   14 41 37 09 51
11 08 79 62 94   14 01 33 17 92   59 74 76 72 77   76 50 33 45 13   39 66 37 75 44
52 70 10 83 37   56 30 38 73 15   16 52 06 96 76   11 65 49 98 93   02 18 16 81 61
57 27 53 68 98   81 30 44 85 85   68 65 22 73 76   92 85 25 58 66   88 44 80 35 84

20 85 77 31 56   70 28 42 43 26   79 37 59 52 20   01 15 96 32 67   10 62 24 83 91
15 63 38 49 24   90 41 59 36 14   33 52 12 66 65   55 82 34 76 41   86 22 53 17 04
92 69 44 82 97   39 90 40 21 15   59 58 94 90 67   66 82 14 15 75   49 76 70 40 37
77 61 31 90 19   88 15 20 00 80   20 55 49 14 09   96 27 74 82 57   50 81 69 76 16
38 68 83 24 86   45 13 46 35 45   59 40 47 20 59   43 94 75 16 80   43 85 25 96 93

25 16 30 18 89   70 01 41 50 21   41 29 06 73 12   71 85 71 59 57   68 97 11 14 03
65 25 10 76 29   37 23 93 32 95   05 87 00 11 19   92 78 42 63 40   18 47 76 56 22
36 81 54 36 25   18 63 73 75 09   82 44 49 90 05   04 92 17 37 01   14 70 79 39 97
64 39 71 16 92   05 32 78 21 62   20 24 78 17 59   45 19 72 53 32   83 74 52 25 67
04 51 52 56 24   95 09 66 79 46   48 46 08 55 58   15 19 11 87 82   16 93 03 33 61

83 76 16 08 73   43 25 38 41 45   60 83 32 59 83   01 29 14 13 49   20 36 80 71 26
14 38 70 63 45   80 85 40 92 79   43 52 90 63 18   38 38 47 47 61   41 19 63 74 80
51 32 19 22 46   80 08 87 70 74   88 72 25 67 36   66 16 44 94 31   66 91 93 16 78
72 47 20 00 08   80 89 01 80 02   94 81 33 19 00   54 15 58 34 36   35 35 25 41 31
05 46 65 53 06   93 12 81 84 64   74 45 79 05 61   72 84 81 18 34   79 98 26 84 16

39 52 87 24 84   82 47 42 55 93   48 54 53 52 47   18 61 91 36 74   18 61 11 92 41
81 61 61 87 11   53 34 24 42 76   75 12 21 17 24   74 62 77 37 07   58 31 91 59 97
07 58 61 61 20   82 64 12 28 20   92 90 41 31 41   32 39 21 97 63   61 19 96 79 40
90 76 70 42 35   13 57 41 72 00   69 90 26 37 42   78 46 42 25 01   18 62 79 08 72
40 18 82 81 93   29 59 38 86 27   94 97 21 15 98   62 09 53 67 87   00 44 15 89 97

34 41 48 21 57   86 88 75 50 87   19 15 20 00 23   12 30 28 07 83   32 62 46 86 91
63 43 97 53 63   44 98 91 68 22   36 02 40 08 67   76 37 84 16 05   65 96 17 34 88
67 04 90 90 70   93 39 94 55 47   94 45 87 42 84   05 04 14 98 07   20 28 83 40 60
79 49 50 41 46   52 16 29 02 86   54 15 83 42 43   46 97 83 54 82   59 36 29 59 38
91 70 43 05 52   04 73 72 10 31   75 05 19 30 29   47 66 56 43 82   99 78 29 34 78
```

```
94 01 54 68 74    32 44 44 82 77    59 82 09 61 63    64 65 42 58 43    41 14 54 28 20
74 10 88 82 22    88 57 07 40 15    25 70 49 10 35    01 75 51 47 50    48 96 83 86 03
62 88 08 78 73    95 16 05 92 21    22 30 49 03 14    72 87 71 73 34    39 28 30 41 49
11 74 81 21 02    80 58 04 18 67    17 71 05 96 21    06 55 40 78 50    73 95 07 95 52
17 94 40 56 00    60 47 80 33 43    25 85 25 89 05    57 21 63 96 18    49 85 69 93 26

66 06 74 27 92    95 04 35 26 80    46 78 05 64 87    09 97 15 94 81    37 00 62 21 86
54 24 49 10 30    45 54 77 08 18    59 84 99 61 69    61 45 92 16 47    87 41 71 71 98
30 94 55 75 89    31 73 25 72 60    47 67 00 76 54    46 37 62 53 66    94 74 64 95 80
69 17 03 74 03    86 99 59 03 07    94 30 47 18 03    26 82 50 55 11    12 45 99 13 14
08 34 58 89 75    35 84 18 57 71    08 10 55 99 87    87 11 22 14 76    14 71 37 11 81

27 76 74 35 84    85 30 18 89 77    29 49 06 97 14    73 03 54 12 07    74 69 90 93 10
13 02 51 43 38    54 06 61 52 43    47 72 46 67 33    47 43 14 39 05    31 04 85 66 99
80 21 73 62 92    98 52 52 43 35    24 43 22 48 96    43 27 75 88 74    11 46 61 60 82
10 87 56 20 04    90 39 16 11 05    57 41 10 63 68    53 85 63 07 43    08 67 08 47 41
54 12 75 73 26    26 62 91 90 87    24 47 28 87 79    30 54 02 78 86    61 73 27 54 54

60 31 14 28 24    37 30 14 26 78    45 99 04 32 42    17 37 45 20 03    70 70 77 02 14
49 73 97 14 84    92 00 39 80 86    76 66 87 32 09    59 20 21 19 73    02 90 23 32 50
78 62 65 15 94    16 45 39 46 14    39 01 49 70 66    83 01 20 98 32    25 57 17 76 28
66 69 21 39 86    99 83 70 05 82    81 23 24 49 87    09 50 49 64 12    90 19 37 95 68
44 07 12 80 91    07 36 29 77 03    76 44 74 25 37    98 52 49 78 31    65 70 40 95 14

41 46 88 51 49    49 55 41 79 94    14 92 43 96 50    95 29 40 05 56    70 48 10 69 05
94 55 93 75 59    49 67 85 31 19    70 31 20 56 82    66 98 63 40 99    74 47 42 07 40
41 61 57 03 60    64 11 45 86 60    90 85 06 46 18    80 62 05 17 90    11 43 63 80 72
50 27 39 31 13    41 79 48 68 61    24 78 18 96 83    55 41 18 56 67    77 53 59 98 92
41 39 68 05 04    90 67 00 82 89    40 90 20 50 69    95 08 30 67 83    28 10 25 78 16

25 80 72 42 60    71 52 97 89 20    72 68 20 73 85    90 72 65 71 66    98 88 40 85 83
06 17 09 79 65    88 30 29 80 41    21 44 34 18 08    68 98 48 36 20    89 74 79 88 82
60 80 85 44 44    74 41 28 11 05    01 17 62 88 38    36 42 11 64 89    18 05 95 10 61
80 94 04 48 93    10 40 83 62 22    80 58 27 19 44    92 63 84 03 33    67 05 41 60 67
19 51 69 01 20    46 75 97 16 43    13 17 75 52 92    21 03 68 28 08    77 50 19 74 27

49 38 65 44 80    26 60 42 35 54    21 78 54 11 01    91 17 81 01 74    29 42 09 04 38
06 31 28 89 40    15 99 56 93 21    47 45 86 48 09    98 18 98 18 51    29 65 18 42 15
60 94 20 03 07    11 89 79 26 74    40 40 56 80 32    96 71 75 42 44    10 70 14 13 93
92 32 99 89 32    78 28 44 63 47    71 20 99 20 61    39 44 89 31 36    25 72 20 85 64
77 93 66 35 74    31 38 45 19 24    85 56 12 96 71    58 13 71 78 20    22 75 13 65 18

38 10 17 77 56    11 65 71 38 97    95 88 95 70 67    47 64 81 38 85    70 66 99 34 06
39 64 16 94 57    91 33 92 25 02    92 61 38 97 19    11 94 75 62 03    19 32 42 05 04
84 05 44 04 55    99 39 66 36 80    67 66 76 06 31    69 18 19 68 45    38 52 51 16 00
47 46 80 35 77    57 64 96 32 66    24 70 07 15 94    14 00 42 31 53    69 24 90 57 47
43 32 13 13 70    28 97 72 38 96    76 47 96 85 62    62 34 20 75 89    08 89 90 59 85

64 28 16 18 26    18 55 56 49 37    13 17 33 33 65    78 85 11 64 99    87 06 41 30 75
66 84 77 04 95    32 35 00 29 85    86 71 63 87 46    26 31 37 74 63    55 38 77 26 81
72 46 13 32 30    21 52 95 34 24    92 58 10 22 62    78 43 86 62 76    18 39 67 35 38
21 03 29 10 50    13 05 81 62 18    12 47 05 65 00    15 29 27 61 39    59 52 65 21 13
95 36 26 70 11    06 65 11 61 36    01 01 60 08 57    55 01 85 63 74    35 82 47 17 08

40 71 29 73 80    10 40 45 54 52    34 03 06 07 26    75 21 11 02 71    36 63 36 84 24
58 27 56 17 64    97 58 65 47 16    50 25 94 63 45    87 19 54 60 92    26 78 76 09 39
89 51 41 17 88    68 22 42 34 17    73 95 97 61 45    30 34 24 02 77    11 04 97 20 49
15 47 25 06 69    48 13 98 67 32    46 87 43 70 88    73 46 50 98 19    58 86 93 52 20
12 12 08 61 24    51 24 74 43 02    60 88 35 21 09    21 43 73 67 86    49 22 67 78 37
```

```
19 61 27 84 30    11 66 19 47 70    77 60 36 56 69    86 86 81 26 65    30 01 27 59 89
39 14 17 74 00    28 00 06 42 38    73 25 87 17 94    31 34 02 62 56    66 45 33 70 16
64 75 68 04 57    08 74 71 28 36    03 46 95 06 78    03 27 44 34 23    66 67 78 25 56
92 90 15 18 78    56 44 12 29 98    29 71 83 84 47    06 45 32 53 11    07 56 55 37 71
03 55 19 00 70    09 48 39 40 50    45 93 81 81 35    36 90 84 33 21    11 07 35 18 03

98 88 46 62 09    06 83 05 36 56    14 66 35 63 46    71 43 00 49 09    19 81 80 57 07
27 36 98 68 82    53 47 30 75 41    53 63 37 08 63    03 74 81 28 22    19 36 04 90 88
59 06 67 59 74    63 33 52 04 83    43 51 43 74 81    58 27 82 69 67    49 32 54 39 51
91 64 79 37 83    64 16 94 90 22    98 58 80 94 95    49 82 95 90 68    38 83 10 48 38
83 60 59 24 19    39 54 20 77 72    71 56 87 56 73    35 18 58 97 59    44 90 17 42 91

24 89 58 85 30    70 77 43 54 39    46 75 87 04 72    70 20 79 26 75    91 62 36 12 75
35 72 02 65 56    95 59 62 00 94    73 75 08 57 88    34 26 40 17 03    46 83 36 52 48
14 14 15 34 10    38 64 90 63 43    57 25 66 13 42    72 70 97 53 18    90 37 93 75 62
27 41 67 56 70    92 17 67 25 35    93 11 95 60 77    06 88 61 82 44    92 34 43 13 74
82 07 10 74 29    81 00 74 77 49    40 74 45 69 74    23 33 68 88 21    53 84 11 05 36

21 44 58 27 93    24 83 19 32 41    14 19 97 62 68    70 88 36 80 02    03 82 91 74 43
72 51 37 64 00    52 22 59 23 48    62 30 89 84 81    29 74 43 31 65    33 14 16 10 20
71 47 94 50 27    76 16 05 74 11    13 78 01 36 32    52 30 87 77 62    88 87 43 36 97
83 21 05 14 66    09 08 85 03 95    26 74 30 53 06    21 70 67 00 01    99 43 98 07 67
68 74 99 51 48    94 89 77 86 36    96 75 00 90 24    94 53 89 11 43    96 69 36 18 86

05 18 47 57 63    47 07 58 81 58    05 31 35 34 39    14 90 80 88 30    60 09 62 15 51
13 65 16 25 46    96 89 22 52 40    47 51 15 84 83    87 34 27 88 18    07 85 53 92 69
00 56 62 12 20    00 29 22 40 69    25 07 22 95 19    52 54 85 40 91    21 28 22 12 96
50 95 81 76 95    58 07 26 89 90    60 32 99 59 55    71 58 66 34 17    35 94 76 78 07
57 62 16 45 47    46 85 03 79 81    38 52 70 90 37    64 75 60 33 24    04 98 68 36 66

09 28 22 58 44    79 13 97 84 35    35 42 84 35 61    69 79 96 33 14    12 99 19 35 16
23 39 49 42 06    93 43 23 78 36    94 91 92 68 46    02 55 57 44 10    94 91 54 81 99
05 28 03 74 70    93 62 20 43 45    15 09 21 95 10    18 09 41 66 13    78 23 45 00 01
95 49 19 79 76    38 30 63 21 92    82 63 95 46 24    72 43 49 26 06    23 19 17 46 93
78 52 10 01 04    18 24 87 55 83    90 32 65 07 85    54 03 46 62 51    35 77 41 46 92

96 34 54 45 79    85 93 24 40 53    75 70 42 08 40    86 58 38 39 44    52 45 67 37 66
77 96 33 11 51    32 36 49 16 91    47 35 74 03 38    23 43 52 40 65    08 45 89 53 66
07 52 01 12 94    23 23 80 17 48    41 69 06 73 28    54 81 43 77 77    10 05 74 23 32
38 42 30 23 09    70 70 38 57 36    46 14 81 42 58    29 23 61 21 52    05 08 86 58 25
02 46 36 55 33    21 19 96 05 55    33 92 80 18 17    07 39 68 92 15    30 72 22 21 02

15 88 09 22 61    17 29 28 81 90    61 78 14 88 98    92 52 52 12 83    88 58 16 00 98
71 92 60 08 19    59 14 40 02 24    30 57 09 01 94    18 32 90 69 99    26 85 71 92 38
64 42 52 81 08    16 55 41 60 16    00 04 28 32 29    10 33 33 61 68    65 61 79 48 34
79 78 22 39 24    49 44 03 04 32    81 07 73 15 43    95 21 66 48 65    13 65 85 10 81
35 33 77 45 38    44 55 36 46 72    90 96 04 18 49    93 86 54 46 08    93 17 63 48 51

05 24 92 93 29    19 71 59 40 82    14 73 88 66 67    43 70 86 63 54    93 69 22 55 27
56 46 39 93 80    38 79 38 57 74    19 05 61 39 39    46 06 22 76 47    66 14 66 32 10
96 29 63 31 21    54 19 63 41 08    75 81 48 59 86    71 17 11 51 02    28 99 26 31 65
98 38 03 62 69    60 01 40 72 01    62 44 84 63 85    42 17 58 83 50    46 18 24 91 26
52 56 76 43 50    16 31 55 39 69    80 39 58 11 14    54 35 86 45 78    47 26 91 57 47

78 49 89 08 30    25 95 59 92 36    43 28 69 10 64    99 96 99 51 44    64 42 47 73 77
49 55 32 42 41    08 15 08 95 35    08 70 39 10 41    77 32 38 10 79    45 12 79 36 86
32 15 10 70 75    83 15 51 02 52    73 10 08 86 18    23 89 18 74 18    45 41 72 02 68
11 31 45 03 63    26 86 02 77 99    49 41 68 35 34    19 18 70 80 59    76 67 70 21 10
12 36 47 12 10    87 05 25 02 41    90 78 59 78 89    81 39 95 81 30    64 43 90 56 14
```

TABLE A.4
Chi-square Distribution*

Value of α

Value of n	0.01	0.02	0.05	0.10	0.20	0.30	0.50	0.70	0.80	0.90	0.95	0.98	0.99
1	0.000157	0.000628	0.00393	0.0158	0.0642	0.148	0.455	1.074	1.642	2.706	3.841	5.412	6.635
2	0.0201	0.0404	0.103	0.211	0.446	0.713	1.386	2.408	3.219	4.605	5.991	7.824	9.210
3	0.115	0.185	0.352	0.584	1.005	1.424	2.366	3.665	4.642	6.251	7.815	9.837	11.341
4	0.297	0.429	0.711	1.064	1.649	2.195	3.357	4.878	5.989	7.779	9.488	11.668	13.277
5	0.554	0.752	1.145	1.610	2.343	3.000	4.351	6.064	7.289	9.236	11.070	13.388	15.086
6	0.872	1.134	1.635	2.204	3.070	3.828	5.348	7.231	8.558	10.645	12.592	15.033	16.812
7	1.239	1.564	2.167	2.833	3.822	4.671	6.346	8.383	9.803	12.017	14.067	16.622	18.475
8	1.646	2.032	2.733	3.490	4.594	5.527	7.344	9.524	11.030	13.362	15.507	18.168	20.090
9	2.088	2.532	3.325	4.168	5.380	6.393	8.343	10.656	12.242	14.684	16.919	19.679	21.666
10	2.558	3.059	3.940	4.865	6.179	7.267	9.342	11.781	13.442	15.987	18.307	21.161	23.209
11	3.053	3.609	4.575	5.578	6.989	8.148	10.341	12.899	14.631	17.275	19.675	22.618	24.725
12	3.571	4.178	5.226	6.304	7.807	9.034	11.340	14.011	15.812	18.549	21.026	24.054	26.217
13	4.107	4.765	5.892	7.042	8.634	9.926	12.340	15.119	16.985	19.812	22.362	25.472	27.688
14	4.660	5.368	6.571	7.790	9.467	10.821	13.339	16.222	18.151	21.064	23.685	26.873	29.141
15	5.229	5.985	7.261	8.547	10.307	11.721	14.339	17.322	19.311	22.307	24.996	28.259	30.578
16	5.812	6.614	7.962	9.312	11.152	12.624	15.338	18.418	20.465	23.542	26.296	29.633	32.000
17	6.408	7.255	8.672	10.085	12.002	13.531	16.338	19.511	21.615	24.769	27.587	30.995	33.409
18	7.015	7.906	9.390	10.865	12.857	14.440	17.338	20.601	22.760	25.989	28.869	32.346	34.805
19	7.633	8.567	10.117	11.651	13.716	15.352	18.338	21.689	23.900	27.204	30.144	33.687	36.191
20	8.260	9.237	10.851	12.443	14.578	16.266	19.337	22.775	25.038	28.412	31.410	35.020	37.566
21	8.897	9.915	11.591	13.240	15.445	17.182	20.337	23.858	26.171	29.615	32.671	36.343	38.932
22	9.542	10.600	12.338	14.041	16.314	18.101	21.337	24.939	27.301	30.813	33.924	37.659	40.289
23	10.196	11.293	13.091	14.848	17.187	19.021	22.337	26.018	28.429	32.007	35.172	38.968	41.638
24	10.856	11.992	13.848	15.659	18.062	19.943	23.337	27.096	29.553	33.196	36.415	40.270	42.980
25	11.524	12.697	14.611	16.473	18.940	20.867	24.337	28.172	30.675	34.382	37.652	41.566	44.314
26	12.198	13.409	15.379	17.292	19.820	21.792	25.336	29.246	31.795	35.563	38.885	42.856	45.642
27	12.879	14.125	16.151	18.114	20.703	22.719	26.336	30.319	32.912	36.741	40.113	44.140	46.963
28	13.565	14.847	16.928	18.939	21.588	23.647	27.336	31.391	34.027	37.916	41.337	45.419	48.278
29	14.256	15.574	17.708	19.768	22.475	24.577	28.336	32.461	35.139	39.087	42.557	46.693	49.588
30	14.953	16.306	18.493	20.599	23.364	25.508	29.336	33.530	36.250	40.256	43.773	47.962	50.892

If X_n^2 has a chi-square distribution, this table gives the value of $X_{\alpha,n}^2$ for which $P(X_n^2 \leq X_{\alpha,n}^2) = \alpha$.

* Abridged from Table IV of Ronald A. Fisher and Frank Yates, "Statistical Tables for Biological, Agricultural and Medical Research," Oliver & Boyd Ltd., Edinburgh, 1962. Used by permission.

TABLE A.5
Student's *t* Distribution*

df	Percentile point						
	70	80	90	95	97.5	99	99.5
1	.73	1.38	3.08	6.31	12.71	31.82	63.66
2	.62	1.06	1.89	2.92	4.30	6.96	9.92
3	.58	.98	1.64	2.35	3.18	4.54	5.84
4	.57	.94	1.53	2.13	2.78	3.75	4.60
5	.56	.92	1.48	2.01	2.57	3.36	4.03
6	.55	.91	1.44	1.94	2.45	3.14	3.71
7	.55	.90	1.42	1.90	2.36	3.00	3.50
8	.55	.89	1.40	1.86	2.31	2.90	3.36
9	.54	.88	1.38	1.83	2.26	2.82	3.25
10	.54	.88	1.37	1.81	2.23	2.76	3.17
11	.54	.88	1.36	1.80	2.20	2.72	3.11
12	.54	.87	1.36	1.78	2.18	2.68	3.06
13	.54	.87	1.35	1.77	2.16	2.65	3.01
14	.54	.87	1.34	1.76	2.14	2.62	2.98
15	.54	.87	1.34	1.75	2.13	2.60	2.95
16	.54	.86	1.34	1.75	2.12	2.58	2.92
17	.53	.86	1.33	1.74	2.11	2.57	2.90
18	.53	.86	1.33	1.73	2.10	2.55	2.88
19	.53	.86	1.33	1.73	2.09	2.54	2.86
20	.53	.86	1.32	1.72	2.09	2.53	2.84
21	.53	.86	1.32	1.72	2.08	2.52	2.83
22	.53	.86	1.32	1.72	2.07	2.51	2.82
23	.53	.86	1.32	1.71	2.07	2.50	2.81
24	.53	.86	1.32	1.71	2.06	2.49	2.80
25	.53	.86	1.32	1.71	2.06	2.48	2.79
26	.53	.86	1.32	1.71	2.06	2.48	2.78
27	.53	.86	1.31	1.70	2.05	2.47	2.77
28	.53	.86	1.31	1.70	2.05	2.47	2.76
29	.53	.85	1.31	1.70	2.04	2.46	2.76
30	.53	.85	1.31	1.70	2.04	2.46	2.75
40	.53	.85	1.30	1.68	2.02	2.42	2.70
50	.53	.85	1.30	1.67	2.01	2.40	2.68
60	.53	.85	1.30	1.67	2.00	2.39	2.66
80	.53	.85	1.29	1.66	1.99	2.37	2.64
100	.53	.84	1.29	1.66	1.98	2.36	2.63
200	.52	.84	1.29	1.65	1.97	2.34	2.60
500	.52	.84	1.28	1.65	1.96	2.33	2.59
∞	.52	.84	1.28	1.64	1.96	2.33	2.58

* From B. J. Winer, "Statistical Principles in Experimental Design," McGraw-Hill Book Company, Inc., New York, 1962.   Used by permission.

df for denom.	$1 - \alpha$	df for numerator											
		1	2	3	4	5	6	7	8	9	10	11	12
1	.75	5.83	7.50	8.20	8.58	8.82	8.98	9.10	9.19	9.26	9.32	9.36	9.41
	.90	39.9	49.5	53.6	55.8	57.2	58.2	58.9	59.4	59.9	60.2	60.5	60.7
	.95	161	200	216	225	230	234	237	239	241	242	243	244
2	.75	2.57	3.00	3.15	3.23	3.28	3.31	3.34	3.35	3.37	3.38	3.39	3.39
	.90	8.53	9.00	9.16	9.24	9.29	9.33	9.35	9.37	9.38	9.39	9.40	9.41
	.95	18.5	19.0	19.2	19.2	19.3	19.3	19.4	19.4	19.4	19.4	19.4	19.4
	.99	98.5	99.0	99.2	99.2	99.3	99.3	99.4	99.4	99.4	99.4	99.4	99.4
3	.75	2.02	2.28	2.36	2.39	2.41	2.42	2.43	2.44	2.44	2.44	2.45	2.45
	.90	5.54	5.46	5.39	5.34	5.31	5.28	5.27	5.25	5.24	5.23	5.22	5.22
	.95	10.1	9.55	9.28	9.12	9.10	8.94	8.89	8.85	8.81	8.79	8.76	8.74
	.99	34.1	30.8	29.5	28.7	28.2	27.9	27.7	27.5	27.3	27.2	27.1	27.1
4	.75	1.81	2.00	2.05	2.06	2.07	2.08	2.08	2.08	2.08	2.08	2.08	2.08
	.90	4.54	4.32	4.19	4.11	4.05	4.01	3.98	3.95	3.94	3.92	3.91	3.90
	.95	7.71	6.94	6.59	6.39	6.26	6.16	6.09	6.04	6.00	5.96	5.94	5.91
	.99	21.2	18.0	16.7	16.0	15.5	15.2	15.0	14.8	14.7	14.5	14.4	14.4
5	.75	1.69	1.85	1.88	1.89	1.89	1.89	1.89	1.89	1.89	1.89	1.89	1.89
	.90	4.06	3.78	3.62	3.52	3.45	3.40	3.37	3.34	3.32	3.30	3.28	3.27
	.95	6.61	5.79	5.41	5.19	5.05	4.95	4.88	4.82	4.77	4.74	4.71	4.68
	.99	16.3	13.3	12.1	11.4	11.0	10.7	10.5	10.3	10.2	10.1	9.96	9.89
6	.75	1.62	1.76	1.78	1.79	1.79	1.78	1.78	1.77	1.77	1.77	1.77	1.77
	.90	3.78	3.46	3.29	3.18	3.11	3.05	3.01	2.98	2.96	2.94	2.92	2.90
	.95	5.99	5.14	4.76	4.53	4.39	4.28	4.21	4.15	4.10	4.06	4.03	4.00
	.99	13.7	10.9	9.78	9.15	8.75	8.47	8.26	8.10	7.98	7.87	7.79	7.72
7	.75	1.57	1.70	1.72	1.72	1.71	1.71	1.70	1.70	1.69	1.69	1.69	1.68
	.90	3.59	3.26	3.07	2.96	2.88	2.83	2.78	2.75	2.72	2.70	2.68	2.67
	.95	5.59	4.74	4.35	4.12	3.97	3.87	3.79	3.73	3.68	3.64	3.60	3.57
	.99	12.2	9.55	8.45	7.85	7.46	7.19	6.99	6.84	6.72	6.62	6.54	6.47
8	.75	1.54	1.66	1.67	1.66	1.66	1.65	1.64	1.64	1.64	1.63	1.63	1.62
	.90	3.46	3.11	2.92	2.81	2.73	2.67	2.62	2.59	2.56	2.54	2.52	2.50
	95	5.32	4.46	4.07	3.84	3.69	3.58	3.50	3.44	3.39	3.35	3.31	3.28
	.99	11.3	8.65	7.59	7.01	6.63	6.37	6.18	6.03	5.91	5.81	5.73	5.67
9	.75	1.51	1.62	1.63	1.63	1.62	1.61	1.60	1.60	1.59	1.59	1.58	1.58
	.90	3.36	3.01	2.81	2.69	2.61	2.55	2.51	2.47	2.44	2.42	2.40	2.38
	.95	5.12	4.26	3.86	3.63	3.48	3.37	3.29	3.23	3.18	3.14	3.10	3.07
	.99	10.6	8.02	6.99	6.42	6.06	5.80	5.61	5.47	5.35	5.26	5.18	5.11
10	.75	1.49	1.60	1.60	1.59	1.59	1.58	1.57	1.56	1.56	1.55	1.55	1.54
	.90	3.28	2.92	2.73	2.61	2.52	2.46	2.41	2.38	2.35	2.32	2.30	2.28
	.95	4.96	4.10	3.71	3.48	3.33	3.22	3.14	3.07	3.02	2.98	2.94	2.91
	.99	10.0	7.56	6.55	5.99	5.64	5.39	5.20	5.06	4.94	4.85	4.77	4.71
11	.75	1.47	1.58	1.58	1.57	1.56	1.55	1.54	1.53	1.53	1.52	1.52	1.51
	.90	3.23	2.86	2.66	2.54	2.45	2.39	2.34	2.30	2.27	2.25	2.23	2.21
	.95	4.84	3.98	3.59	3.36	3.20	3.09	3.01	2.95	2.90	2.85	2.82	2.79
	.99	9.65	7.21	6.22	5.67	5.32	5.07	4.89	4.74	4.63	4.54	4.46	4.40
12	.75	1.46	1.56	1.56	1.55	1.54	1.53	1.52	1.51	1.51	1.50	1.50	1.49
	.90	3.18	2.81	2.61	2.48	2.39	2.33	2.28	2.24	2.21	2.19	2.17	2.15
	.95	4.75	3.89	3.49	3.26	3.11	3.00	2.91	2.85	2.80	2.75	2.72	2.69
	.99	9.33	6.93	5.95	5.41	5.06	4.82	-4.64	4.50	4.39	4.30	4.22	4.16

F Distribution*

					df for numerator								$1 - \alpha$	df for denom.
15	20	24	30	40	50	60	100	120	200	500	∞			
9.49	9.58	9.63	9.67	9.71	9.74	9.76	9.78	9.80	9.82	9.84	9.85	.75		
61.2	61.7	62.0	62.3	62.5	62.7	62.8	63.0	63.1	63.2	63.3	63.3	.90	1
246	248	249	250	251	252	252	253	253	254	254	254	.95		
3.41	3.43	3.43	3.44	3.45	3.45	3.46	3.47	3.47	3.48	3.48	3.48	.75		
9.42	9.44	9.45	9.46	9.47	9.47	9.47	9.48	9.48	9.49	9.49	9.49	.90	2
19.4	19.4	19.5	19.5	19.5	19.5	19.5	19.5	19.5	19.5	19.5	19.5	.95		
99.4	99.4	99.5	99.5	99.5	99.5	99.5	99.5	99.5	99.5	99.5	99.5	.99		
2.46	2.46	2.46	2.47	2.47	2.47	2.47	2.47	2.47	2.47	2.47	2.47	.75		
5.20	5.18	5.18	5.17	5.16	5.15	5.15	5.14	5.14	5.14	5.14	5.13	.90	3
8.70	8.66	8.64	8.62	8.59	8.58	8.57	8.55	8.55	8.54	8.53	8.53	.95		
26.9	26.7	26.6	26.5	26.4	26.4	26.3	26.2	26.2	26.2	26.1	26.1	.99		
2.08	2.08	2.08	2.08	2.08	2.08	2.08	2.08	2.08	2.08	2.08	2.08	.75		
3.87	3.84	3.83	3.82	3.80	3.80	3.79	3.78	3.78	3.77	3.76	3.76	.90	
5.86	5.80	5.77	5.75	5.72	5.70	5.69	5.66	5.66	5.65	5.64	5.63	.95	4
14.2	14.0	13.9	13.8	13.7	13.7	13.7	13.6	13.6	13.5	13.5	13.5	.99		
1.89	1.88	1.88	1.88	1.88	1.88	1.87	1.87	1.87	1.87	1.87	1.87	.75		
3.24	3.21	3.19	3.17	3.16	3.15	3.14	3.13	3.12	3.12	3.11	3.10	.90	
4.62	4.56	4.53	4.50	4.46	4.44	4.43	4.41	4.40	4.39	4.37	4.36	.95	5
9.72	9.55	9.47	9.38	9.29	9.24	9.20	9.13	9.11	9.08	9.04	9.02	.99		
1.76	1.76	1.75	1.75	1.75	1.75	1.74	1.74	1.74	1.74	1.74	1.74	.75		
2.87	2.84	2.82	2.80	2.78	2.77	2.76	2.75	2.74	2.73	2.73	2.72	.90	6
3.94	3.87	3.84	3.81	3.77	3.75	3.74	3.71	3.70	3.69	3.68	3.67	.95		
7.56	7.40	7.31	7.23	7.14	7.09	7.06	6.99	6.97	6.93	6.90	6.88	.99		
1.68	1.67	1.67	1.66	1.66	1.66	1.65	1.65	1.65	1.65	1.65	1.65	.75		
2.63	2.59	2.58	2.56	2.54	2.52	2.51	2.50	2.49	2.48	2.48	2.47	.90	7
3.51	3.44	3.41	3.38	3.34	3.32	3.30	3.27	3.27	3.25	3.24	3.23	.95		
6.31	6.16	6.07	5.99	5.91	5.86	5.82	5.75	5.74	5.70	5.67	5.65	.99		
1.62	1.61	1.60	1.60	1.59	1.59	1.59	1.58	1.58	1.58	1.58	1.58	.75		
2.46	2.42	2.40	2.38	2.36	2.35	2.34	2.32	2.32	2.31	2.30	2.29	.90	8
3.22	3.15	3.12	3.08	3.04	3.02	3.01	2.97	2.97	2.95	2.94	2.93	.95		
5.52	5.36	5.28	5.20	5.12	5.07	5.03	4.96	4.95	4.91	4.88	4.86	.99		
1.57	1.56	1.56	1.55	1.55	1.54	1.54	1.53	1.53	1.53	1.53	1.53	.75		
2.34	2.30	2.28	2.25	2.23	2.22	2.21	2.19	2.18	2.17	2.17	2.16	.90	9
3.01	2.94	2.90	2.86	2.83	2.80	2.79	2.76	2.75	2.73	2.72	2.71	.95		
4.96	4.81	4.73	4.65	4.57	4.52	4.48	4.42	4.40	4.36	4.33	4.31	.99		
1.53	1.52	1.52	1.51	1.51	1.50	1.50	1.49	1.49	1.49	1.48	1.48	.75		
2.24	2.20	2.18	2.16	2.13	2.12	2.11	2.09	2.08	2.07	2.06	2.06	.90	10
2.85	2.77	2.74	2.70	2.66	2.64	2.62	2.59	2.58	2.56	2.55	2.54	.95		
4.56	4.41	4.33	4.25	4.17	4.12	4.08	4.01	4.00	3.96	3.93	3.91	.99		
1.50	1.49	1.49	1.48	1.47	1.47	1.47	1.46	1.46	1.46	1.45	1.45	.75		
2.17	2.12	2.10	2.08	2.05	2.04	2.03	2.00	2.00	1.99	1.98	1.97	.90	11
2.72	2.65	2.61	2.57	2.53	2.51	2.49	2.46	2.45	2.43	2.42	2.40	.95		
4.25	4.10	4.02	3.94	3.86	3.81	3.78	3.71	3.69	3.66	3.62	3.60	.99		
1.48	1.47	1.46	1.45	1.45	1.44	1.44	1.43	1.43	1.43	1.42	1.42	.75		
2.10	2.06	2.04	2.01	1.99	1.97	1.96	1.94	1.93	1.92	1.91	1.90	.90	12
2.62	2.54	2.51	2.47	2.43	2.40	2.38	2.35	2.34	2.32	2.31	2.30	.95		
4.01	3.86	3.78	3.70	3.62	3.57	3.54	3.47	3.45	3.41	3.38	3.36	.99		

df for denom.	$1 - \alpha$	df for numerator											
		1	2	3	4	5	6	7	8	9	10	11	12
13	.75	1.45	1.54	1.54	1.53	1.52	1.51	1.50	1.49	1.49	1.48	1.47	1.47
	.90	3.14	2.76	2.56	2.43	2.35	2.28	2.23	2.20	2.16	2.14	2.12	2.10
	.95	4.67	3.81	3.41	3.18	3.03	2.92	2.83	2.77	2.71	2.67	2.63	2.60
	.99	9.07	6.70	5.74	5.21	4.86	4.62	4.44	4.30	4.19	4.10	4.02	3.96
14	.75	1.44	1.53	1.53	1.52	1.51	1.50	1.48	1.48	1.47	1.46	1.46	1.45
	.90	3.10	2.73	2.52	2.39	2.31	2.24	2.19	2.15	2.12	2.10	2.08	2.05
	.95	4.60	3.74	3.34	3.11	2.96	2.85	2.76	2.70	2.65	2.60	2.57	2.53
	.99	8.86	6.51	5.56	5.04	4.69	4.46	4.28	4.14	4.03	3.94	3.86	3.80
15	.75	1.43	1.52	1.52	1.51	1.49	1.48	1.47	1.46	1.46	1.45	1.44	1.44
	.90	3.07	2.70	2.49	2.36	2.27	2.21	2.16	2.12	2.09	2.06	2.04	2.02
	.95	4.54	3.68	3.29	3.06	2.90	2.79	2.71	2.64	2.59	2.54	2.51	2.48
	.99	8.68	6.36	5.42	4.89	4.56	4.32	4.14	4.00	3.89	3.80	3.73	3.67
16	.75	1.42	1.51	1.51	1.50	1.48	1.48	1.47	1.46	1.45	1.45	1.44	1.44
	.90	3.05	2.67	2.46	2.33	2.24	2.18	2.13	2.09	2.06	2.03	2.01	1.99
	.95	4.49	3.63	3.24	3.01	2.85	2.74	2.66	2.59	2.54	2.49	2.46	2.42
	.99	8.53	6.23	5.29	4.77	4.44	4.20	4.03	3.89	3.78	3.69	3.62	3.55
17	.75	1.42	1.51	1.50	1.49	1.47	1.46	1.45	1.44	1.43	1.43	1.42	1.41
	.90	3.03	2.64	2.44	2.31	2.22	2.15	2.10	2.06	2.03	2.00	1.98	1.96
	.95	4.45	3.59	3.20	2.96	2.81	2.70	2.61	2.55	2.49	2.45	2.41	2.38
	.99	8.40	6.11	5.18	4.67	4.34	4.10	3.93	3.79	3.68	3.59	3.52	3.46
18	.75	1.41	1.50	1.49	1.48	1.46	1.45	1.44	1.43	1.42	1.42	1.41	1.40
	.90	3.01	2.62	2.42	2.29	2.20	2.13	2.08	2.04	2.00	1.98	1.96	1.93
	.95	4.41	3.55	3.16	2.93	2.77	2.66	2.58	2.51	2.46	2.41	2.37	2.34
	.99	8.29	6.01	5.09	4.58	4.25	4.01	3.84	3.71	3.60	3.51	3.43	3.37
19	.75	1.41	1.49	1.49	1.47	1.46	1.44	1.43	1.42	1.41	1.41	1.40	1.40
	.90	2.99	2.61	2.40	2.27	2.18	2.11	2.06	2.02	1.98	1.96	1.94	1.91
	.95	4.38	3.52	3.13	2.90	2.74	2.63	2.54	2.48	2.42	2.38	2.34	2.31
	.99	8.18	5.93	5.01	4.50	4.17	3.94	3.77	3.63	3.52	3.43	3.36	3.30
20	.75	1.40	1.49	1.48	1.46	1.45	1.44	1.42	1.42	1.41	1.40	1.39	1.39
	.90	2.97	2.59	2.38	2.25	2.16	2.09	2.04	2.00	1.96	1.94	1.92	1.89
	.95	4.35	3.49	3.10	2.87	2.71	2.60	2.51	2.45	2.39	2.35	2.31	2.28
	.99	8.10	5.85	4.94	4.43	4.10	3.87	3.70	3.56	3.46	3.37	3.29	3.23
22	.75	1.40	1.48	1.47	1.45	1.44	1.42	1.41	1.40	1.39	1.39	1.38	1.37
	.90	2.95	2.56	2.35	2.22	2.13	2.06	2.01	1.97	1.93	1.90	1.88	1.86
	.95	4.30	3.44	3.05	2.82	2.66	2.55	2.46	2.40	2.34	2.30	2.26	2.23
	.99	7.95	5.72	4.82	4.31	3.99	3.76	3.59	3.45	3.35	3.26	3.18	3.12
24	.75	1.39	1.47	1.46	1.44	1.43	1.41	1.40	1.39	1.38	1.38	1.37	1.36
	.90	2.93	2.54	2.33	2.19	2.10	2.04	1.98	1.94	1.91	1.88	1.85	1.83
	.95	4.26	3.40	3.01	2.78	2.62	2.51	2.42	2.36	2.30	2.25	2.21	2.18
	.99	7.82	5.61	4.72	4.22	3.90	3.67	3.50	3.36	3.26	3.17	3.09	3.03
26	.75	1.38	1.46	1.45	1.44	1.42	1.41	1.40	1.39	1.37	1.37	1.36	1.35
	.90	2.91	2.52	2.31	2.17	2.08	2.01	1.96	1.92	1.88	1.86	1.84	1.81
	.95	4.23	3.37	2.98	2.74	2.59	2.47	2.39	2.32	2.27	2.22	2.18	2.15
	.99	7.72	5.53	4.64	4.14	3.82	3.59	3.42	3.29	3.18	3.09	3.02	2.96
28	.75	1.38	1.46	1.45	1.43	1.41	1.40	1.39	1.38	1.37	1.36	1.35	1.34
	.90	2.89	2.50	2.29	2.16	2.06	2.00	1.94	1.90	1.87	1.84	1.81	1.79
	.95	4.20	3.34	2.95	2.71	2.56	2.45	2.36	2.29	2.24	2.19	2.15	2.12
	.99	7.64	5.45	4.57	4.07	3.75	3.53	3.36	3.23	3.12	3.03	2.96	2.90

F Distribution (Continued)*

					df for numerator									1 − α	df for denom.
15	20	24	30	40	50	60	100	120	200	500	∞				
1.46	1.45	1.44	1.43	1.42	1.42	1.42	1.41	1.41	1.40	1.40	1.40			.75	
2.05	2.01	1.98	1.96	1.93	1.92	1.90	1.88	1.88	1.86	1.85	1.85			.90	13
2.53	2.46	2.42	2.38	2.34	2.31	2.30	2.26	2.25	2.23	2.22	2.21			.95	
3.82	3.66	3.59	3.51	3.43	3.38	3.34	3.27	3.25	3.22	3.19	3.17			.99	
1.44	1.43	1.42	1.41	1.41	1.40	1.40	1.39	1.39	1.39	1.38	1.38			.75	
2.01	1.96	1.94	1.91	1.89	1.87	1.86	1.83	1.83	1.82	1.80	1.80			.90	
2.46	2.39	2.35	2.31	2.27	2.24	2.22	2.19	2.18	2.16	2.14	2.13			.95	14
3.66	3.51	3.43	3.35	3.27	3.22	3.18	3.11	3.09	3.06	3.03	3.00			.99	
1.43	1.41	1.41	1.40	1.39	1.39	1.38	1.38	1.37	1.37	1.36	1.36			.75	
1.97	1.92	1.90	1.87	1.85	1.83	1.82	1.79	1.79	1.77	1.76	1.76			.90	15
2.40	2.33	2.29	2.25	2.20	2.18	2.16	2.12	2.11	2.10	2.08	2.07			.95	
3.52	3.37	3.29	3.21	3.13	3.08	3.05	2.98	2.96	2.92	2.89	2.87			.99	
1.41	1.40	1.39	1.38	1.37	1.37	1.36	1.36	1.35	1.35	1.34	1.34			.75	
1.94	1.89	1.87	1.84	1.81	1.79	1.78	1.76	1.75	1.74	1.73	1.72			.90	16
2.35	2.28	2.24	2.19	2.15	2.12	2.11	2.07	2.06	2.04	2.02	2.01			.95	
3.41	3.26	3.18	3.10	3.02	2.97	2.93	2.86	2.84	2.81	2.78	2.75			.99	
1.40	1.39	1.38	1.37	1.36	1.35	1.35	1.34	1.34	1.34	1.33	1.33			.75	
1.91	1.86	1.84	1.81	1.78	1.76	1.75	1.73	1.72	1.71	1.69	1.69			.90	17
2.31	2.23	2.19	2.15	2.10	2.08	2.06	2.02	2.01	1.99	1.97	1.96			.95	
3.31	3.16	3.08	3.00	2.92	2.87	2.83	2.76	2.75	2.71	2.68	2.65			.99	
1.39	1.38	1.37	1.36	1.35	1.34	1.34	1.33	1.33	1.32	1.32	1.32			.75	
1.89	1.84	1.81	1.78	1.75	1.74	1.72	1.70	1.69	1.68	1.67	1.66			.90	18
2.27	2.19	2.15	2.11	2.06	2.04	2.02	1.98	1.97	1.95	1.93	1.92			.95	
3.23	3.08	3.00	2.92	2.84	2.78	2.75	2.68	2.66	2.62	2.59	2.57			.99	
1.38	1.37	1.36	1.35	1.34	1.33	1.33	1.32	1.32	1.31	1.31	1.30			.75	
1.86	1.81	1.79	1.76	1.73	1.71	1.70	1.67	1.67	1.65	1.64	1.63			.90	19
2.23	2.16	2.11	2.07	2.03	2.00	1.98	1.94	1.93	1.91	1.89	1.88			.95	
3.15	3.00	2.92	2.84	2.76	2.71	2.67	2.60	2.58	2.55	2.51	2.49			.99	
1.37	1.36	1.35	1.34	1.33	1.33	1.32	1.31	1.31	1.30	1.30	1.29			.75	
1.84	1.79	1.77	1.74	1.71	1.69	1.68	1.65	1.64	1.63	1.62	1.61			.90	20
2.20	2.12	2.08	2.04	1.99	1.97	1.95	1.91	1.90	1.88	1.86	1.84			.95	
3.09	2.94	2.86	2.78	2.69	2.64	2.61	2.54	2.52	2.48	2.44	2.42			.99	
1.36	1.34	1.33	1.32	1.31	1.31	1.30	1.30	1.30	1.29	1.29	1.28			.75	
1.81	1.76	1.73	1.70	1.67	1.65	1.64	1.61	1.60	1.59	1.58	1.57			.90	22
2.15	2.07	2.03	1.98	1.94	1.91	1.89	1.85	1.84	1.82	1.80	1.78			.95	
2.98	2.83	2.75	2.67	2.58	2.53	2.50	2.42	2.40	2.36	2.33	2.31			.99	
1.35	1.33	1.32	1.31	1.30	1.29	1.29	1.28	1.28	1.27	1.27	1.26			.75	
1.78	1.73	1.70	1.67	1.64	1.62	1.61	1.58	1.57	1.56	1.54	1.53			.90	24
2.11	2.03	1.98	1.94	1.89	1.86	1.84	1.80	1.79	1.77	1.75	1.73			.95	
2.89	2.74	2.66	2.58	2.49	2.44	2.40	2.33	2.31	2.27	2.24	2.21			.99	
1.34	1.32	1.31	1.30	1.29	1.28	1.28	1.26	1.26	1.26	1.25	1.25			.75	
1.76	1.71	1.68	1.65	1.61	1.59	1.58	1.55	1.54	1.53	1.51	1.50			.90	26
2.07	1.99	1.95	1.90	1.85	1.82	1.80	1.76	1.75	1.73	1.71	1.69			.95	
2.81	2.66	2.58	2.50	2.42	2.36	2.33	2.25	2.23	2.19	2.16	2.13			.99	
1.33	1.31	1.30	1.29	1.28	1.27	1.27	1.26	1.25	1.25	1.24	1.24			.75	
1.74	1.69	1.66	1.63	1.59	1.57	1.56	1.53	1.52	1.50	1.49	1.48			.90	28
2.04	1.96	1.91	1.87	1.82	1.79	1.77	1.73	1.71	1.69	1.67	1.65			.95	
2.75	2.60	2.52	2.44	2.35	2.30	2.26	2.19	2.17	2.13	2.09	2.06			.99	

df for denom.	$1 - \alpha$	df for numerator											
		1	2	3	4	5	6	7	8	9	10	11	12
30	.75	1.38	1.45	1.44	1.42	1.41	1.39	1.38	1.37	1.36	1.35	1.35	1.34
	.90	2.88	2.49	2.28	2.14	2.05	1.98	1.93	1.88	1.85	1.82	1.79	1.77
	.95	4.17	3.32	2.92	2.69	2.53	2.42	2.33	2.27	2.21	2.16	2.13	2.09
	.99	7.56	5.39	4.51	4.02	3.70	3.47	3.30	3.17	3.07	2.98	2.91	2.84
40	.75	1.36	1.44	1.42	1.40	1.39	1.37	1.36	1.35	1.34	1.33	1.32	1.31
	.90	2.84	2.44	2.23	2.09	2.00	1.93	1.87	1.83	1.79	1.76	1.73	1.71
	.95	4.08	3.23	2.84	2.61	2.45	2.34	2.25	2.18	2.12	2.08	2.04	2.00
	.99	7.31	5.18	4.31	3.83	3.51	3.29	3.12	2.99	2.89	2.80	2.73	2.66
60	.75	1.35	1.42	1.41	1.38	1.37	1.35	1.33	1.32	1.31	1.30	1.29	1.29
	.90	2.79	2.39	2.18	2.04	1.95	1.87	1.82	1.77	1.74	1.71	1.68	1.66
	.95	4.00	3.15	2.76	2.53	2.37	2.25	2.17	2.10	2.04	1.99	1.95	1.92
	.99	7.08	4.98	4.13	3.65	3.34	3.12	2.95	2.82	2.72	2.63	2.56	2.50
120	.75	1.34	1.40	1.39	1.37	1.35	1.33	1.31	1.30	1.29	1.28	1.27	1.26
	.90	2.75	2.35	2.13	1.99	1.90	1.82	1.77	1.72	1.68	1.65	1.62	1.60
	.95	3.92	3.07	2.68	2.45	2.29	2.17	2.09	2.02	1.96	1.91	1.87	1.83
	.99	6.85	4.79	3.95	3.48	3.17	2.96	2.79	2.66	2.56	2.47	2.40	2.34
200	.75	1.33	1.39	1.38	1.36	1.34	1.32	1.31	1.29	1.28	1.27	1.26	1.25
	.90	2.73	2.33	2.11	1.97	1.88	1.80	1.75	1.70	1.66	1.63	1.60	1.57
	.95	3.89	3.04	2.65	2.42	2.26	2.14	2.06	1.98	1.93	1.88	1.84	1.80
	.99	6.76	4.71	3.88	3.41	3.11	2.89	2.73	2.60	2.50	2.41	2.34	2.27
∞	.75	1.32	1.39	1.37	1.35	1.33	1.31	1.29	1.28	1.27	1.25	1.24	1.24
	.90	2.71	2.30	2.08	1.94	1.85	1.77	1.72	1.67	1.63	1.60	1.57	1.55
	.95	3.84	3.00	2.60	2.37	2.21	2.10	2.01	1.94	1.88	1.83	1.79	1.75
	.99	6.63	4.61	3.78	3.32	3.02	2.80	2.64	2.51	2.41	2.32	2.25	2.18

* From B. J. Winer, "Statistical Principles in Experimental Design," McGraw- and H. O. Hartley, eds., "Biometrika Tables for Statisticians," 2d ed., vol. 1, Cam- mission of E. S. Pearson and the trustees of *Biometrika*.

F Distribution (*Continued*)*

df for numerator													
15	20	24	30	40	50	60	100	120	200	500	∞	$1 - \alpha$	df for denom.
1.32	1.30	1.29	1.28	1.27	1.26	1.26	1.25	1.24	1.24	1.23	1.23	.75	
1.72	1.67	1.64	1.61	1.57	1.55	1.54	1.51	1.50	1.48	1.47	1.46	.90	30
2.01	1.93	1.89	1.84	1.79	1.76	1.74	1.70	1.68	1.66	1.64	1.62	.95	
2.70	2.55	2.47	2.39	2.30	2.25	2.21	2.13	2.11	2.07	2.03	2.01	.99	
1.30	1.28	1.26	1.25	1.24	1.23	1.22	1.21	1.21	1.20	1.19	1.19	.75	
1.66	1.61	1.57	1.54	1.51	1.48	1.47	1.43	1.42	1.41	1.39	1.38	.90	40
1.92	1.84	1.79	1.74	1.69	1.66	1.64	1.59	1.58	1.55	1.53	1.51	.95	
2.52	2.37	2.29	2.20	2.11	2.06	2.02	1.94	1.92	1.87	1.83	1.80	.99	
1.27	1.25	1.24	1.22	1.21	1.20	1.19	1.17	1.17	1.16	1.15	1.15	.75	
1.60	1.54	1.51	1.48	1.44	1.41	1.40	1.36	1.35	1.33	1.31	1.29	.90	60
1.84	1.75	1.70	1.65	1.59	1.56	1.53	1.48	1.47	1.44	1.41	1.39	.95	
2.35	2.20	2.12	2.03	1.94	1.88	1.84	1.75	1.73	1.68	1.63	1.60	.99	
1.24	1.22	1.21	1.19	1.18	1.17	1.16	1.14	1.13	1.12	1.11	1.10	.75	
1.55	1.48	1.45	1.41	1.37	1.34	1.32	1.27	1.26	1.24	1.21	1.19	.90	120
1.75	1.66	1.61	1.55	1.50	1.46	1.43	1.37	1.35	1.32	1.28	1.25	.95	
2.19	2.03	1.95	1.86	1.76	1.70	1.66	1.56	1.53	1.48	1.42	1.38	.99	
1.23	1.21	1.20	1.18	1.16	1.14	1.12	1.11	1.10	1.09	1.08	1.06	.75	
1.52	1.46	1.42	1.38	1.34	1.31	1.28	1.24	1.22	1.20	1.17	1.14	.90	200
1.72	1.62	1.57	1.52	1.46	1.41	1.39	1.32	1.29	1.26	1.22	1.19	.95	
2.13	1.97	1.89	1.79	1.69	1.63	1.58	1.48	1.44	1.39	1.33	1.28	.99	
1.22	1.19	1.18	1.16	1.14	1.13	1.12	1.09	1.08	1.07	1.04	1.00	.75	
1.49	1.42	1.38	1.34	1.30	1.26	1.24	1.18	1.17	1.13	1.08	1.00	.90	∞
1.67	1.57	1.52	1.46	1.39	1.35	1.32	1.24	1.22	1.17	1.11	1.00	.95	
2.04	1.88	1.79	1.70	1.59	1.52	1.47	1.36	1.32	1.25	1.15	1.00	.99	

Hill Book Company, Inc., New York, 1962.   Abridged from Table 18 of E. S. Pearson bridge University Press, New York, 1958.   Originally reproduced with kind per-

Arcsin Transformation ($\phi = 2$ arcsin $\sqrt{X}$)*

X	ϕ	X	ϕ	X	ϕ	X	ϕ	X	ϕ
.001	.0633	.041	.4078	.36	1.2870	.76	2.1177	.971	2.7993
.002	.0895	.042	.4128	.37	1.3078	.77	2.1412	.972	2.8053
.003	.1096	.043	.4178	.38	1.3284	.78	2.1652	.973	2.8115
.004	.1266	.044	.4227	.39	1.3490	.79	2.1895	.974	2.8177
.005	.1415	.045	.4275	.40	1.3694	.80	2.2143	.975	2.8240
.006	.1551	.046	.4323	.41	1.3898	.81	2.2395	.976	2.8305
.007	.1675	.047	.4371	.42	1.4101	.82	2.2653	.977	2.8371
.008	.1791	.048	.4418	.43	1.4303	.83	2.2916	.978	2.8438
.009	.1900	.049	.4464	.44	1.4505	.84	2.3186	.979	2.8507
.010	.2003	.050	.4510	.45	1.4706	.85	2.3462	.980	2.8578
.011	.2101	.06	.4949	.46	1.4907	.86	2.3746	.981	2.8650
.012	.2195	.07	.5355	.47	1.5108	.87	2.4039	.982	2.8725
.013	.2285	.08	.5735	.48	1.5308	.88	2.4341	.983	2.8801
.014	.2372	.09	.6094	.49	1.5508	.89	2.4655	.984	2.8879
.015	.2456	.10	.6435	.50	1.5708	.90	2.4981	.985	2.8960
.016	.2537	.11	.6761	.51	1.5908	.91	2.5322	.986	2.9044
.017	.2615	.12	.7075	.52	1.6108	.92	2.5681	.987	2.9131
.018	.2691	.13	.7377	.53	1.6308	.93	2.6062	.988	2.9221
.019	.2766	.14	.7670	.54	1.6509	.94	2.6467	.989	2.9315
.020	.2838	.15	.7954	.55	1.6710	.95	2.6906	.990	2.9413
.021	.2909	.16	.8230	.56	1.6911	.951	2.6952	.991	2.9516
.022	.2978	.17	.8500	.57	1.7113	.952	2.6998	.992	2.9625
.023	.3045	.18	.8763	.58	1.7315	.953	2.7045	.993	2.9741
.024	.3111	.19	.9021	.59	1.7518	.954	2.7093	.994	2.9865
.025	.3176	.20	.9273	.60	1.7722	.955	2.7141	.995	3.0001
.026	.3239	.21	.9521	.61	1.7926	.956	2.7189	.996	3.0150
.027	.3301	.22	.9764	.62	1.8132	.957	2.7238	.997	3.0320
.028	.3363	.23	1.0004	.63	1.8338	.958	2.7288	.998	3.0521
.029	.3423	.24	1.0239	.64	1.8546	.959	2.7338	.999	3.0783
.030	.3482	.25	1.0472	.65	1.8755	.960	2.7389		
.031	.3540	.26	1.0701	.66	1.8965	.961	2.7440		
.032	.3597	.27	1.0928	.67	1.9177	.962	2.7492		
.033	.3654	.28	1.1152	.68	1.9391	.963	2.7545		
.034	.3709	.29	1.1374	.69	1.9606	.964	2.7598		
.035	.3764	.30	1.1593	.70	1.9823	.965	2.7652		
.036	.3818	.31	1.1810	.71	2.0042	.966	2.7707		
.037	.3871	.32	1.2025	.72	2.0264	.967	2.7762		
.038	.3924	.33	1.2239	.73	2.0488	.968	2.7819		
.039	.3976	.34	1.2451	.74	2.0715	.969	2.7876		
.040	.4027	.35	1.2661	.75	2.0944	.970	2.7934		

* From B. J. Winer, "Statistical Principles in Experimental Design," McGraw-Hill Book Company, Inc., New York, 1962. Used by permission.

TABLE A.8
Control Chart Constants, Sample Sizes to 15*

Number of observations in sample, n	Chart for averages			Chart for standard deviations					Chart for ranges				
	Factors for control limits			Factor for central line	Factors for control limits				Factor for central line	Factors for control limits			
	A	A_1	A_2	c_2	B_1	B_2	B_3	B_4	d_2	D_1	D_2	D_3	D_4
2	2.121	3.760	1.880	0.5642	0	1.843	0	3.267	1.128	0	3.686	0	3.267
3	1.732	2.394	1.023	0.7236	0	1.858	0	2.568	1.693	0	4.358	0	2.575
4	1.500	1.880	0.729	0.7979	0	1.808	0	2.266	2.059	0	4.698	0	2.282
5	1.342	1.596	0.577	0.8407	0	1.756	0	2.089	2.326	0	4.918	0	2.115
6	1.225	1.410	0.483	0.8686	0.026	1.711	0.030	1.970	2.534	0	5.078	0	2.004
7	1.134	1.277	0.419	0.8882	0.105	1.672	0.118	1.882	2.704	0.205	5.203	0.076	1.924
8	1.061	1.175	0.373	0.9027	0.167	1.638	0.185	1.815	2.847	0.387	5.307	0.136	1.864
9	1.000	1.094	0.337	0.9139	0.219	1.609	0.239	1.761	2.970	0.546	5.394	0.184	1.816
10	0.949	1.028	0.308	0.9227	0.262	1.584	0.284	1.716	3.078	0.687	5.469	0.223	1.777
11	0.905	0.973	0.285	0.9300	0.299	1.561	0.321	1.679	3.173	0.812	5.534	0.256	1.744
12	0.866	0.925	0.266	0.9359	0.331	1.541	0.354	1.646	3.258	0.924	5.592	0.284	1.716
13	0.832	0.884	0.249	0.9410	0.359	1.523	0.382	1.618	3.336	1.026	5.646	0.308	1.692
14	0.802	0.848	0.235	0.9453	0.384	1.507	0.406	1.594	3.407	1.121	5.693	0.329	1.671
15	0.775	0.816	0.223	0.9490	0.406	1.492	0.428	1.572	3.472	1.207	5.737	0.348	1.652

Statistic	Standards given		Analysis of past data	
	Central line	Limits	Central line	Limits
Average, $\bar{X}$	$\bar{X}'$	$\bar{X}' \pm A\sigma_X'$	$\bar{\bar{X}}$	$\bar{\bar{X}} \pm A_1\bar{\sigma}_X$ or $\bar{\bar{X}} \pm A_2\bar{R}$
Standard deviation, σ_X	$c_2\sigma_X'$	$B_1\sigma_X', B_2\sigma_X'$	$\bar{\sigma}_X$	$B_3\bar{\sigma}_X, B_4\bar{\sigma}_X$
Range, R	$d_2\sigma_X'$	$D_1\sigma_X', D_2\sigma_X'$	$\bar{R}$	$D_3\bar{R}, D_4\bar{R}$

* From Irving W. Burr, "Engineering Statistics and Quality Control," McGraw-Hill Book Company, Inc., New York, 1953. Reprinted by kind permission from "Quality Control of Materials," American Society for Testing Materials, Special Technical Publication 15-C, Philadelphia, 1951, pp. 63, 72.

TABLE A.8

Control Chart Constants, Sample Sizes 2 to 15

INDEX